Engineering drawing and computer graphics

Engineering drawing and computer graphics

B.L. DAVIES and A. YARWOOD

Van Nostrand Reinhold (UK) Co. Ltd

First published in 1986 by
Van Nostrand Reinhold (UK) Co. Ltd
Molly Millars Lane, Wokingham, Berkshire, England

Typeset in Plantin 10/11pt by
Columns Ltd, Reading

Printed in Great Britain by
J.W. Arrowsmith Ltd, Bristol

ISBN 0 442 30616 4

Contents

Preface

This text is aimed at teaching the basic principles of engineering drawing and of computer aided graphics to undergraduate, 'A' level and TEC students. It also discusses the way in which engineering drawing is changing due to the introduction of computer aided drawing. The need for the text arose from the authors' experiences over a number of years in teaching and examining engineering drawing and computer graphics at both undergraduate and 'A' level. It was found that many staff and students were finding difficulty in understanding the newer areas associated with computer graphics. This was found to be so because available texts were often written from the viewpoint of a computer scientist with a great deal of unexplained specialist terminology and knowledge. Many other texts go into great detail on the methods for drawing pictures using a specific computer or require knowledge of particular computer language. This approach is confusing to those who are teaching or learning about engineering drawing, not only because it presumes a knowledge of computers and computing which is not available, but also because it treats computer graphics within the narrow confines of drawing lines on a screen. This latter treatment neglects the more exciting application issues of how the design and manufacture processes are being changed by the use of computer graphics. This text attempts to redress this imbalance by linking the process of engineering drawing with that of computer graphics in a way which requires no prior computing knowledge.

This book is also written for those who require a knowledge of engineering drawing and the way in which computer graphics is changing the subject. The basic principles of engineering drawing are covered in a complete but succinct way which is appropriate to modern courses in this subject. The role and methodology of computer graphics hardware is also covered, together with the basic principles of computer graphics software ranging from simple draughting systems through to an understanding of the methods used in solid modelling. The application of computer graphics is also dealt with in a chapter covering a typical draughting system, a commercial solid modeller, finite element analysis and the link to computer aided manufacture. A comprehensive set of exercises is provided both for engineering drawing and for computer graphics.

The book will also be of interest to those in industry and education who are already familiar with the processes of engineering drawing, but who would like to have a fundamental appreciation of the technology of computer graphics, how it affects engineering drawing and how it is changing industry across a wide range of disciplines.

The authors feel the text is much needed in filling the gap between the traditional engineering drawing texts and the extremely specialist texts on computer graphics. It is hoped that it will advance this important area in all branches of education and industry.

Acknowledgements

The authors wish to place on record here their appreciation for the help given by representatives of the following organizations in granting permission to reproduce in this book copyright illustrations:

J.C. Bamford (Excavators) Limited (Fig. 1.1)
Harley Reece and Company (Fig. 2.2)
The University of Cambridge Local Examinations Syndicate (Fig. 12.14 and associated text)
The Welsh Joint Education Committee (Fig. 12.15 and Fig. 12.16, together with associated text)
The University of London School Examinations Board (Fig. 12.17 and associated text)
The Associated Examining Board (Fig. 12.18 and associated text)
Robocom Limited (Fig. 14.2, Fig. 14.18 and Fig. B.1)
D.E.C. Limited (Fig. 14.3 and Fig. 14.26)
Tektronix Limited (UK) (Fig. 14.4 and Fig. 14.27)
Autodesk Limited (Fig. 14.6)
Benson Electronics Limited (Fig. 14.21, Fig. 14.25, Fig. 14.28 and Fig. 14.29)
The School of Industrial Design, Royal College of Art, London (Fig. 16.9 and Fig. 16.10)
CAE International (Figs. 16.11 to 16.24, Figs. 16.28 to 16.30)
Pathtrace Limited (Fig. 16.31 and Fig. 16.32)
GRASP Simulation, BYG Systems Limited (Fig. 16.33)

1 Introduction

ENGINEERING DRAWING AND THE ENGINEERING PROCESS

An engineer can be defined as a person who is concerned with working with tools and machines to produce devices which will aid mankind. A physicist deals with fundamental principles. The engineer differs from the physicist in that he takes the underlying concepts and ideas evolved by physicists and uses them to amend, change or produce artefacts. To succeed in this, engineers must engage in a range of activities such as analysis, design, drawing and manufacture, which are concerned with communicating ideas about artefacts. Engineering drawing plays a crucial role in this communication process. The graphical form is ideal for quickly conveying complex ideas in an unambiguous manner. Anyone attempting to write a complete description of an engineering component will realize the difficulties of producing a concise and unambiguous description and will readily agree the truth in the saying that 'a simple picture is worth a thousand words'. If a set of rules and procedures can be agreed and adopted for the methods by which the pictures are to be set out, and if sufficient separate views are drawn, any assembly can be completely and exactly described without ambiguity, no matter how complex the assembly may be. The subject *Engineering Drawing* is an attempt to set down these rules and procedures in a systematic graphical form.

It is not only the manufacturer who finds engineering drawings of value. Engineering drawings are also used by the designer; as he sketches and draws he carries on a dialogue with himself and others to refine his design ideas step by step. The analyst and the researcher define the precise geometry of parts for mathematical analysis from drawings. Managers in industry discuss aspects such as length of manufacturing times, costs of manufacturing parts, materials requirements and other such detail with the aid of sets of engineering drawings. The draughtsman will use a range of drawings to ensure that parts are correct to shape and form, have the correct dimensions and tolerances and will assemble together properly into a working device. Engineering drawings therefore provide an essential means of communication between a wide variety of types of engineers. Despite the advent of computer graphics (covered in the latter half of this book), the ability to read and understand engineering drawings remains an essential part of any engineer's background knowledge.

The ability to be able to interpret the various views from engineering drawings and to form them into mental visualizations of the three-dimensional nature of artefacts is as essential now as it ever was before the introduction of computing into engineering drawings. The need to be able to understand the conventions and terminology employed in drawings is as essential as ever. However, the physical skills involved in setting out and drawing on paper with pencil or pen will clearly diminish as computer graphics become more widely available for the production of engineering drawings.

Conventions and standards

To ensure that engineers have a common language available for communicating by graphical means, a commonly accepted set of conventions, terminology and symbols is specified in a number of British Standards published by the British Standards Institution. That most widely used in engineering drawing is BS 308: *Engineering drawing practice* which is published in three parts. A shorter version of this Standard for students is available, this being PD 7308: *Engineering drawing practice for schools and colleges*. PD 7308 is published as a single booklet. BS 308 and PD 7308 cover most of the conventions and symbols required for engineering drawing. The drawings throughout this book have been drawn to the methods laid down in BS 308. Other British Standards referred to in this book are as follows:

BS 4500: *Limits and fits* which, together with BS 308 Parts 2 and 3, specifies the methods by which parts in drawings should be dimensioned to ensure they can be joined together in an assembly, with a particular quality of fit to meet a required function.
BS 3463: *ISO metric screw threads* deals with thread forms and sizes of nuts, bolts and other threaded parts as recommended by the International Standards Organization (ISO).
BS 499: Part 2 *Welding symbols* covers the range of symbols which can be added to drawings to specify the sizes and types of weld. This Standard also deals with the preparation of materials ready for welding to be carried out.
BS 3939: *Graphical symbols for electrical power, telecommunications and electronics diagrams* covers the huge range of symbols for electrical, electronic and telecommunication circuits.
BS 2917: *Fluid symbols: CETOP* covers the range of symbols for hydraulic, pneumatic and fluidic circuits.
BS 4058: *Flow chart symbols*. The descriptions of flow charts given in Chapter 13 are based upon the details given in this Standard.

Reprographics

It is not possible to send an original drawing to the workshop for parts to be manufactured because the drawing could be lost or become damaged and there would then be no permanent record of the drawing. Because of this there is a necessity to copy or reproduce the original. This topic is known as *reprographics*. Most methods of copying require the original to be on a semi-transparent medium, e.g. tracing paper, tracing cloth or tracing plastic film.

Blueprints

The original system for reproducing drawings used a blue paper with white lines, hence the term *blueprint*. The paper for this process had one side chemically treated. An original drawing is placed on the paper and exposed to light. The paper is then washed in water and coated with a solution of potassium dichromate to *fix* the print. The print is then dried by being passed through heated rollers. Because this system requires the use of liquids and the paper dried after fixing, it has largely fallen out of use in favour of other procedures.

Diazo process

This process produces generally blue lines on white paper. An original drawing is placed on the yellow side of a chemically treated paper and exposed to light in a machine. The light burns out the chemical leaving the paper white with a yellow drawing. The lines are then fixed in a separate developing unit by exposure to ammonia fumes which turn the yellow lines blue.

In both blueprint and diazo methods, lines on an original drawing must be dark and dense to avoid prints which have fuzzy, unclear lines.

Microfilming

This is a photographic process in which drawings are photographed on 16 mm or 35 mm film. Each film is mounted on a card for filing purposes thus eliminating the need to file large and bulky drawings. The cards on which the film is mounted can be readily sorted and assessed through a computer system. The cards can also be placed in a machine for viewing and prints from the film can be made on paper of any standard size.

Xerography

This process, commonly known as *photocopying*, uses a powder which is electrostatically attracted to the paper, enabling untreated paper to be used for copying. This process is becoming increasingly popular for the copying of drawings, particularly on sheet sizes such as A4 and A3. The addition of colour in xerography is also possible.

Types of engineering drawing

In order to communicate as much information as possible in a concise form, a system of drawing of views known as *orthographic projection* has been developed. Two forms of orthographic projection are widely used in engineering drawing. These are *First Angle* and *Third Angle orthographic projections*. These two methods of projection are described in Chapter 4. Orthographic projections show single views of faces alongside other views seen from directions which are at right angles to each other. Hence orthographic, from orthogonal, meaning at right angles. With the aid of the methods of orthographic projection, views of individual component parts can be drawn and fully dimensioned to specify their precise geometry, size, shape and form. An example of a single part orthographic projection drawing is given in Fig. 1.1. This drawing has been reproduced by courtesy of

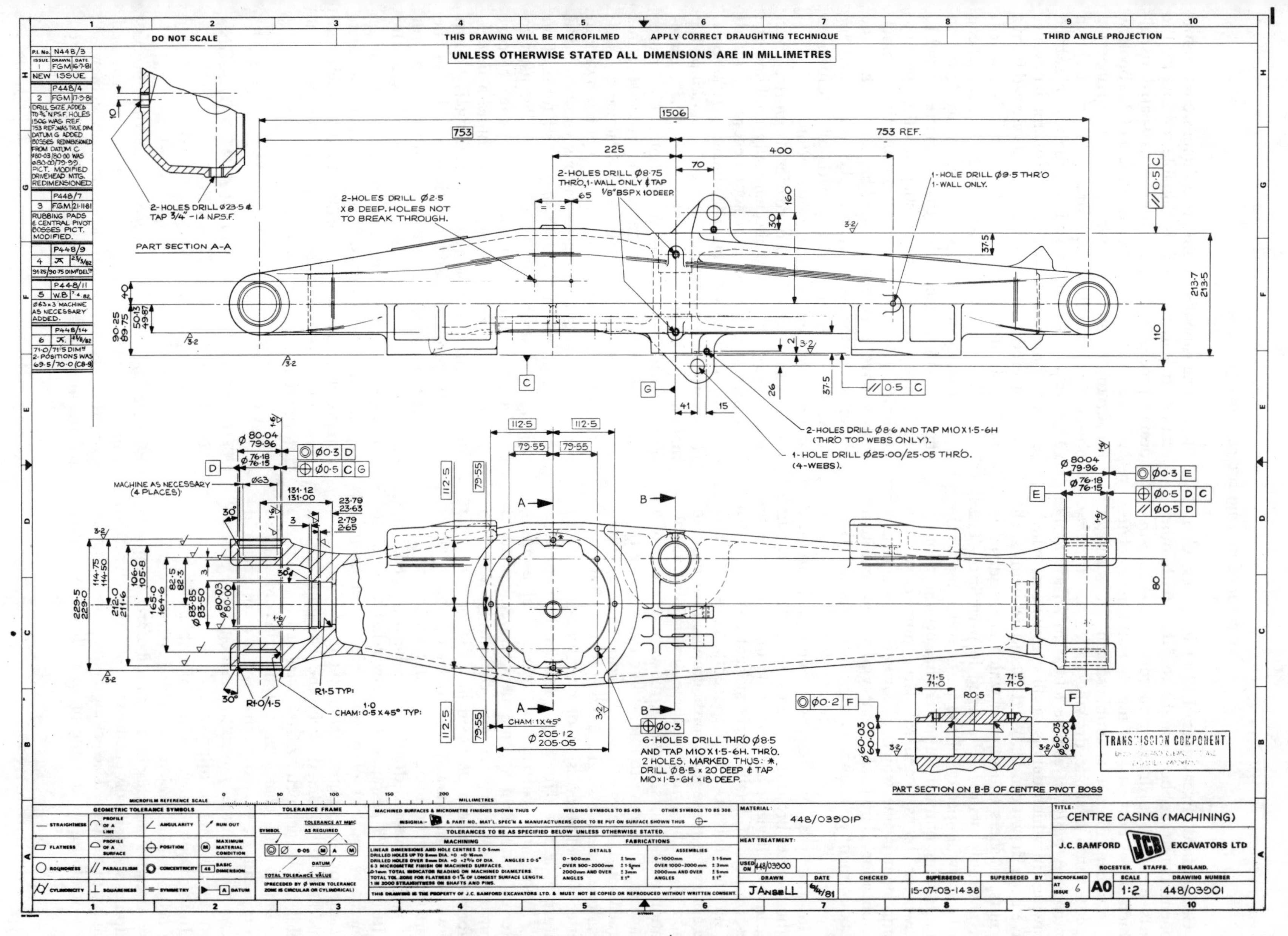

Fig.1.1 A detail drawing. A Third Angle orthographic projection

J. C. Bamford (Excavators) Ltd of Rocester. Component parts can be brought together with other parts in a single drawing to form a *sub-assembly* which shows how parts fit together and inter-relate. A number of sub-assemblies can be brought together into a single drawing called an *assembly drawing*. A *parts list* can be added to an assembly drawing, in which details of all components which have been drawn can be listed. Standard items such as nuts, washers and screws, which are required in the assembly, will also be listed in parts lists. The parts list will specify all the parts either by a title and drawing number if the item has been previously drawn or by a standard parts number if the component is one which is covered by a standard specification. The final assembly of a complete item of equipment is known as a *general assembly* (GA) drawing.

In the past it has been necessary to use orthographic projection views to a great extent because such views are very good for giving precise descriptions of details of components, in particular of internal features of components. However, it is necessary for those using orthographic projection to build up in their minds a three-dimensional visualization of the parts shown in the various views of a drawing. They have to inter-relate the separate two-dimensional views. Pictorial views showing more than one face in a single drawing will quickly give a better overall impression of the three-dimensional nature of a part. However, pictorial drawings lead to ambiguity particularly when representing internal features of a component. Several pictorial drawings may be necessary to convey as much information as can be given in a few orthographic views. More time is required to draw pictorial views than to draw orthographically and so, in the past, the use of pictorial drawings has been limited.

In computer graphics it is now relatively easy to generate a number of pictorial views seen from a variety of directions. Such pictorial views are generated from the data in the computer which holds all the geometry of the part being displayed. As the use of computer graphics becomes more widespread, it is likely that the use of pictorial views will eventually result in orthographic projection diminishing in importance.

In this book a fairly traditional emphasis is placed on orthographic projection. This is partly because a few decades are liable to pass before computer graphics substantially changes the emphasis on orthographic projection. Also orthographic projection is an ideal medium for training of an ability to visualize three-dimensionally from two-dimensional information. In particular this is valuable training for the design process in engineering. Thus spatial visualizational ability is developed in the text of this book by the examples and exercises in which engineering objects are visualized and drawn, particularly in Chapters 4, 5 and 6. In addition the use of section planes to show internal features and of auxiliary views is also covered in order to show objects viewed from a number of directions so that they are fully defined.

The objects shown in this book have mainly been taken from typical components generally found in engineering practice, rather than being restricted to simple non-functional block shapes, although some preliminary exercises using non-functional block shapes have been included. This is to allow the reader to become familiar with the conventions for drawing typical engineering parts in addition to gaining practice in spatial visualization.

It is possible to draw a third view from two given views by the process of mechanically applying the principles of projection, without necessarily building up a three-dimensional image of a part. However, the reader is encouraged to attempt the mental processes of visualizing the three-dimensional (3-D) forms throughout. No matter how little innate talent he or she possesses, this ability to visualize will grow with practice.

In addition to being able to interpret a drawing in the sense of inter-relating its various views to build a visual concept of the 3-D shape and form of an object, an assembly drawing can also be used to give a clear understanding as to how a part functions, without the need first to build a model. This can only be achieved if something is known about the properties and functions of some of the standard engineering parts encountered in an engineering drawing. This is a further reason why the objects portrayed in these pages are mainly of engineering components. The inclusion of such components enables the reader to determine the functioning of an assembly from the graphical information given by the drawing.

THE ROLE OF COMPUTER AIDED DESIGN AND ITS IMPLICATIONS FOR ENGINEERING DRAWING

Engineering design is a decision-making process which requires a wide range of knowledge and expertise. Early design activities, in which all calculations were performed manually, required that the models being analysed were greatly simplified in order that the mathematics involved were sufficiently simple to allow standard techniques of analysis to be applied. However, the simplifications were often so extreme that the resulting mathematical model bore little relationship to reality. With the tremendous processing power of computers as an aid to the design process, the models can be much more complex. In fact some analytical techniques, such as finite element analysis, can only be effectively carried out by using a computer. Thus, until recently, it has been the calculation power of the computer which has had the most impact on the process of engineering analysis and design. The introduction of the low cost microcomputer, available on the desk of the majority of engineers, has meant that the computer is available as a standard tool for a number of calculations requiring relatively small programs with simple graphical output, e.g. graphs and diagrams to represent shear force and bending moments. The storage of data and standard codes of practice on a computer disk, together with purpose written programs, can give the engineer the guidance and step-by-step advice at his computer terminal that was previously only obtainable from specialist consultants.

INTERACTIVE COMPUTER GRAPHICS

Until recently graphical computing aids for the engineer were restricted to graphs and 2-D draughting systems. The 2-D draughting systems were comparatively simple and contained no intrinsic knowledge of the geometry of the part to be drawn. It was therefore necessary for the designer to be able to specify, e.g. hidden features by showing them by hidden detail lines or by showing cross-hatching lines for sectioned planes. This information is not part of the data base for a simple 2-D draughting system. Relatively few companies, typically those which often draw parts with only small differences between them, could justify what used to be expensive equipment for such a restricted task.

The advent of a type of 3-D computer graphics, known as 2½-D, has improved this situation. The dramatic reduction in the computer graphics hardware costs has also helped. A 2½-D system is one which is used only for shapes where a 2-D profile is translated linearly by a small distance to make a 3-D object of constant depth. Alternatively a 2-D profile of an object can be rotated through 360° to make a roughly cylindrical type of 2½-D component. These shapes are of particular value because they are of a type that is often used in engineering and which is relatively easy to produce on a simple numerically controlled lathe or milling machine. The programs can now be provided on relatively small and cheap microcomputers and graphical displays. The use of 2½-D facilities in 2-D draughting has meant that many design offices have been able to show savings of a factor of 3 or 4 on productivity.

It is in the area of computer graphics in which a full 3-D *solid* model of the product can be constructed, that the greatest potential for change is envisaged. This is an area that has only recently been developed on a large scale, partly because the high cost of computer hardware has recently come down to more acceptable levels, and partly because of advances in computer programs which have produced many new techniques. The ability to produce a full solid model, or an outline of an object as a *wire frame*, means that the full 3-D geometry of a part is available as a data base. This data based geometry is then available, not only to produce 2-D drawings of an assembly and its constituent parts, but is also available for transmission to other computer programs for design, analysis and manufacture. This central nature of the geometric data base, together with the manner in which it integrates with a range of design and manufacture activities, is shown in Fig. 1.2. This figure shows that it is the graphics display screen which produces the geometry of the part. This can then be used in design and analysis, e.g. to pass to a finite element pre-processor which breaks down the geometry into a mesh which can then be analysed by a further program. The other major area where the geometric data base is used is in manufacture and management activities. Not only is the information of value for the automatic generation of numerical control machine tool motions, but also for such activities as scheduling the motions of robots and automated guided vehicles. The total computer information is also available for management activities in planning production and maintenance, in costing, sales and marketing. Although any single one of these activities may only have a marginal cost advantage taken on its own, by bringing them all together into an integrated activity, the whole process becomes very cost effective. The result is that the engineer is relieved of many routine tasks and can use his time more

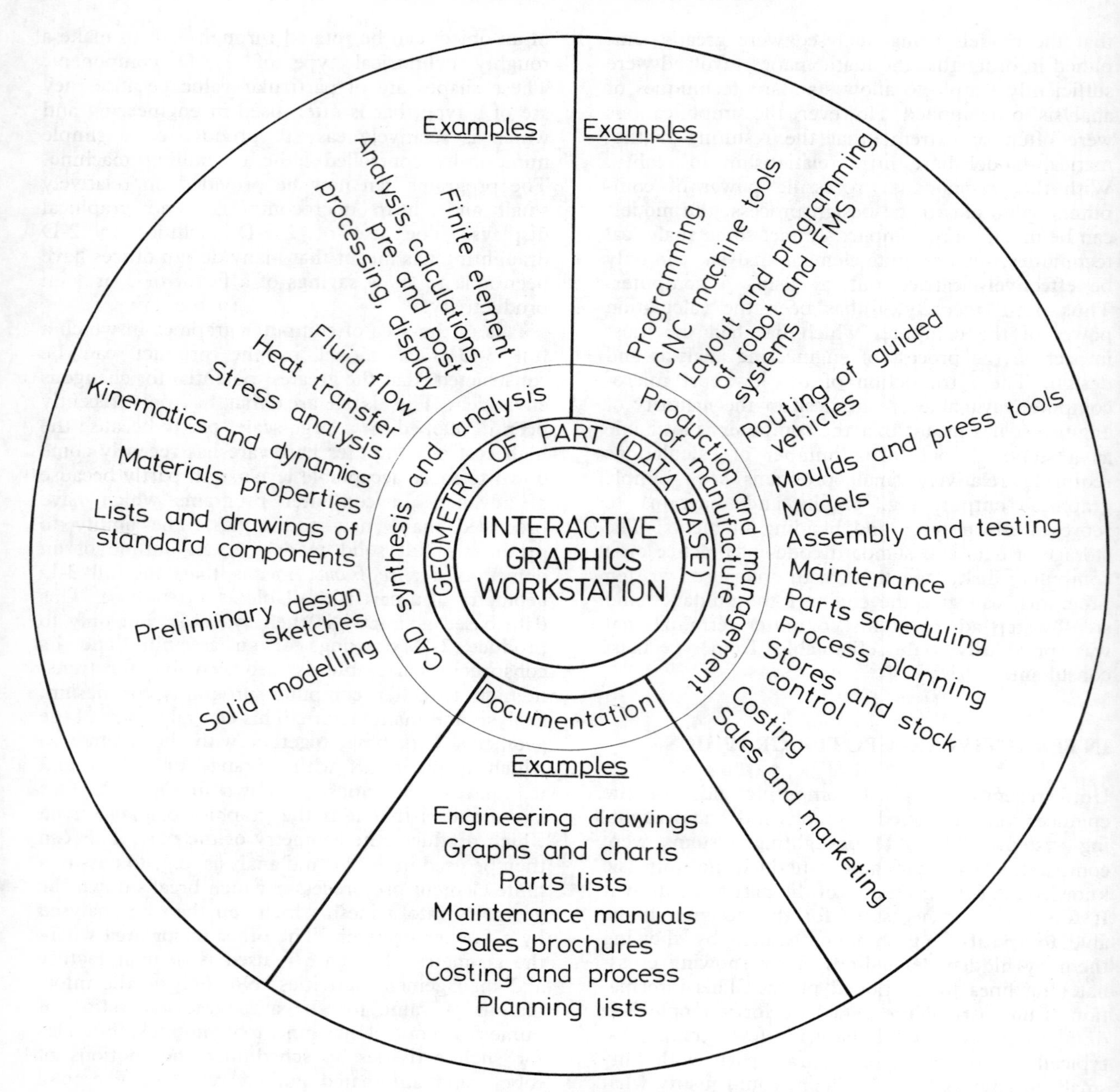

Fig.1.2 The central role of graphics in CAD/CAM

creatively. The availability of specially written programs means that a small business can have access to information, expertise and guidance which was previously only available to larger corporations. This process is likely to change the skills required of the engineer. The knowledge of a large number of detailed standards and procedures will no longer be necessary as they can be accessed directly from a computer. The emphasis on analytic ability is also likely to decrease for the general engineer who will rely more on the standard analysis tools available on the computer. For a small number of mathematicians and researchers, who will be responsible for developing or updating computer programs, the mathematical process will remain important. For the average engineer, however, the main activity is likely to become one of using the computer as a synthesis tool to enhance his creativity. This reliance on the use of standard computer programs implies that their integrity must be fully verified and that the limitations of their application are well documented and understood. Until the time when totally integrated sophisticated computer graphics systems are in widespread use, it is generally thought necessary for every engineer to understand at least the basic analytical principles of a range of engineering subjects and to be able to understand the type of thinking and processes that underlie existent computer programs.

It is this need for a fundamental understanding of the graphics hardware, software and methods of application which has resulted in the provision of the chapters on computer graphics in this book. These chapters provide an introduction to computer graphics in a way that those with a general knowledge of engineering drawing, as provided by the earlier chapters, will be able to understand. The subjects of computing and computer graphics are full of terminology (often contradictory) which makes it difficult for the beginner to be able to read even an introductory specialist text and understand what is happening. The introductory texts used with commercial computer graphics hardware often require a knowledge of terminology and procedures which is beyond the experience of the normal beginner. The constraints and reasons for a particular type of hardware or software system are also seldom discussed in such texts. It is hoped that the chapters in this book will give a sound appreciation of basic principles and processes which are used in and by most computer graphics systems. This aspect has been presented with the assumption that the reader is not well versed in any particular computer language. Similarly the text has not been based on any particular computer hardware system, but covers a range of categories from the simple to the complex. It is hoped that these chapters on computer graphics will be of interest to those about to use computer graphics for the first time and also to those who wish to extend their knowledge beyond the smaller microcomputer-based systems.

The trends in computer graphics are towards larger systems with more memory and faster operation at a competitive price. This implies that the computer aided design (CAD) systems which are currently being used by the larger companies will, within a decade, be produced at a cost which is within the reach of smaller companies and colleges. To meet this challenge it is essential for all those who have a knowledge of the more traditional engineering drawing processes to become familiar with the terminology and techniques of computer graphics.

2 Equipment, lines and terms in engineering drawing

SIZES OF DRAWING SHEETS

The most common range of sheet sizes for engineering drawings is the ISO (International Standards Organization) A series. This range is based upon an A0 size of an area equal to one square metre. All other sizes in the range are exact halves of each preceding sheet.

The recommended A range sheet sizes

A0 – 1189 mm × 841 mm = 1 square metre
A1 – 841 mm × 594 mm
A2 – 594 mm × 420 mm
A3 – 420 mm × 297 mm
A4 – 297 mm × 210 mm

Engineering drawings may be laid out on the drawing sheet in either a *landscape* format, in which the longest edges of the sheet are horizontal, or in a *portrait* format in which the longest sheet edges are vertical.

TYPES OF DRAWINGS

Detail drawing

A drawing of a single object. This is sometimes referred to as a *single part drawing*. Detail drawings should include all necessary dimensions, tolerances, materials and finishes, necessary for the making of the object.

Assembly drawing

A drawing showing two or more parts of an assembly assembled together. Assembly drawings should contain all information, all dimensions and other information needed to ensure that assembly is possible.

Combined drawing

A drawing which includes with an assembly drawing detail drawings of the assembly's various parts and a list of items required to make up the assembly, all gathered together on the same drawing sheet.

Arrangement drawing

A drawing of the complete final manufactured product, showing how assemblies are arranged together. Any functional features of the product should also be included.

Parts or items lists

A list of all the parts needed to make up an assembly. Such lists may be included with an assembly drawing or shown as a separate list.

Drawings list

A list of all the drawings required for manufacturing an assembly.

LETTERS AND FIGURES

All letters and figures on an engineering drawing must be clearly drawn or printed so as to ensure that the meanings of dimensions and notes, etc., are completely unambiguous. Letters and figures may be drawn freehand, with the aid of stencils, by machine printing or from dry transfer sheets.

Letters and figures should vary in height according to the size of the drawing sheet. Thus 7 mm high printing is suitable for items such as drawing numbers and titles on drawings made on sheets of size A0 to A3, but 5 mm high print for such details is better for drawings on A4 sheets. Dimensions, notes and other such information should be 4 mm high on A0 to A3 sheets and 3 mm on A4 sheets. Examples of suitable figures and letters are given in Fig. 2.1.

ENGINEERING DRAWING 1234567890
Design drawing Computer graphics
DETAIL DRAWING No975 1234567890
Parts list Languages Basic Fortran
ABCDEFGHIJKLMNOPQRSTUVWXYZ 1234567890
COMPONENT PART 24/7906
Arrangement drawing 3471 showing assemblies 46/9 and 35/72

Fig.2.1 Letters and figures

EQUIPMENT

When producing engineering drawings by hand methods the following items of equipment will be required.

Drawing tables, stands or boards

A drawing/design office in an industrial undertaking will be equipped with drawing stands or tables often of a size suitable for A0 sheets of paper (1189 mm × 841 mm). These stands will be equipped with draughting machine heads which can be quickly placed at any position on the drawing sheet and adjusted for drawing any angle. Schools and colleges may also have similar tables or stands although tables on which A1 size sheets of paper (841 mm × 594 mm) can be placed are more common. Also more common in schools and colleges are tables equipped with parallel motion rules, which can be easily slid up and down the drawing surface for either drawing parallel lines or on which set squares can be placed to draw vertical lines or lines at angles to the horizontal.

The student may well have to use drawing boards and Tee squares for his or her drawings. A suitable size of drawing board is one which will take A2 size sheets (594 mm × 420 mm). Drawing boards are usually made of wood with both surfaces sanded to a fine smooth surface and with edges straight and square against which Tee squares are placed for drawing horizontal parallel lines. Special plastic, self-adhesive sheet material can be glued on drawing boards to provide an excellent base when working with pencil or with pen.

Other equipment

Tee squares

When working with a drawing board, a Tee square is needed. The blade should be sufficiently long to enable horizontal lines to be drawn across an A2 size sheet. Edges must be straight.

Set squares

Either a pair of set squares – a 30°, 60° square and a 45° square, or an adjustable set square is required. An adjustable set square can be adjusted and locked at any angle between 0° and 90° to the horizontal.

Pencils

Most drawings will be in pencil. Although 17 grades of pencil can be purchased, from very black (6B) to very hard (9H), engineering drawings are most often drawn using a range of pencils from B to 3H – B, HB, H, 2H and 3H. Either the common wood and graphite pencil or a *clutch* pencil in which long pencil *leads* can be held is suitable.

Erasers

A good pencil eraser is essential.

Pens

Technical pens of the *Rotring* type can be of value when producing finished drawings. Technical pens with special black or coloured inks will draw a defined width of line. Pen nibs to draw lines of thicknesses such as 0.18 mm, 0.25 mm, 0.35 mm, 0.4 mm, 0.6 mm, 0.7 mm and so on up to 2 mm width can be purchased. Technical pens are designed for use with reservoirs which enable continuous working with the pens without constantly having to recharge the nibs. Fig. 2.2 shows a technical pen in use.

Compasses

At least two pairs of compasses are needed. A compass which will draw arcs and circles of radii up to about 200 mm and a spring bow compass for drawing smaller arcs and circles of radii up to about 25 mm. These compasses should be of a type which take pencil leads. If technical pen nibs are to be used for drawing arcs and circles, purpose-made compasses manufactured for the specific make of pen being used are necessary.

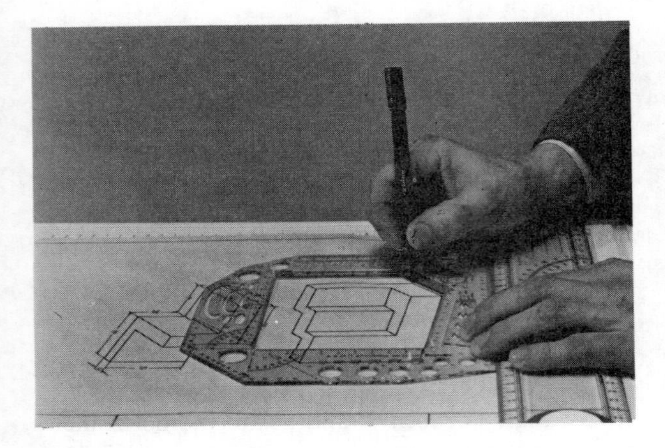

Fig.2.2 Technical pen used with a Rotring template

Drawing aids

Aids for drawing curves and shapes – flexicurves; French curves; radius curves; nut and bolt templates; ellipse, circle and hexagon templates; letter and figure stencils; and other such drawing aids assist in the production of clean, accurate drawings.

Rules

Good quality rules marked in millimetres are essential. That most commonly used is of 300 mm length. Rule tapes are of occasional value.

LINES IN ENGINEERING DRAWING

The black lines of engineering drawings may be produced with pencils or in ink. All lines should be dense and black, so as to reproduce well by the various forms of copying employed in drawing/design offices or by being photographed on 35 mm film or other forms of microphotography.

Two thicknesses of line should be used – thick and thin, thick lines being approximately twice as thick as thin lines. Suitable line thicknesses, depending upon the drawing size and on any necessary scale reduction, should be as follows:

thick 2.0 mm	thin 1.0 mm
thick 1.4 mm	thin 0.7 mm
thick 1.0 mm	thin 0.5 mm
thick 0.7 mm	thin 0.35 mm
thick 0.5 mm	thin 0.25 mm

TYPES OF LINE

The various types of line used in engineering drawings are shown in the example given in Fig. 2.3 and 2.4.

Thick lines

Outlines All outlines should be drawn with thick and continuous lines.

Thick chain line A thick chain line drawn adjacent to an outline indicates a surface requiring special treatment.

Thick dashed line Hidden detail is usually shown in drawings produced in the UK by thin dashed lines. Do not mix thick and thin hidden detail lines on the same drawing.

End of cutting plane lines Cutting plane lines should finish with thick lines.

Thin lines

Continuous thin lines are used for the following purposes:

Dimension lines Commonly ending in arrows touching projection lines.

Projection lines Commonly commencing about 3 mm from the point on an outline to which they refer and projecting about 3 mm beyond dimension lines.

Hatching lines

Leader lines May end in an arrow, if ending on an outline; with a dot if ending on a surface; with neither if ending on a dimension line.

Imaginary lines of intersection

Limits of partial or interrupted views May be either a thin continuous, but irregular, line if the limit is not axial. A continuous straight line with zig-zags if the limit line lies along an axis.

Broken thin lines

These are used for the following:

Hidden detail line A dashed line to indicate hidden outlines and hidden edges.

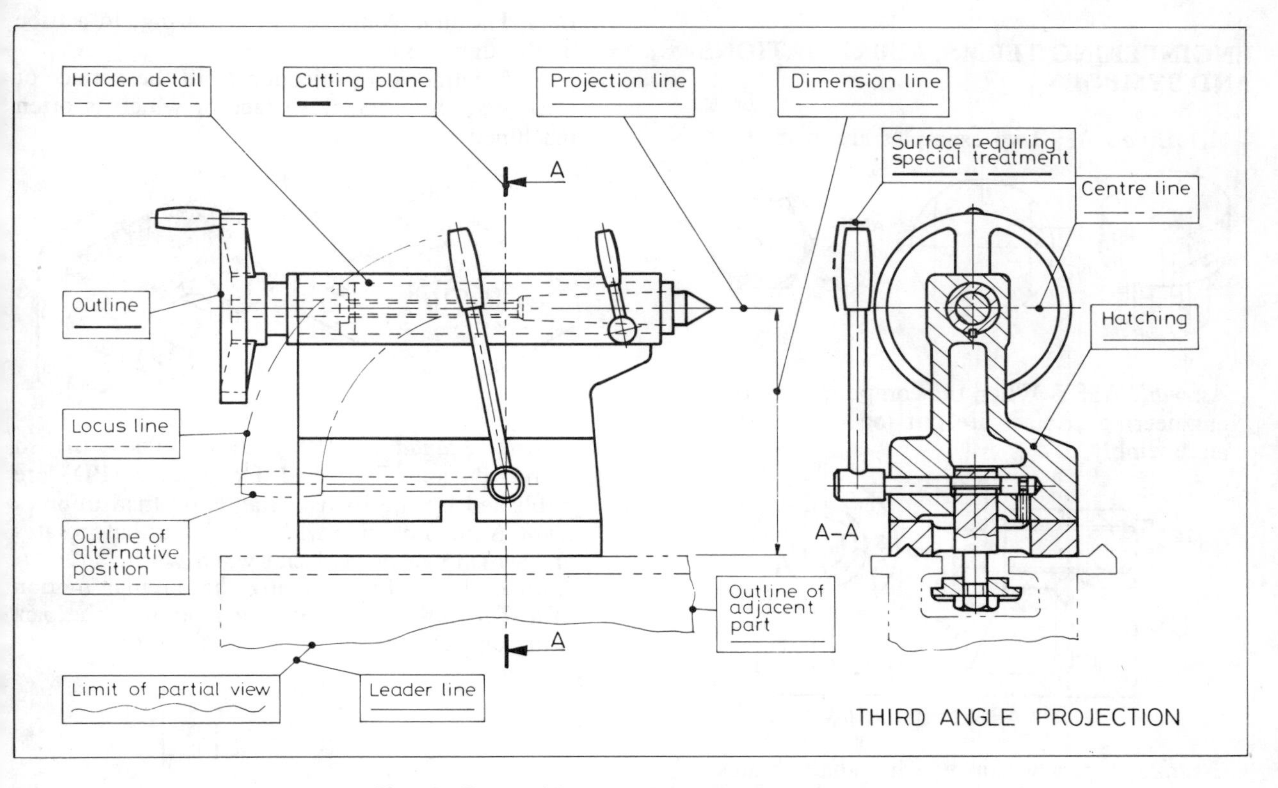

Fig.2.3 Types of lines used in engineering drawings

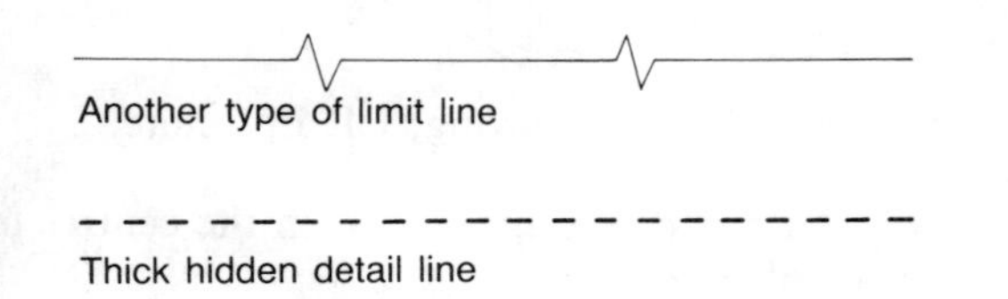

Fig.2.4 Second type of limit line: thick hidden detail lines

Chain line The most common use of thin chain lines is for centre lines. Thin chain lines are also used to indicate lines of symmetry, loci and pitch lines. Cutting plane lines are thin chain lines ending in thick lines.

Double dashed chain line To indicate any of the following details – outlines of adjacent parts; outlines of the alternative positions of movable parts; outlines prior to forming.

Notes on lines

Where different types of line coincide, the order of priority of their importance should be:

(1) outlines
(2) hidden detail
(3) cutting planes
(4) centre lines
(5) outlines of adjacent parts
(6) projection lines.

Chain lines Should start and end with long dashes. Centre lines should cross at long dashes. Centre lines should project only a short distance beyond the feature. Centre lines should not be used as dimension lines although they may be used as projection lines.

Hidden detail lines Should start and end on outline lines or on other hidden detail lines, but if the hidden detail line continues an outline line, a dash should occur between the two types of line. Hidden detail dashes should meet at tangents and corners.

ENGINEERING TERMS, ABBREVIATIONS AND SYMBOLS

- *Across flats* AF Two examples are given.

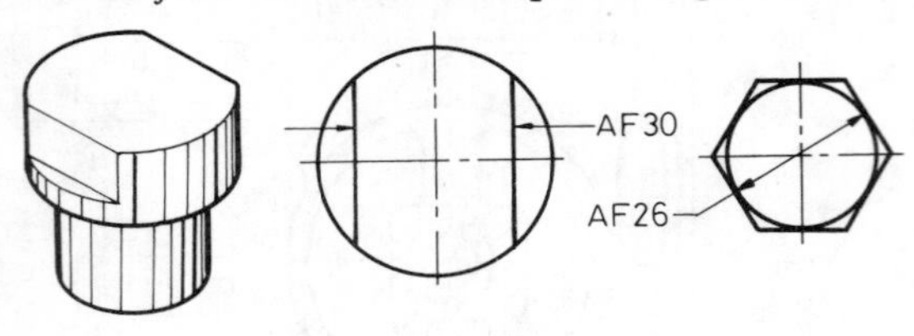

- *Assembly* ASSY When the component parts of an engineering artefact are put together, they form an assembly.

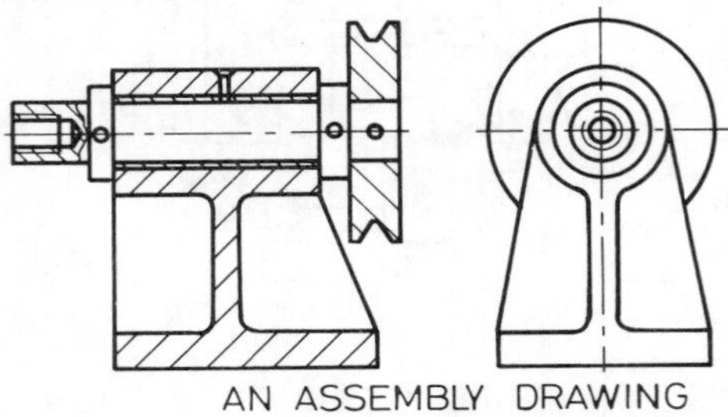

AN ASSEMBLY DRAWING

- *Bearing* A part within which a shaft rotates.

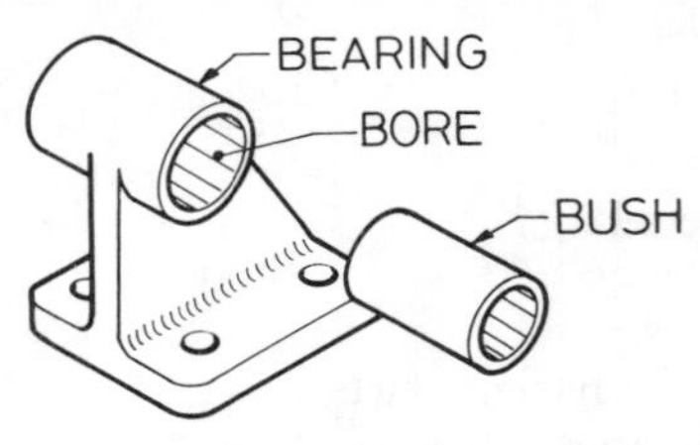

- *Blind hole* A hole which is not drilled through a component.

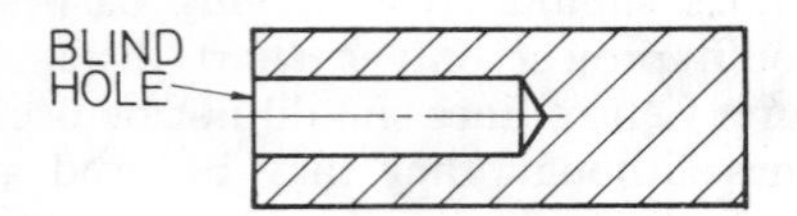

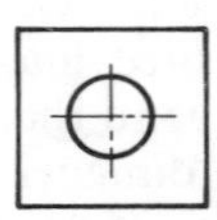

- *Bolt* A fastening device containing a screw thread. If the thread is cut along the complete length of the rod of the fastening, it is common practice to refer to the fastener as a *screw*.

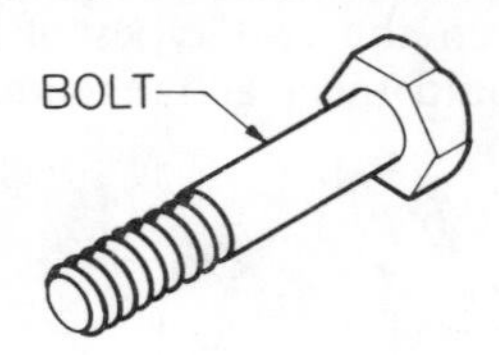

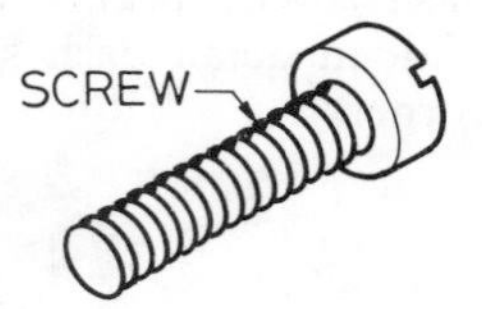

- *Bore* The hole contained in a bearing, in a tube or through a bore.
- *Boss* A cylindrical projection from the surface of a casting, the circular surface of which is often machined smooth.

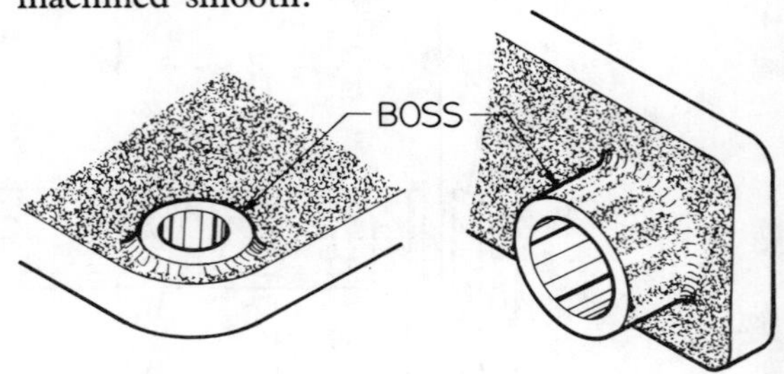

- *British Standards* (BS.) Over 4000 British Standards and Published Documents (PD) are published by the British Standards Institution.
- *Bush* A plain bearing within which a shaft rotates and which can be replaced when worn.
- *Cam* A device for changing the circular motion of a shaft into a reciprocating motion of the part fiting on the eccentric surface of the cam.

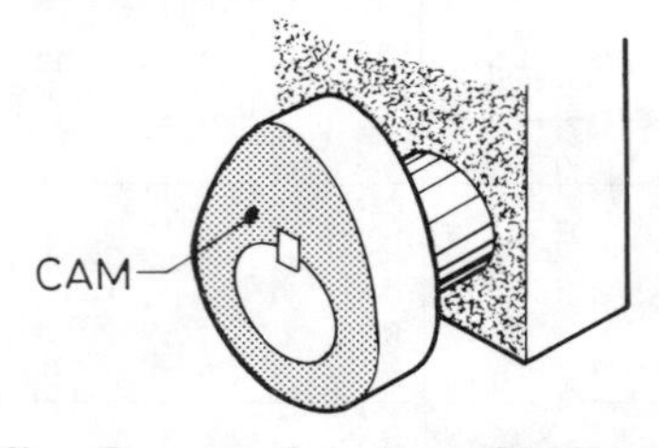

- *Centre line* ℄ on a drawing; CL in a note.
- *Centre of gravity* CG
- *Centres* CRS The distance between the centres of holes or of other parts.

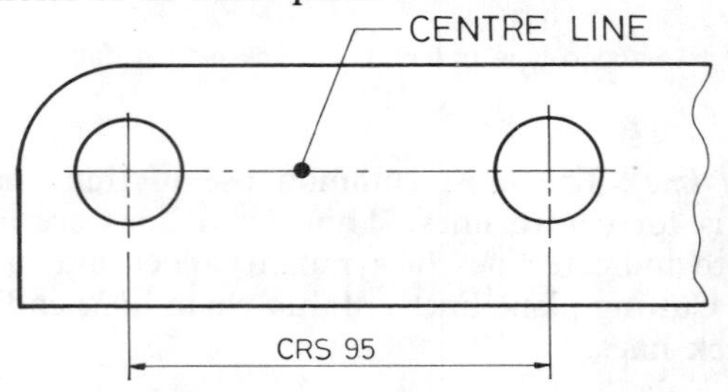

- *Chamfer* CHAM

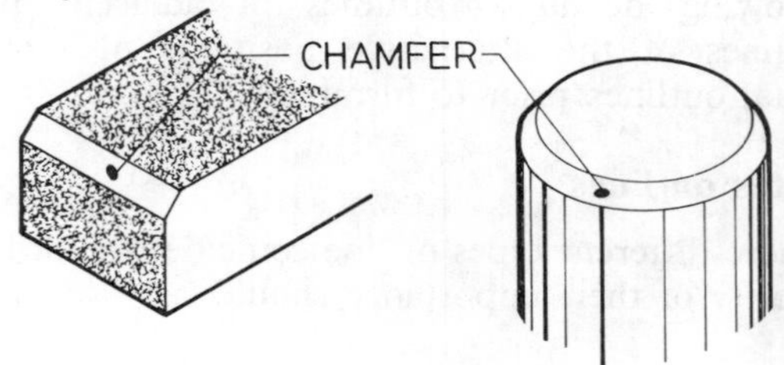

– *Cheese head* CH HD

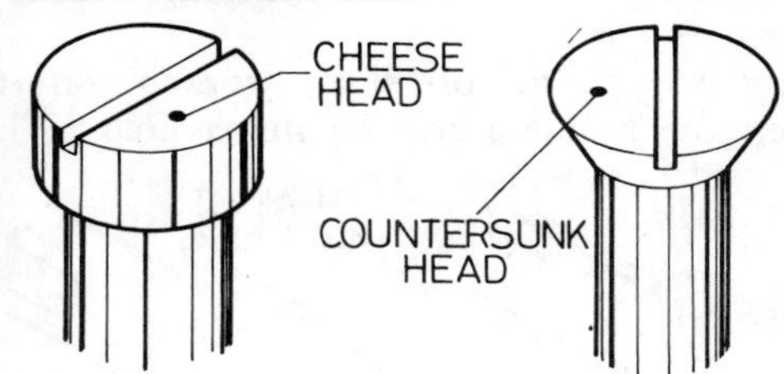

– *Collar* A ring which can be fixed to a shaft to restrict its movement in the direction of its axis.

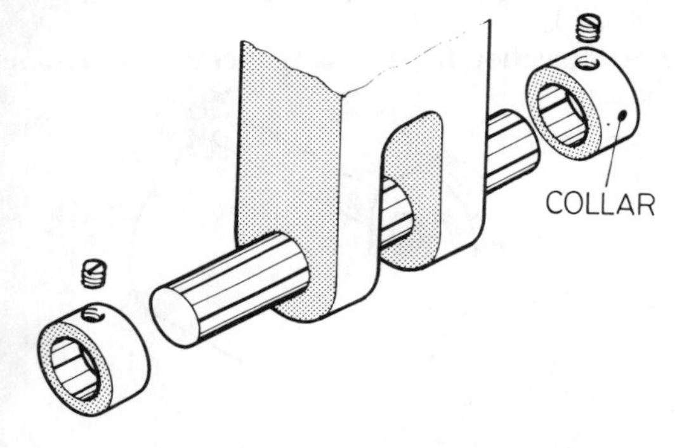

– *Counterbore* CBORE The enlargement of the top of a hole to receive the head of a bolt or to receive a nut.

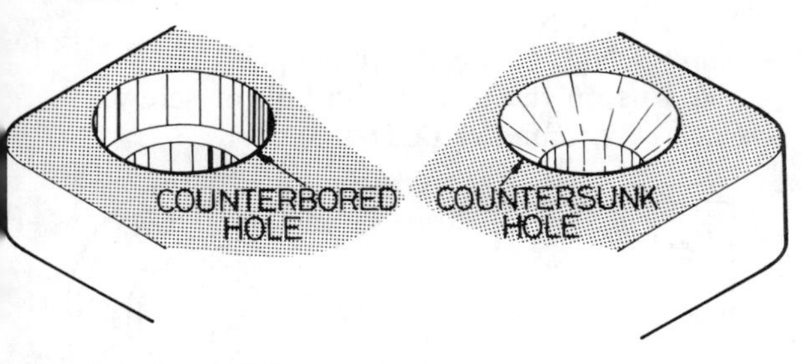

– *Countersunk* CSK The enlargement of the top of a hole to receive a countersunk bolt, rivet or screw (also CSK HD).
– *Cylinder* CYL

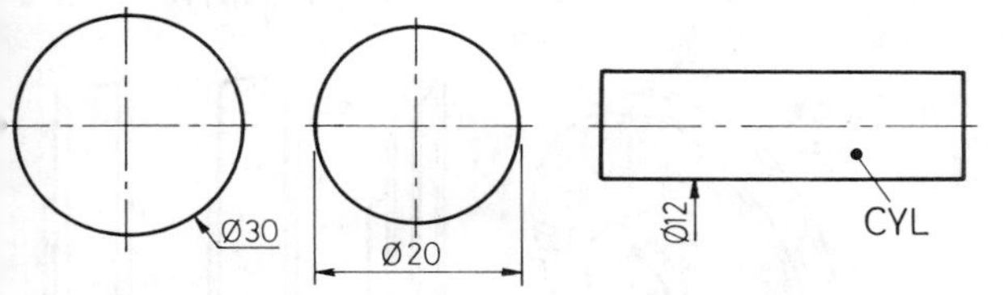

– *Diameter* Ø preceding a dimension on a drawing; DIA in a note.
– *Dimension* DIM. (Note the fullstop.)

– *Dovetail* A wedge shaped part which allows movement along only one axis.

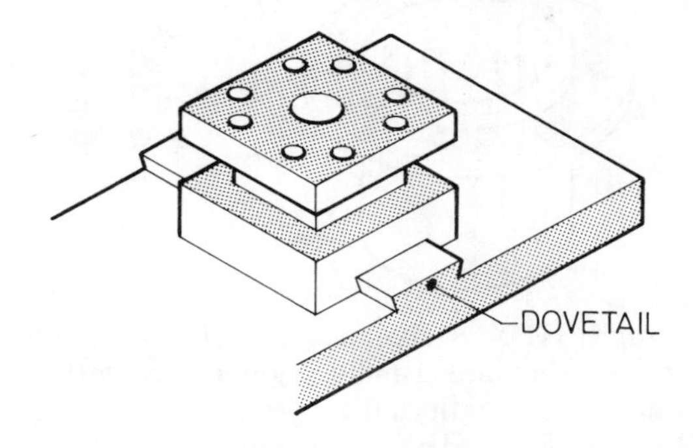

– *Dowel* Projecting pins which allow accurate positioning of one part on another.

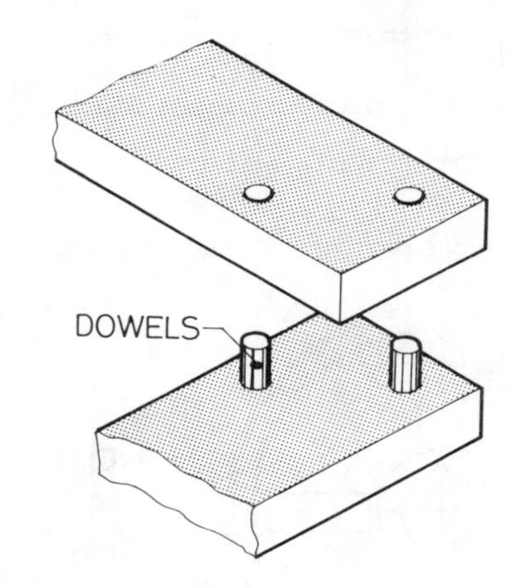

– *Drawing* DRG
– *Equally spaced* EQUI SP
– *External* EXT
– *Figure* FIG. (Note the fullstop.)
– *Fillet* A corner in a casting, shaped to allow molten metal to flow into the corner without setting up stress conditions.

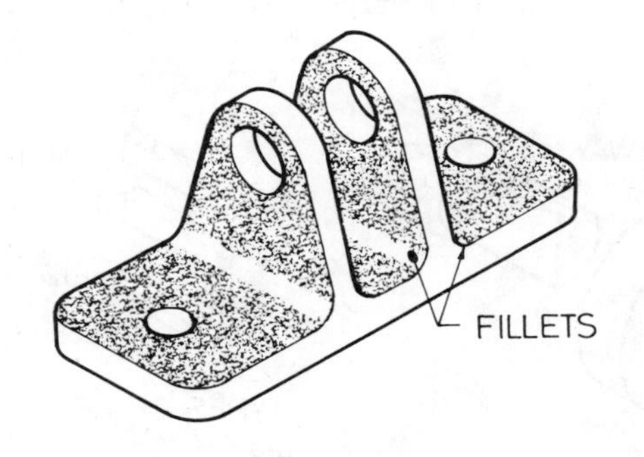

- *Flange* A thin projecting disk.

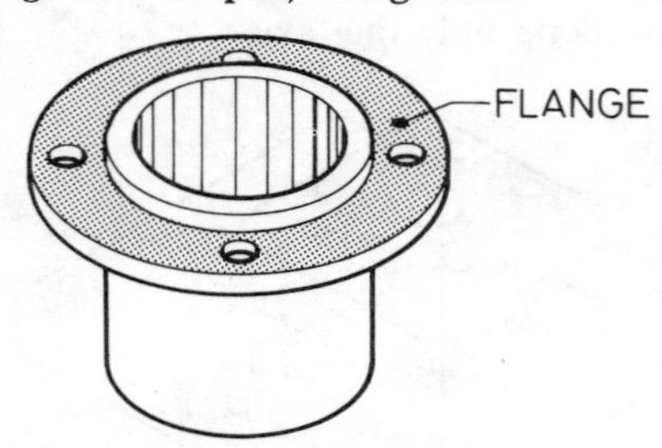

- *Hexagon* HEX A six-sided polygon. In engineering hexagons are usually regular, i.e. with sides of an equal length and angles of 135°.
- *Hexagon head* HEX HD The head of a bolt which is hexagonal in shape.

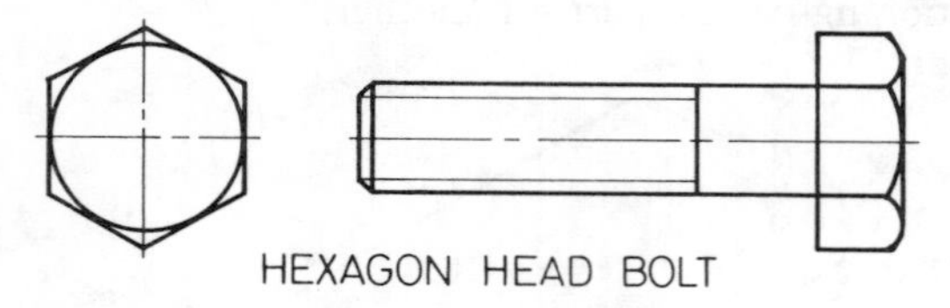

- *Hub* The central part of a wheel or pulley.

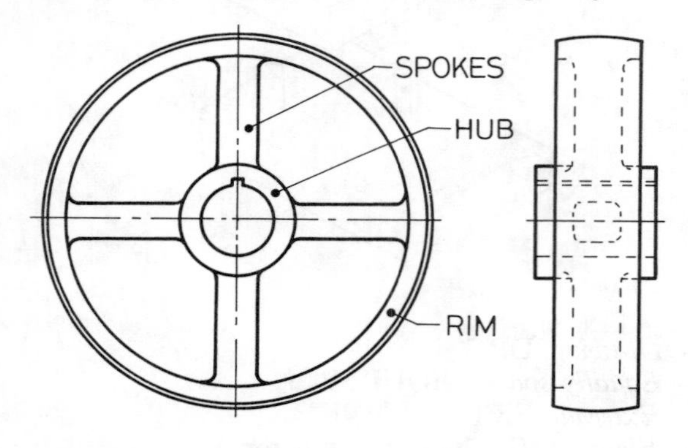

- *Insulation* INSUL
- *Internal* INT
- *Key* A small shaped piece of metal fitted between a shaft and a hub to prevent rotation between them.

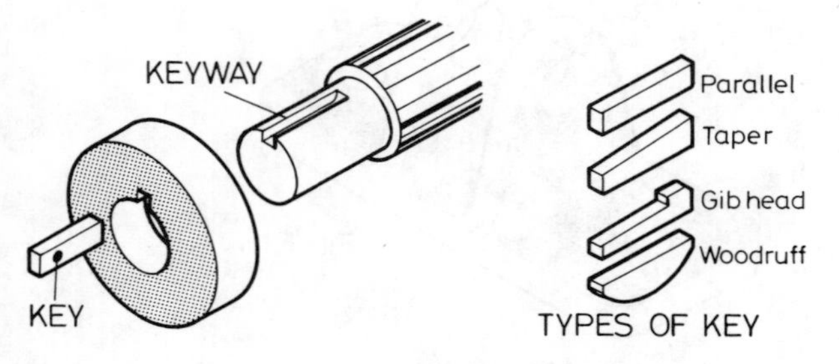

- *Keyway* The slot in a shaft or hub into which a key fits.
- *Knurling* A pattern of slots worked on to cylinders to provide a grip for finger holds.

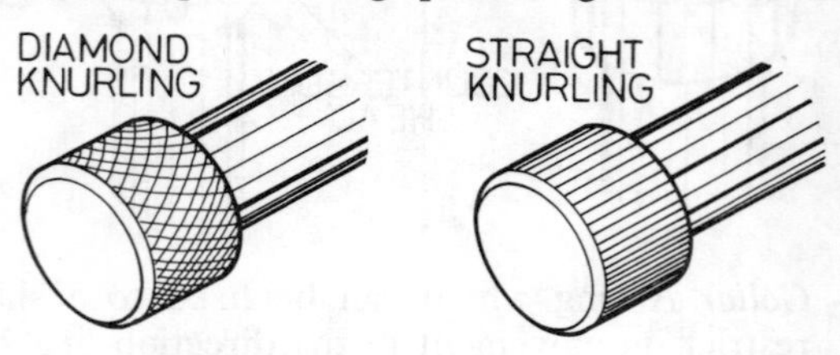

- *Left hand* LH
- *Lug* A projection from a component for fastening purposes.

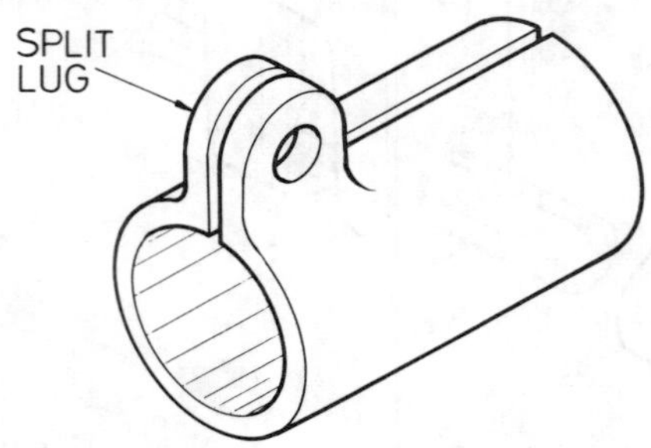

- *Maximum* MAX
- *Minimum* MIN
- *Not to scale* NTS
- *Number* NO. (Note the fullstop.)
- *Nut* Fits on the thread of a bolt or screw.
- *Pitch circle diameter* PCD

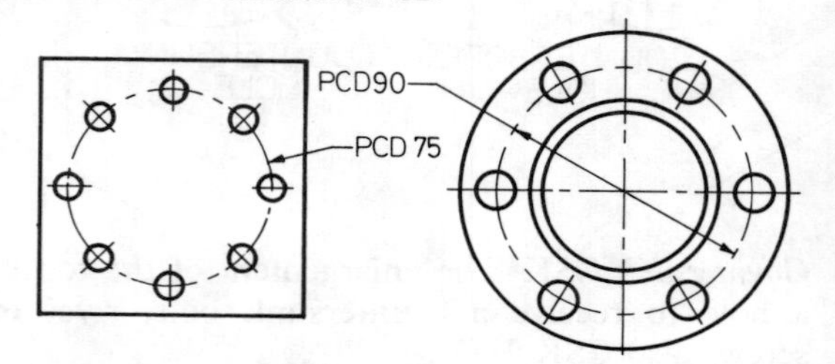

- *Pulley* A wheel designed to carry a belt for driving a shaft, or for transmitting drive from a shaft.

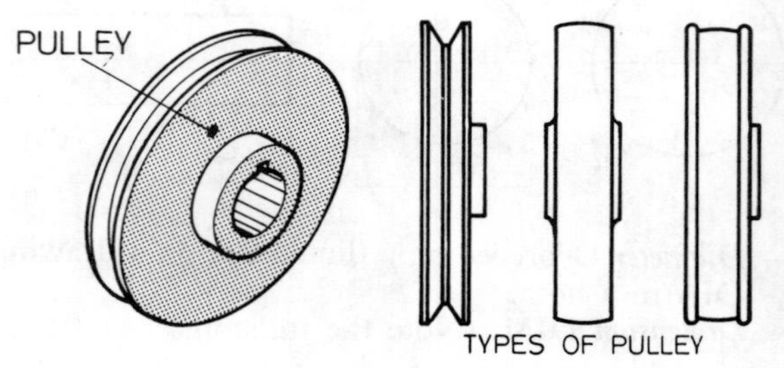

– *Radius* R Preceding a dimension; RAD in a note.
– *Recess* A hole made to receive a spigot.

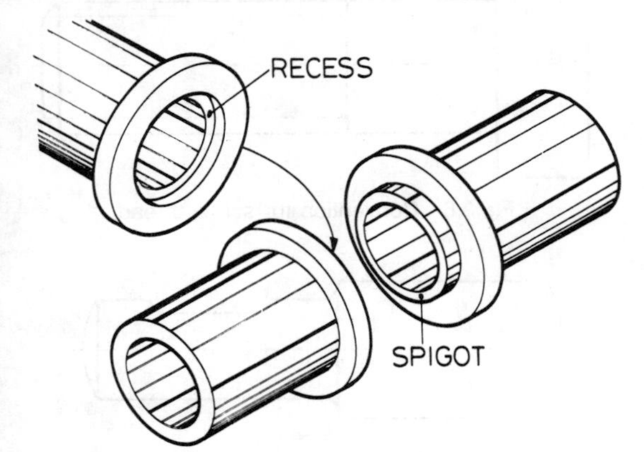

– *Rib* See Web.
– *Right hand* RH
– *Rim* The outer part of a wheel. See Hub.
– *Round head* RH
– *Screw* SCR
– *Shaft* A rod which rotates to which parts can be fitted for the transmission of circular movement.

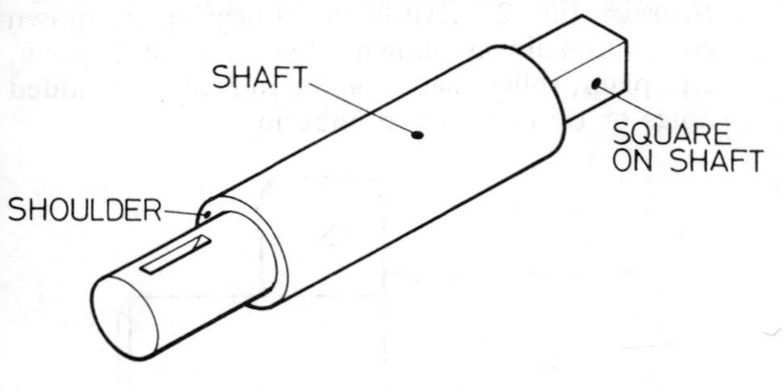

– *Shoulder* A surface at right angles to the axis caused by a change in diameter in a shaft.
– *Slot* An elongated hole.

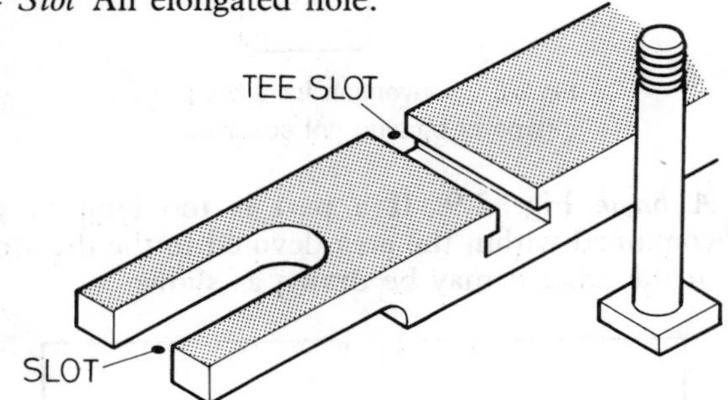

– *Specification* SPEC
– *Spherical* SPHERE SØ preceding a spherical diameter; SR preceding a spherical radius.

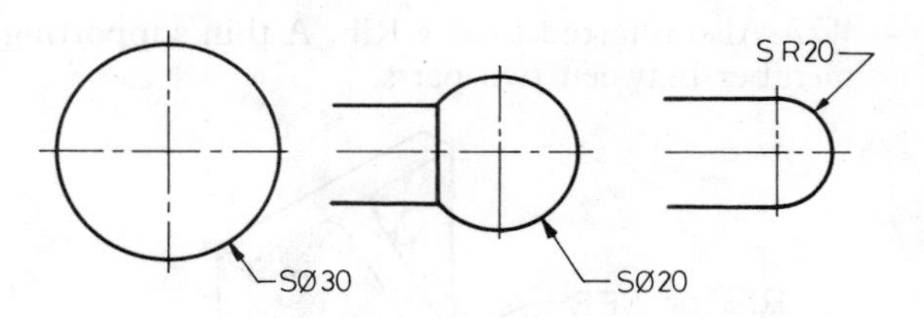

– *Spigot* See Recess. A protrusion, cylindrical in shape, allowing for accurate fitting between parts.

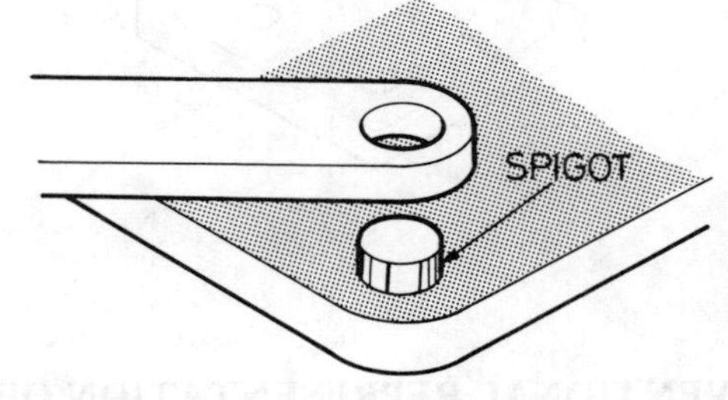

– *Spoke* The parts between the hub and rim of a wheel.
– *Spotface* SFACE A machined surface around a hole to allow accurate seating of a bolt head, washer or nut.

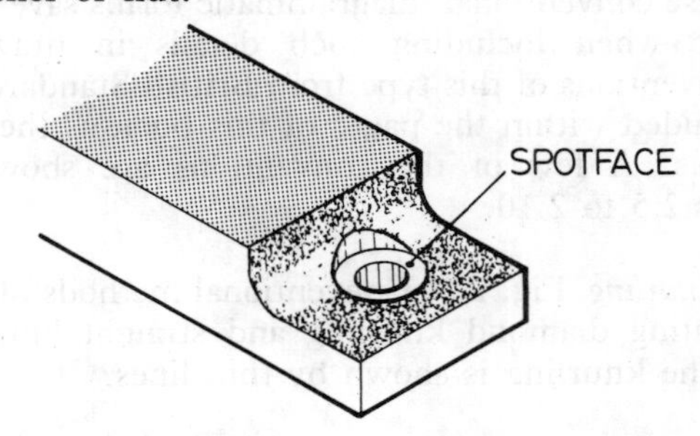

– *Square* Preceding a dimension; SQ in a note.
– *Standard* STD
– *Taper* A gradual change in diameter between two parts of a rod-shaped part.

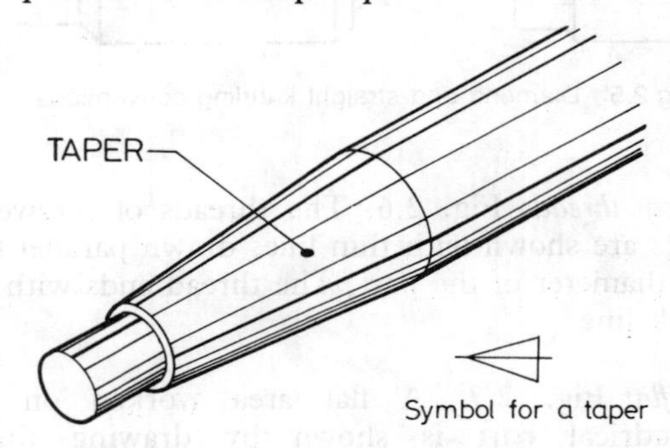

– *Tolerance* TOL

– *Web* Also referred to as a Rib. A thin supporting member between two parts.

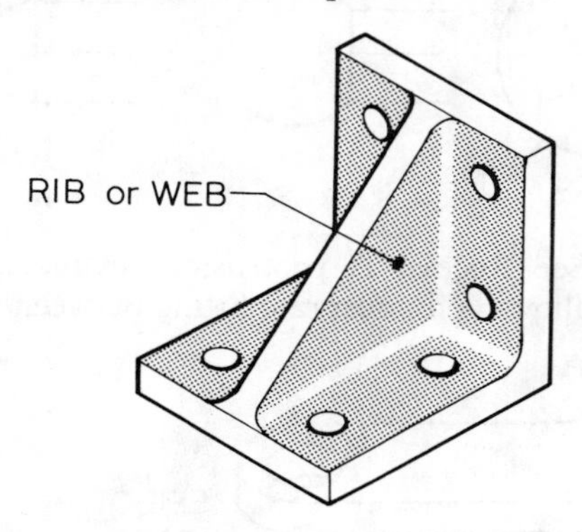

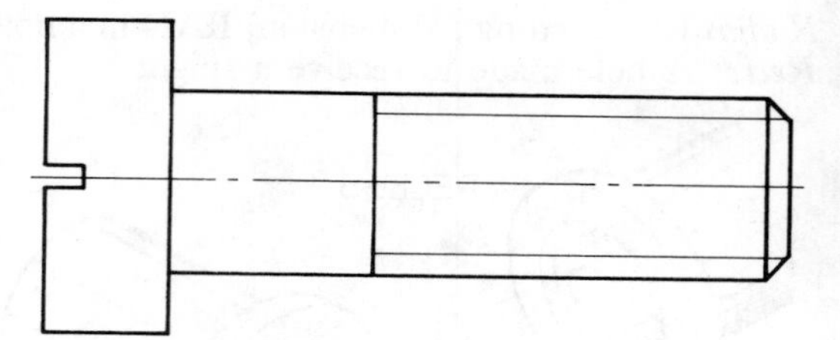

Fig.2.6 Convention for screw thread

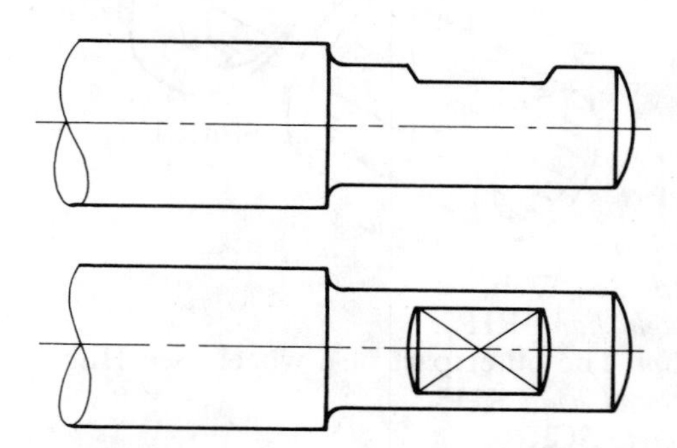

Fig.2.7 Convention for a flat on a shaft

CONVENTIONAL REPRESENTATION OF PARTS

A number of conventional methods of showing engineering details are given in British Standards. These conventional, diagrammatic forms save much time when including such details in drawings. Conventions of this type from British Standards are included within the pages of this book as the need arises. A few of the conventions are shown by Figs 2.5 to 2.10.

– *Knurling* Fig. 2.5. Conventional methods of indicating diamond knurling and straight knurling. The knurling is shown by thin lines.

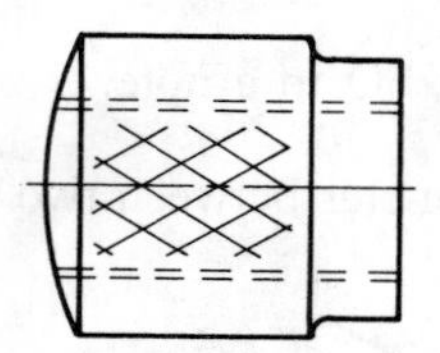

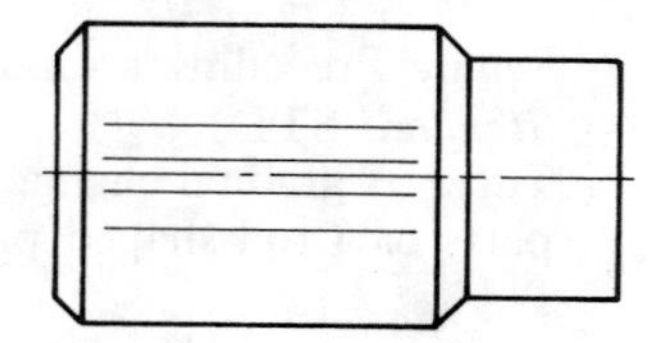

Fig.2.5 Diamond and straight knurling conventions

– *Screw threads* Fig. 2.6. The threads of screwed parts are shown with thin lines drawn parallel to the diameter of the part. The thread ends with a thick line.

– *A flat* Fig. 2.7. A flat area worked on a cylindrical part is shown by drawing thin diagonal lines across the flat.

– *Bearings* Fig. 2.8. All forms of bearing are drawn conventionally as shown. The type of bearing, e.g. plain, roller, ball, may be indicated by added notes or by reference numbering.

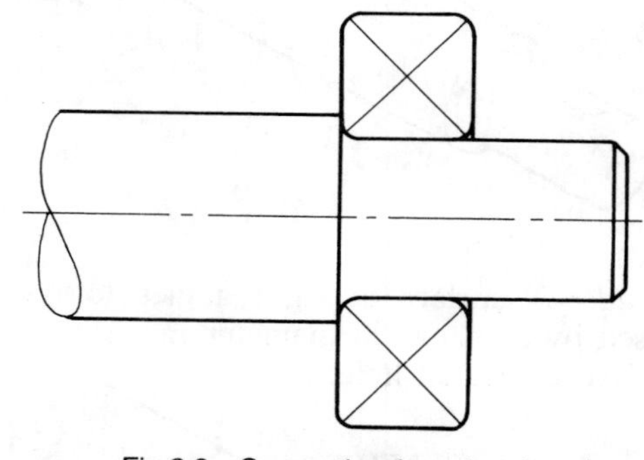

Fig.2.8 Convention for a bearing (type of bearing not specified)

– *A break* Fig. 2.9. If a part is too long to be contained within the area devoted to the drawing of the part, it may be drawn as shown.

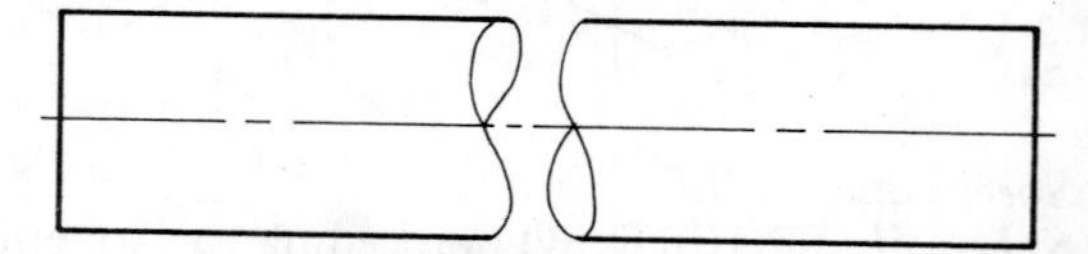

Fig.2.9 Convention for a break

- *Repetition of features* Fig. 2.10. When a number of identical features in a drawing occur, the method shown in the two drawings of Fig. 2.10 can be adopted. Common practice is to add a note to such drawings, e.g. in the examples given 14 HOLES Ø 10 and 8 HOLES Ø 8 at 45°.

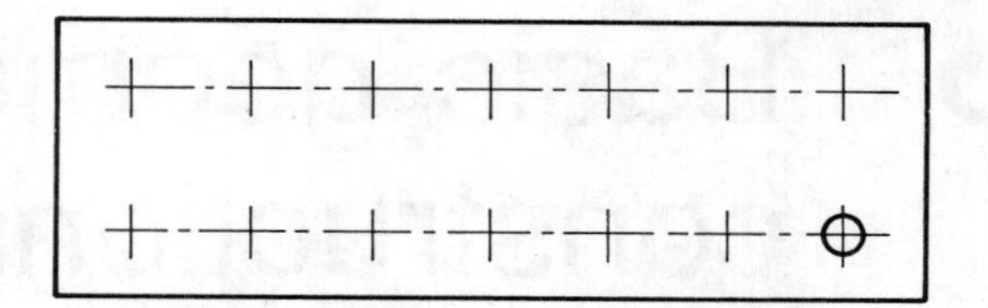

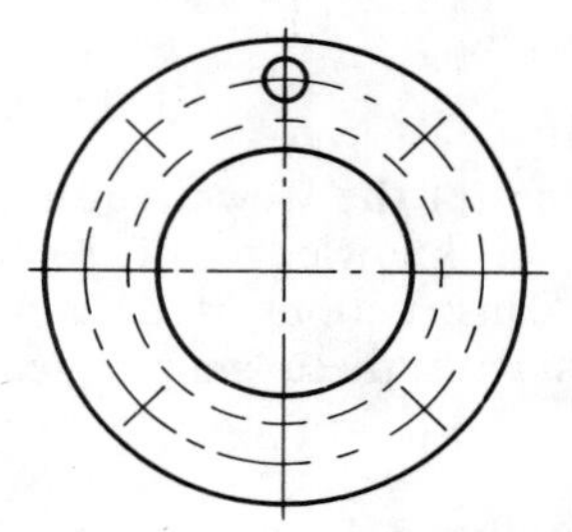

Fig.2.10 Convention to show repeated parts

3 Basic geometrical constructions

When producing the outlines of the views required in engineering drawings, a knowledge of some simple basic geometrical constructions is of good value. This chapter deals with these simple geometrical constructions.

Bisection of a straight line Fig. 3.1

(1) Draw the line AB of any required length.
(2) Set a compass to about two-thirds of the length of AB.
(3) With the compass centred at A draw two arcs, a, above and below the line.
(4) Without altering the set of the compass, and centred at B, draws arcs b crossing arcs a.
(5) Draw a straight line between the intersections of the arcs a and b to cross AB at C.
(6) C bisects line AB and AC = CB.

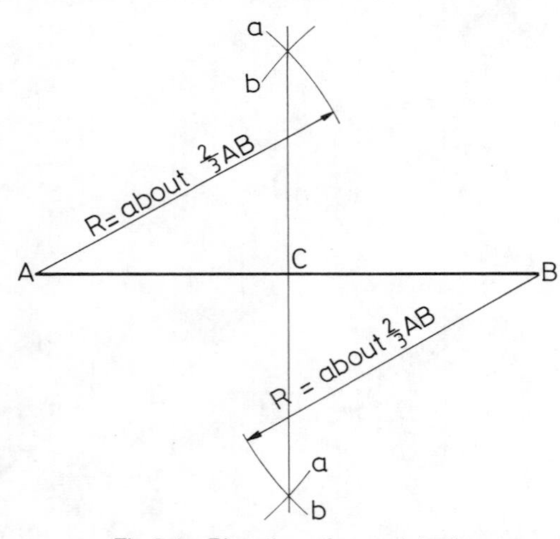

Fig.3.1 Bisection of a straight line

An example of the use of bisection Fig. 3.2

A pair of holes A and B are to be drawn centrally along a bar with the centre of B half way between the centre of A and the end of the bar. The positions of the hole centres are found by bisections are shown.

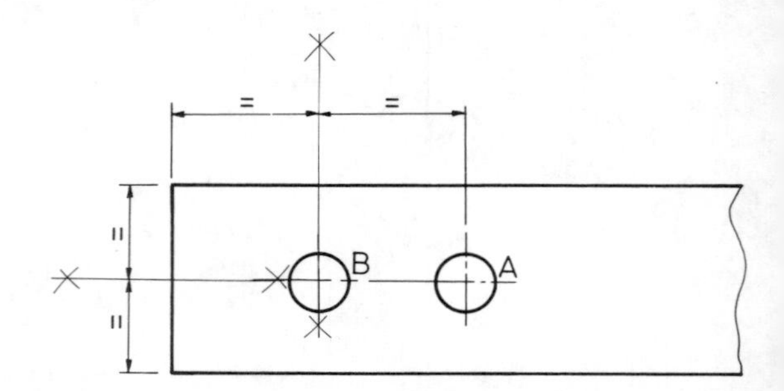

Fig.3.2 Example of an application of bisection of a line

Drawing lines parallel to each other Fig. 3.3

(1) Draw the first line AB.
(2) With a compass set to *r*, the distance that the lines are to be apart, draw an arc with the compass centred at any point along AB.
(3) Adjust two set squares, or a set square and a straightedge so that one edge of set square S rests on AB and another edge of S is resting on the second set square T.
(4) Hold the set square T firmly in position on the drawing sheet and slide set square S along its edge until a line can be drawn tangential to the arc of radius *r* from AB.
(5) The process can be repeated to draw other lines at distance *r* apart, all parallel to AB.

Division of line into equal parts Fig. 3.4

The line AB is to be divided into a number of parts of equal length – in this example into five equal parts.

(1) Draw the line AB of the required length.
(2) Draw AC at any convenient angle to AB.
(3) With a compass set to any convenient length mark off five equal spaces along AC to give the points 1 to 5.
(4) Join point 5 to B.
(5) Draw lines parallel to B5 through points 1 to 4.
(6) Where this series of parallel lines meet AB are the points of equal divisions along AB.

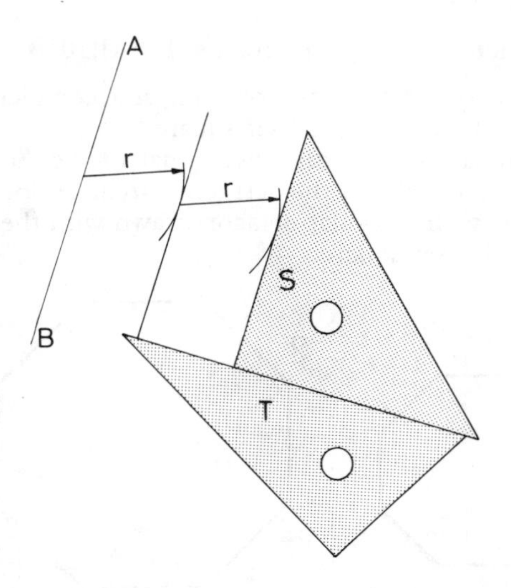

Fig.3.3 Drawing lines parallel to each other

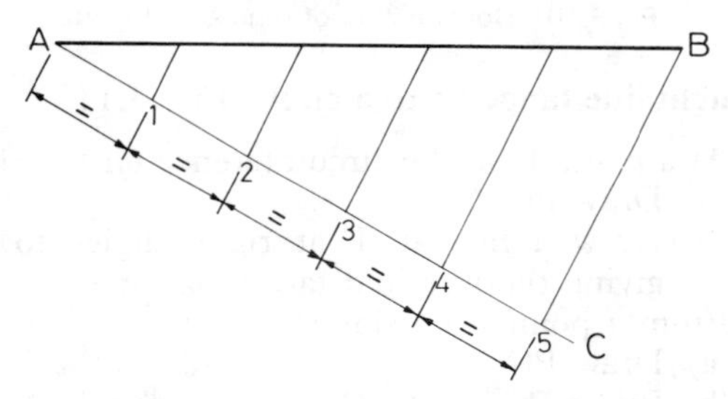

Fig.3.4 Division of a line into equal parts

An example of the use of the division of a line Fig. 3.5

Eight holes with their centres equally spaced along a straight line are to be drawn. Locate the positions of the first and last holes. Divide the line so obtained into seven equal parts. Note that there is no need to draw all the circles of the holes.

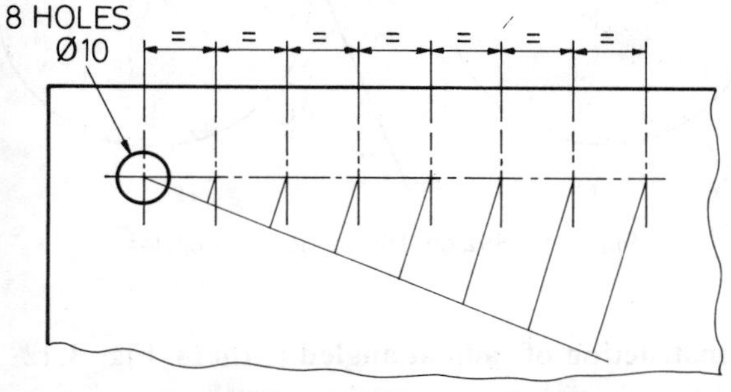

Fig.3.5 Example of an application of dividing a line into equal parts

Construction of regular hexagons Fig. 3.6

Three methods are shown.

(1) Draw a circle of a radius that is equal to one side of the required regular hexagon. Draw a diameter of the circle. From each end of the diameter draw arcs of circle radius to cross the circle. Join the points so obtained.
(2) Draw a circle of a radius that is equal to one side of the required regular hexagon. Draw a diameter of the circle. From each end of the diameter draw lines with a 30°, 60° set square as shown.
(3) Draw a circle of a diameter equal to the Across Flats (AF) size of the required regular hexagon. Circumscribe the circle with the hexagon as shown, with the aid of a 30°, 60° set square.

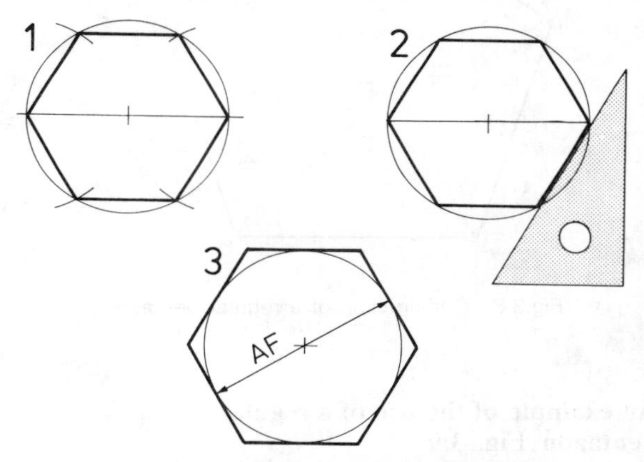

Fig.3.6 Construction of regular hexagons

Examples of the use of regular hexagons Fig. 3.7

One of the most common applications of the use of regular hexagons seen in engineering drawings is in the outlines of nuts and of bolt heads. Drawing 1 shows a hexagonal headed bolt in plan; Drawing 2 shows a hexagonal nut.

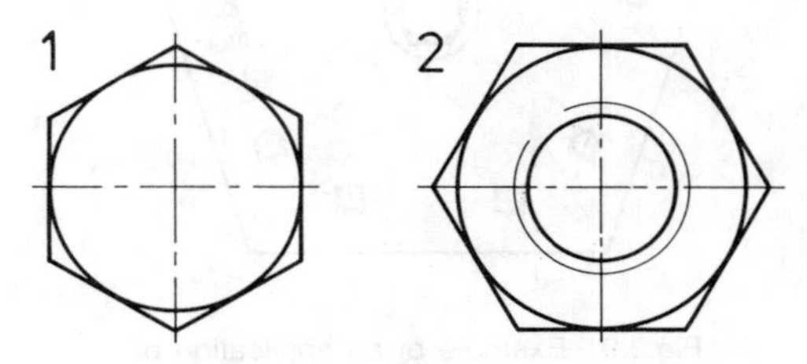

Fig.3.7 Examples of regular hexagons in applications

Construction of a regular pentagon Fig. 3.8

(1) Draw side AB of the required length.
(2) Draw AC and BC at 45° to AB, to meet at C.
(3) Draw AD and BD at 60° to AB, to meet at D.
(4) Bisect CD to give E.
(5) Set a compass to radius EA (or EB) and draw a circle centred at E.
(6) Set a compass to AB and from B and A mark off F and H.
(7) Produce CD to meet the circle at G.
(8) Join BF, FG, GH and HA to complete the required regular pentagon.

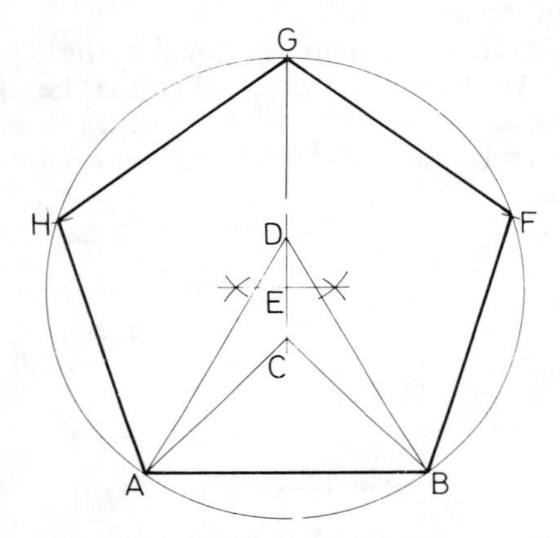

Fig.3.8 Construction of a regular pentagon

An example of the use of a regular pentagon Fig. 3.9

The plan of a five-tool turret from a capstan lathe is in the form of a regular pentagon.

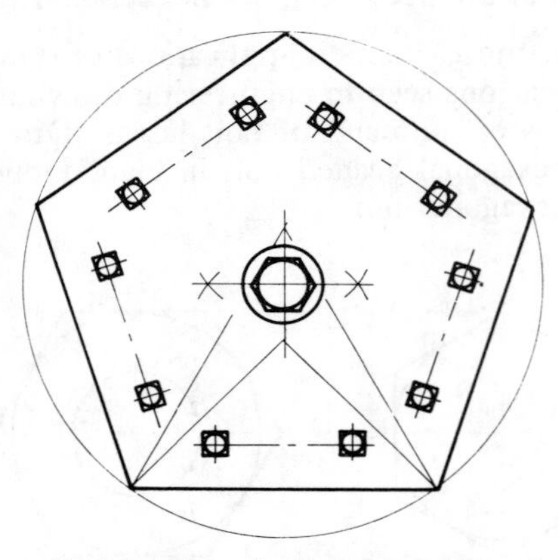
Fig.3.9 Example of an application of the construction of a regular pentagon

Construction of regular octagon Fig. 3.10

(1) Draw one side of the octagon and complete it with the aid of a 45° set square.
(2) Draw a circle of diameter equal to the Across Flats (AF) size of the octagon. Circumscribe the circle with a regular octagon drawn with the aid of a 45° set square.

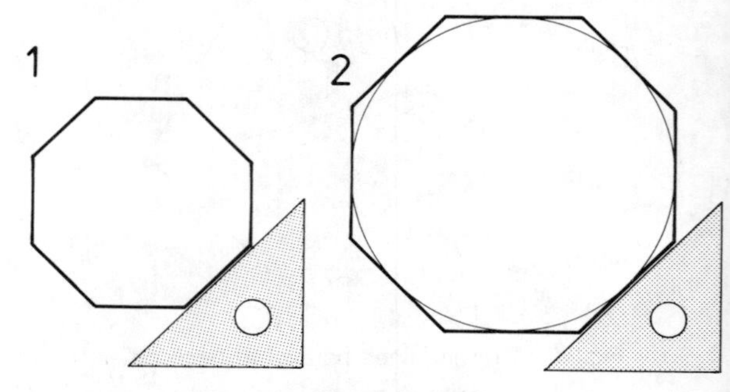

Fig.3.10 Construction of regular octagons

Straight line tangents to a circle Fig. 3.11

(1) At a point T on the circumference on the circle
 (a) Draw line OT.
 (b) Draw a line at T at right angles to OT giving the required tangential line.
(2) From a point P outside the circle
 (a) Draw PO.
 (b) Bisect PO giving C.
 (c) Draw the semi-circle on OP centred at C.
 (d) T, where the semi-circle crosses the circle is the point of tangency.
 (e) Draw PT – the required tangent.

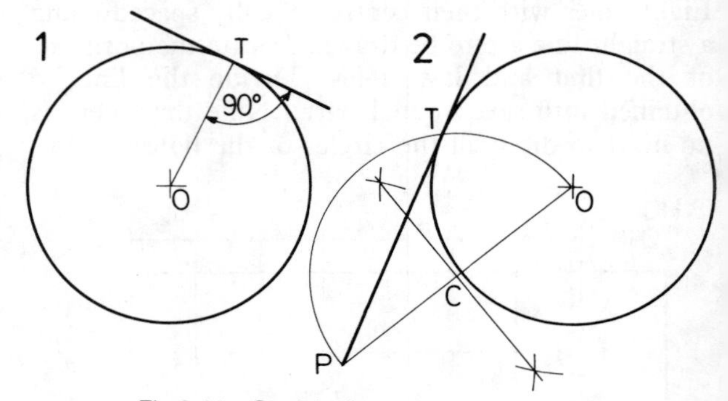

Fig.3.11 Straight line tangents to circles

Construction of radii at angled corners Fig. 3.12

Examples of radii drawn at a right angled corner (1), an acute angled corner of less than 90° (2) and an obtuse angled corner of between 90° and 180° (3), are given. The constructions show methods of obtaining a smooth join between the straight lines forming the angle and the arc of radius R joining the two lines of the angle.

Right angled corner

In drawing 1, the angle at A is 90°. To find the centre of an arc of radius R joining the arms of the angle.

(1) Set a compass to R.
(2) From the corner A of the angle strike arcs along each arm.
(3) From the points where these arcs meet the lines of the angle strike arcs to meet at C. C is the required arc centre.

Acute angled corner

(1) Draw lines at distance R parallel to each arm of the angle.
(2) Where the two lines meet at C is the centre of the required arc.

Obtuse angled triangle

Follow the same procedure as for an acute angle to find the centre C of the required arc.

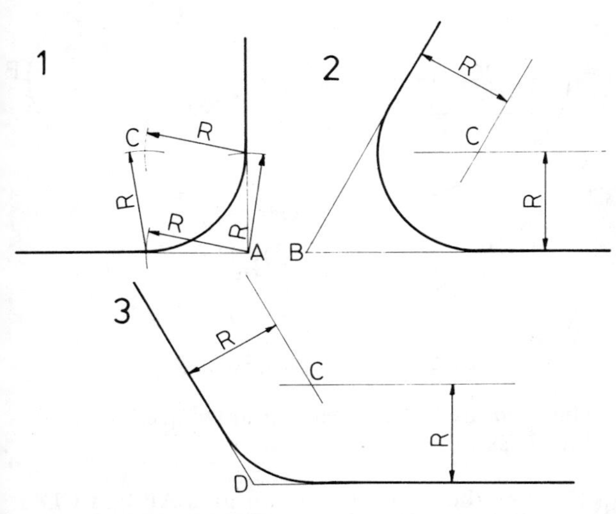

Fig.3.12 Construction of centres for radii at angled corners

Tangency between arcs of circles

When it is required to draw arcs of circles to meet so as to form a smooth join, the arcs must meet at the points of tangency between the curves. Two examples are given.

Arcs of circles meeting internally Fig. 3.13 An arc of radius R is joined internally by arcs of radius r.

From the centre of the arc of radius R draw an arc of a radius equal to the difference $(R - r)$ of the two radii. The centres C_1 and C_2 of the arcs of radius r will be on the arc of radius $R - r$. Note that the lines OC_1 and OC_2 produced pass through the points of tangency T of the smaller and larger joining arcs.

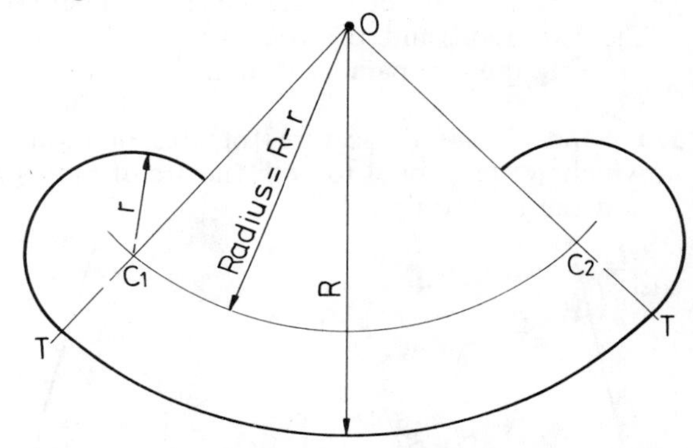

Fig.3.13 Tangency between arcs of circles meeting internally

Arcs of circles meeting externally Fig. 3.14 An arc of radius R is joined externally by arcs of radius r.

From the centre of the arc of radius R draw an arc of a radius equal to the sum $(R + r)$ of the two radii. The centres C_1 and C_2 of the arcs of radius r will be on the arc of radius $R + r$.

Note that the lines OC_1 and OC_2 pass through the points of tangency of the smaller and larger joining arcs.

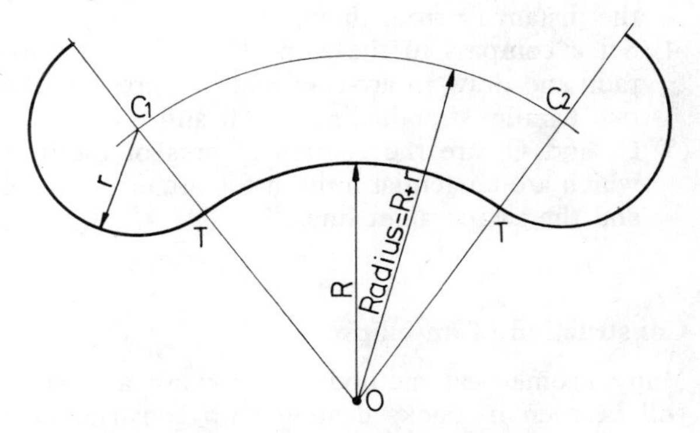

Fig.3.14 Tangency between arcs of circles meeting externally

Arcs of circles meeting straight lines

When it is required to draw arcs of circles to meet straight lines so as to form a smooth join between the arcs and lines, proceed as shown in Figs 3.15 and 3.16.

Example 1 Fig. 3.15

(1) Draw the arc of radius R centred at O.
(2) Draw the two straight lines.
(3) Draw lines parallel to the two straight lines at the distance r from them.
(4) Set a compass to the difference $(R - r)$ between the two radii and draw an arc centred at O crossing the two parallel straight lines at C_1 and C_2.
(5) C_1 and C_2 are the centres of arcs of radius r which are tangential to both the arc of radius R and the two straight lines.

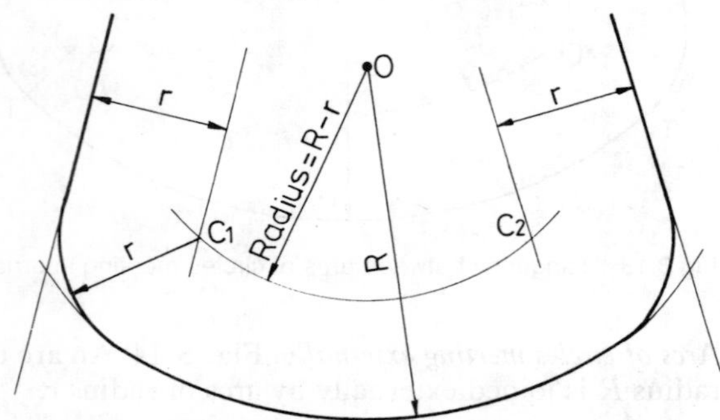

Fig.3.15 Arcs of circles meeting straight lines – Example 1

Example 2 Fig. 3.16

(1) Draw the arc of radius R centred at O.
(2) Draw the two straight lines.
(3) Draw lines parallel to the two straight lines at the distance r from them.
(4) Set a compass to the sum $(R + r)$ of the two radii and draw an arc centred at O, crossing the two parallel straight lines at C_1 and C_2.
(5) C_1 and C_2 are the centres of arcs of radius r which are tangential to both the arc of radius R and the two straight lines.

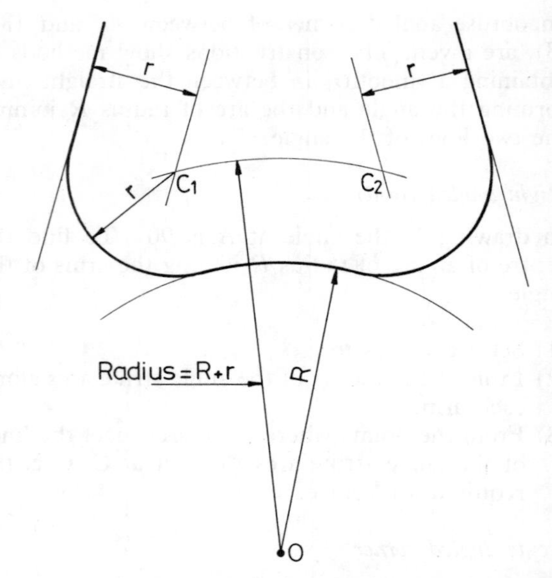

Fig.3.16 Arcs of circles meeting straight lines – Example 2

Construction of an ellipse

Many geometrical methods of drawing an ellipse will be seen in books dealing with constructional geometry. Only one is shown here. This method (Fig. 3.17) is quite suitable for drawing ellipses

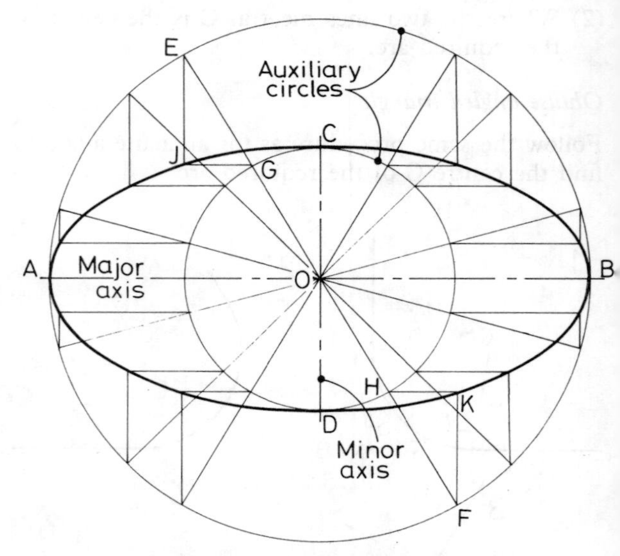

Fig.3.17 Construction for an ellipse

when required in engineering drawings. The procedure is as follows:

(1) Draw the major and minor axes AB and CD at right angles to each other, meeting at the ellipse centre O.
(2) With a compass set to OA (or OB) and centred at O, draw the major auxiliary circle.
(3) With a compass set to OC (or OD) and centred at O, draw the minor auxiliary circle.

(4) Draw a number of diagonals crossing both major and minor auxiliary circles. EOF is one such diagonal.
(5) Taking each diagonal in turn, draw lines parallel to the major axis from the points where the diagonals cross the minor auxiliary circle. The lines GJ and HK are examples.
(6) Taking each diagonal in turn, draw lines parallel to the minor axis from the points where the diagonals meet the major auxiliary circle. The lines EJ and FK are examples.
(7) The intersections of these lines parallel to the major and minor axes are points on the curve of the ellipse. Thus J and K are on the ellipse.
(8) Draw a fair curve between all the points so obtained to complete the ellipse.

Straight line tangents to an ellipse

At a point on the ellipse Fig. 3.18

(1) Set a compass to half the major axis – in this example ½AB. With the compass centred at either end of the minor axis draw arcs across the major axis. This gives the points f_1 and f_2 – the two *focal points* of the ellipse.
(2) Draw lines from f_1 and f_2 through the point T at which the straight line tangent is to touch.
(3) Bisect the angle between the lines f_1T and f_2T to obtain the required tangent.

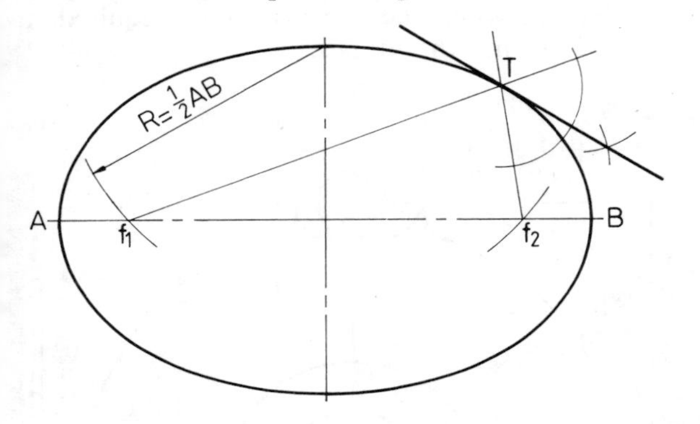

Fig.3.18 Construction of tangent to ellipse

From a point outside the ellipse Fig. 3.19

(1) Construct the two foci f_1 and f_2.
(2) With radius Pf_1 and centre P draw an arc.
(3) With radius equal to the major axis and centre f_2 draw an arc crossing that from P at C and D.
(4) Draw the lines f_2C and f_2D crossing the ellipse at T_1 and T_2.
(5) Draw the tangents PT_1 and PT_2.

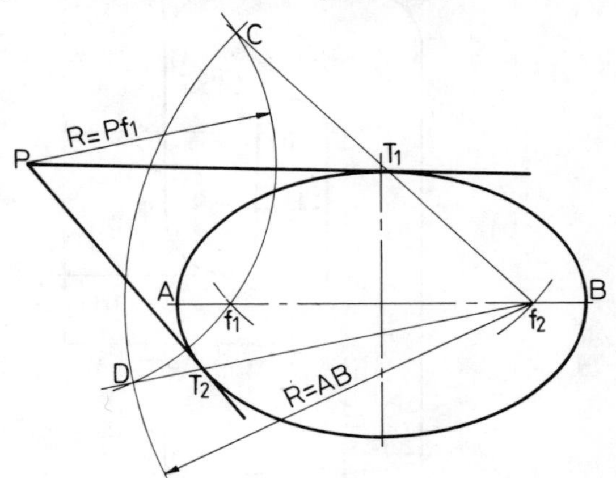

Fig.3.19 Construction of tangent to ellipse – from point outside the ellipse

Exercises

(1) The given drawing is a front view of a handle made from Ø6 mm rod. Make an accurate scale 1:1 drawing of the handle showing how the centres of all the arcs were obtained.

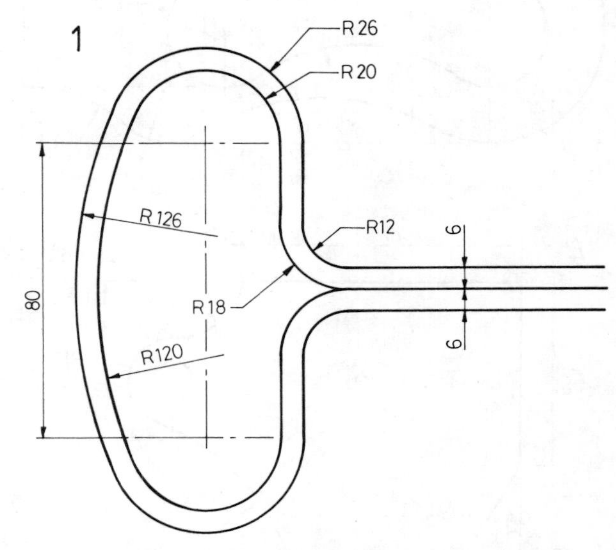

(2) A view of part of a clip is given. Copy the given view to a scale of 1:1. Your drawing should show the constructions required to find the centres of all arcs.

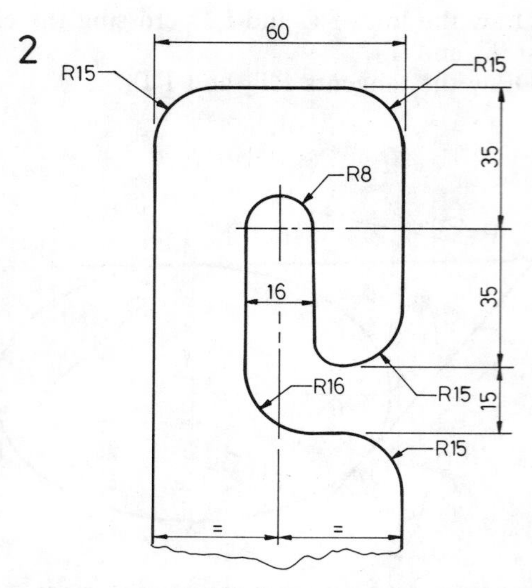

(3) A handle from a machine is shown. Make an accurate scale 1:1 drawing of the handle showing the constructions used to find the centres of all arcs.

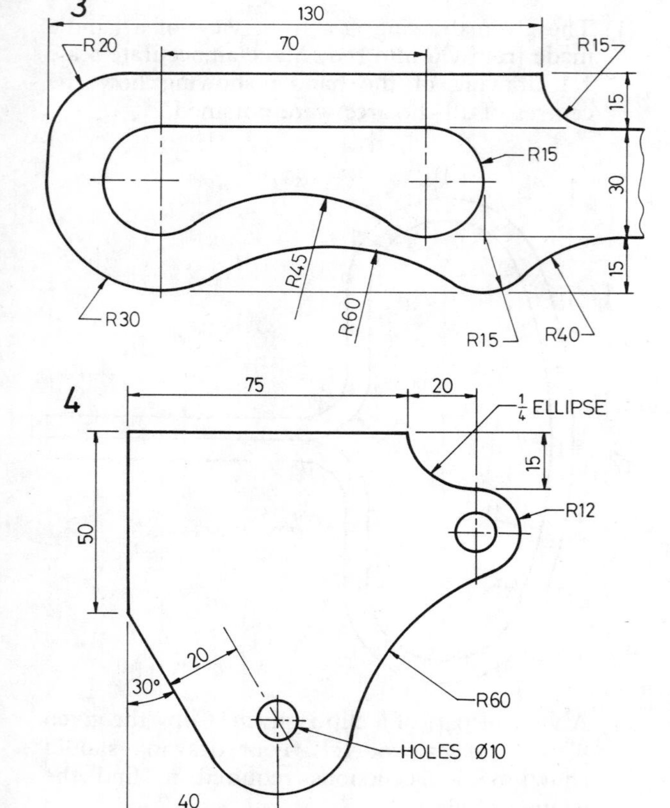

(4) A piece of steel plate is to be made to the outline shown. Construct an accurate scale 1:1 drawing of the outline of the plate showing the geometrical constructions used to obtain the outline.

(5) A front view of a locking clip from a screw cutting machine is given. Draw, scale 1:1, an accurate copy of the given front view. Include in your drawing all the constructional lines for finding the arc centres.

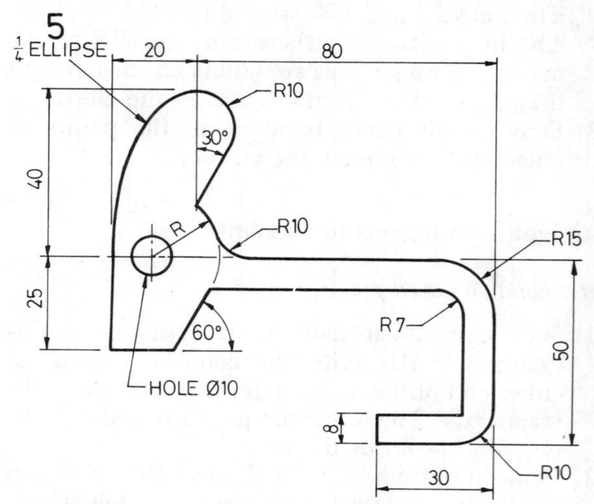

(6) A plan of the base from a hand-held router machine is shown. Draw, scale 1:1, the given plan showing the constructions required to achieve smooth outlines.

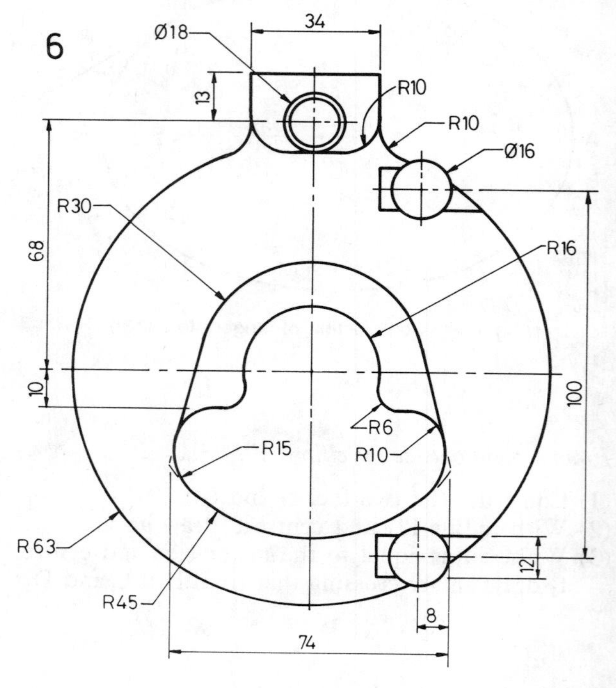

Construction of a parabola

A parabola may be regarded as the *locus* of a point which moves so as to be always the same distance from a fixed point (the *focus*) as it is from a fixed line (the *directrix*). A parabola is also one of the curves in the *conic section* series (see page 76). The actual shape of a parabolic curve will vary according to the perpendicular distance of its focus from its directrix. Fig. 3.20 shows the construction of a parabola, the focus of which is 25 mm from its directrix.

(1) Draw the directrix dd.
(2) Draw the axis of the parabola at right angles to the directrix.
(3) Mark f (the focus) 25 mm from dd along the axis.
(4) Find the vertex (V), half way between f and dd. V is one point on the parabola.
(5) Draw lines AA, BB, CC, etc., parallel to and *any* distances from dd.
(6) Set a compass to the perpendicular distance that AA is from dd. With the compass centred at f strike arcs across AA.
(7) Repeat step 6 with the compass set to the perpendicular distances that BB, CC, etc., are from dd, and strike arcs across BB, CC, etc., with the compass set at f in each case.
(8) The points where this series of arcs cross the lines AA, BB, CC, etc., are on the parabola.
(9) Draw a fair curve through V and the points of intersection to obtain the curve of the parabola.

Construction of a hyperbola

A hyperbola may be regarded as the locus of a point which moves so that it is always a greater distance from a given focus than it is perpendicularly from a given directrix by a constant ratio greater than 1. This ratio is known as the *eccentricity* (*e*) of the hyperbola. Note that the eccentricity of a parabola is always 1. Also note that an ellipse can be regarded as the locus of a point in which the eccentricity is always less than 1. The hyperbola can also be regarded as a conic section (see page 76). Fig. 3.21 shows the construction of a hyperbola with an eccentricity of 1.25 and with its focus 25 mm from its directrix.

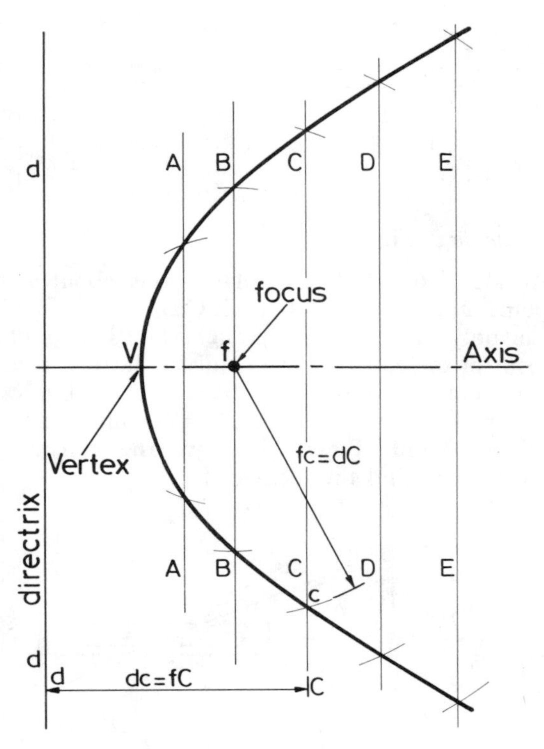

Fig.3.20 Construction of a parabola

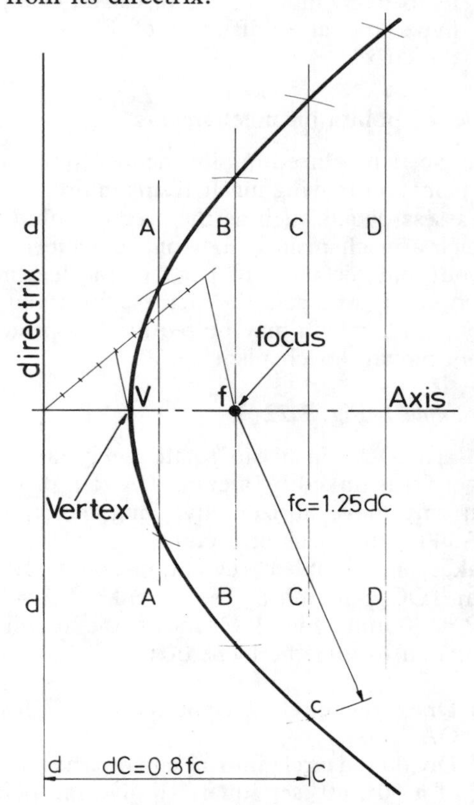

Fig.3.21 Construction of a hyperbola

(1) Draw the directrix and axis and mark the focus f.
(2) Draw lines AA, BB, CC, etc., at *known* distances from dd.
(3) Find V so that ddV:Vf = 4:5. This gives a ratio Vf:ddV = 1.25.
(4) Set a compass to 1.25 of the distance that AA is perpendicularly from dd. With the compass at f strike arcs across the line AA.
(5) Repeat on lines BB, CC, etc., remembering that the distance to the lines from f is always 1.25 that which the lines are from dd.
(6) Draw a fair curve through the intersections of the arcs and the lines and also through the vertex V to obtain the required hyperbolic curve.

Exercises

(1) Draw a parabola whose focus is 20 mm from its directrix. Complete the parabola at a distance of 60 mm from the directrix.
(2) Draw a hyperbola of eccentricity 1.2 and with its focus 30 mm from its directrix. Complete the hyperbola at a distance of 80 mm from the directrix.

Loci of points on mechanisms

Engineers may need to plot the loci (plural of locus) of points on moving mechanisms in order to be able to assess details such as the area or volume within which a mechanism is moving; to achieve a correct layout and distances of parts of mechanisms from each other; to assess the shapes, form and sizes of any guards which may be required to protect users from moving mechanisms.

Example 1 Fig. 3.22

An arm OC which can rotate freely about a fixed pivot O, is linked by a crank CA to a piston which can only move horizontally along the straight line OA. Plot the locus of a point P on CA as the arm makes one complete revolution about O. Let the arm OC = 35 mm; the crank CA = 80 mm; AP = 30 mm. Fig. 3.23 shows the required construction to find the locus of P.

(1) Draw the circle OC of 35 mm radius. Draw OA.
(2) Divide the circle into 12 equal parts with the aid of a 30°, 60° set square to give the points 1 to 12.

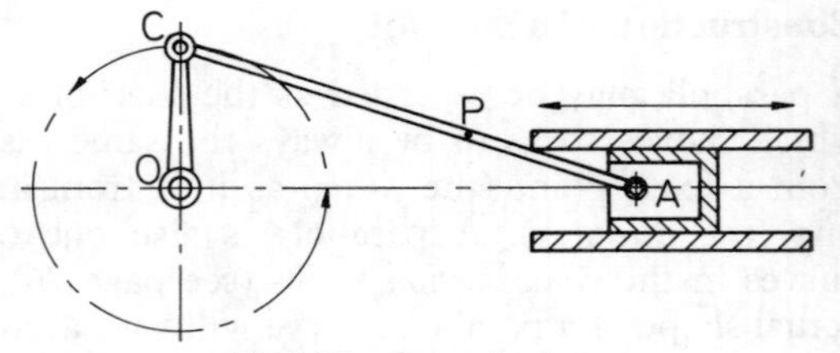

Fig.3.22 Example 1

(3) Set a compass to the length CA (80 mm) and with the compass centred at the points 1 to 12 in turn strike arcs along the line OA. Join the points 1 to 12 to the points where these arcs cross OA. One example is labelled CA.
(4) Set a compass to AP (30 mm) and mark from each of the points A on circle OA along the lines AC to give 12 positions of P along the lines CA.
(5) Join the 12 positions of P so found with a fair curve to obtain the required locus.

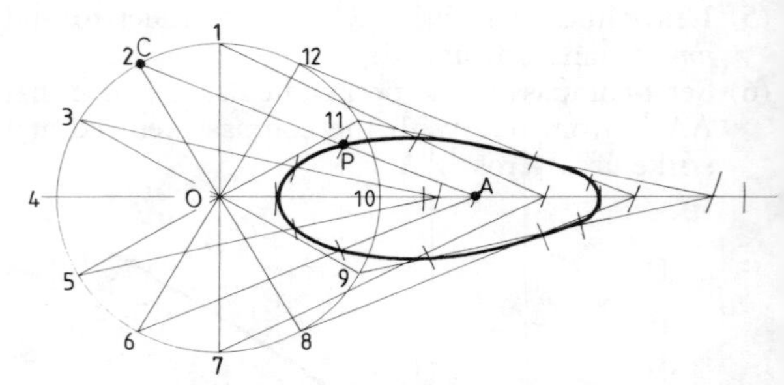

Fig.3.23 Construction for Example 1

Example 2 Fig. 3.24

An arm OC which can rotate freely about a fixed point O, is linked by a crank CAL to a slide which can only move along a straight line OA. Plot the locus of the end L of the crank as the arm makes a complete revolution about O. Let the arm = 40 mm; the length CA = 90 mm; the length AL = 30 mm. Fig. 3.25 shows the construction required to find the locus of L.

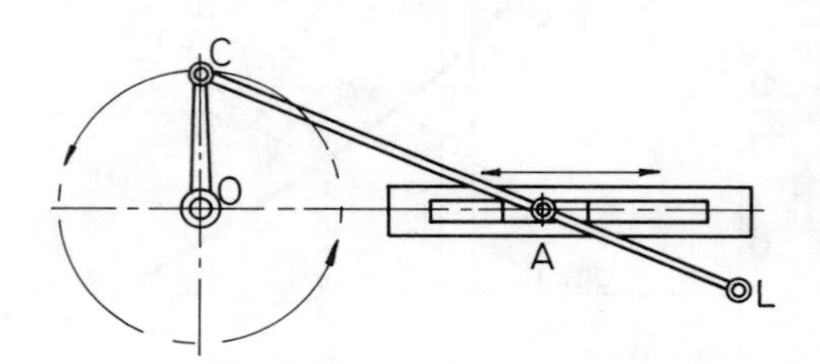

Fig.3.24 Example 2

(1) Draw the circle OC of radius 40 mm. Draw OA.
(2) Divide the circle into 12 equal parts with the aid of a 30°, 60° set square to give the points 1 to 12.
(3) Set a compass to CA (90 mm) and with the compass centred at the points 1 to 12 in turn, strike arcs along the line OA. Join the points 1 to 12 to the points where these arcs cross OA and produce each line beyond OA. One example is labelled CAL.
(4) Set a compass to the length AL (30 mm) and from the points A along OA mark off along the lines CAL the 30 mm lengths to give the 12 positions of the end L as OC rotates.
(5) Draw a fair curve through these 12 positions of L to obtain the required locus.

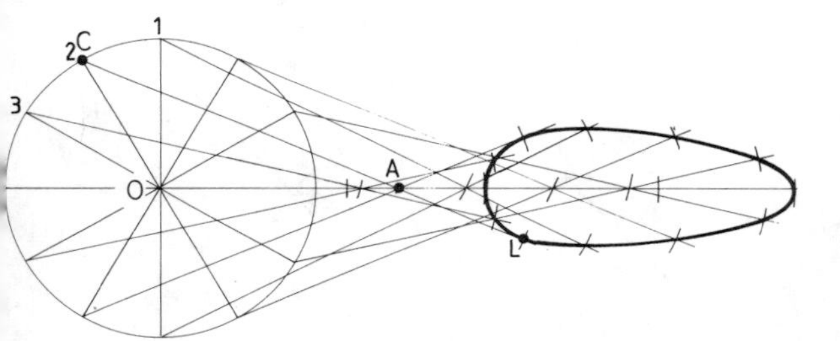

Fig.3.25 Construction for Example 2

Example 3 Fig. 3.26

The end A of a link AB is constrained to move only horizontally by a slider. The end B of link AB is constrained to move only vertically by a slider. Plot the loci of points P_1 and P_2 as the end A slides from left to right as far as is possible in both directions along its horizontal path. Let AB = 120 mm; BP_1 = 40 mm; AP_2 = 35 mm. Fig. 3.27 shows the construction for finding the two locus curves.

(1) Draw two lines at right angles to each other to give the horizontal and vertical paths of A and B.
(2) Mark along the vertical line any number of convenient positions of B. Fig. 3.27 shows 10 such positions.
(3) Set a compass to the length AB (120 mm) and with the compass centred at points 2 to 10 in turn strike arcs across the horizontal path line of A to give 10 positions of the end A. These are labelled A to K.
(4) Join the points 2 to 9 to the points B to J with straight lines.

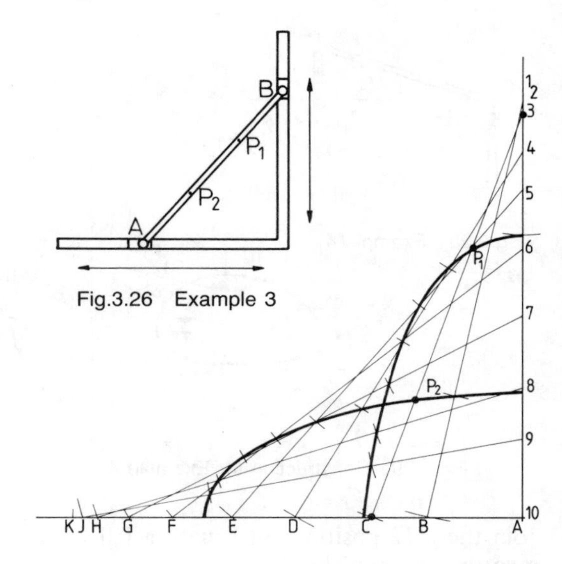

Fig.3.26 Example 3

Fig.3.27 Construction for Example 3

(5) Set a compass to 40 mm and with it mark along the lines from 1 to 10 to give 10 positions of P_1.
(6) Set a compass to 35 mm and with it mark along the lines from A to K to give 10 positions of P_2.
(7) Join the two sets of points with fair curves to obtain the two locus curves.

Example 4 Fig. 3.28

An arm OA which can rotate freely about a fixed pivot O, is linked by a crank AC to another arm BC. B is a second fixed pivot about which C is free to rotate with both clockwise and anti-clockwise movements. Plot the locus of the point P on AC as the arm OA makes a complete revolution about O. Let arm OA = 40 mm; arm BC = 50 mm; crank AC = 170 mm; OC = 165 mm; AP = 80 mm. Fig. 3.29 shows the construction for finding the locus of P.

(1) Divide the circle OA into 12 equal parts with the aid of a 30°, 60° set square, to give points 1 to 12.
(2) Draw the arc BC.
(3) Set a compass to AC (170 mm) and with it centred at points 1 to 12 in turn strike arcs on the arc BC. Join the points 1 to 12 to their respective points on arc BC by straight lines.
(4) Set a compass to AP (30 mm) and with it mark from each of the points A on circle OA along the lines AC to give 12 positions of P along AC.

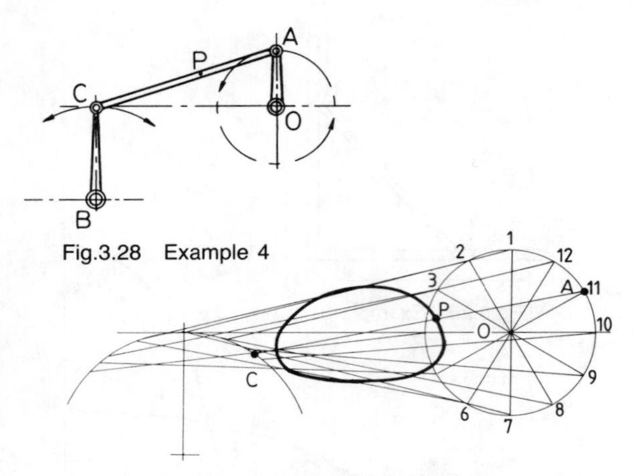

Fig.3.28 Example 4

Fig.3.29 Construction for Example 4

(5) Join these 12 positions of P with a fair curve to give the required locus.

Exercises

Fig. 3.30 explains the symbols in the drawings 1 to 4 on which the four exercises are based.

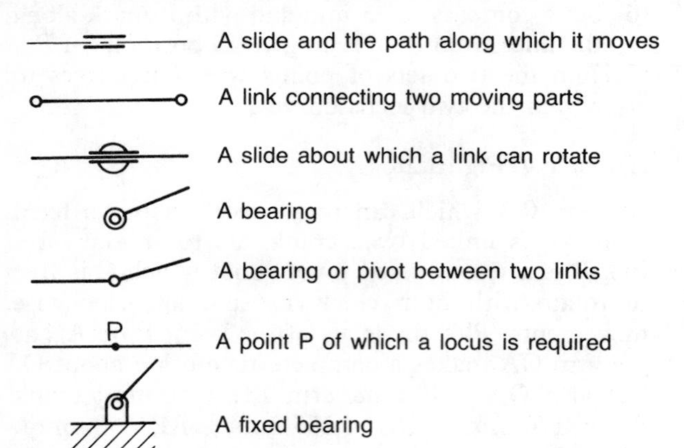

Fig.3.30 Symbols for exercises

(1) An arm OA is free to rotate about a bearing O. The end S of a link AS can only slide horizontally along the line OS. Plot the locus of the point P on AS.

(2) The link SP_2 is restrained to move along AB and AC by slider pivots S and L as shown in the given drawing. Plot the loci of P_1 and P_2 as the end S moves from A towards B and the slider L moves vertically to A.

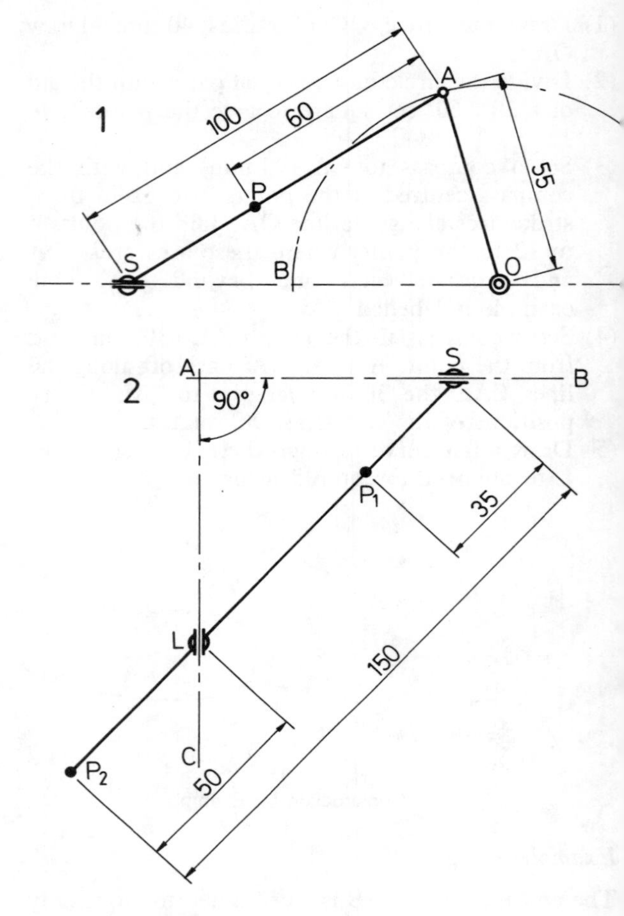

(3) An arm OA is free to move about a bearing O. OA is connected to a second arm BC by a link AB. BC is free to rotate in either direction about the pivot C. Plot the locus of P on AB as OA makes one complete revolution.

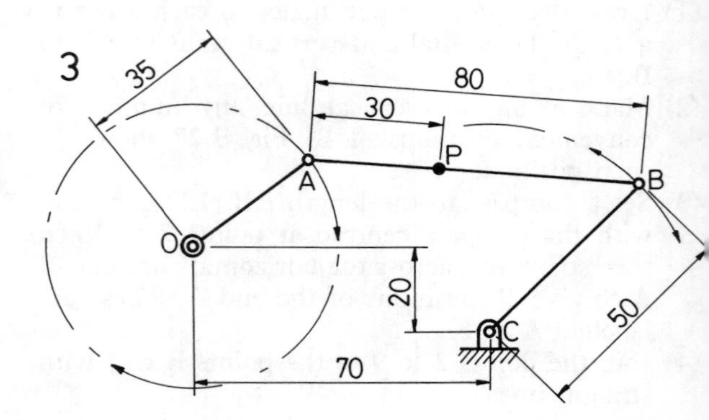

(4) An arm OA is free to rotate about a pivot O. OA is connected at A by a pivot which allows a link AB to slide through a fixed pivot at B. Plot the locus of the two ends P_1 and P_2 of the link AB.

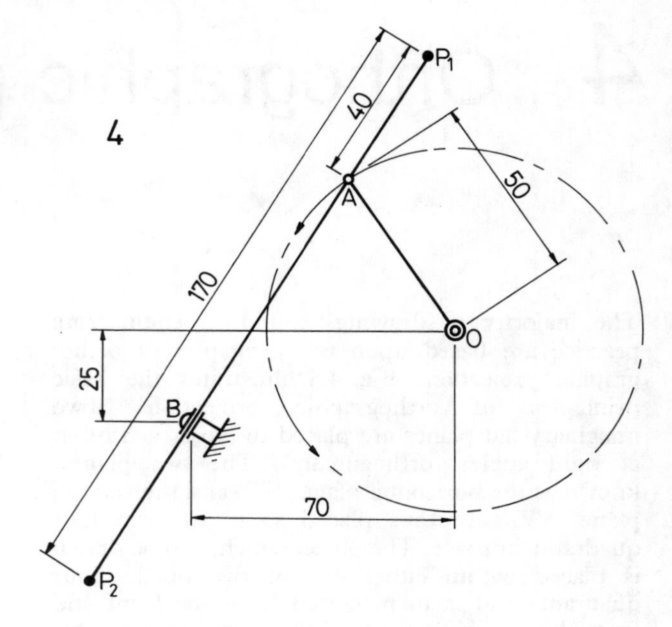

4 Orthographic projection

The majority of drawings found in engineering practice are based upon the principles of orthographic projection. Fig. 4.1 illustrates the basic principles of orthographic projection. Two imaginary flat planes are placed to cross each other at right angles (orthogonally). The two planes, known as the horizontal plane (HP) and the vertical plane (VP), are thus placed so as to form four quadrants in space. The object which is to be drawn is placed within either one of two of the four quadrants and is then viewed from the front and from above. The outlines of the shapes seen by this viewing are then projected on to the two planes. The projection lines involved are parallel to each other, no allowance being made for perspective – i.e. they are orthogonal to the plane on to which the projections are made. It will be noted that, of the four quadrants formed by the horizontal and vertical planes, only two are suitable for orthographic projections. These two quadrants are known as the First Angle and the Third Angle. The second and fourth angles are not suitable for producing sensible projections for engineering drawings and are therefore not used.

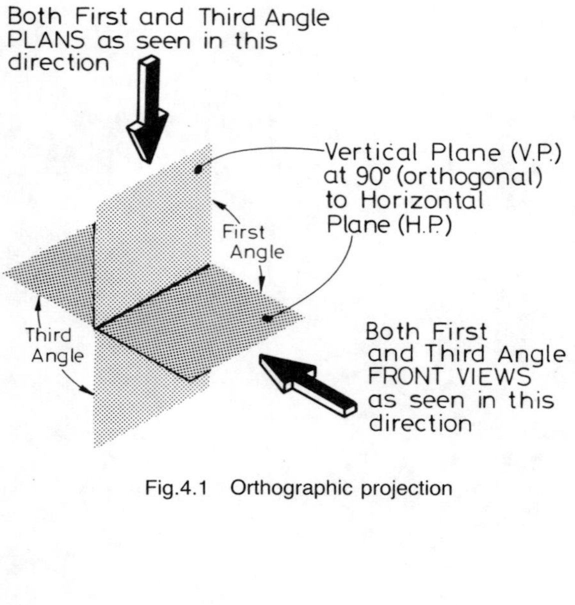

Fig.4.1 Orthographic projection

In the British Isles, First and Third Angle projections are given equal prominence. In the United States of America common practice in engineering drawing is to use the Third Angle system. In Europe generally, First Angle projections are more common. Third Angle projection is sometimes referred to as 'American projection' and you will occasionally hear First Angle projection referred to as 'European projection'. The student is advised to learn the methods of both angles of orthographic projection.

By placing further planes within this system, views can be projected from viewing positions other than from the front or from above. With additional planes views can be projected to obtain views from either end, from below, from the rear, or at angles to either, or both, the horizontal and vertical planes.

FIRST ANGLE ORTHOGRAPHIC PROJECTION

An example of the theory given above as applied to a First Angle orthographic projection is illustrated by Fig. 4.2. This shows how a First Angle projection of a UNIVERSAL JOINT YOKE from the differential system of a motor car has been obtained. Following on from the information given by Fig. 4.1, the component is placed in the space within the First Angle quadrant. It is then viewed from the front, and what is seen is drawn on to the vertical plane (VP). This gives a *front view*. A second viewing position from above allows a projection to be drawn on the horizontal plane (HP) to give a *plan*. A second vertical plane is placed on the right hand of the component and a viewing position to the left of the yoke provides the projections on to the second VP to obtain an *end view*. In this example then we have three views of the article – a front view, a plan and an end view.

It is then imagined that the HP and the second VP are both swung through 90° to lie in the same

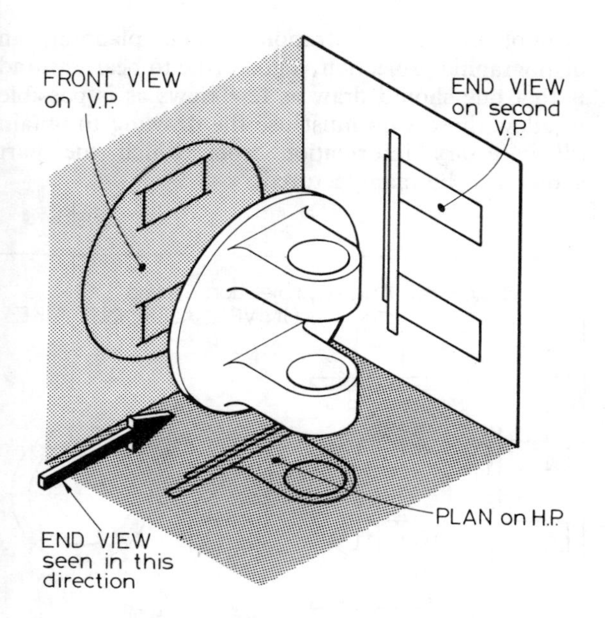

Fig.4.2 First Angle orthographic projection

plane as the first VP – Fig. 4.3. The resulting two-dimensional drawing forms the basis for the views a draughtsman would produce on a drawing sheet. Fig. 4.4 is a draughtsman's detail drawing, or single-part drawing, of the universal joint yoke.

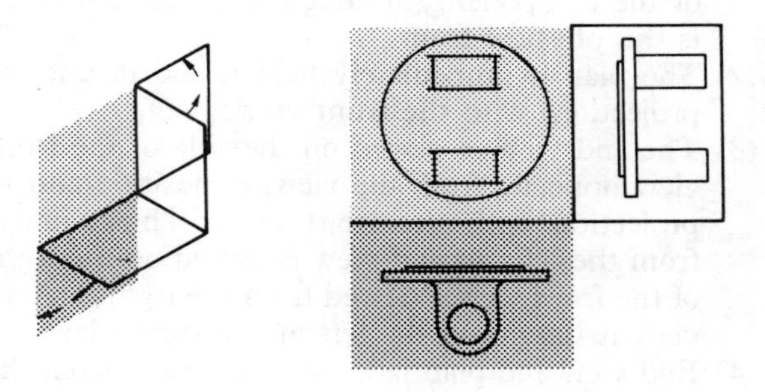

Fig.4.3 The three planes swung into a two-dimensional position

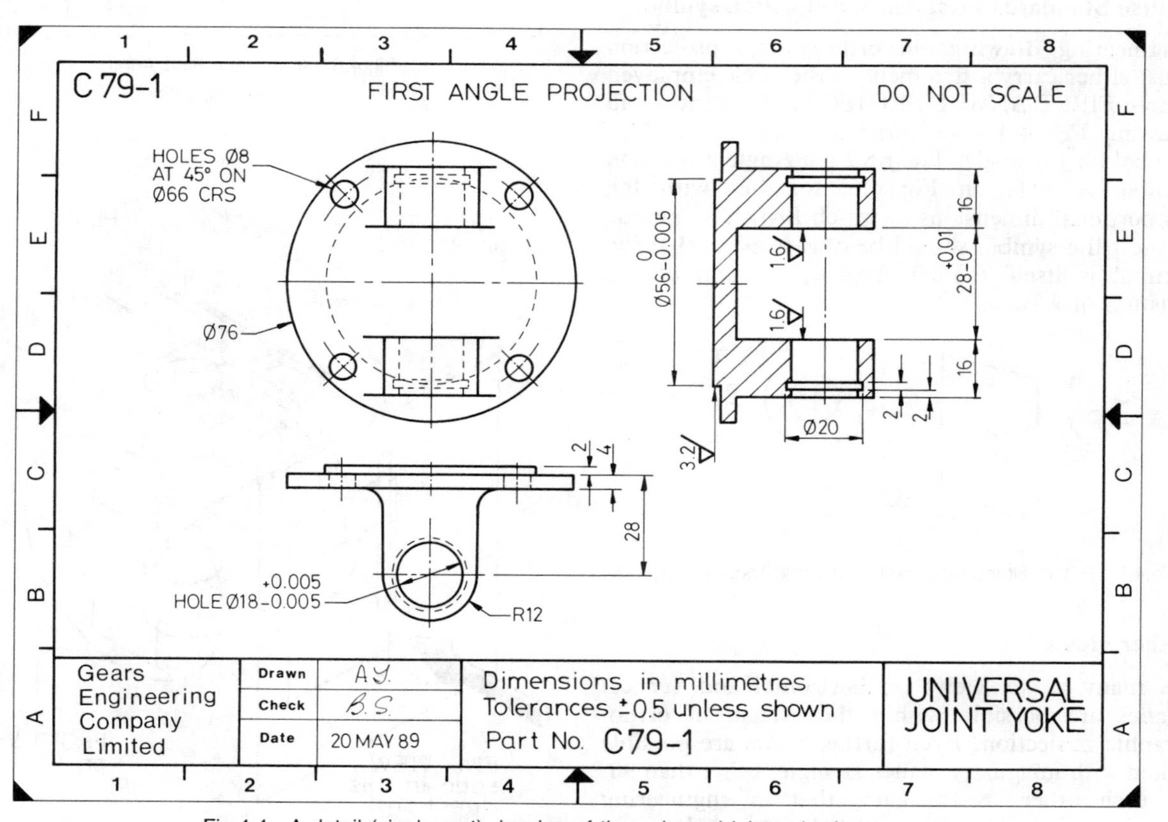

Fig.4.4 A detail (single-part) drawing of the universal joint yoke from a car – First Angle projection

Note the following details, which always apply when a First Angle projection is to be drawn:

(1) The front view is chosen as that view which gives the most information for drawing purposes. It need not necessarily be the actual front of the component, although in practice it often is the physical front.
(2) The plan is immediately below, and in line (or projection) with the front view.
(3) The end view is placed on the side of the front view opposite from the viewing position and in projection with the front view. Thus viewed from the left, an end view is drawn on the right of the front view. Viewed from the right, an end view is drawn on the left of the front view.
(4) End view and plan face *outwards*, away from the front view.
(5) The views are not labelled as such. It is unnecessary, and hence incorrect, to label the views as front view, end view and plan.

British Standards First Angle projection symbol

Engineering drawings in orthographic projection must either carry a statement of the angle employed – note FIRST ANGLE PROJECTION in the detail drawing Fig. 4.4 – or carry the British Standard symbol for the angle. The BS First Angle projection symbol is given in Fig. 4.5, together with the proportional dimensions to which British Standards suggest the symbol should be drawn. Note that the symbol is itself a First Angle projection of the frustum of a cone.

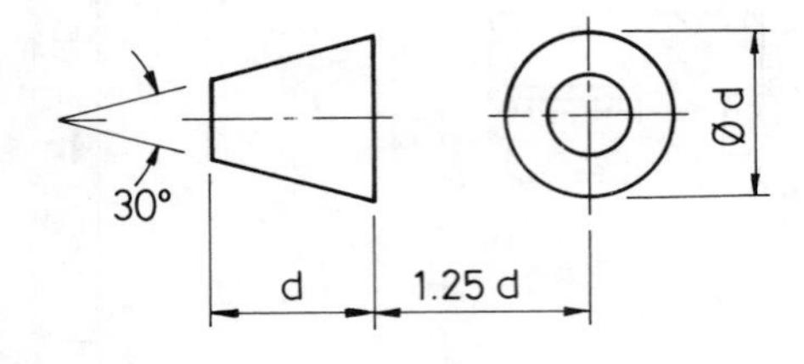

Fig.4.5 British Standards symbol of First Angle projection

Other views

As many as six views on horizontal and vertical planes are possible within the system of orthographic projection. Even further views are possible taken with imaginary planes at angles other than 90° to each other. Note again, that in engineering drawing it is bad practice to label views as shown in Fig. 4.6. Note also the inclusion of the First Angle symbol in this illustration. When planning an orthographic projection, a good rule to bear in mind is that one should draw as few views as is possible to allow those who must use the drawing to obtain *all* necessary information from which the part shown can be manufactured.

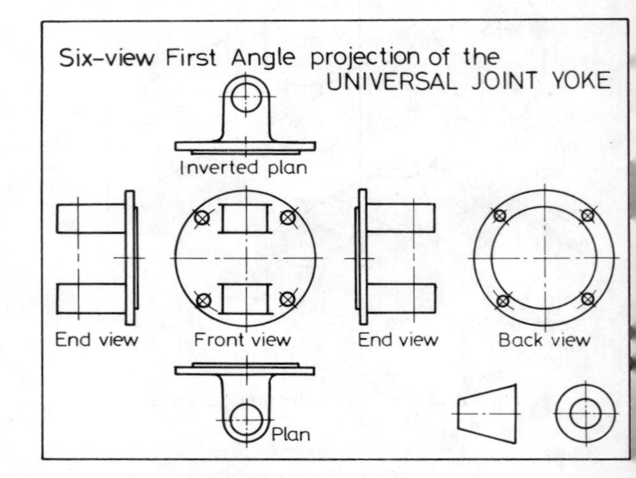

Fig.4.6 A six-view First Angle orthographic projection

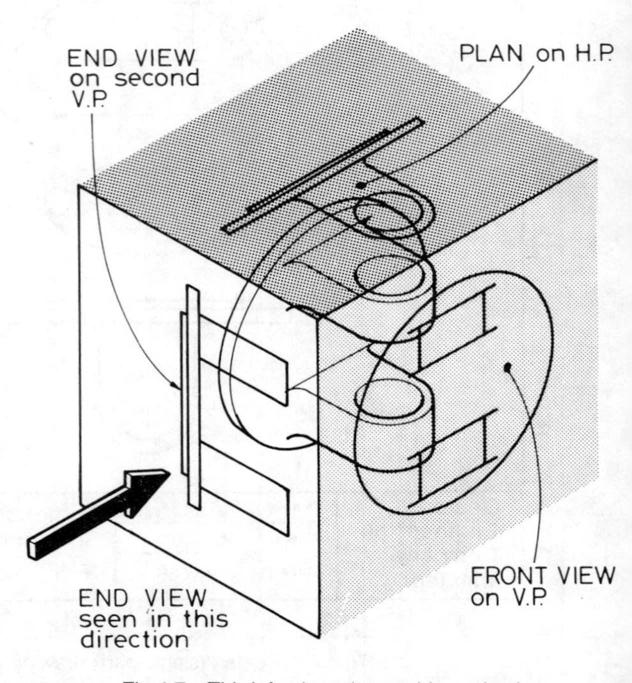

Fig.4.7 Third Angle orthographic projection

THIRD ANGLE ORTHOGRAPHIC PROJECTION

Taking as an example the same UNIVERSAL JOINT YOKE which was used to portray First Angle projection, Fig. 4.7 shows the principles illustrated by Fig. 4.1 as they are applied to Third Angle orthographic projection. The component is placed in the space within the Third Angle quadrant which is formed by the two orthogonally placed vertical and horizontal planes. The directions of viewing to obtain projections are the same as those employed in First Angle projection. The required views are drawn on to the planes *through* which the component can be seen. Thus the front view is drawn on to the vertical plane in front of the component and through which it can be seen. Similarly a plan is drawn on to the horizontal plane which is above the component and through which it can be seen. An end view drawn on a second vertical plane placed on the left of the component completes a three-view projection in Third Angle.

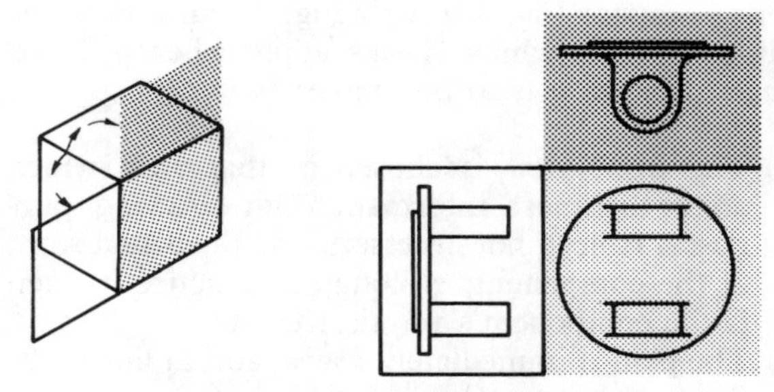

Fig.4.8 The three planes swung into a two-dimensional position

Now imagine the HP and second VP to be rotated through 90° so as they both lie in the same plane as the first VP – Fig. 4.8. The resulting two-dimensional drawing forms the basis of views which a draughtsman would produce on a drawing sheet. Fig. 4.9 is a detail drawing of the universal joint yoke in Third Angle projection. Fig. 4.10 is the British Standards symbol for Third Angle projec-

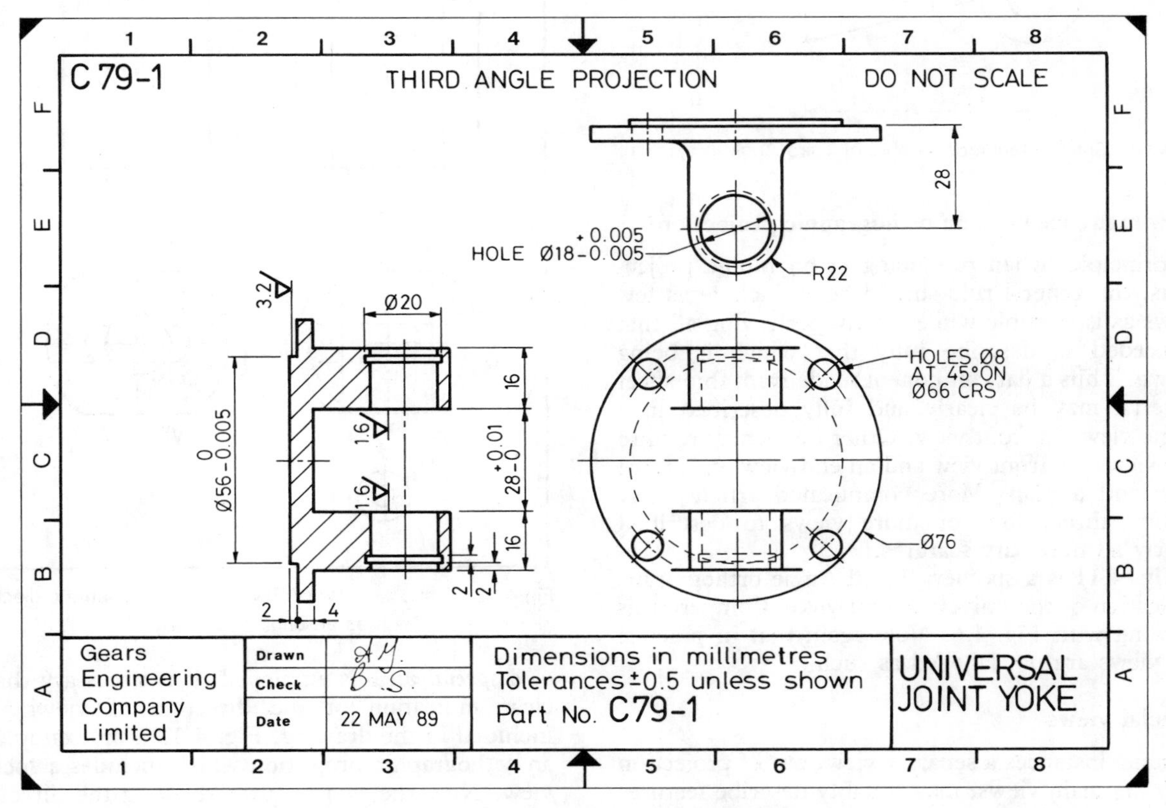

Fig.4.9 A Third Angle projection of the universal joint yoke

tion. Compare Fig. 4.9 with Fig. 4.4 and note the following rules which always apply when a Third Angle projection is to be drawn:

(1) The front view is chosen as that view which gives the most information for drawing purposes. It need not necessarily be the actual front of the component, although in practice it often is the component's physical front.
(2) The plan is immediately *above*, and in line with, the front view.
(3) The end view is placed to the side of, and in line with, the front view on the same side as the viewing position. Thus viewed from the left, the end view is placed to the left of the front view. Viewed from the right, the end view is placed to the right of the front view.
(4) End views and plan face inwards – towards the front view.
(5) The views should *not* be labelled.

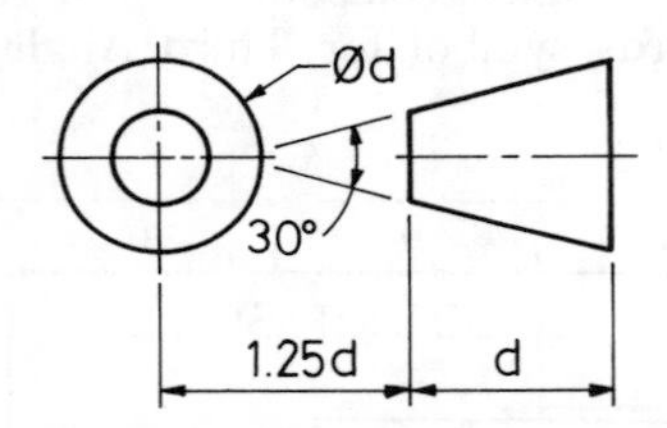

Fig.4.10 British Standards symbol of Third Angle projection

How many views in an orthographic projection?

In principle, when producing orthographic projections, the general rule should be to include as few views as is possible while clearly portraying all that is needed to describe fully that which is being drawn. Thus a flat component made from thin sheet material may be clearly and fully described in a single view – a front view. Other items may require two views – a front view and an end view, or a front view and a plan. More complicated articles may require three, four or more views to described clearly all necessary features.

Fig. 4.11 is a six-view Third Angle orthographic projection of the universal joint yoke. Compare this drawing with Fig. 4.6. Note again that in practice the views are not labelled as such.

Special views

In some instances a separate view, out of projection with the main views, may suitably describe features not clearly shown by the main views. When the idea of a *special view* is employed, it is necessary that a clear indication of the direction of viewing is included in the drawing. Fig. 4.12 is an example of an orthographic projection which includes a special view. Note the two features showing the direction of viewing.

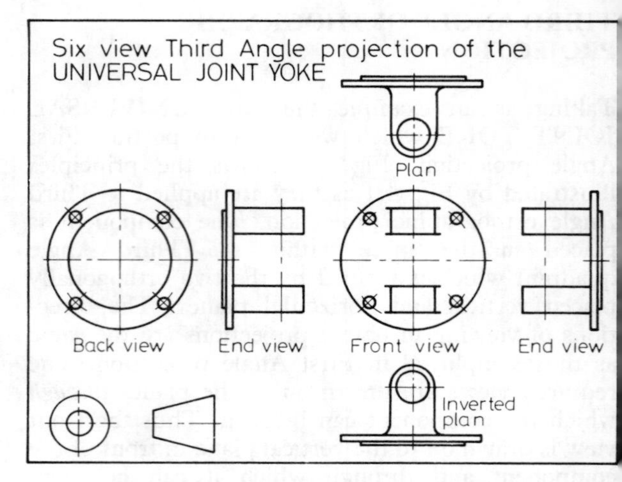

Fig.4.11 A six-view Third Angle projection

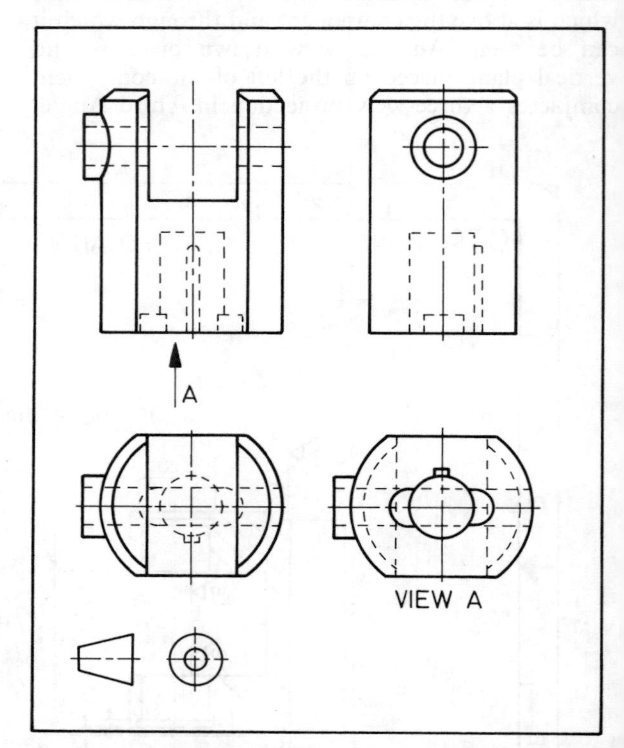

Fig.4.12 A special view (VIEW A) not in the same projection as an original drawing

(1) The arrow labelled A.
(2) The special view itself labelled VIEW A.

Exercises (non-functional)

In order to allow the reader to gain practice in applying the principles of orthographic projection, ten pictorial drawings of non-functional shaped block forms are given on this page and page 00. Each of the ten blocks has been drawn on a 5 mm isometric grid to enable sizes for parts of the blocks to be determined.

For each of the ten exercises:

(1) Determine how many orthographic projection views will show the form of the block without ambiguity.
(2) Working in either First or Third Angle projection draw the views as determined. Practice in both First and Third Angle projections is advisable.
(3) Make the drawings either full size, or if preferred to scale 2:1, i.e. double each of the sizes as found by counting the spaces along the isometric grid lines.
(4) Work either freehand or with instruments on either square grid paper or plain paper as preferred.

These ten exercises involving non-functional block forms are followed by a further twenty-four exercises each involving a component which has an engineering function.

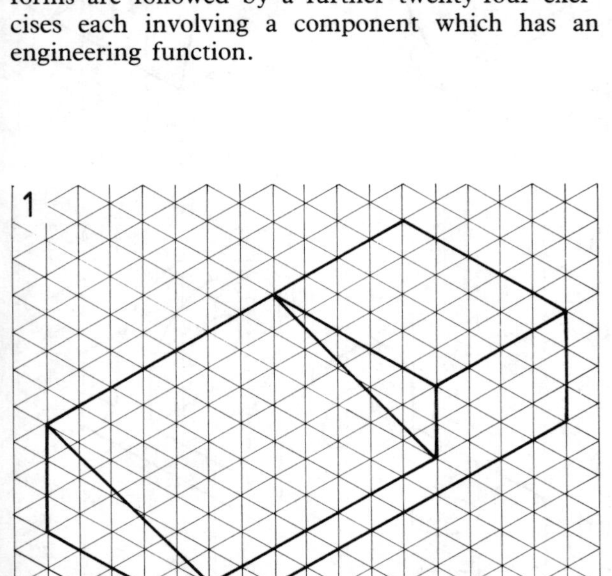

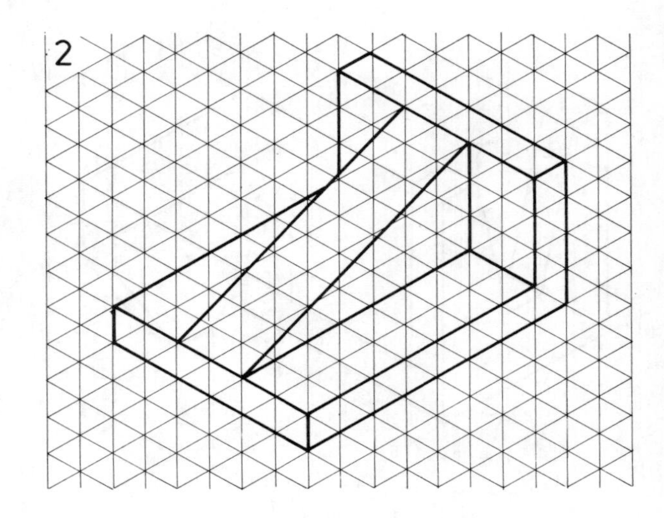

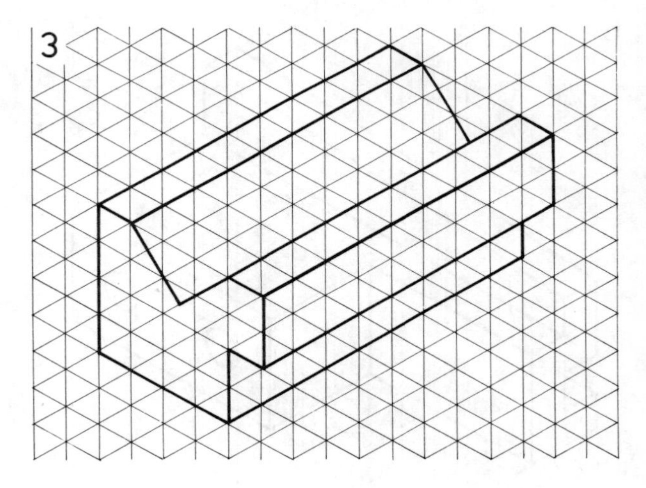

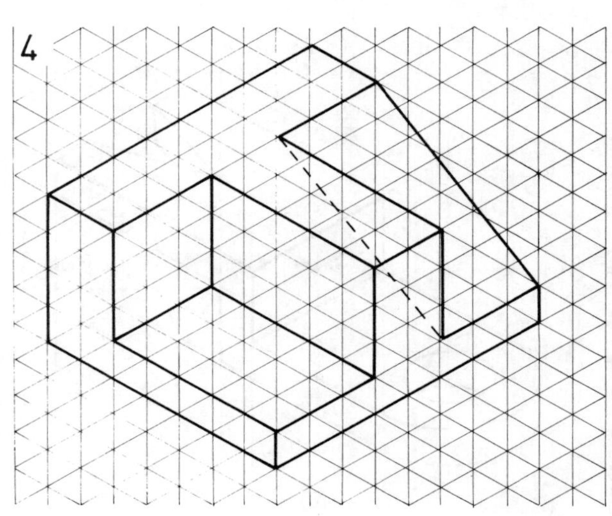

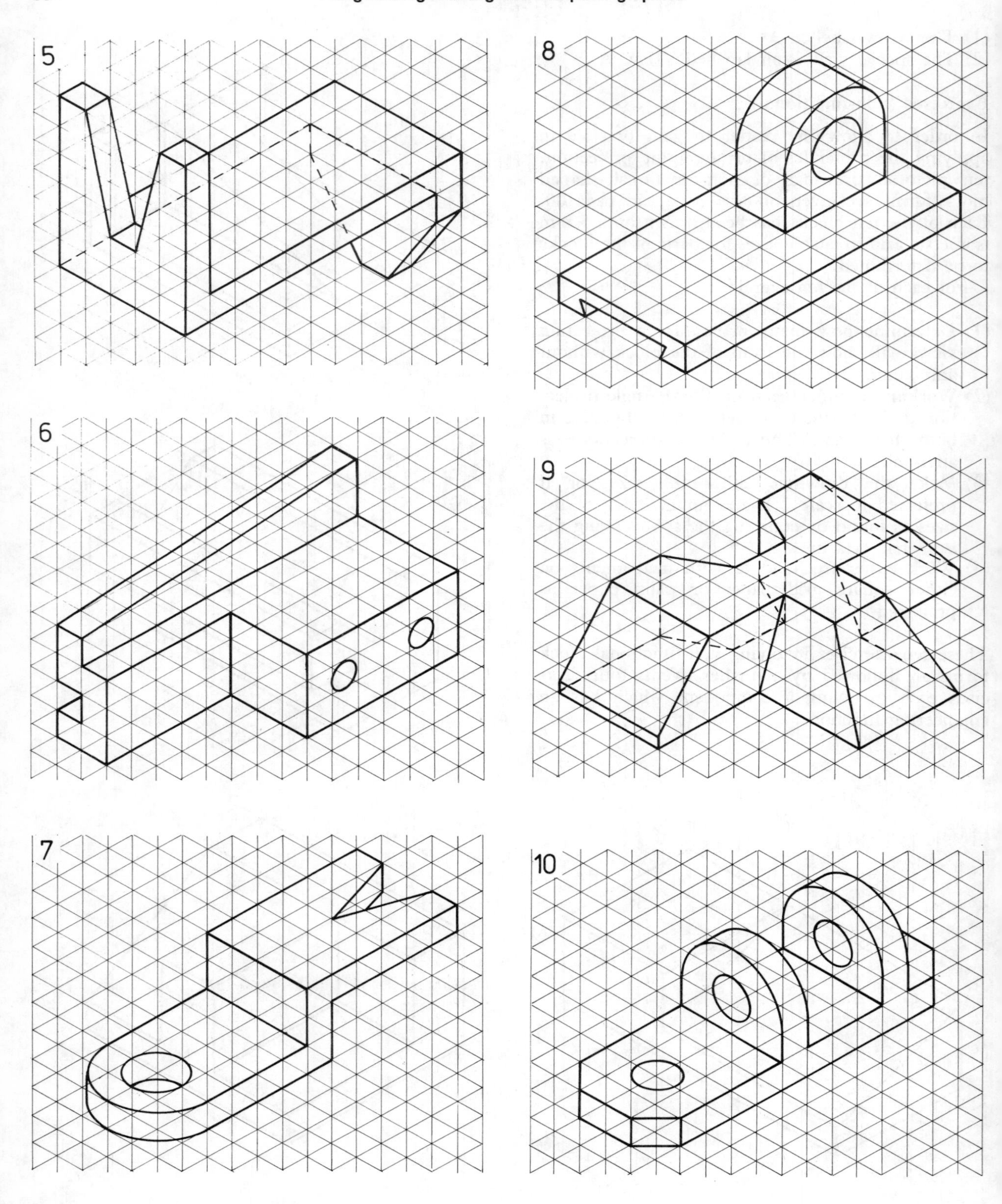
5
8
6
9
7
10

Exercises (functional)

Twenty-four exercises are given in the pages which follow. Answering these will enable the student to practise and to understand the principles of drawing views in First and Third Angle orthographic projections. An answer to each exercise can be drawn full size (scale 1:1) on an A4 sheet of paper with the aid of drawing instruments. These exercises are intended to allow practice in drawing orthographic projections. It is not necessary to include dimensions in the answers.

A variety of methods of presenting the exercises have been adopted – some are drawn on isometric or square grids, some are dimensioned pictorial drawings and some are dimensioned orthographic views. When the exercises have been drawn on grids, the student should assume the grid spacings to be at 10 mm intervals. Sizes can be estimated from the given drawings by counting the grid spacings.

Example

Fig. 4.13 is an example of one of the exercises. The question relating to this exercise is: Draw in Third Angle projection as many views as are necessary to describe clearly the shape of the bracket shown by Fig. 4.13.

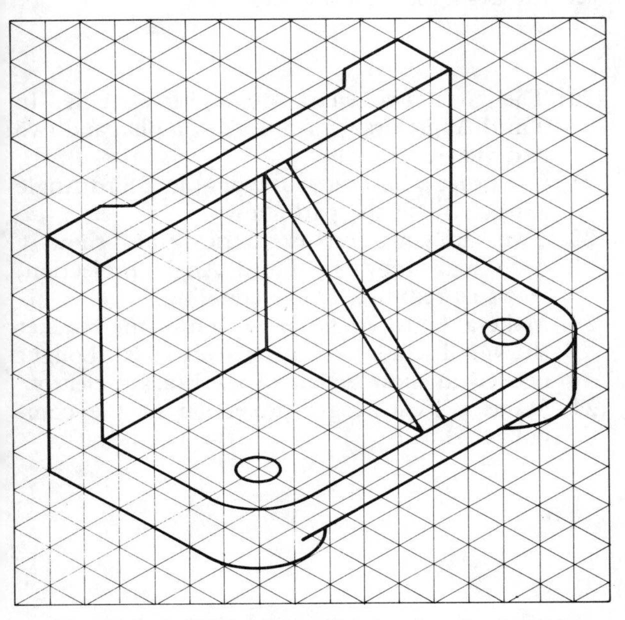

Fig..4.13 A pictorial (isometric) drawing of a bracket drawn on a 10 mm isometric grid

Fig. 4.14 is an answer to the question. The answer has been drawn on a sheet of A4 paper with the aid of drawing instruments. A special view taken from a viewing position below the bracket has been included in the answer.

Note The shape underneath the bracket cannot be clearly related to the isometric drawing. The special view (VIEW A) of Fig. 4.14 is included here to give a second example of such special views in addition to the example given by Fig. 4.12.

Exercises

(1) Make a two-view drawing in First Angle projection of the component shown by drawing 1.
(2) Draw a three-view projection in Third Angle of the given item.
(3) Construct a First Angle projection of the component using as many views as thought necessary to show clearly all details of its shape.
(4) Draw, in Third Angle, a three-view projection of the article.
(5) Using First Angle projection draw a front view, two end views and a plan of the fork end.
(6) Make a Third Angle projection of the slide with as many views as thought necessary.
(7) Draw in First Angle projection three views of the component shown.
(8) Construct a Third Angle projection of this component.
(9) The drawing on an isometric grid includes a partial second drawing showing the shape of the boss on its right hand end. Draw, in First Angle projection a front view, two end views and a plan of the part described by the drawing.
(10) In Third Angle projection draw as many views as necessary to describe fully the component shown by drawing 10.
(11) Draw a First Angle projection of the component.
(12) Third Angle projection. Two or three views?
(13) Draw a front view and a plan of the spanner. Use First Angle projection.
(14) The given drawings are in Third Angle projection. Draw, in First Angle projection, a front view, an end view and a plan.
(15) A front view and an inverted plan of a brake shoe from a car which is given in Third Angle projection. Draw, in First Angle projection, a

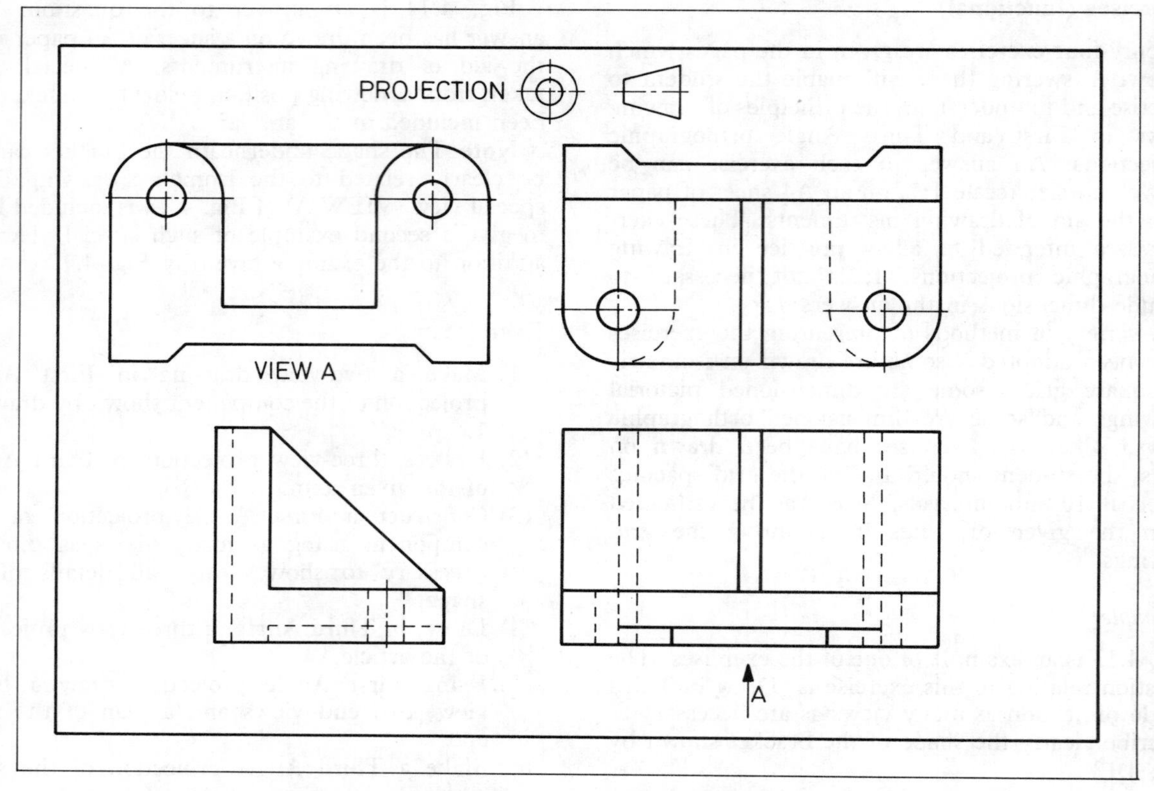

Fig.4.14 A Third Angle projection of the bracket to include a special view (VIEW A)

front view, end view and plan. Add a special view as thought necessary.

(16) The tool rest from a grinding machine is drawn in Third Angle projection. Working in First Angle produce a three-view drawing of the tool rest.

(17) The given views are in Third Angle. Construct a three-view First Angle projection of the component.

(18) A draw bar is shown in First Angle projection. Construct a three-view Third Angle projection of the draw bar.

(19) Draw in Third Angle projection, three views of the component shown. The end view is given.

(20) The given two views are in First Angle. In Third Angle draw a front view, a plan and two end views.

(21) Construct a four-view drawing, in Third Angle projection, of the part shown.

(22) Two drawings on isometric grids show a coupling. Draw, in Third Angle projection, views as required of the coupling.

(23) Make a Third Angle projection of the bracket shown. Include as many views as thought needed to show details of the bracket clearly.

(24) Make a First Angle projection of the component shown.

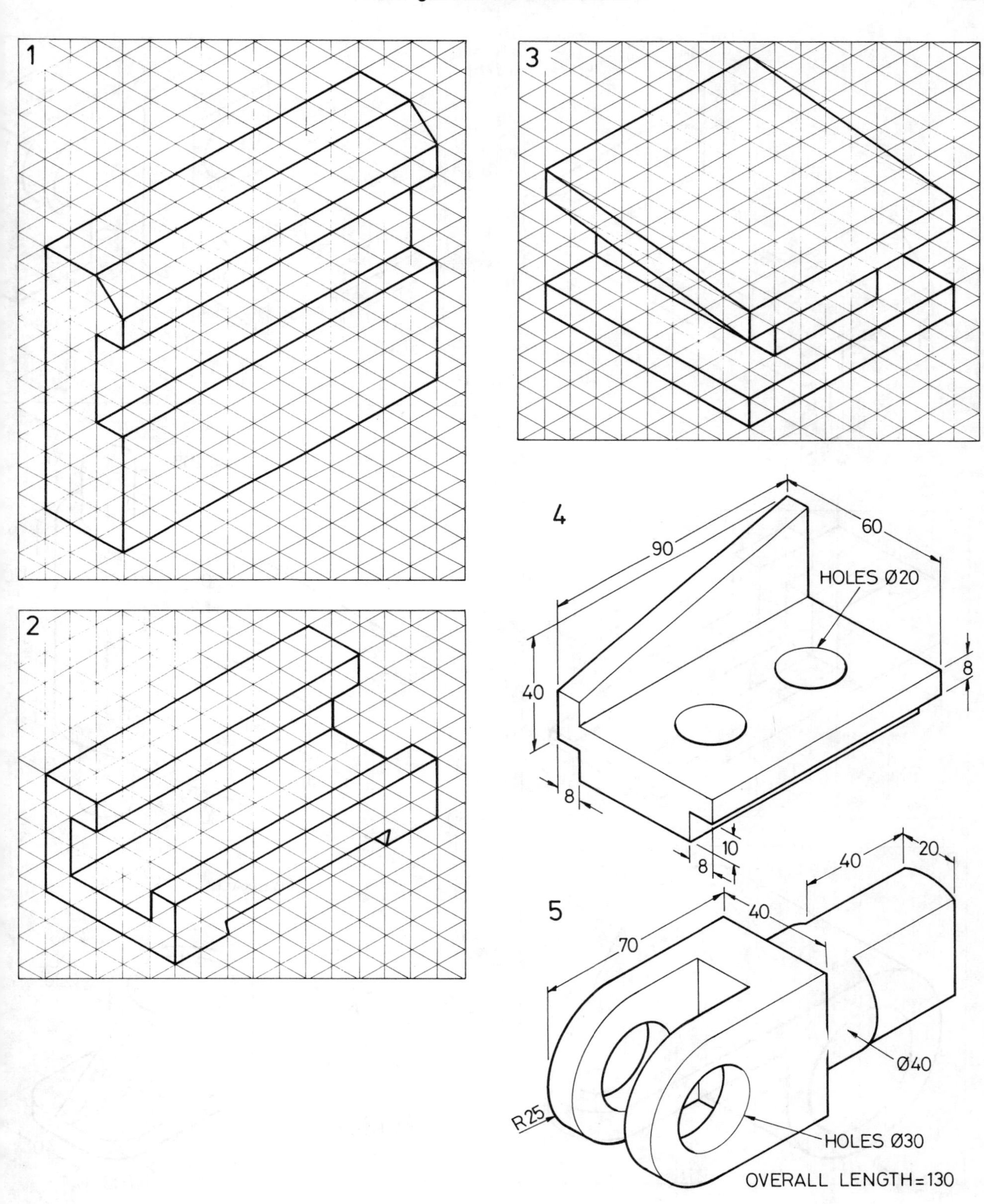
1
2
3
4
90
60
HOLES Ø20
40
8
8
10
8
5
40
20
40
70
Ø40
R25
HOLES Ø30
OVERALL LENGTH=130

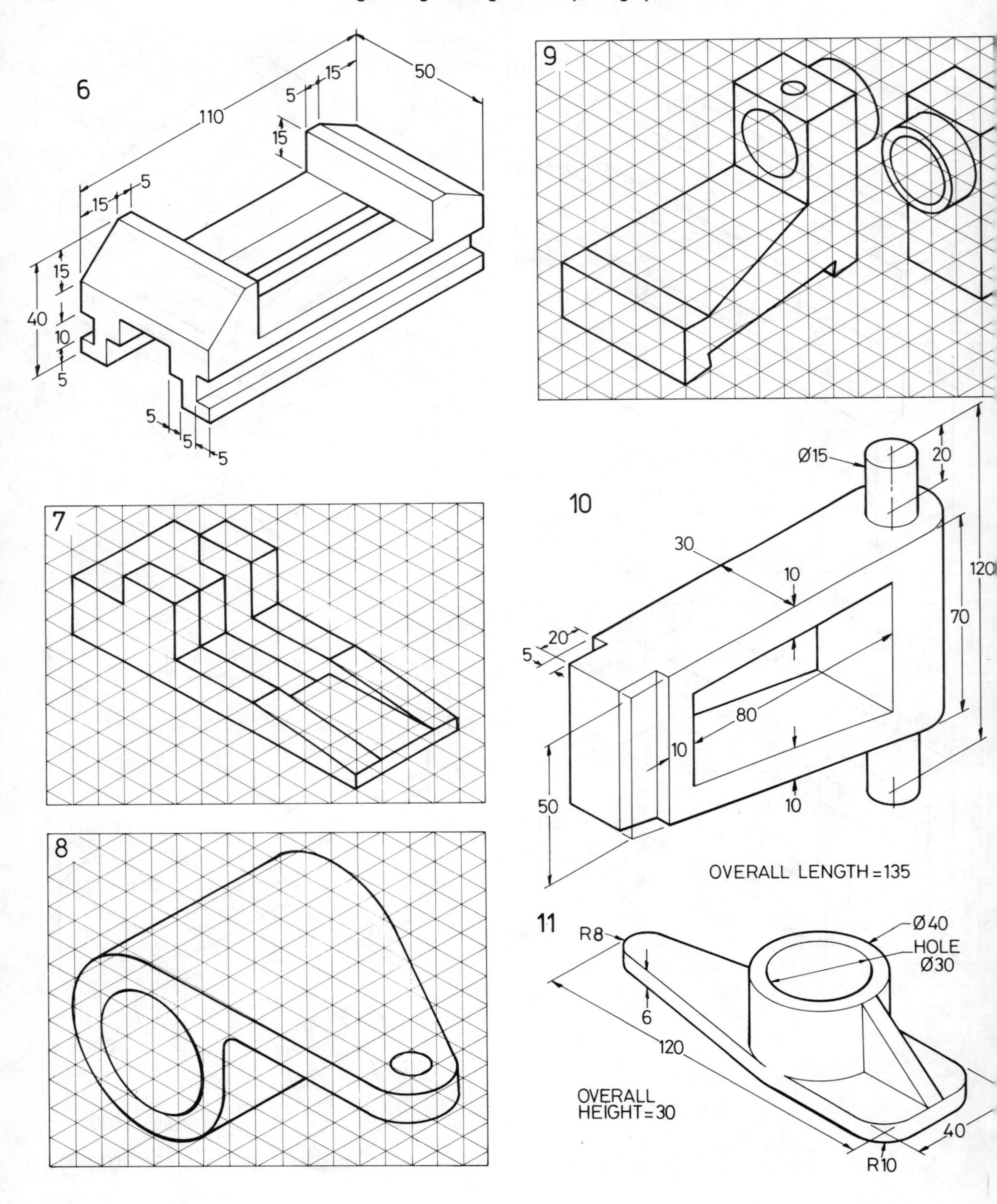
6
110
50
15
5
15
15
5
15
40
10
5
5
5
5
7
8
9
10
Ø15
20
30
10
120
70
20
5
80
10
50
10
OVERALL LENGTH = 135
11
R8
Ø40
HOLE
Ø30
6
120
OVERALL
HEIGHT = 30
40
R10

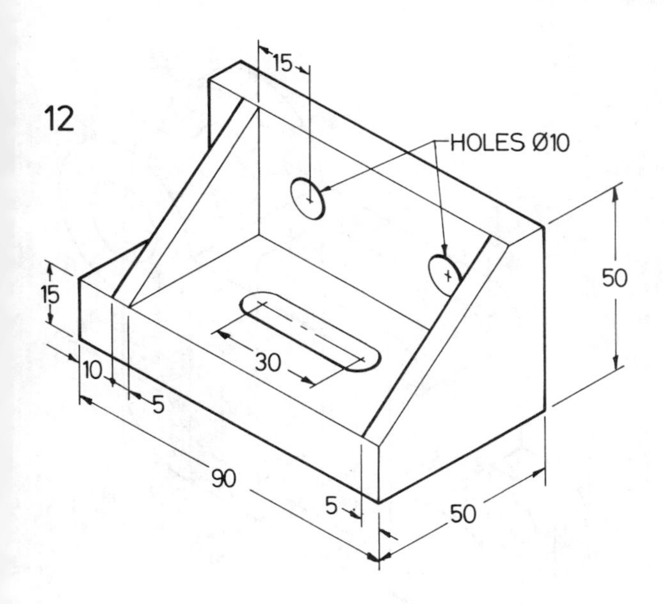
12
15
HOLES Ø10
15
10
5
30
50
90
5
50

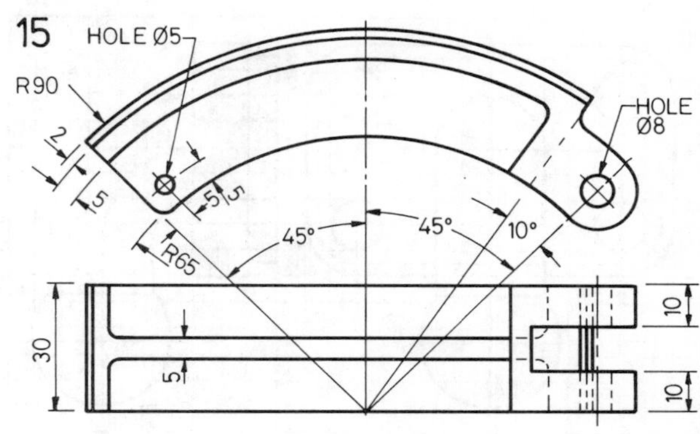
15
HOLE Ø5
R90
HOLE Ø8
2
5
5
5
R65
45°
45°
10°
30
5
10
10

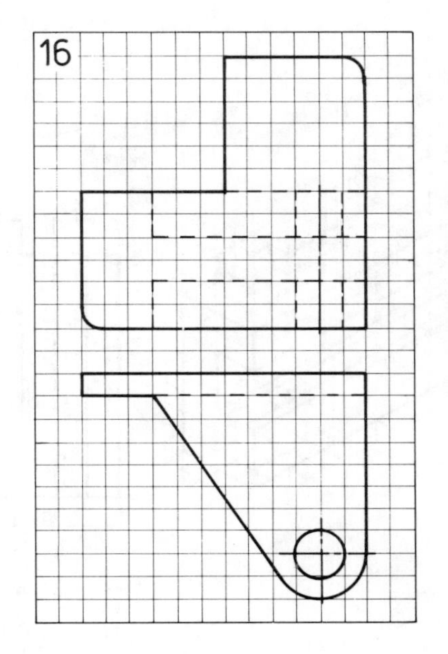
16

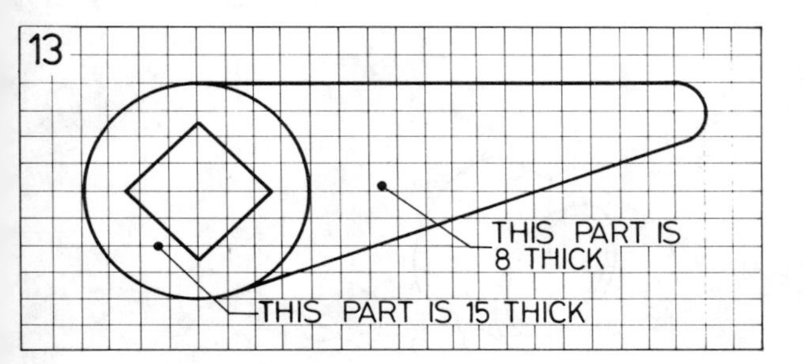
13
THIS PART IS 8 THICK
THIS PART IS 15 THICK

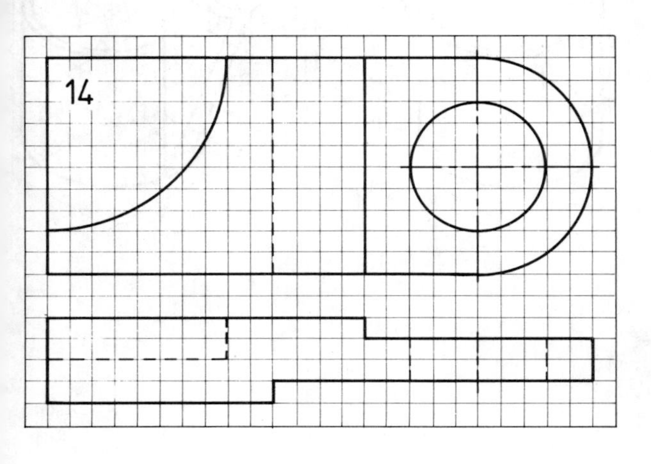
14

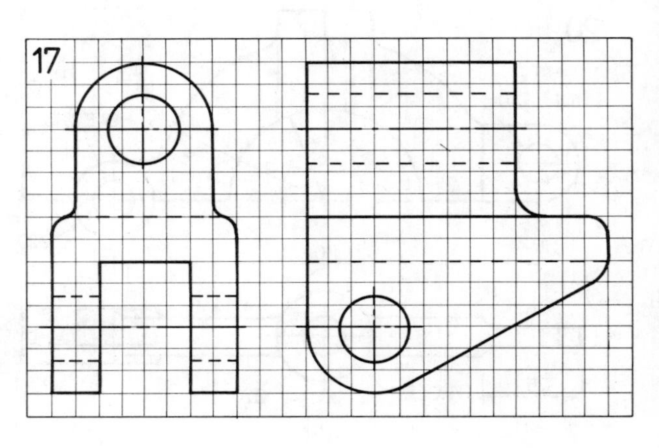
17

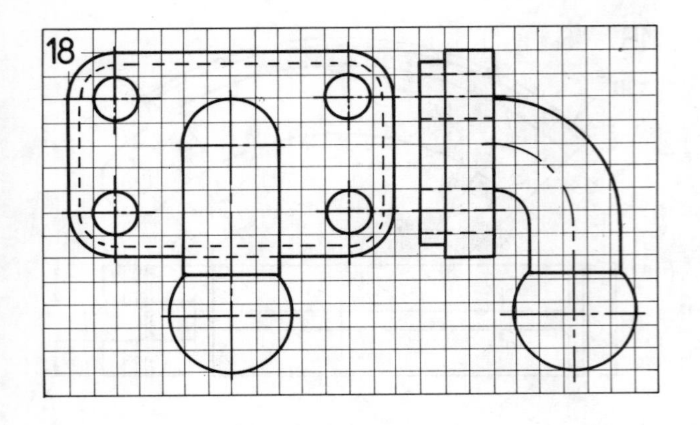
18

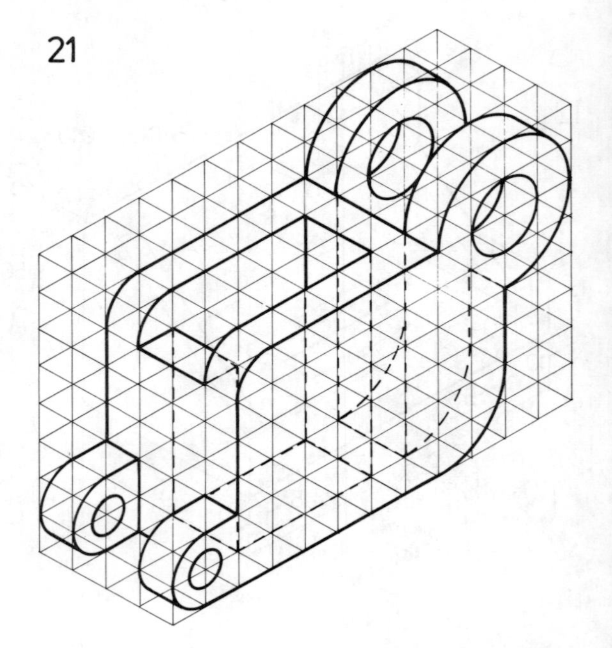
21

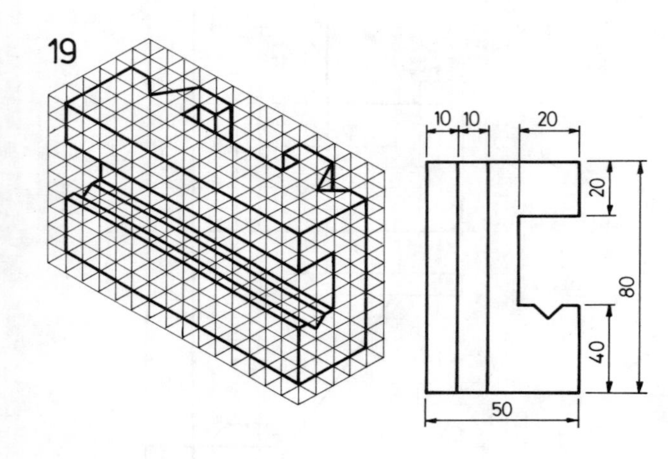
19
10
10
20
20
80
40
50

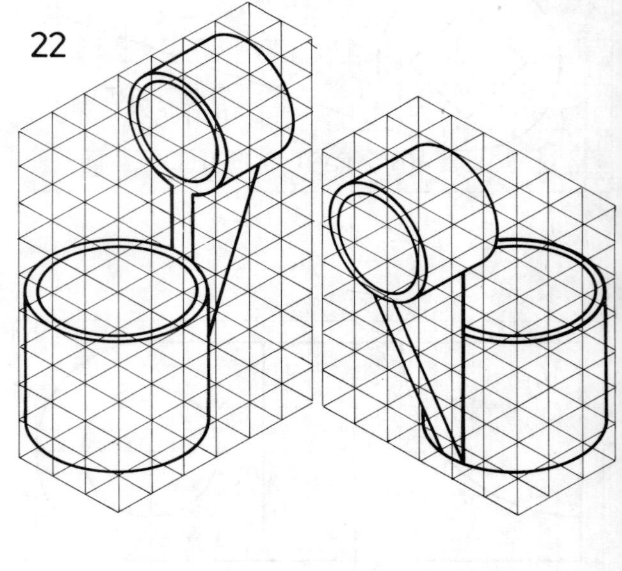
22

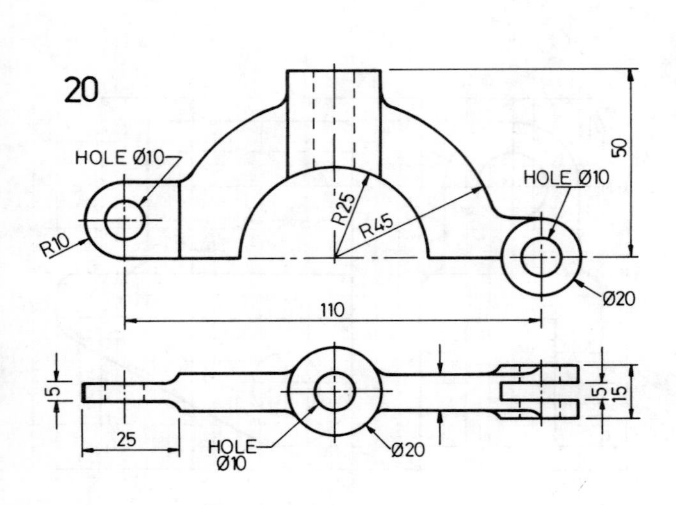
20
HOLE Ø10
R10
R25
R45
HOLE Ø10
50
Ø20
110
5
25
HOLE
Ø10
Ø20
5
15

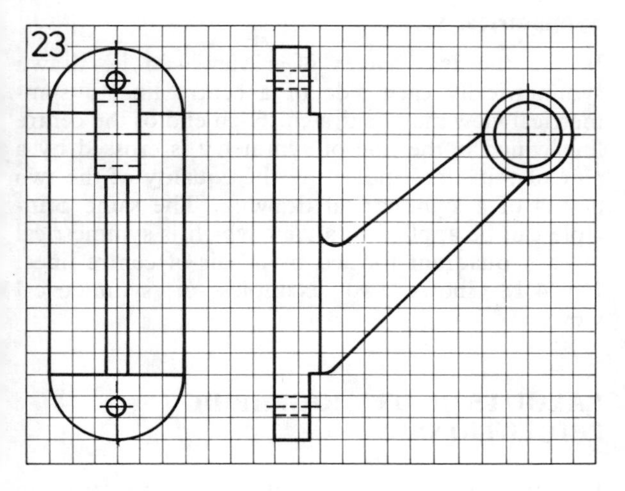

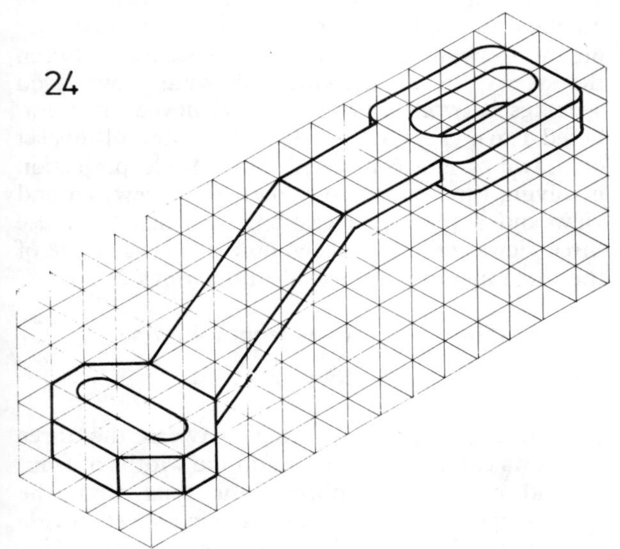

OTHER TYPES OF VIEWS

Partial views showing true shape

Fig. 4.15 shows two examples of partial views which have been added to a front view drawing of a brake shoe (see also Exercise 15). In each example the direction of viewing, as indicated by the arrows labelled A and B, has been taken at right angles to that part of the component the shape of which needs to be truly represented. The views A and B are only partial views because in the case of view A, only the true shape of the end of the brake shoe is drawn, and in the case of view B, the view is terminated by a thin broken line. Partial views of this type can either be placed on the drawing sheet out of projection with a main view as in view A, or in line with and projected from a main view as in view B.

Auxiliary views

Fig. 4.16 is an example of an auxiliary view drawn to determine the true shape of a sloping surface. This example is in Third Angle projection but could equally as well have been drawn in First Angle projection. There is an advantage in drawing auxiliary views in Third Angle projection in that the face showing the required true shape will project to a position adjacent to the part being viewed. Note again the arrow A indicating clearly in which direction the face is being viewed and the labelling

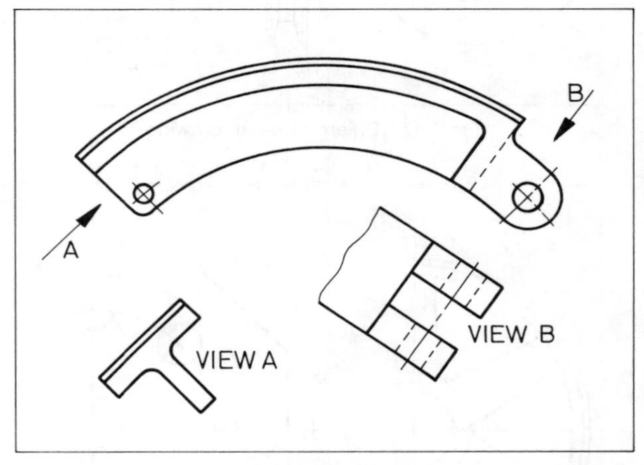

Fig.4.15 Partial views showing true shapes

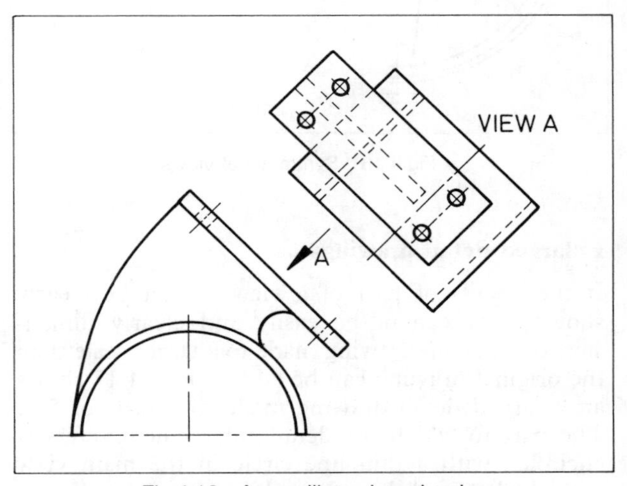

Fig.4.16 An auxiliary view showing true shape of a sloping surface

of the true shape view as view A in order to identify the view with the direction in which it is seen. Note also the differences between an auxiliary view, in which parts behind the true shape surface are included, and a partial view which shows only that part of the item of which a true shape is required.

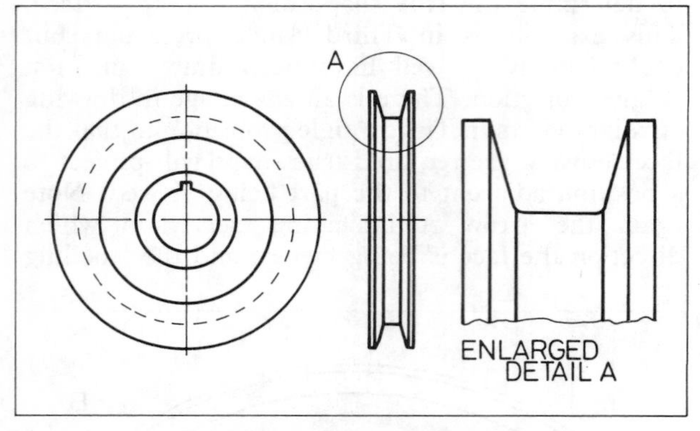

Fig.4.17 Enlarged detail drawing

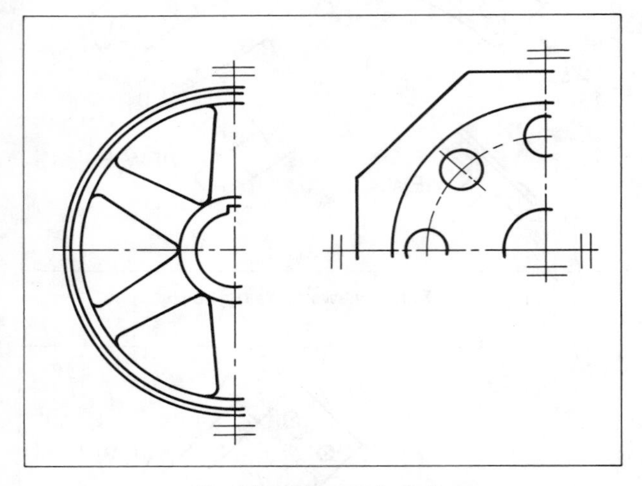

Fig.4.18 Symmetrical views

Enlarged detail drawings

If the details of part of a view cannot be clearly shown – or cannot be easily and clearly dimensioned – a detail drawing made to a larger scale than the original drawing can be added. Fig. 4.17 shows an enlarged detail drawing made to a scale of 5:1. The part to which the detail enlargement refers is encircled with a thin line circle in the main view and labelled, and the enlarged drawing is labelled to identify it as that part within the circle.

Symmetrical views

Where the two halves of a view can be drawn symmetrically each side of a centre line, a symmetrical view may be drawn. Each end of the centre line which is the line of symmetry is crossed by a pair of thin lines indicating the equality of the two halves of a symmetrical drawing. The same principle can be applied to a view which is symmetrical in each quadrant formed by a pair of centre lines. Fig. 4.18 shows two examples of symmetrical views.

LAYOUTS OF ORTHOGRAPHIC PROJECTIONS

Drawings in orthographic projection are easier to read and to understand if the views are well laid out on the drawing sheet with good spacings between the views. Four drawings showing how good spacings between views can be achieved are numbered 1 to 4 (Figs 4.19 to 4.22). The first of this set of drawings is a completed First Angle projection involving three views. It shows front view, an end view and a plan of a casting. Spacings for these three views could have been obtained by any one of the three methods described in drawings 2, 3 or 4.

First method – projections from a 45° line

Proceed as follows – drawing 2:

(1) The approximate spacings between the three views can be estimated – add the widths of front and end views; subtract the total from the available space across the drawing sheet; divide the remainder by three. Similarly, vertically – add the heights of front view and plan; subtract the total from the available space vertically on the drawing sheet; divide the remainder by three.
(2) In the example given, draw the plan first. From the plan project upwards to produce the widths of the front view. Heights of the front view should be obtained by measuring.
(3) Draw line AB at 45° to the base of the front view. Project horizontally from the plan on to line AB. From points so obtained project vertically to obtain widths of the end view.
(4) Heights of the end view are then projected from the front view.
(5) Further details can be added to the three views as necessary by projections on to line AB.

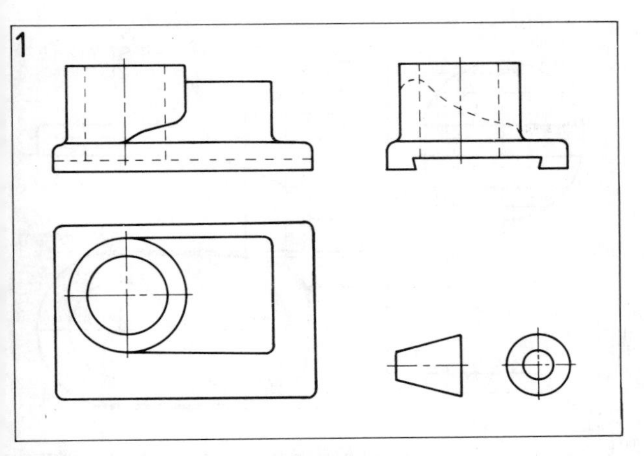

Fig.4.19 An example of a layout of three views in orthographic projection

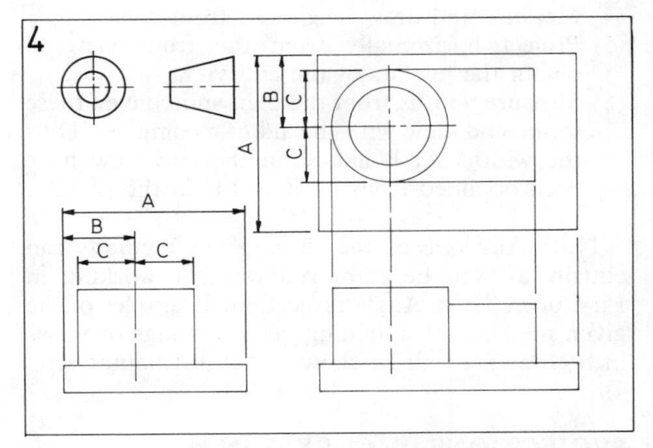

Fig.4.22 Projections from an end view by measurements

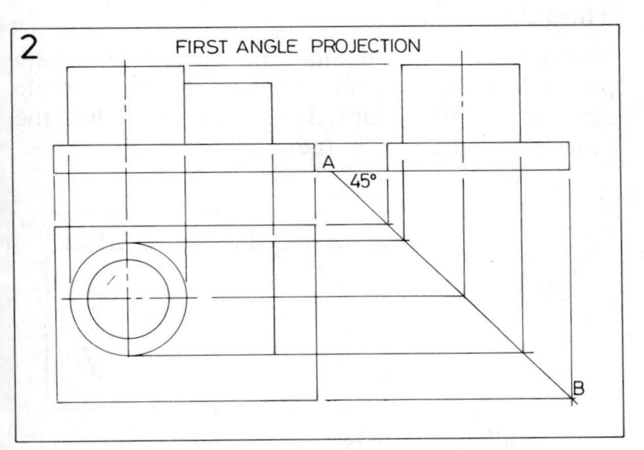

Fig.4.20 Projection from a 45° line

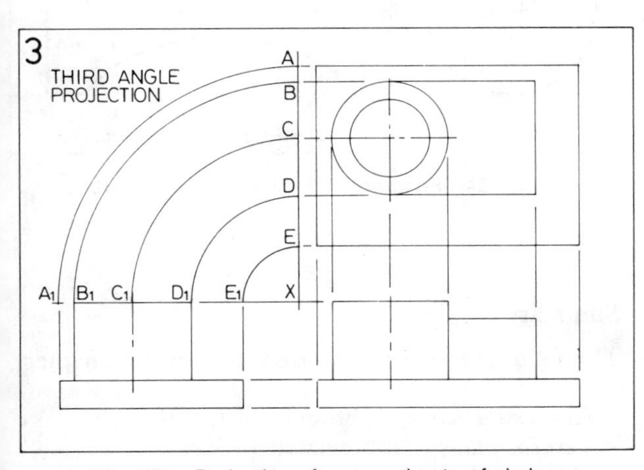

Fig.4.21 Projections from quadrants of circles

Second method – projections from quadrants of circles

Proceed as follows – drawing 3:

(1) Obtain approximate spacings for the three views by simple arithmetical calculation – as for Method 1.
(2) Again as with Method 1 – in this example – draw the plan first. Project downwards to obtain widths of the front view.
(3) Heights of the front view can now be measured and drawn.
(4) Project horizontally from the front view to obtain the heights of the end view.
(5) Project widths for the end view from the plan on to a line XA drawn at right angles to a horizontal line projected from the front view. These projections give the points A, B, C, D and E.
(6) With compasses centred at X and set to XA, XB, XC, XD and XE in turn, draw arcs to obtain points A_1, B_1, C_1, D_1 and E_1 which provide widths for the end view.

Third method – projections into end view by measurements

Proceed as follows – drawing 4:

(1) Obtain approximate spacings by simple arithmetical calculation.
(2) Draw plan.
(3) Project widths of front view vertically from plan.

(4) Measure and draw heights of front view.
(5) Project horizontally from the front view to obtain the heights of the end view.
(6) Measure widths from the plan and convey these to the end view with the aid of a compass. Thus the widths A, B and C in the end view have been obtained from A, B and C in the plan.

Note Any one of the three given methods can equally as well be employed whether working in First or in Third Angle projection. Examples of the given methods of obtaining good spacings of views in both angles will be shown later in Chapter 7.

PROJECTIONS OF CURVES IN ORTHOGRAPHIC PROJECTION

Two examples of the method by which curves can be projected from one view to another in an orthographic projection are given in Figs 4.23 and 4.24. The first is in First Angle and the second in Third Angle. It will be noted that:

(1) In both examples the method of projection from one view to another via a 45° line is employed. Either of the other two methods illustrated by Fig. 4.21 or 4.22 could equally as well be used.
(2) The method of projection of curves between views is the same, irrespective of the angle of projection.

First Angle example

(1) Draw front view and end view.
(2) Draw 45° line AB.
(3) Project outline of plan from front view and end view via line AB.
(4) To obtain points on the curved line in the plan follow the pattern of projection given by the numbered sequence 1 to 7.
(5) Imagine the plane C–C cutting across the front and end views. C–C cuts the front view at point 1 and the end view at points 2 and 3.
(6) Project from points 2 and 3 to points 4 and 5 on line AB.
(7) From 1 project downwards on to the plan.
(8) From 4 and 5 project horizontally to meet the line projected from point 1. The intersections of these projections give points 6 and 7. Points 6 and 7 are on the line of the curve in the plan.
(9) Follow the same procedure with several other cutting planes similar to C–C. Join the points so obtained in the plan with a fair freehand line.

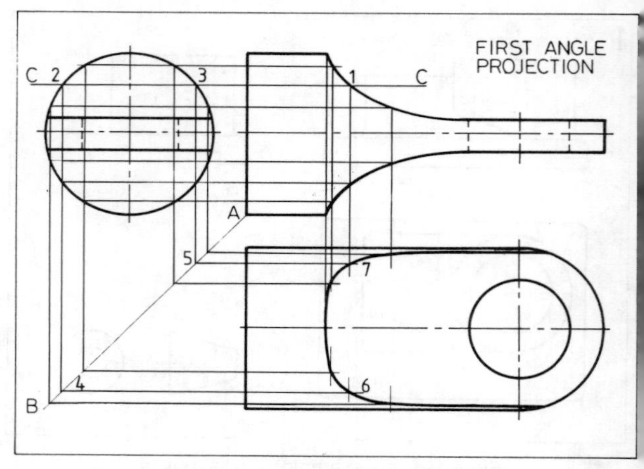

Fig.4.23 Projections of curves – First Angle

Third Angle example

The procedure for obtaining the curved line in the plan follows that given above in the First Angle example. In this Third Angle example follow the procedure indicated by the sequence 1 to 10.

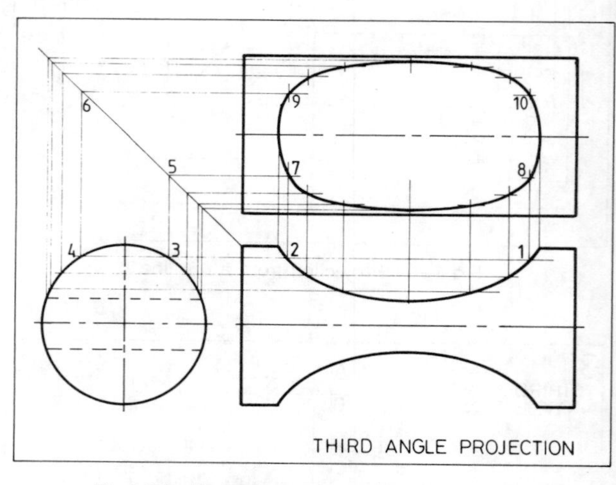

Fig.4.24 Projections of curves – Third Angle

Summary

The following terms have been used in this chapter:

– *Horizontal plane* – abbreviated to HP.
– *Vertical plane* – abbreviated to VP.
– *Orthogonal* – a line or a plane which is perpen-

dicular to another plane is said to be *orthogonal* to the second plane.

- *Dihedral* – the angles between planes are known as *dihedral* angles.
- *View* – a common practice is to use the term '*elevation*' in place of the term '*view*'. The two words have the same meaning.
- *First Angle projection* – in which views are obtained from viewing articles placed in the first dihedral angle.
- *Third Angle projection* – in which views are obtained from viewing articles placed in the third dihedral angle.
- *Front view* – a view drawn as seen when an article is viewed from that part selected as its '*front*'.
- *End view* – a view drawn as seen when an article is viewed as seen from an end. The term '*side view*' will also be seen in place of '*end view*'. '*End view*' is to be preferred.
- *Plan* – a view drawn as seen from above.
- *Inverted plan* – a view drawn as seen from below.
- *Special views* – views to show details not clearly described by main views in orthographic projection. Special views are commonly drawn out of projection with main views.
- *Partial views* – special views showing part of what is seen in a defined direction of viewing.
- *Auxiliary views* – views as seen in a direction perpendicular to a given face in order to show the true shape of the face.
- *Enlarged detail drawing* – a part view drawn to a larger scale than the main drawing, in order to show details of the part more clearly.

5 Sectional views

When producing orthographic projections for engineering drawing, it may not be possible to give sufficient information concerning the internal features of components and assemblies in views showing details of external features. Even when internal features are drawn on external views with hidden detail lines, the outlines and shapes of internal parts may not be clearly indicated in the drawing. In such cases sectional views can be included in engineering drawings to define clearly internal shapes and forms. *Sectional views* (or *sections*) are the result of imagining that section cutting planes pass through the article being drawn to allow the draughtsman to see and draw the actual outlines and details of the surfaces which have been cut by the section cutting plane. A number of different types of sectional views have been developed for the purpose of producing engineering drawings. Details of the various types of sections and the rules governing them are given in this chapter.

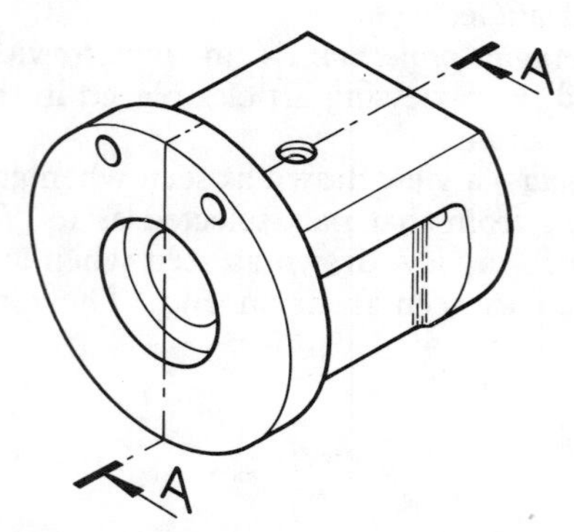

Fig.5.1 Pictorial drawing of LEAD SCREW SUPPORT showing line of sectional cut

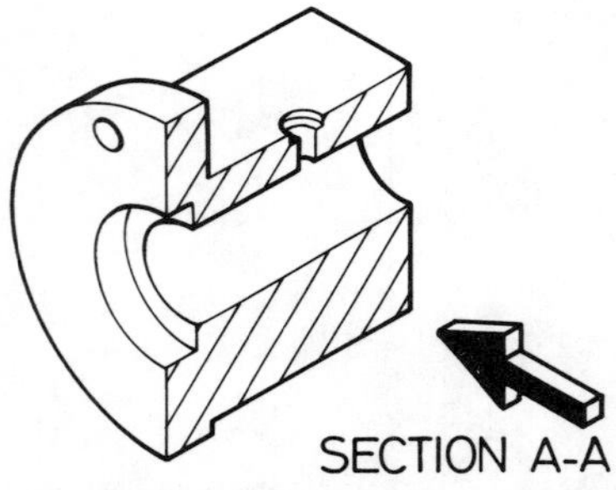

Fig.5.2 Pictorial drawing of LEAD SCREW SUPPORT showing surfaces cut by section plane

GENERAL PRINCIPLES

Two pictorial drawings – Figs 5.1 and 5.2 – show the principle of section cutting planes. Both illustrations are drawings showing the same LEAD SCREW SUPPORT from a screw cutting lathe. In the first drawing, the outline of a sectional cutting plane is shown tracing a cut which is to be made vertically through the centre of the component. In the second drawing, one must imagine that the front half of the component has been removed to reveal the whole of the surfaces through which the sectional cutting plane has passed. These surfaces have been shown by drawing 'hachure' lines across them.

Fig. 5.3 shows the application of this principle to a three-view First Angle orthographic projection of the LEAD SCREW SUPPORT. In this drawing, the front view is 'in section' – it is a *sectional front view*. Note the following:

(1) As is obvious from reading the three views, the section plane has been taken vertically through the centre of the main hole of the component. In such instances, when the route of the section plane does not require to be defined, there is no need to show the exact location of the cutting plane in any view.
(2) The surfaces which have been cut by the section plane have been 'hatched' with thin lines drawn at 45° to the centre line of the front view. The common spacing of hachure lines is about 4 mm, although as will be shown later, this spacing may vary.

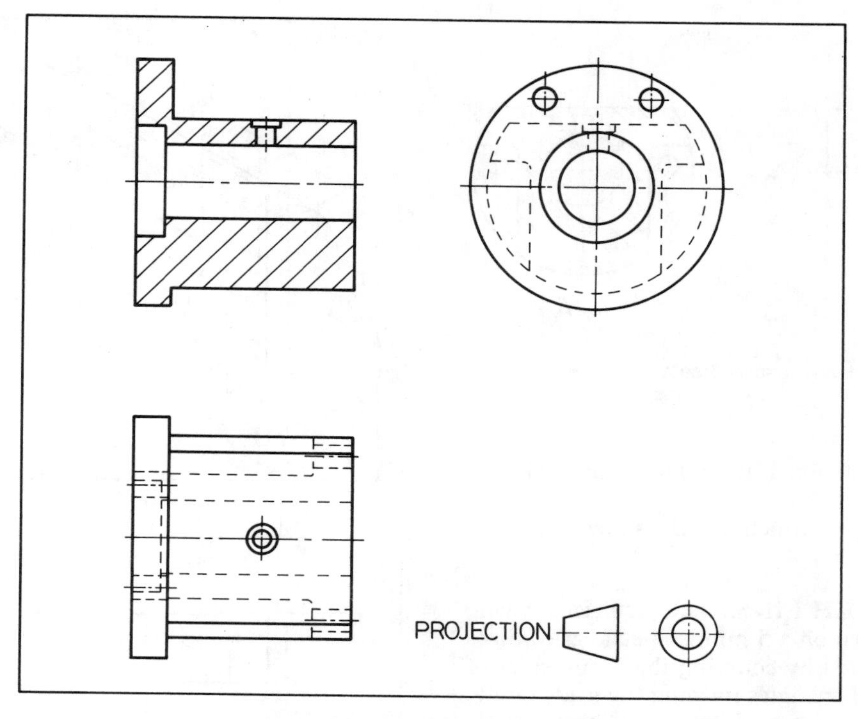

Fig.5.3 Three-view First Angle projection which includes a section

(3) All those parts which lie behind the cut surface and can be seen are shown in the sectional view.
(4) Hidden detail may, or may not, be included within a sectional view. In this example hidden detail lines have not been included because it is thought that all details of the component are quite clearly portrayed without the addition of hidden detail in the section. Hidden detail has, however, been included in the other two views of the projection.

Section plane line

Fig. 5.4 shows a two-view First Angle projection of the same component. In this example it should be noted that the position of the cutting plane, on which the sectional end view is taken, has been quite clearly defined in the front view. When it is not quite clear as to the exact location of the cutting plane, it is essential to show its position and also to label the sectional view resulting from the section cutting plane.

Note the following in Fig. 5.4:

(1) The section cutting plane line is a centre line which terminates at each end in a thick line. A short dash of the centre line occurs immediately before each of the thick lines at the ends.
(2) Arrows showing the direction of viewing to see the sectional cut, touch the thick lines at the ends of the section plane line.
(3) The arrows showing the direction of viewing are labelled – usually with letters of the alphabet.
(4) The sectional view resulting from the cut made by the section plane is labelled. In this example by A–A. If it is thought necessary for the sake of clarity, the sectional view could be given the label SECTION A–A.

Note Hatching lines need not be drawn on the surfaces of sectional views, if the meaning of the view is quite clear without the inclusion of the hatching lines. It is probably advisable for students always to draw hatching lines across sectional views during the period of their training.

Exercises

(1) SUPPORT SLIDE. Work to scale 1:1 in either First or Third Angle projection. Draw three views:

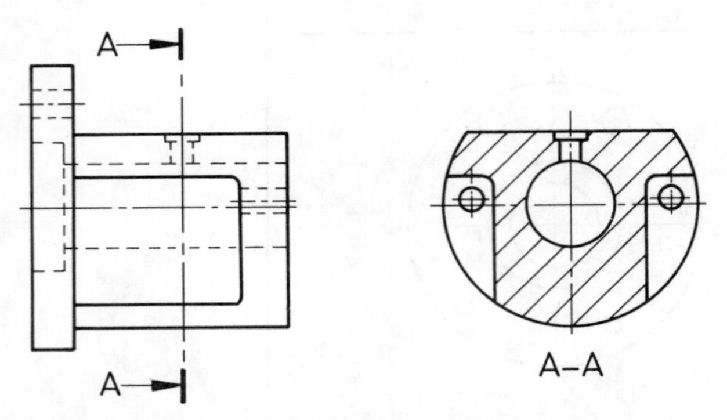

Fig.5.4 Front view and end sectional view of LEAD SCREW SUPPORT

(a) a front sectional view taken through the central hole;
(b) an end view which clearly shows the slide guides;
(c) a plan.

(2) GEAR CLUTCH LINK. The pictorial drawing has been drawn on a 5 mm isometric grid. Sizes can be estimated by counting the 5 mm sides of the equilateral triangles forming the grid. Draw, scale 1:1 in either First or Third Angle projection:
(a) the sectional front view DD;
(b) an end view;
(c) a plan.

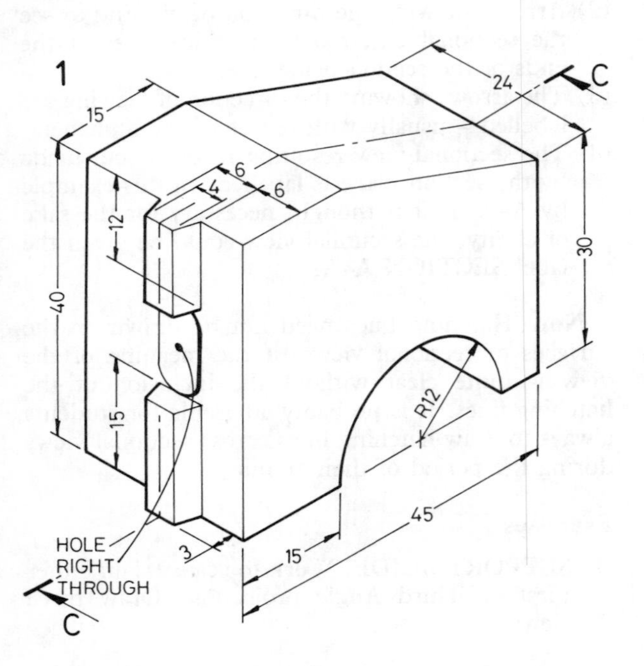

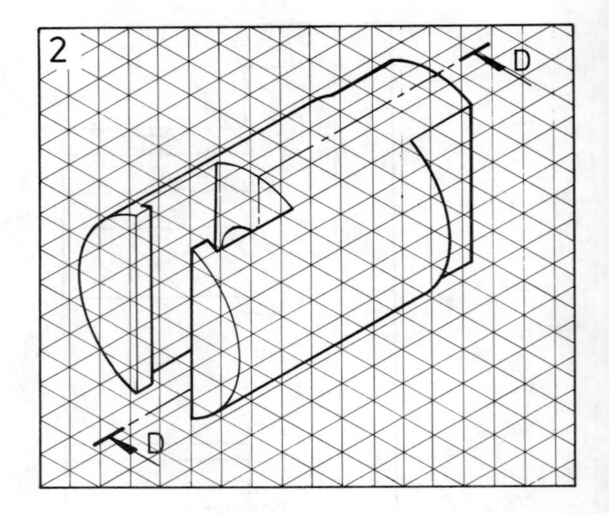

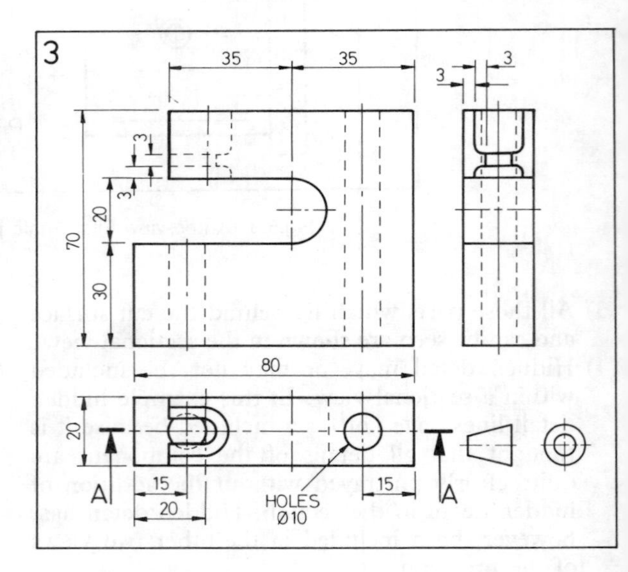

(3) GUDGEON PIN REMOVAL TOOL. Work to scale 1:1 in Third Angle projection. Draw:
(a) section AA;
(b) an end view;
(c) a plan.

(4) TAPER TURNING ATTACHMENT GUIDE. Work to scale 1:1 in First Angle projection. Draw:
(a) section BB;
(b) an end view;
(c) a plan.

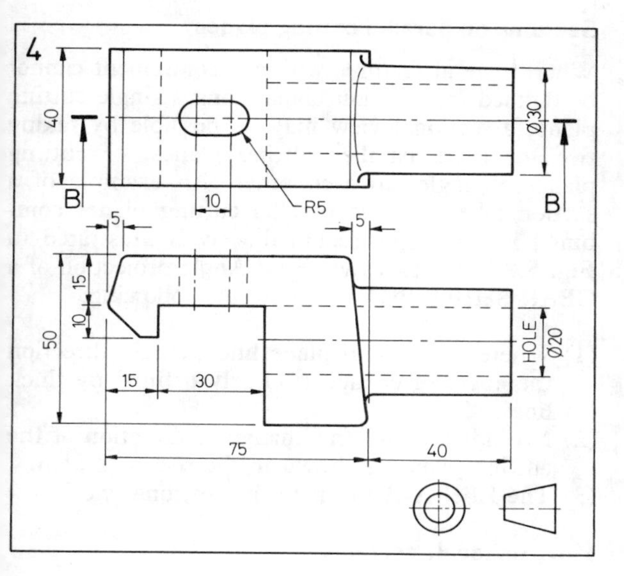

OTHER TYPES OF SECTIONS

Hatching at alternate angles

A sectional view through a ball race bearing within the hub of a wheel is shown in Fig. 5.5. In this assembly drawing, hatching is required on a number of different parts. In order to prevent confusion as to the meaning of each part, the hatching is varied in direction. Some of the hatching lines slope at 45° to the right, some at 45° to the left. The spacing between the hatching lines is also varied. Small parts within the assembly are hatched with lines closer together than those of the larger parts.

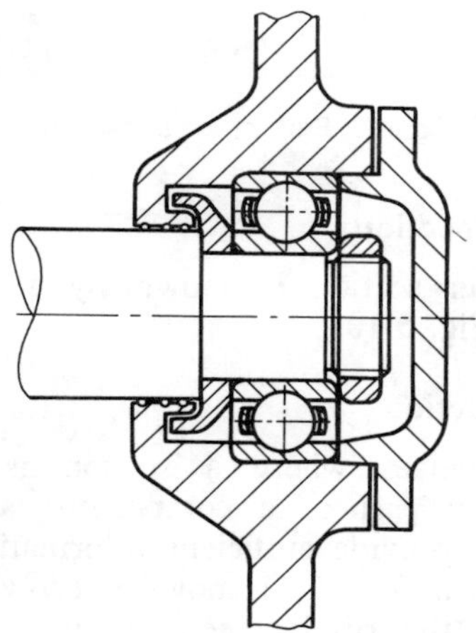

Fig.5.5 Hatching at alternate angles

Bolts, ribs, etc., within sectional views

One of the more important rules governing the drawing of sectional views is that, when a section plane cuts through bolts, keys, nuts, ribs, screws, shafts, spindles, spokes, washers, webs and similar parts, such parts are shown by outside views within the sectional view. Note that this only applies when the section plane cuts *longitudinally along or through* these parts. When a section plane cuts *across* such parts they are treated like any other part in sections. This rule is illustrated in the two-view Third Angle projection of a DRAUGHTING MACHINE SUPPORT SWIVEL shown in Fig. 5.6. In the sectional view of this drawing, the screw and the web are shown by outside views – they are not sectioned. Other examples of the application of this rule will be found throughout this book.

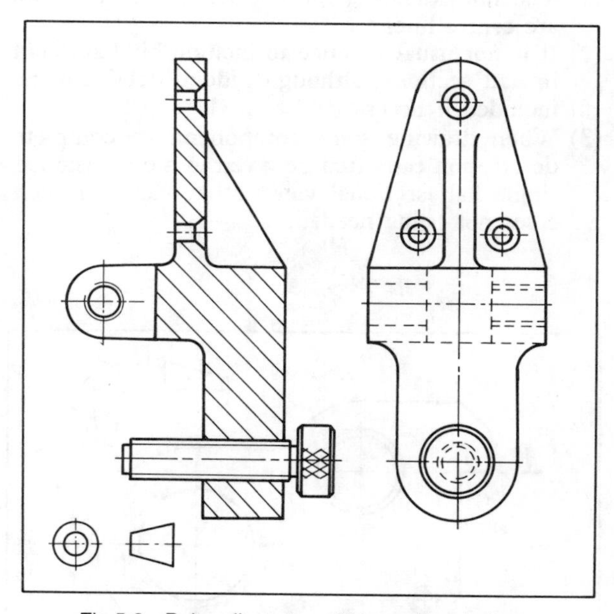

Fig.5.6 Bolts, ribs, etc., within sectional views

Half sections

If a component or an assembly is symmetrical about an axis, details of its shape and form can often be clearly defined by a half section. Two examples of half sections are given in Fig. 5.7. The first – a SEAL REMOVING COLLAR – is a single-part component. The second – a SEALING BUNG – is an assembly drawing. In both examples the following rules apply:

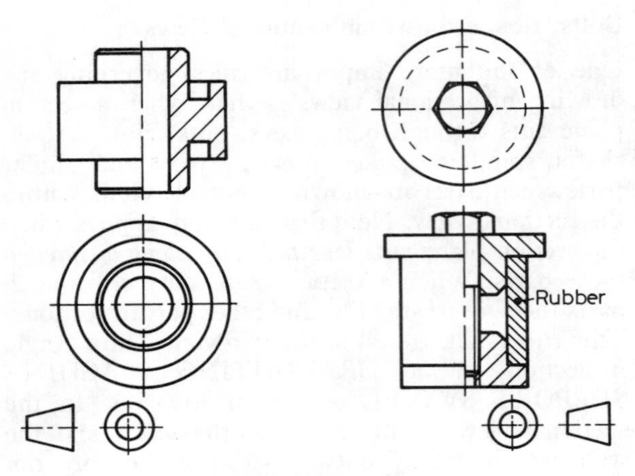

Fig.5.7 Half sections

(1) The lines dividing the two halves of the views are centre lines.
(2) It is not usual practice to include hidden detail in half sections, although hidden detail can be included if necessary.
(3) When drawing some components, a complete description can often be given in a dimensioned single half sectional view, other views in such cases not being needed.

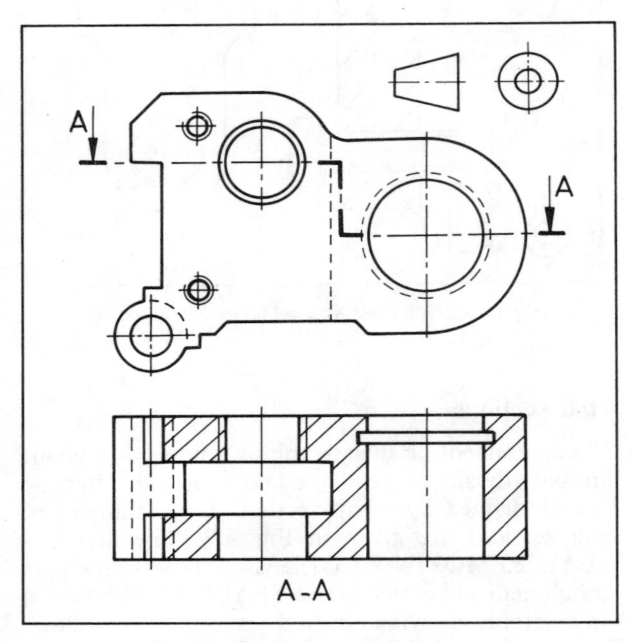

Fig.5.8 Section on parallel planes

Sections on parallel cutting planes

Where several features within a component cannot be defined in a section taken along a single cutting plane, a sectional view may be possible by taking two, or more parallel cutting planes, or cutting planes at angles to each other. An example of a section taken on two parallel cutting planes combined into a single sectional view is illustrated in Fig. 5.8 in the two-view First Angle projection of a GEAR SHIFT PLATE. Note the following:

(1) Where the section plane line changes direction the angle of change is clearly defined by thick lines.
(2) No indication of the change of direction of the cutting planes is shown in the sectional plan.
(3) The label A–A given to the sectional view.

Part, or local, sections

If, in order to define the internal shape of a component clearly, only part of a view requires to be sectioned, a part section, or local section, may be sufficient. Fig. 5.9 shows the HANDLE from a lathe handwheel drawn by two views in Third Angle projection. Note the following:

(1) The line showing the break between the part section and the outside view is a thin wavy line.
(2) No indication of the position of the section cutting plane is needed.

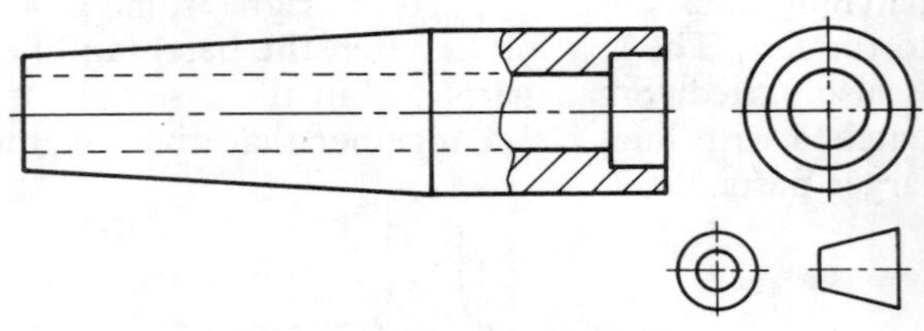

Fig.5.9 Part, or local, section

Thin sheet section

A thin sheet section is shown by a thick line drawing – Fig. 5.10.

Revolved section

In circumstances where a section is required through only part of a component, a revolved section may provide sufficient information of the detail required. Fig. 5.11 shows a revolved section taken along the rib between the two ends of a CONNECTING ROD.

Note that the outline of the revolved section is a thin line.

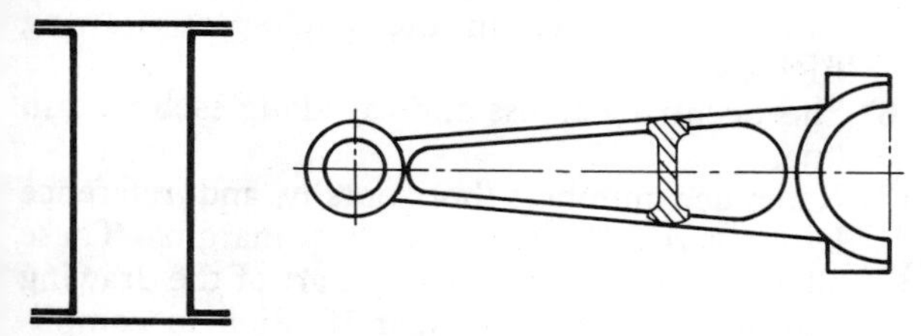

Fig.5.10 Thin sheet section

Fig.5.11 Revolved section

Removed sections

Two drawings of Fig. 5.12 show the methods of drawing a removed section in which the section cutting plane has been taken at right angles to a part of the component which is itself at an angle to the horizontal. Although the given example shows a section taken at an angle to the horizontal the method can, if required, equally as well be applied to removed sections taken vertically or horizontally to the main views of a drawing. Note that in Fig. 5.12 the views are drawn in First Angle projection. Either of the two methods shown can be adopted – the removed section can be drawn in projection, with the direction of viewing, or can be drawn in any convenient position on the drawing sheet. Whichever of the two positions is adopted, it is important that:

(1) The removed section is clearly labelled to relate it to its section cutting plane.
(2) The outline of the sectional view is drawn with thick lines.

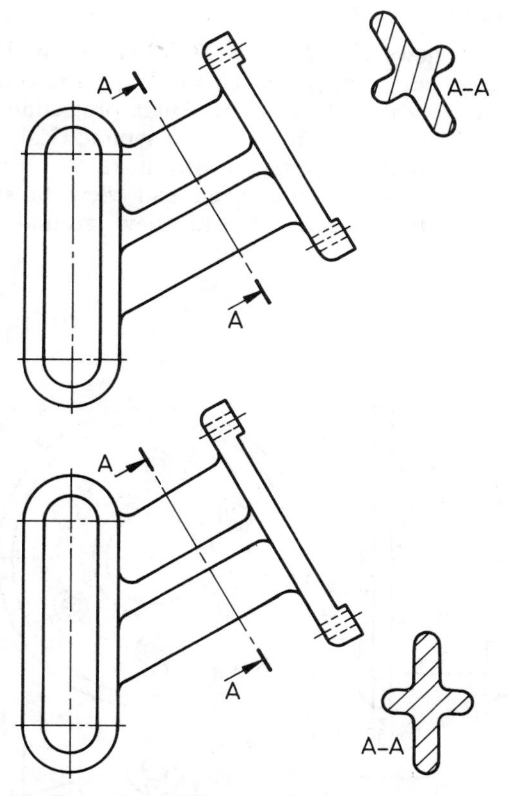

Fig.5.12 Examples of different methods of removed sections

Successive sections

Fig. 5.13 is an example of a series of successive sections taken at suitable positions along a shaft to show clearly the different sectional outlines along the component. The drawing is in First Angle projection. Note the following details concerning successive sections:

(1) Section plane lines determine the positions at which the sections are to be taken.
(2) Each section plane line is labelled with letters of the alphabet.
(3) The required sectional views have been drawn in line with the section plane lines.
(4) The outlines of the sectional views are thick lines.
(5) Each sectional view is labelled A–A, B–B, etc., to ensure correspondence with the section plane line to which it relates.

Successive sectional views can be placed in line

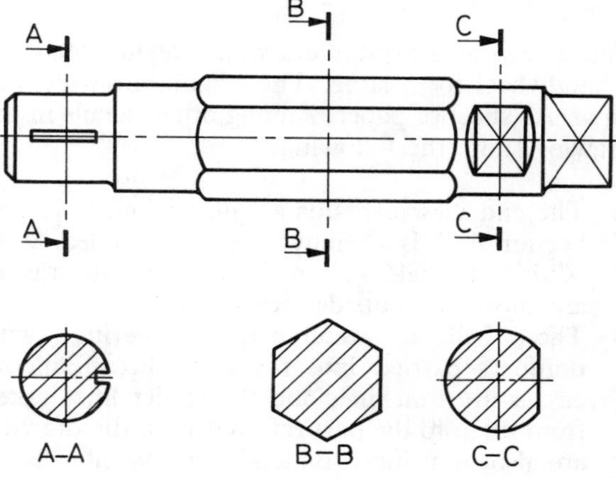

Fig.5.13 Successive sections

with the centre line of the axis of the component if such a positioning is thought to be more suitable.

Symmetrical sections

In order to save time and space on the drawing sheet, sectional views which are symmetrical about a centre line may be drawn as shown in the example of Fig. 5.14. In this example both the view from which the section has been taken and the sectional view are symmetrical around centre lines. Although it can be seen that the keyway of the given sectional view renders the view non-symmetrical, the drawing is quite clear as to its meaning.

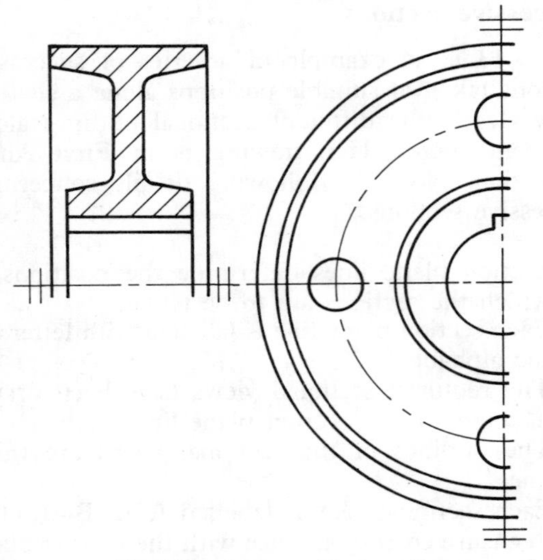

Fig.5.14 A symmetrical section

AN EXAMPLE OF AN ASSEMBLY DRAWING

Fig. 5.15 is an assembly drawing showing details of a handwheel for a lathe. The original drawing was on an A3 sheet of paper. Among other details in the drawing, note the following:

(1) The end view contains a half section.
(2) Section A–A is a removed section labelled A–A.
(3) Within the half section the bolt and its washer are shown by outside views.
(4) The 'balloon' reference numbering with numbers carried into the parts list. 'Balloon' circles are thin lines and the leader lines taken from them to the part referred to in the drawing are also thin lines. 'Balloons' are usually placed in line either vertically or horizontally and in sequence, numbering either clockwise or anti-clockwise.
(5) Trimming marks at the sheet corners. Compare with those shown in the single-part drawing Fig. 4.4.
(6) Sheet centring across midway along each margin line.
(7) Reference numbers horizontally and reference letters vertically along the sheet margins. These allow quick reference to any part of the drawing and are a good aid to identification in complicated drawings. As an example, the handle (part 3) is drawn in space A3.
(8) The millimetre scale along one of the margins, although this drawing should not be scaled – see note DO NOT SCALE along top edge of drawing.
(9) The drawing is not dimensioned – it is an assembly drawing showing how the parts of the handwheel are assembled. *Detail* or *part* drawings of each of the four parts of the handwheel will have been drawn. These part drawings will be dimensioned.

Exercises

(1) Two views of a SEALING CAP are given. They have been drawn in Third Angle projection. Draw, scale 1:1, in Third Angle projection:
   (a) The given front view as a symmetrical view around the vertical centre line.
   (b) In place of the given end view, a symmetrical sectional end view around the horizontal centre line.

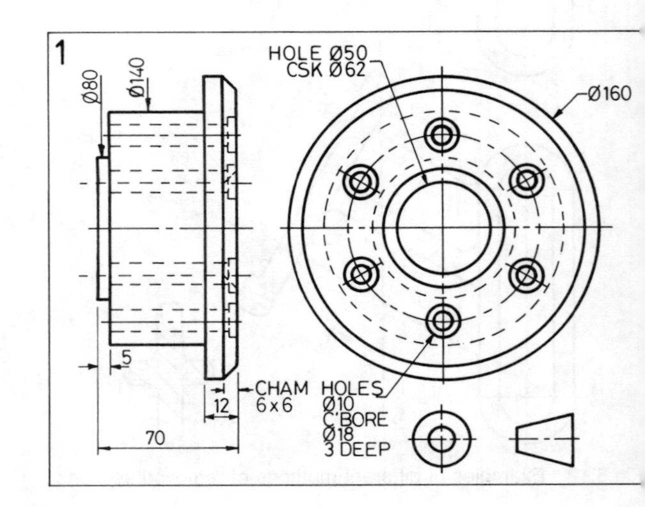

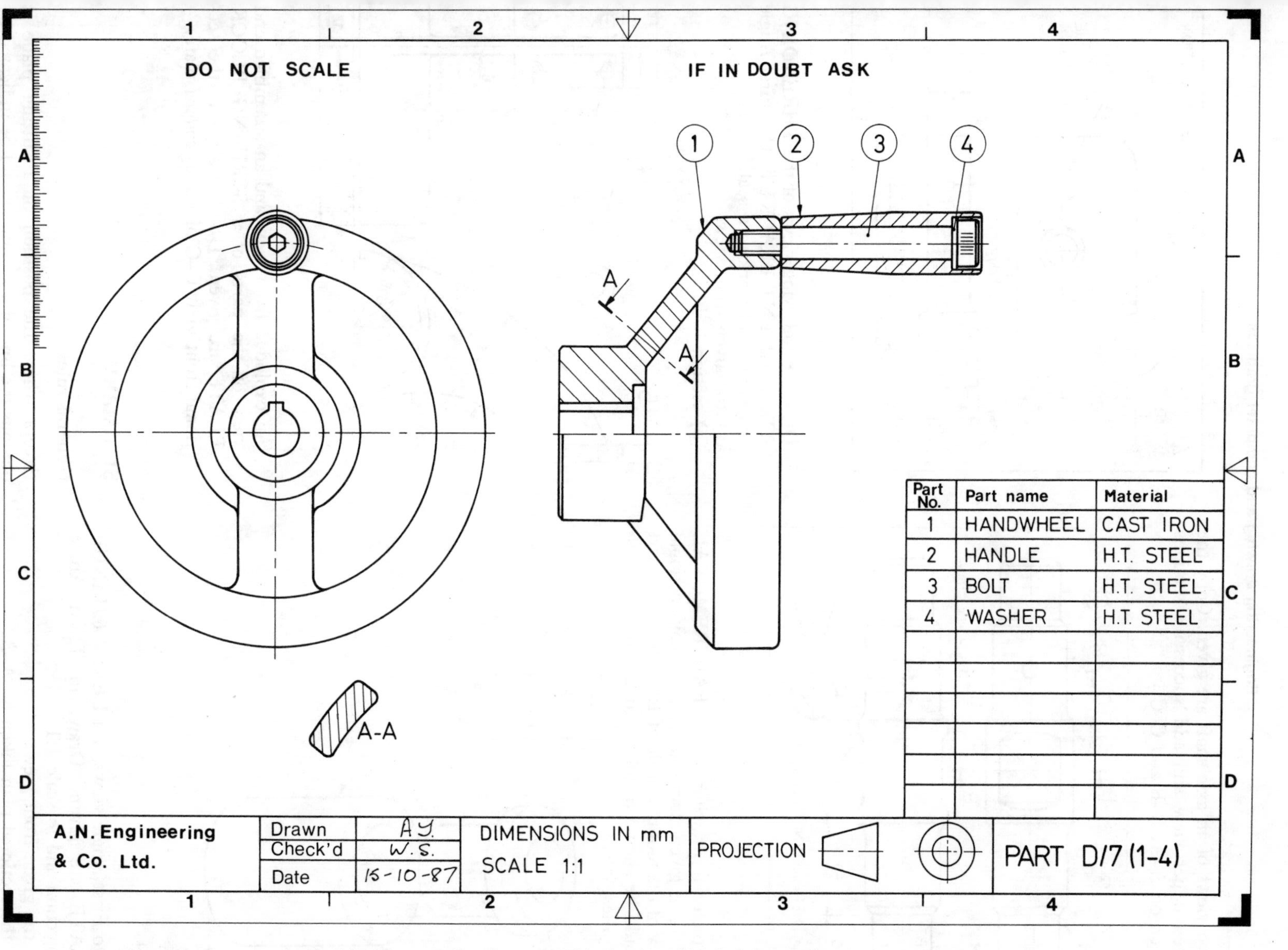

Fig.5.15 An example of an assembly drawing which includes sections

(2) Two views of an axle shaft are given. Copy the given upper view and add successive sections taken on A–A, B–B and C–C.

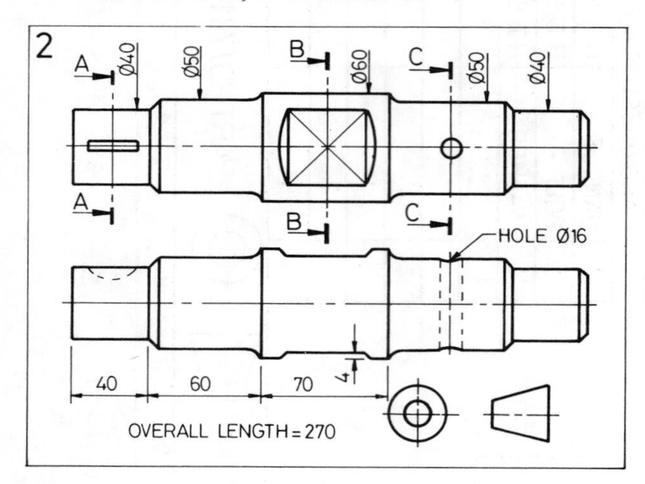

(3) A pictorial drawing of a SEAL REMOVAL TOOL is given. Draw an accurate half-sectional view of the tool to a scale of 1:1. The upper part should be shown bedded into the lower part to its fullest extent.

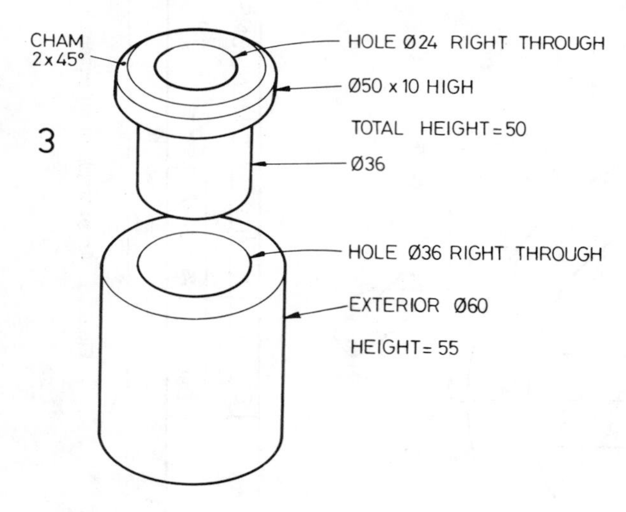

(4) Two First Angle views of a LEVER CHANGE PLATE are given. Draw, in Third Angle projection and to scale 1:1:
(a) the given front view;
(b) the sectional plan taken on A–A.

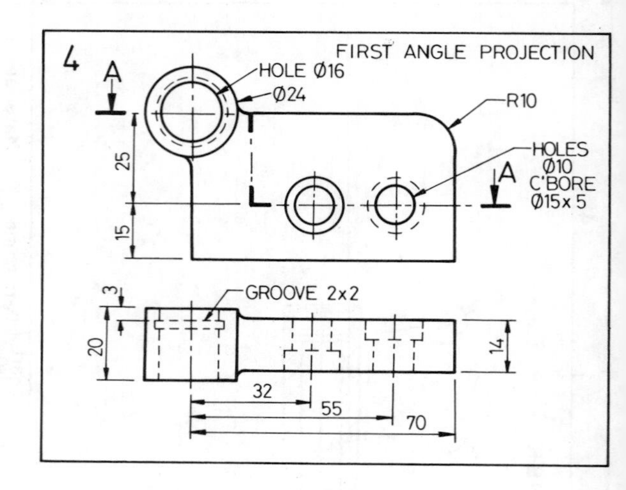

(5) Draw the following views of the THREADING ATTACHMENT BRACKET. Use First Angle projection and work to a scale of 1:1:
(a) the given front view;
(b) section B–B.

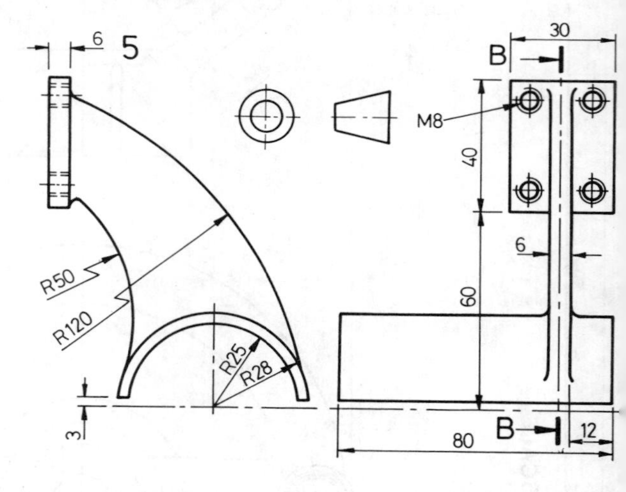

(6) An exploded front view and an assembled end view of the parts of a SCRIBING BLOCK PLATE are given. Draw, scale 2:1, the sectional front view C–C of the *assembled* plate.

SUMMARY

General rules

Except where the position of a cutting plane is obvious the line of a section should be indicated by

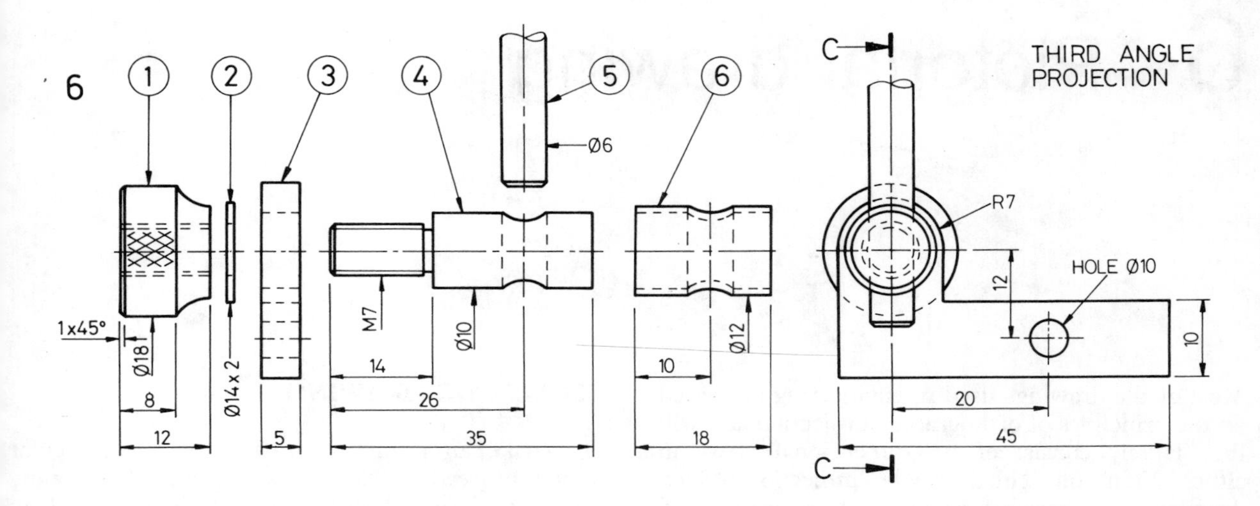

a section plane line. The line should be labelled with a letter of the alphabet.

Sectional views should be labelled to correspond with the section cutting plane to which they refer.

In general cut surfaces in a sectional view should be hachured with thin lines drawn at 45° to the axis of the section.

Where a section cutting plane passes longitudinally along items such as bolts, keys, ribs, screws, shafts and similar parts, such parts are shown as outside views.

Other types of sections

- Half sections
- Sections on parallel cutting planes
- Part, or local sections
- Thin sheet sections
- Revolved sections
- Removed sections
- Successive sections
- Symmetrical sections.

6 Pictorial drawing

Most of the drawings used in engineering are based on the principles of orthographic projection and will thus largely consist of two-dimensional views in either First or Third Angle projection. Such drawings will therefore consist of front views, end views, plans, sectional views and the like – two-dimensional 'true views'. There are occasions when it will be found necessary to produce pictorial three-dimensional drawings to explain, or to enable easier comprehension of, orthographic projections. Pictorial drawings are also of value when explanations of design features, design details and functions are required. Although many geometrical methods for producing pictorial drawings have been developed, only three are shown here. These are the three in most common use – isometric drawing, cabinet oblique drawing and simple perspective drawing. In both isometric and cabinet drawing, the projections on which the drawings are based are always parallel to each other on each face of the drawing. In perspective drawings the projections diverge on one, two or three faces, depending on which method of perspective is selected. It should be noted that none of the methods of pictorial drawing given here gives a true picture as seen by an observer. They are intended to give the observer a picture which clearly describes the object being drawn. Drawings produced by any of the three methods may be made with the aid of instruments or may be drawn freehand. It is, however, common practice to draw isometric and cabinet drawings with the assistance of instruments and to use perspective methods working freehand, or with minimal aid from instruments. All three types of drawing can also be produced on grid papers, working either with instruments or working freehand. Isometric drawings may be produced on isometric grid papers, cabinet drawings on square grid papers and perspective drawings on perspective grid papers.

ISOMETRIC DRAWING

To make an isometric drawing of a rectangular block proceed as shown in Fig. 6.1. All sloping lines are drawn at 30° to a base line AB and all verticals are drawn at 90° to AB. The measurements of length (*L*), width (*W*) and height (*H*) are taken directly along the sloping and vertical lines, with no scale allowance made to allow for the fact that they slope away from the observer. The lines of the block are drawn with the aid of a 30°, 60° set square or with the aid of a draughting head set to draw lines at 30° and at 90°.

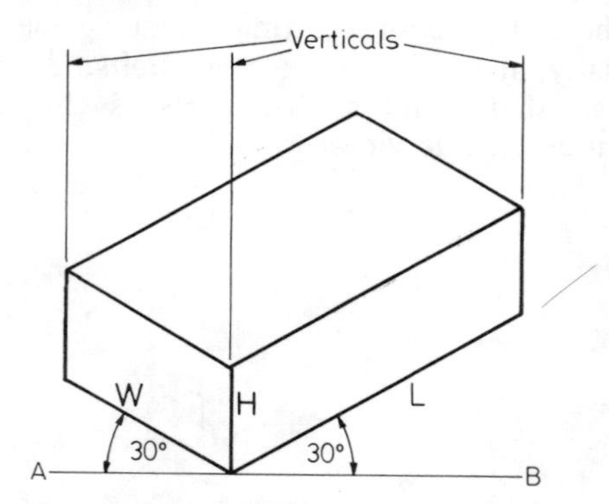

Fig.6.1 Basis of isometric drawing

Isometric scale

Fig. 6.2 compares an isometric drawing of a cube with an isometric projection of a cube of the same edge lengths. The isometric projection of the cube is an end view, in First Angle orthographic projection, of the cube resting on one corner A so that a line passing through corners B and C is parallel to the plane on which the corner of the cube rests. Note the difference in size between the isometric drawing and the isometric projection. An isometric scale could be drawn and used to take

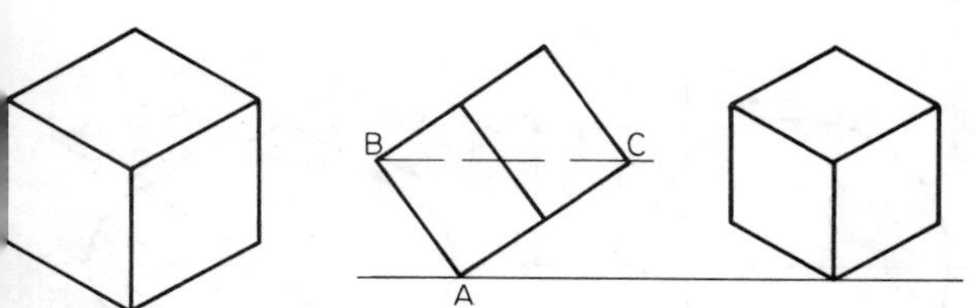

Fig.6.2 Isometric drawing of a cube compared with isometric projection of the cube

account of this difference in size, but it is rarely of any practical consequence to ensure that an isometric drawing is drawn to such a scale. As far as this book is concerned isometric scale is ignored.

A simple isometric drawing Fig. 6.3

The shape of a catch is given in front and plan views in First Angle projection. Drawings 1 and 2 show stages in producing an isometric drawing of the catch.

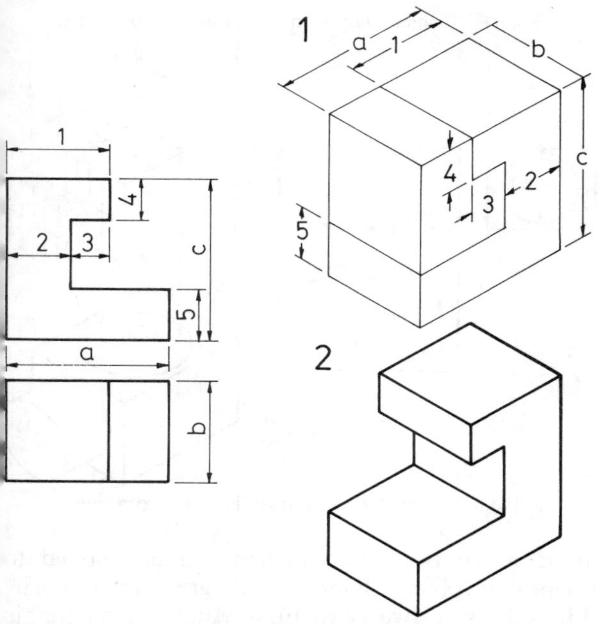

Fig.6.3 A simple isometric drawing

Drawing 1

Draw the outline of a rectangular block of length *a*, width *b* and height *c* within which the catch is contained. Draw the shapes of the outlines of the catch on the sloping faces by taking measurements from the orthographic views and transferring them along the 30° and vertical axes of the isometric block. Lengths 1, 2, 3, 4 and 5 are obtained in this manner. Draw sloping lines at 30° and vertical lines at 90° to produce the shapes on each face.

Drawing 2

Complete the isometric drawing as shown.

Sloping faces in an isometric drawing

When drawing sloping lines in an isometric drawing, measurements can only be made along either 30° or along vertical axes and never along the slope of the line itself. Figs. 6.4 and 6.5 show applications of this principle.

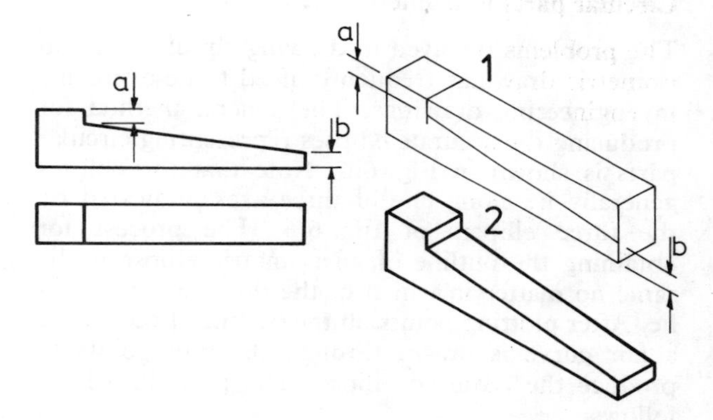

Fig.6.4 Sloping faces in an isometric drawing – a key

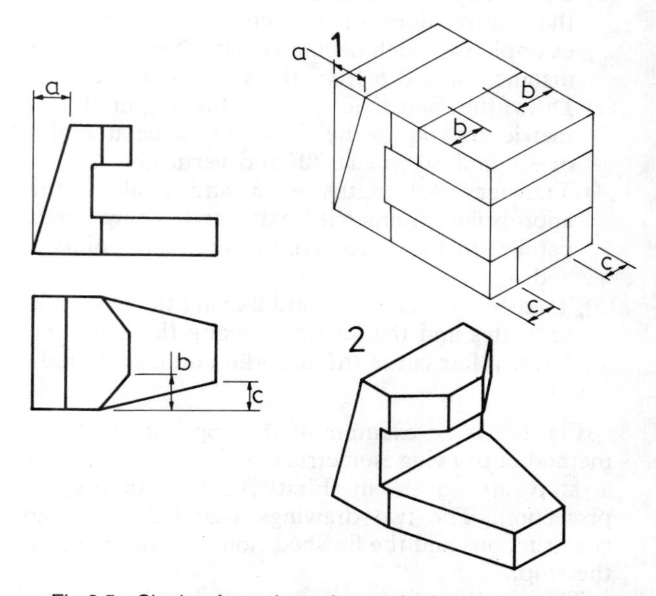

Fig.6.5 Sloping faces in an isometric drawing – a slide

To obtain the lines of the sloping face of the key in the isometric drawing, the lengths *a* and *b* must be transferred from the orthographic projection to vertical lines of the isometric drawing (Fig. 6.4). When the positions of the ends of the sloping lines have been so obtained, the actual slope lines can be drawn.

To obtain the various sloping lines of the slide the lengths *a*, *b* and *c* must be transferred from the orthographic projection to the 30° axes of the isometric drawing (Fig. 6.5). When the ends of the slopes have been plotted along the isometric axes, the slope lines can be drawn.

Circular parts in isometric drawings

The problems involved in drawing circular parts in isometric drawings frequently need to be overcome in engineering drawings. The general method for producing the accurate ellipses representing circular parts is shown in Fig. 6.6. Note that the ellipses generally lie along one of three axes, indicated by the three ellipses of Fig. 6.6. The process for obtaining the outline of an isometric ellipse is the same no matter in which of the directions the axes lie. After plotting points on the outline of the ellipse a fair curve is drawn through the plot points to produce the required ellipse. The procedure is as follows:

(1) Draw a front view of the circle.
(2) Draw a number of ordinates parallel to one of the centre lines of the circle. In the given example two such ordinates have been drawn at distances *a* and *b* from the vertical centre line.
(3) Draw the isometric axes of the required isometric drawing of the circle. These lie at angles of 30° and 30°, or at 30° and vertically.
(4) Transfer the lengths *a*, *b* and *c* along the appropriate isometric axis and draw lines parallel to the other axis through the points *a* and *b*.
(5) Transfer the lengths 1 and 2 along the isometric ordinates and the lengths 3 along the axis.
(6) Draw a fair curve through the points so found.

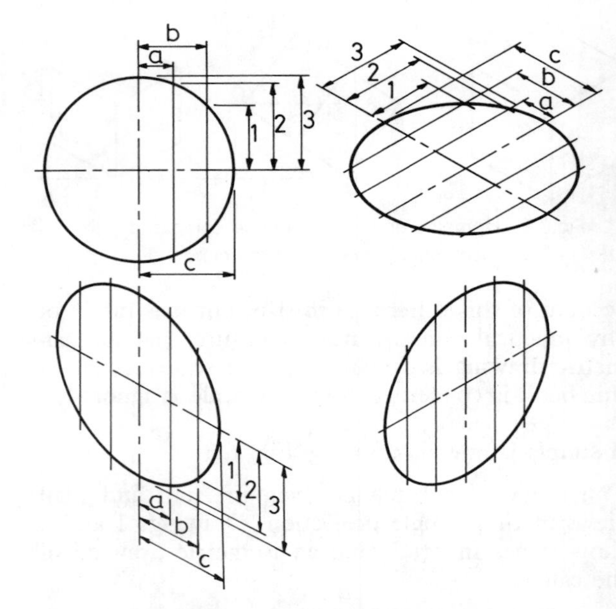

Fig.6.6 Constructing isometric drawings of circles

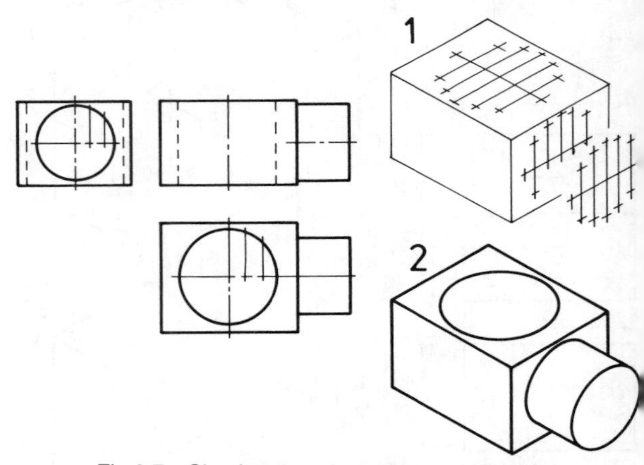

Fig.6.7 Circular parts in an isometric drawing

Fig. 6.7 is an example of the application of this method of drawing isometric curves. Three views of a stop are given in First Angle orthographic projection. The two drawings 1 and 2 show the constructions and the finished isometric drawings of the stop.

This method of constructing and drawing circular parts in an isometric drawing can be applied to shapes involving lines which are not circular. Fig. 6.8 is a two-view First Angle orthographic projection of a clip, together with an isometric drawing of the clip. The two curves in the front view are semi-ellipses. Following the procedure outlined for obtaining the isometric drawings of circles given in Fig. 6.6, the positions and lengths of the ordinates *a*, *b*, *c* and *d* have been transferred from the front view to the isometric drawing to obtain points through which the curves representing the semi-ellipses in the isometric drawing can be drawn. Note that the length of the lines AB at 30°

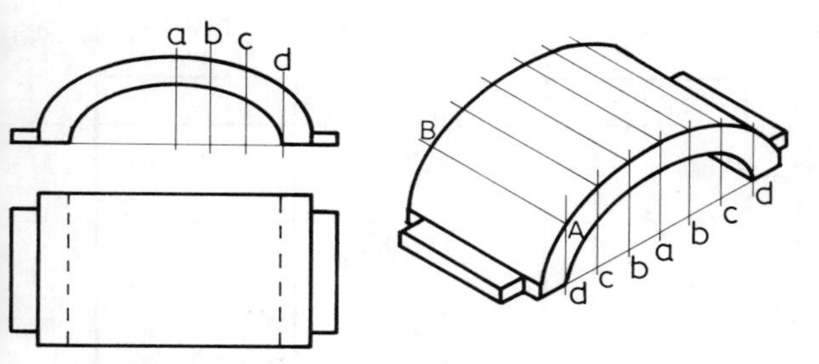

Fig.6.8 Isometric drawing involving shapes which are not parts of circles

on the isometric drawing are all the same to ensure that the curve at the rear is the same as the curve at the front of the drawing.

Exploded isometric drawing

Exploded isometric drawings are commonly found in maintenance manuals and in engineering drawings which show how the parts of an assembly fit together. An example of an exploded isometric drawing is given in Fig. 6.9. The construction lines on which details of this drawing were based are given in Fig. 6.10. The 'explosions' in this form of drawing are usually made with the parts of the assembly in line with the position in which they fit. Thus the parts are drawn in line along either the 30° or the vertical axes. Exploded pictorial drawings will be seen which have been drawn using methods other than isometric.

Isometric grids

It was stated earlier that isometric drawings could be drawn on grid papers. Isometric grid papers are

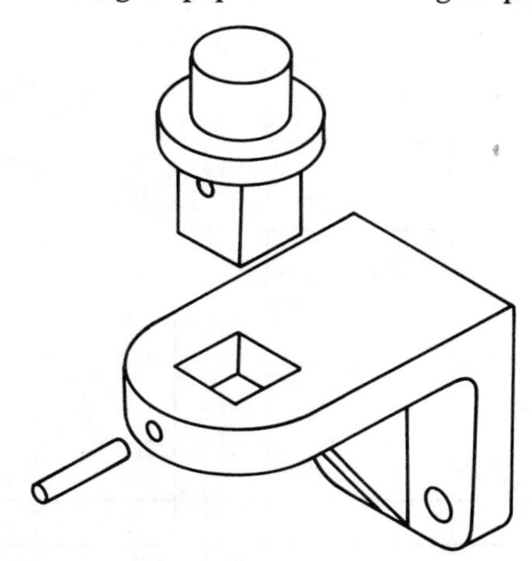

Fig.6.9 A simple exploded isometric drawing

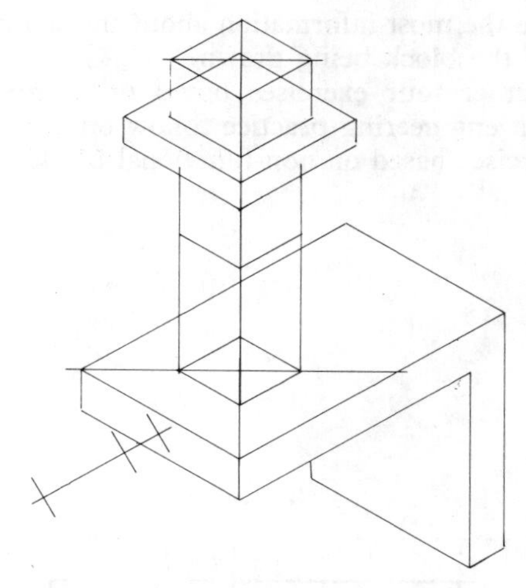

Fig.6.10 Construction for the exploded isometric drawing Fig.6.9

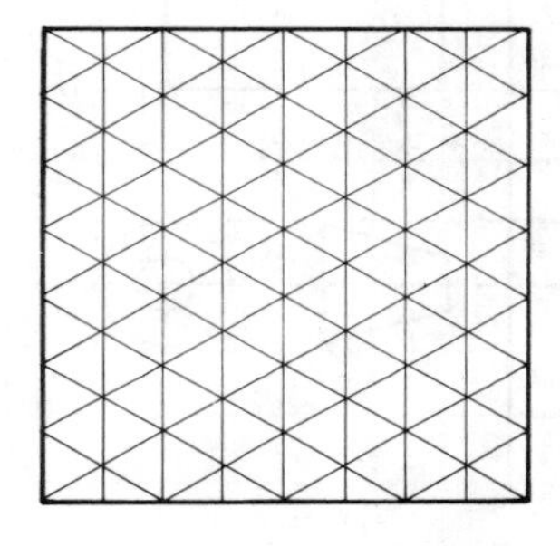

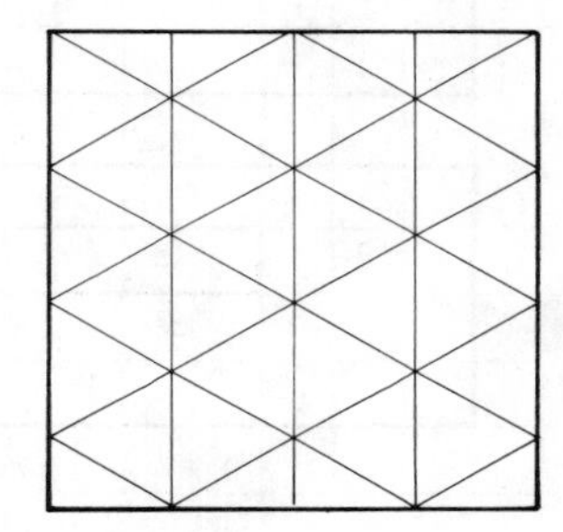

Fig.6.11 5 mm and 10 mm isometric grid papers

commonly printed with grid lines at 5 mm or 10 mm intervals, as shown in the two drawings of Fig. 6.11. The grid lines are usually printed in blue.

Exercises (non-functional)

To allow the reader practice in the making of isometric drawings ten orthographic projections on square grids have been included on page 62 and page 63. These ten drawings show non-functional block shapes devised to give drawing practice. Each of the blocks is drawn in either First or in Third Angle projection, indicated by a BS angle symbol on each drawing. The grids are spaced at 5 mm and the answers to the exercises may be drawn either full size or at a scale of 2:1. Dimensions can be gained by counting the grid spaces.

Work on plain paper with instruments. Select a viewing position for each of your answers which will give the most information about the shapes and form of the block being drawn.

A further four exercises based on components found in engineering practice follow on from these ten exercises based on non-functional block shapes.

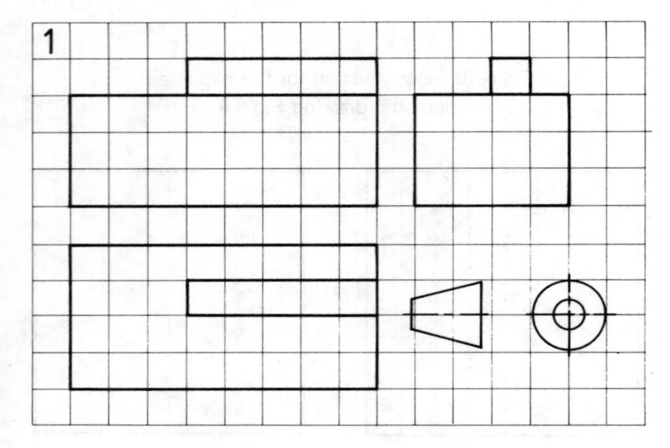

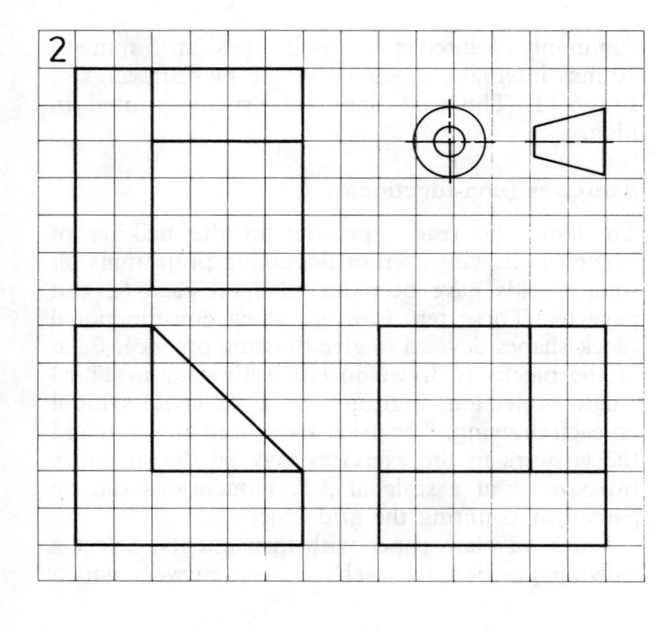

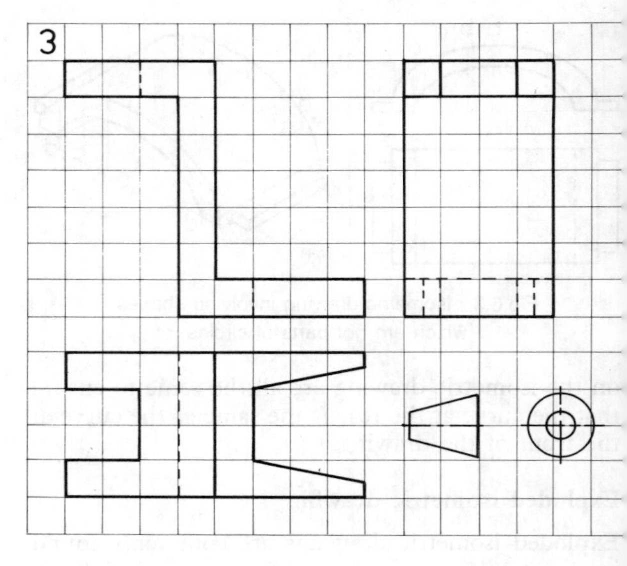

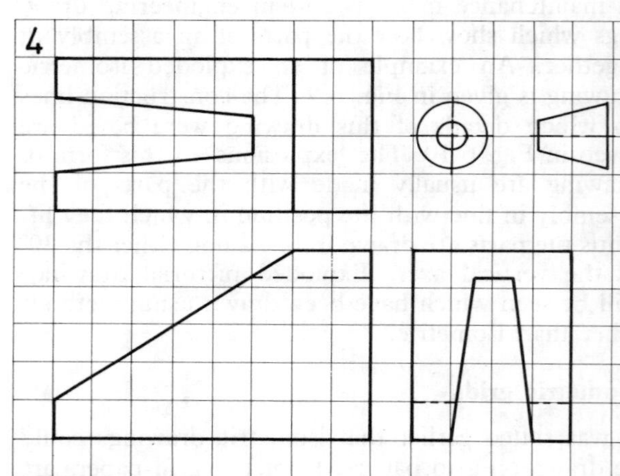

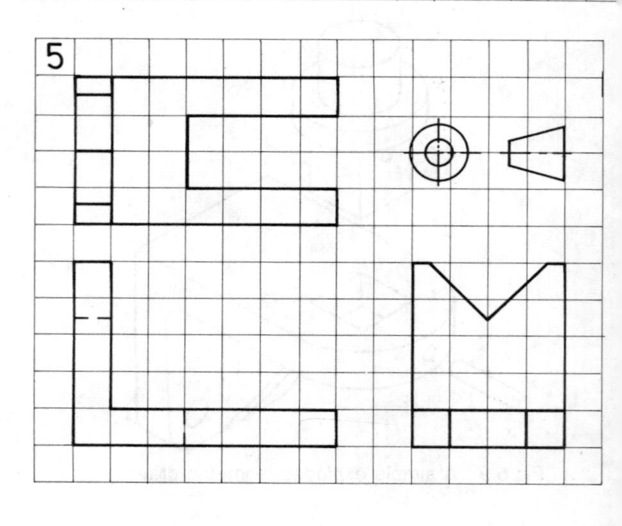

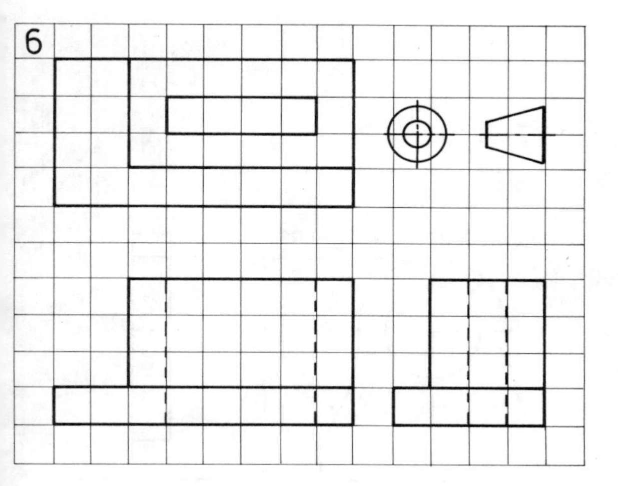

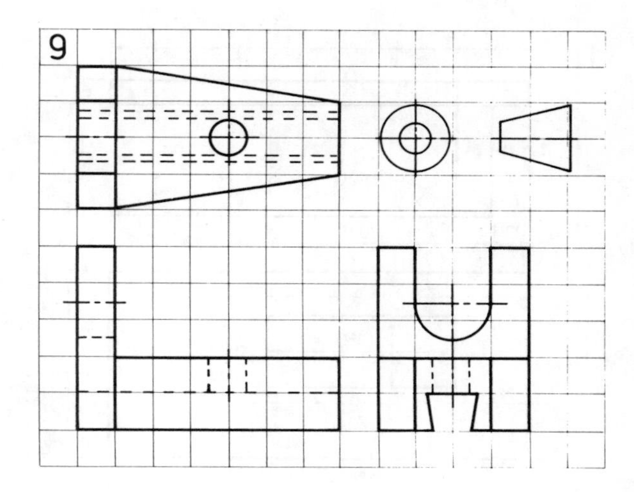

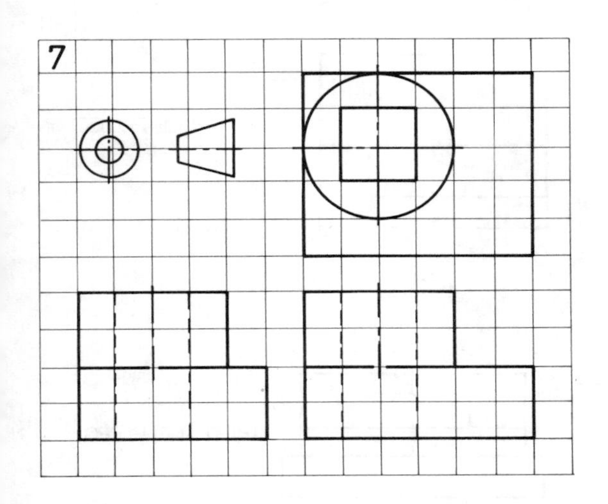

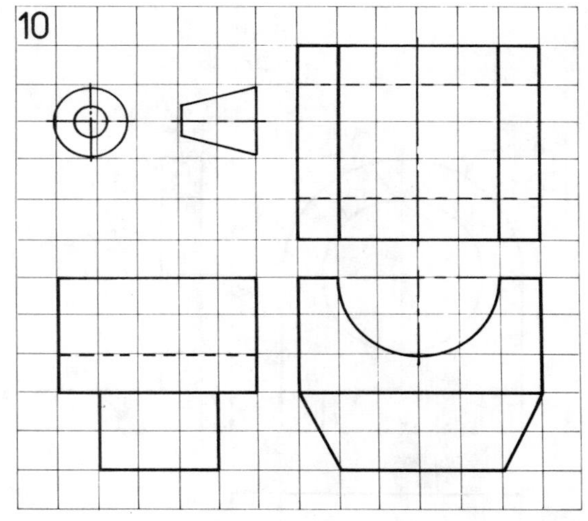

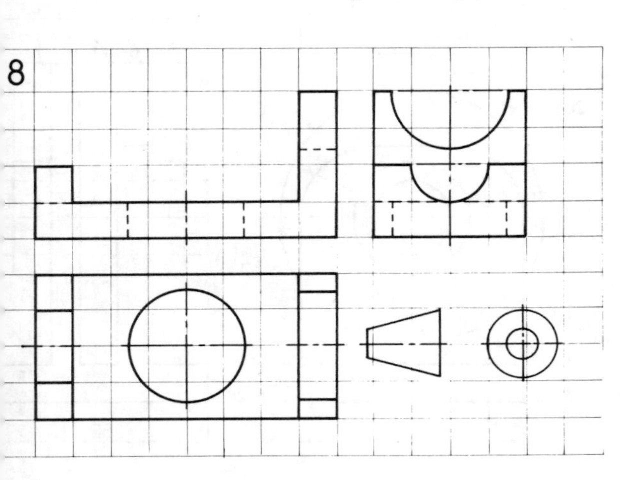

Exercises (functional)

Four exercises designed to give the reader some practice in isometric drawing are given below. When drawing the answers to these four exercises, work to a scale of 1:1 (full size).

(1) The two given views of the component are in First Angle projection. Draw the component in isometric drawing.
(2) Three First Angle views of a bracket are given. Make an accurate isometric drawing of the bracket.
(3) Draw an isometric view of the slide.
(4) In the given orthographic drawing Part A is a disk, Part B is a bearing, Parts C are collars and Part D is a spindle. Make an accurate exploded drawing of the assembly.

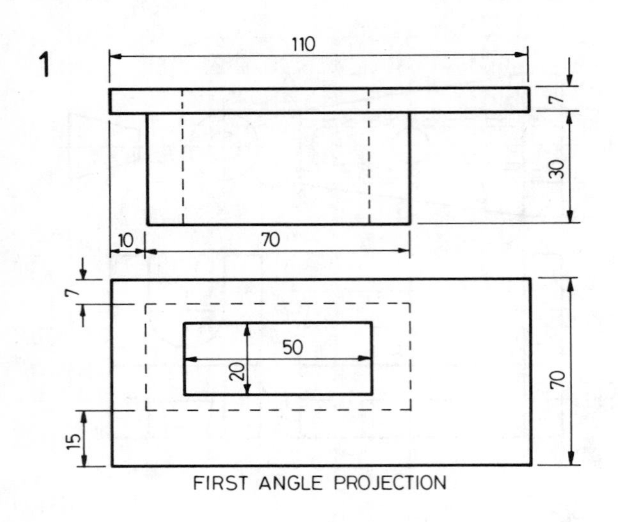
1
110
7
30
10
70
7
50
20
70
15
FIRST ANGLE PROJECTION

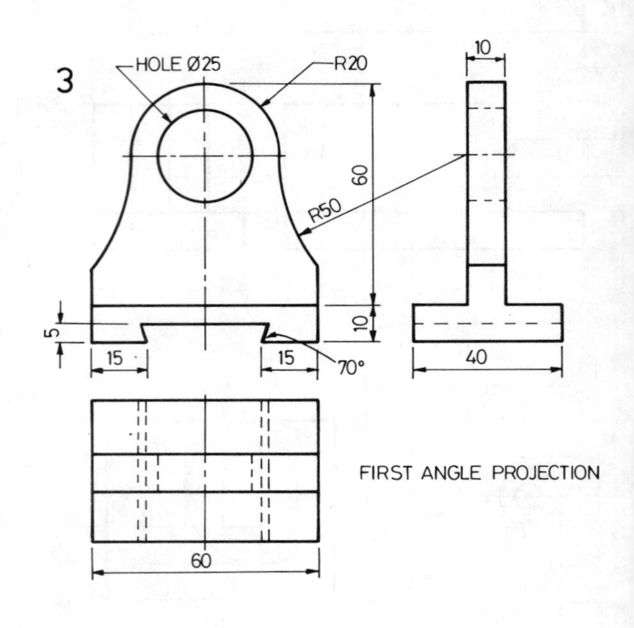
3
HOLE Ø25
R20
10
60
R50
5
10
15
15
70°
40
60
FIRST ANGLE PROJECTION

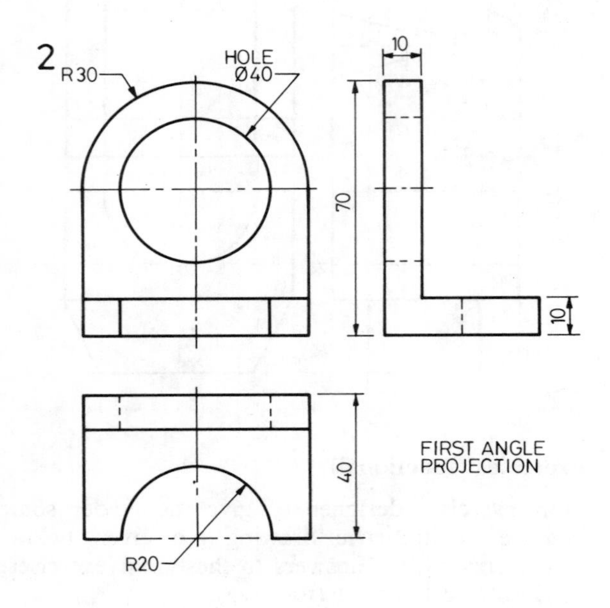
2
R30
HOLE
Ø40
10
70
10
40
FIRST ANGLE
PROJECTION
R20

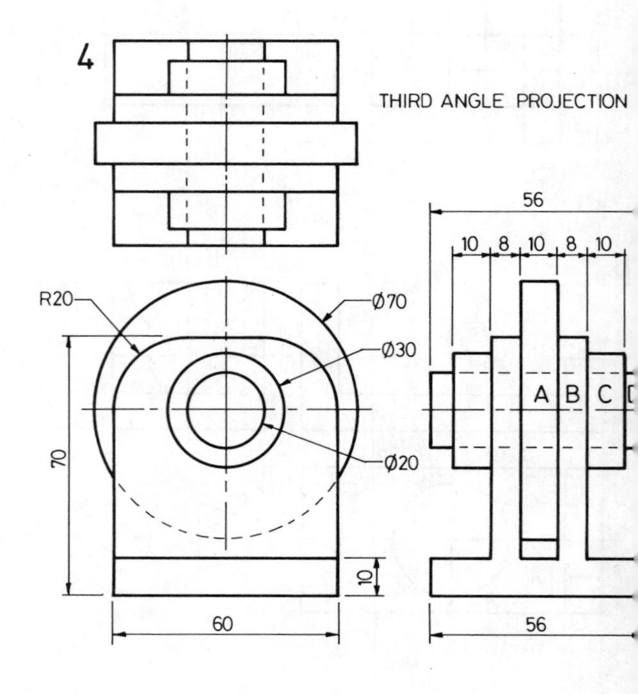
4
THIRD ANGLE PROJECTION
56
10
8
10
8
10
R20
Ø70
Ø30
A
B
C
70
Ø20
10
60
56

OBLIQUE CABINET DRAWING

Oblique drawing is a form of pictorial drawing in which front facing surfaces are drawn as true views of the front face of the object and receding edges are drawn parallel to each other at angles of 30°, 45° or 60°. It is common practice when making oblique drawings to use the same drawing scale along receding edges as for the front facing surfaces.

Cabinet drawing is a particular form of oblique drawing in which receding edges are drawn at an angle of 45° to the front surfaces and measurements along the 45° edges are taken at half size (scale 1:2) of the drawing scale. Fig. 6.12 compares cabinet drawing with oblique drawing.

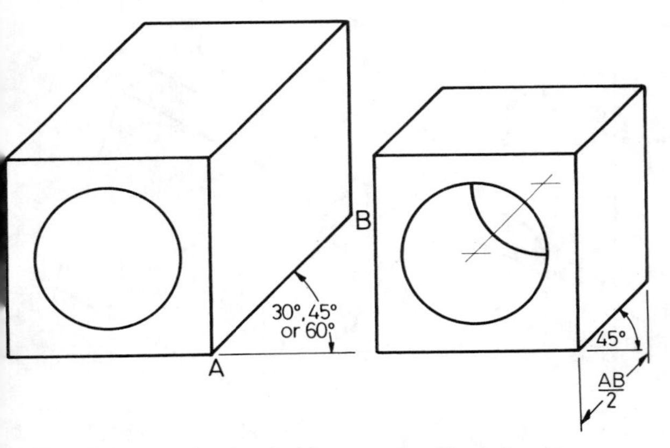

Fig.6.12 Basis of oblique and cabinet drawing

The reason for adopting cabinet drawing in preference to oblique is to avoid the appearance of distortion of depth which occurs when applying oblique drawing methods. By the scaling of receding edge lengths to half size, cabinet drawing tends to avoid this distortion. Cabinet drawing is a useful form of pictorial drawing to be used when the object being drawn tends to have complicated shapes in one face.

Fig. 6.13 shows the method of producing either an oblique drawing or a cabinet drawing of a simple bracket bearing. Proceed as follows:

(1) Draw a front view of the bearing.
(2) Draw lines at 45° from the corners of the base and from the circle centres.
(3) Measure full size lengths along the 45° lines in the case of the oblique drawing or half size lengths in the case of the cabinet drawing.
(4) Complete the drawing as shown.

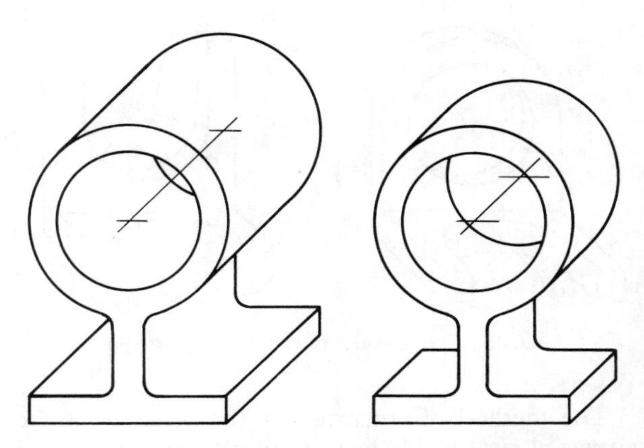

Fig.6.13 An example of an oblique and of a cabinet drawing

Note The receding edges of the oblique drawing may be drawn at angles other than 45°. In these two examples 45° has been chosen for the oblique drawing in order that a comparison may be made with a cabinet drawing of the same object.

Cabinet drawing with curves along the 45° axes

If one wishes to make a cabinet drawing of an object which has curves along the 45° axes, it becomes necessary to devise a method by which the measurements taken along all 45° edges are at a scale of 1:2. Fig. 6.14 is a three-view Third Angle projection of an angle clip. Fig. 6.15 shows two cabinet drawings of the clip. The left hand of the two drawings shows the clip resting on the face containing a slot. The right hand drawing shows the clip resting on the face which contains a hole.

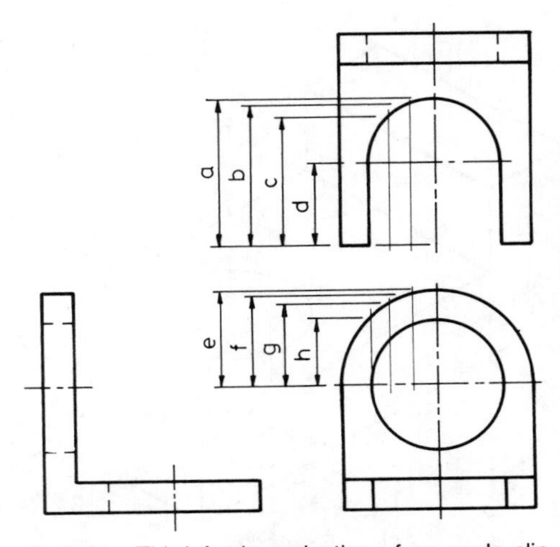

Fig.6.14 Third Angle projection of an angle clip

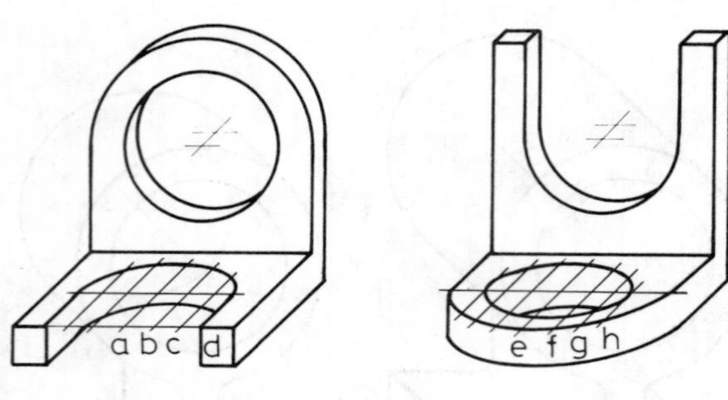

Fig.6.15 Two cabinet drawings of the angle clip

The method of constructing the outlines of the curves along the 45° faces is similar to the method employed when drawing curves in isometric drawings (see Figs 6.6 and 6.7). Ordinates are drawn on the orthographic views of the object being drawn and the positions and half lengths of these ordinates then transferred to the cabinet drawing. Note the difference between the method as used for an isometric drawing and as used for a cabinet drawing – full lengths of the ordinates are transferred to an isometric drawing, but half scale lengths of ordinates are transferred to a cabinet drawing. Thus in Fig. 6.15 the lengths of ordinates a to h in the two cabinet drawings are half the length of the same ordinates in the orthographic view of Fig. 6.14.

Exercises (non-functional)

To allow the reader to obtain practice in producing cabinet drawings, ten exercises based on non-functional block forms are given on this page and pages 67 and 68. The first four of the blocks have been drawn on 5 mm isometric grids and the remaining six are on 5 mm square grids. Proceed as follows:

(1) Work with instruments on plain paper either to a scale of 1:1 or scale 2:1, from dimensions given by counting the grid spacings.
(2) Select that face of each block which is the most complicated as the face of your cabinet drawing.
(3) Make an accurate cabinet drawing of each block.

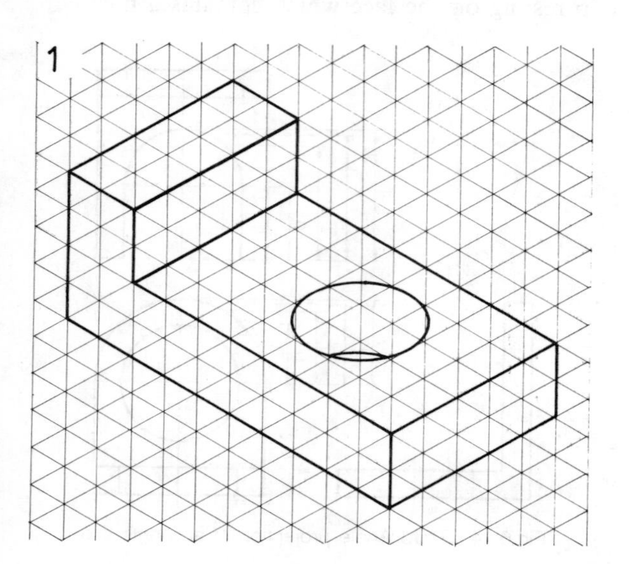

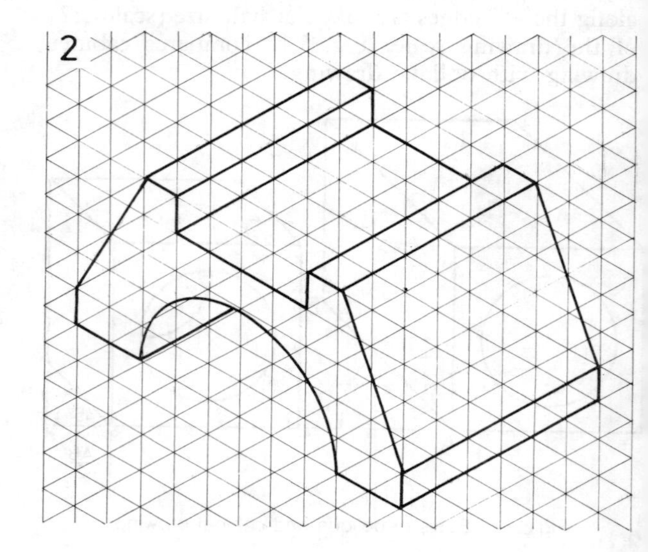

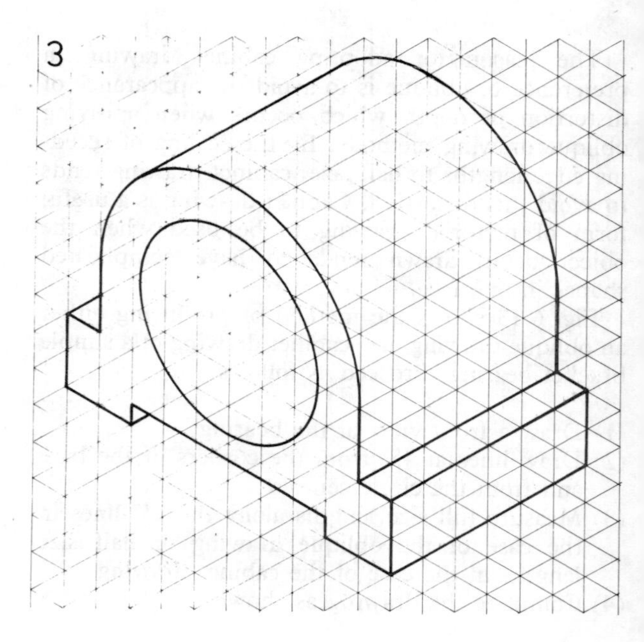

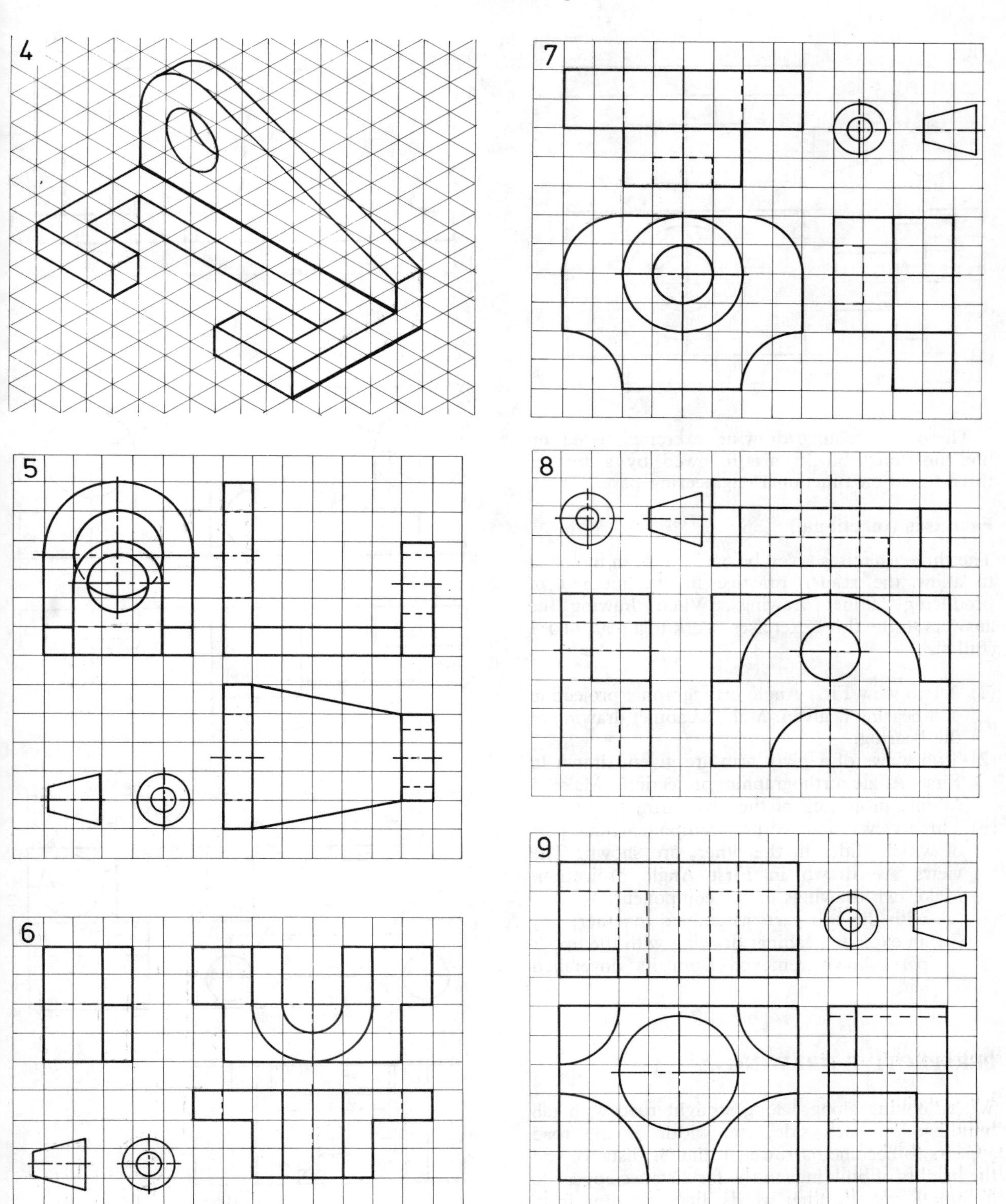
4
5
6
7
8
9

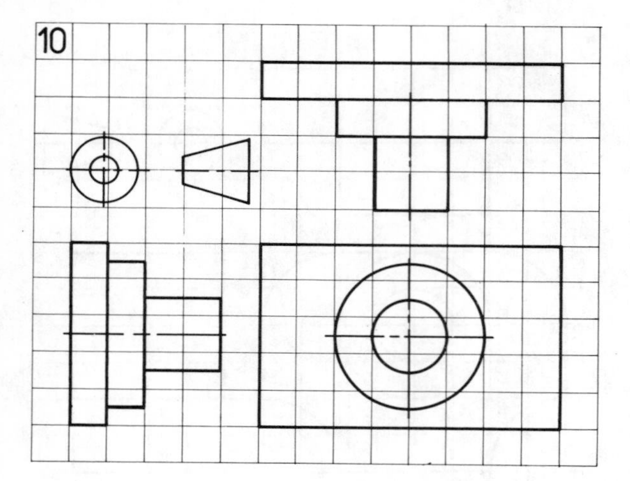

These ten cabinet drawing exercises based on non-functional blocks are followed by a further three based on functional engineering parts.

Exercises (functional)

The three exercises given below have been included to allow the reader practice in the method of producing cabinet drawings. When drawing the answers to the three exercises, work to a scale of 1:1 (full size).

(1) A two-view First Angle orthographic projection of a bearing is given. Make a cabinet drawing of the bearing.
(2) Two views of a pivot arm are given, drawn in First Angle orthographic projection. Make a cabinet projection of the pivot arm.
(3) Three views of a two-part component, one part of which slides in the other, are shown. The views are drawn in First Angle projection. Make two drawings of the component:
  (a) with the two parts assembled together;
  (b) an exploded cabinet drawing with the upper part shown removed from its dovetailed slide.

PERSPECTIVE DRAWING

When looking along a long straight road with tall buildings on each side, the width of the road appears to become narrower in the far distance and the heights of buildings in the far distance appear to become lower. In other words, lines receding from

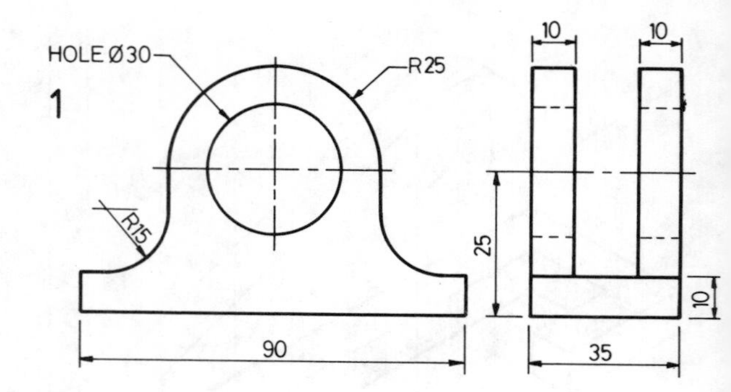

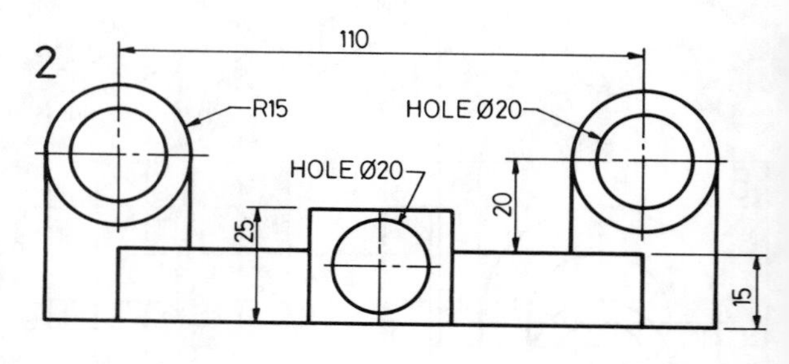

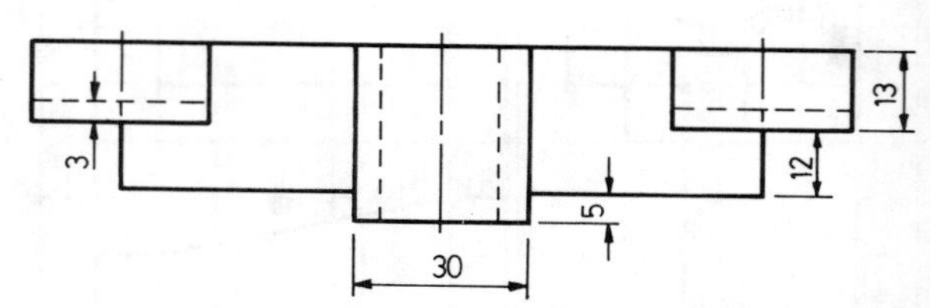

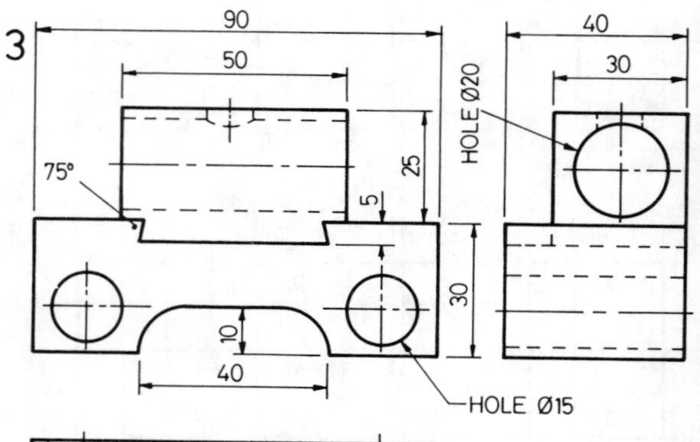

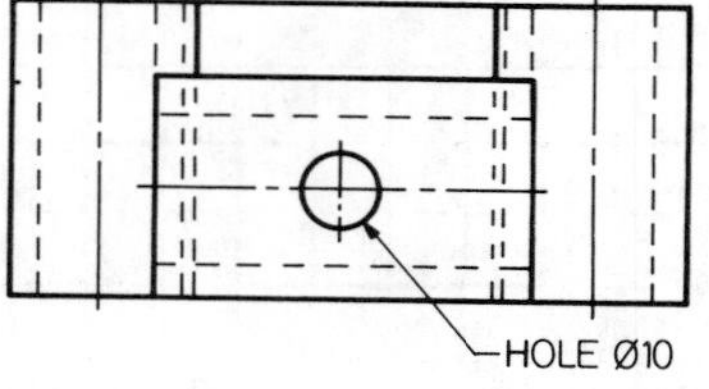

the observer appear to converge towards a point in the distance. This commonly observed phenomenon forms the basis of perspective drawing. In technical drawings of the type with which we are concerned here, perspective drawing is assumed to be based upon the use of one, two or three vanishing points towards which lines converge. The technical methods of perspective are therefore referred to as one-point, two-point or three-point perspective.

We will not be dealing in these pages with the various forms of perspective drawing in which vanishing points are located on the drawing sheet with regard to laid down rules based on geometrical concepts. If the reader wishes to learn how to lay out perspective drawings to such geometrical concepts as architect's perspective, measured point perspective, among others, there are many textbooks available which fully describe the processes by which such perspective drawings can be achieved. Here we are only concerned with what is known as estimated perspective drawing, in which vanishing points are placed at positions judged to give reasonable perspective representation of that which is being drawn.

Single-point perspective

Four single-point perspective drawings of a cube are shown in Fig. 6.16. In each example a single vanishing point (VP) is placed above the cube at a scaled position approximating to the height of the eye level of the observer looking at the cube. Note the following:

(1) A front view of the cube is drawn.
(2) The VP is placed to the left, to the right, or above the front view according to the part of the cube which needs most emphasis.
(3) Lines are drawn from the corners of the front view of the cube to the VPs.
(4) Lengths along the receding edges of the cube are smaller than the lengths of the edges of the face of the cube. In estimated perspective drawing the lengths of receding edges are also estimated.

Two-point perspective

The two-point perspective drawings of a cube are shown in Figs 6.17 and 6.18. In both examples two vanishing points (VP1 and VP2) are placed in line with each other, at positions approximating to the scaled height of the observer viewing the cubes. In the first example, the cube is placed below the level

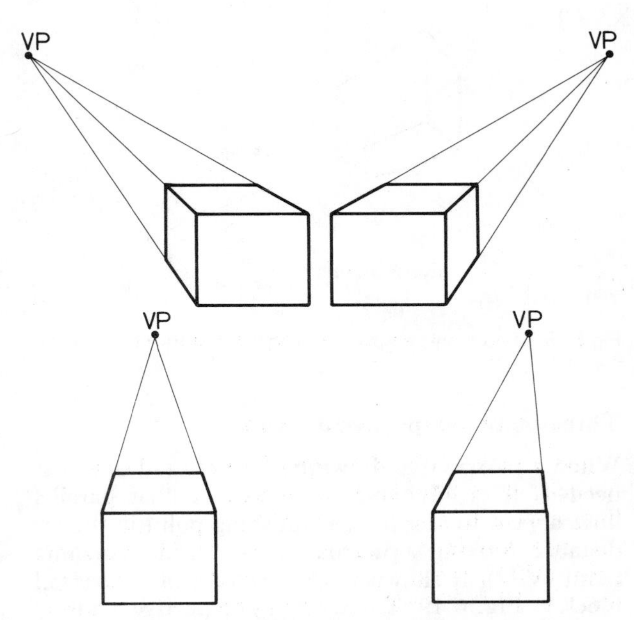

Fig.6.16 Single-point perspective

of the observer's eyes. Note the following in both examples:

(1) The distances along the receding sides are less than the actual length of a cube edge. These lengths are estimated according to the position of the drawing within the space below or above the VPs.
(2) The two drawings commenced with a drawing of the front vertical edge of the cube from the ends of which lines were taken to the two VPs.
(3) Rear vertical edges are drawn parallel to the front vertical edge.

Two-point estimated perspective drawing is commonly used to make pictorial freehand drawings of engineering components when such drawings are deemed to be necessary.

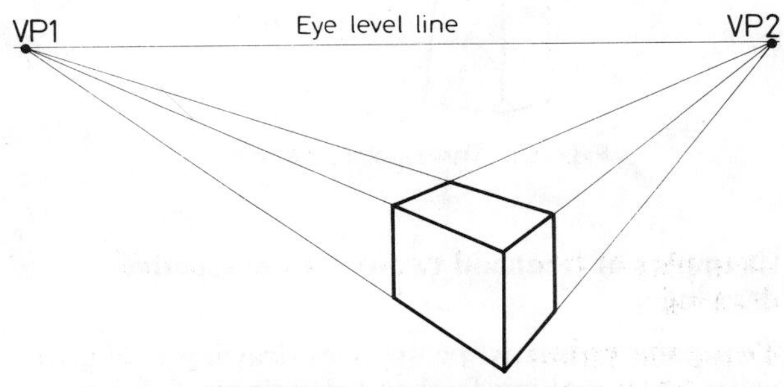

Fig.6.17 Two-point perspective

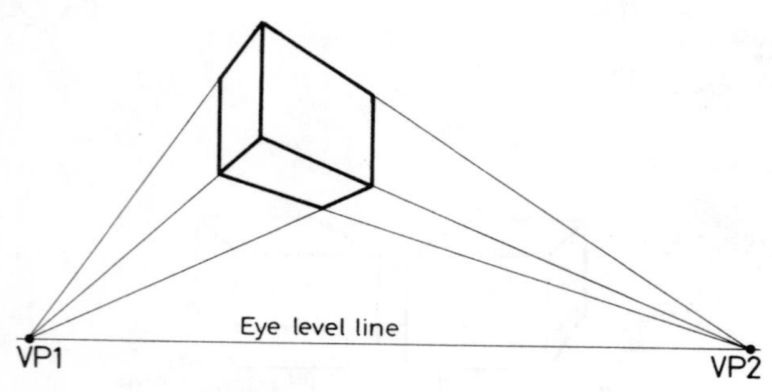

Fig.6.18 Two-point perspective of an object above the eye line

Three-point perspective drawing

When a perspective drawing of a very tall object is needed, it is advisable to remember that parallel lines appear to recede to a vanishing point in the far distance looking upwards. This, third vanishing point (VP3), is shown in the drawing of a very tall block in Fig. 6.19. Three-point perspective is rarely needed in engineering drawing.

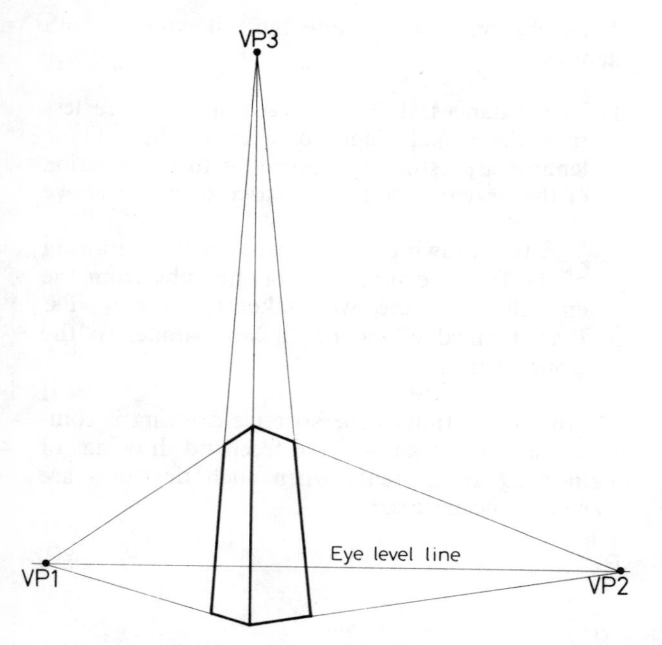

Fig.6.19 Three-point perspective

Examples of freehand two-point perspective drawing

Two-point estimated perspective drawing is of good value when making freehand drawings of engineering parts. Three examples are given in Figs 6.20, 6.21 and 6.22.

Drawing of a V block

Note the following in the two-point perspective drawing of a V block given in Fig. 6.20.

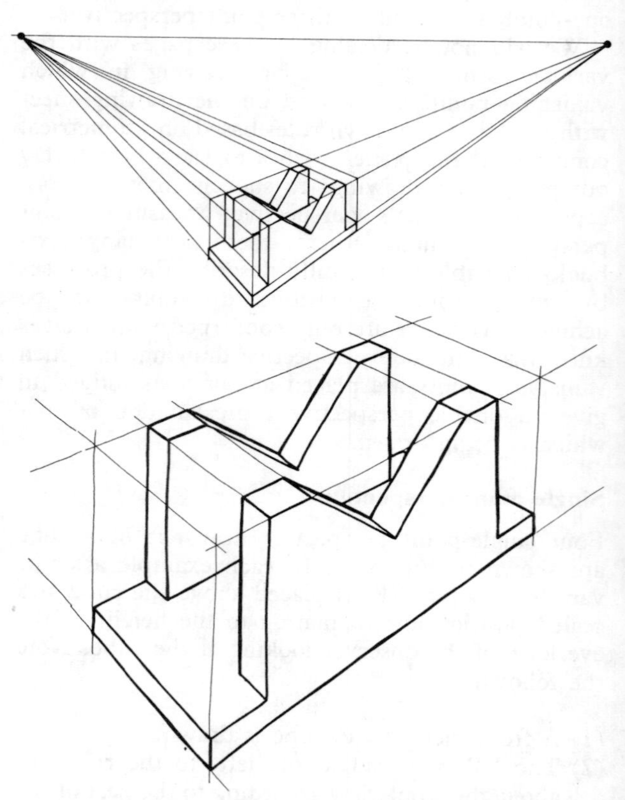

Fig.6.20 V block drawn in freehand two-point perspective

(1) A small-scale instrument drawing indicates the approximate location of the two VPs.
(2) When producing such freehand drawings there is no need actually to locate vanishing points on the drawing sheet. One should, however, estimate a position for the two VPs on the sheet or drawing board and keep the location of their positions 'in the mind's eye' so that the receding lines are drawn towards the imaginary VPs.
(3) The block in which the drawing of the V block fits is first drawn with thin, fine construction lines. This assists in obtaining reasonable proportions.

Exploded two-point perspective drawing

Fig. 6.21 is an exploded two-point perspective drawing of a tractor hitch, with the towing pin drawn in an exploded position. Note again the drawing was boxed with fine construction lines.

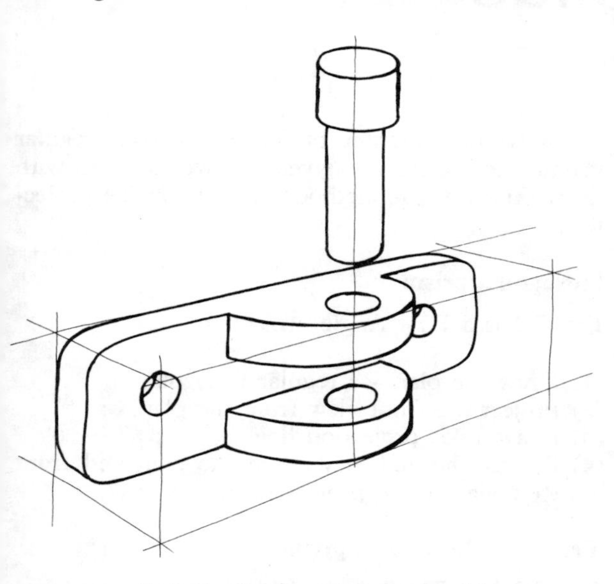

Fig.6.21 Simple exploded two-point perspective freehand drawing

Two-point perspective drawing from below

Fig. 6.22 is a two-point estimated perspective drawing, drawn freehand, of a hanging bracket as seen from below.

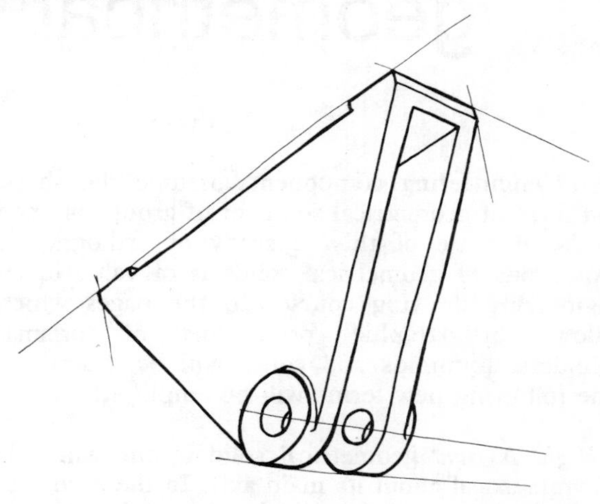

Fig.6.22 Freehand two-point perspective drawing of a hanging bracket

7 Orthographic projections of geometrical solids

Many engineering components assume the shape and form of geometrical solids or of groups of such solids. Because of this, a study of orthographic projections of geometrical solids is of value in an engineering drawing course. In the pages which follow, orthographic projections of prisms, cylinders, pyramids and cones will be described. The following new terms will be employed:

- *Right* A *right* geometrical solid is one which is symmetrical about its main axis. In the examples which follow, each solid is assumed as being capable of standing on a flat base with its main axis at right angles to that base.
- *Frustrum* The remainder of a regular right solid, part of which has been cut off by a plane parallel to its base.
- *Truncated* A truncated solid is one which has had a part (or parts) cut off by planes not necessarily parallel to the base of the solid.

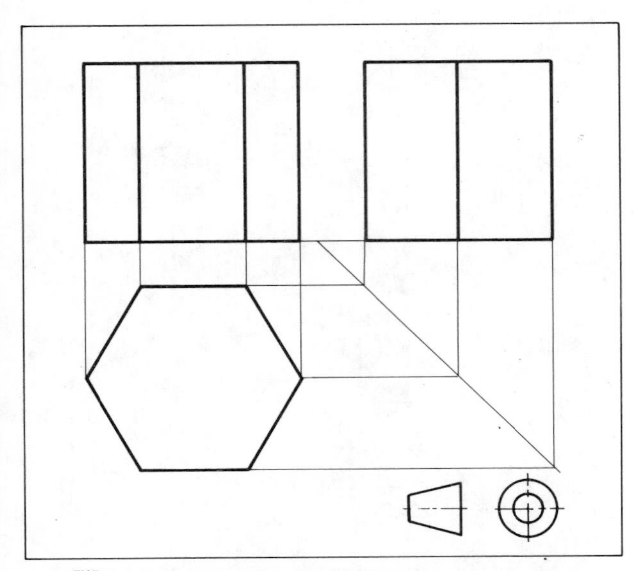

Fig.7.1 First Angle projection of a hexagonal prism

Twelve orthographic projections of right regular geometrical solids are given below, together with descriptions of the methods of drawing the projections.

Hexagonal prism

Fig. 7.1 is a First Angle projection.

(1) Draw the plan – a regular hexagon.
(2) Project the front view from the plan.
(3) Draw a 45° projection line.
(4) Project the end view from the plan and front view via the 45° projection line.

Truncated hexagonal prism

Fig. 7.2 is a Third Angle projection to include an auxiliary view.

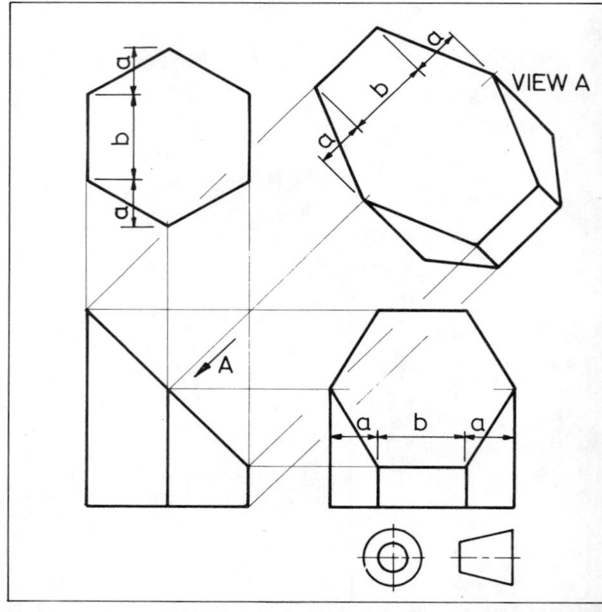

Fig.7.2 Third Angle projection of truncated hexagonal prism including an auxiliary view

(1) Draw the plan – a regular hexagon.
(2) Project the front view from the plan. Draw the truncation plane line – in this example at 45° to the base of the prism.
(3) Project the end view from the front view and plan, transferring the measurements *a* and *b* from the plan with compasses.
(4) Project lines at right angles to the truncated face in the front view and transfer the measurements *a* and *b* along these projection lines from the plan with compasses.
(5) Complete the auxiliary VIEW A as shown.

Cylinder

Fig. 7.3 is a Third Angle projection.

(1) Draw the plan – a circle.
(2) Project the front view from the plan.
(3) Project the end view from the plan and front view via quadrant arcs as shown.
(4) Add centre lines.

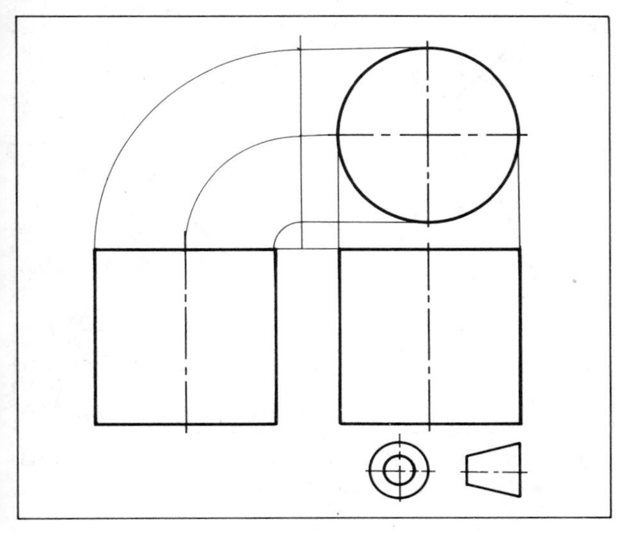

Fig.7.3 Third Angle projection of a cylinder

Truncated cylinder

Fig. 7.4 is a First Angle projection to include an auxiliary view.

(1) Draw the plan – a circle.
(2) Project the front view from the plan and draw its truncation line – in this example at 30° to the base of the cylinder.
(3) To obtain the end view:
  (a) divide the plan circle into 12 equal parts by drawing lines at 30° and 60° to the horizontal centre line. This will give the points on the circle numbered 1 to 12;
  (b) project points 1 to 12 in the plan on to the truncation plane line in the front view;
  (c) project from the points 1 to 12 on the truncation plane line horizontally;
  (d) draw the centre line of the end view in any convenient position;
  (e) transfer the measurements *a*, *b* and *c* from the plan to each side of the end view centre line. Draw verticals through the points so obtained;
  (f) draw a fair freehand curve through the points 1 to 12 in the end view;
  (g) complete the end view as shown.
(4) To obtain the auxiliary view – VIEW B:
  (a) from points 1 to 12 on the truncation plane line in the front view, project lines at right angles;
  (b) draw the centre line of the auxiliary view parallel to the truncation plane in the front view, in any convenient position;
  (c) transfer the measurements *a*, *b* and *c* from the plan each side of the centre line of the

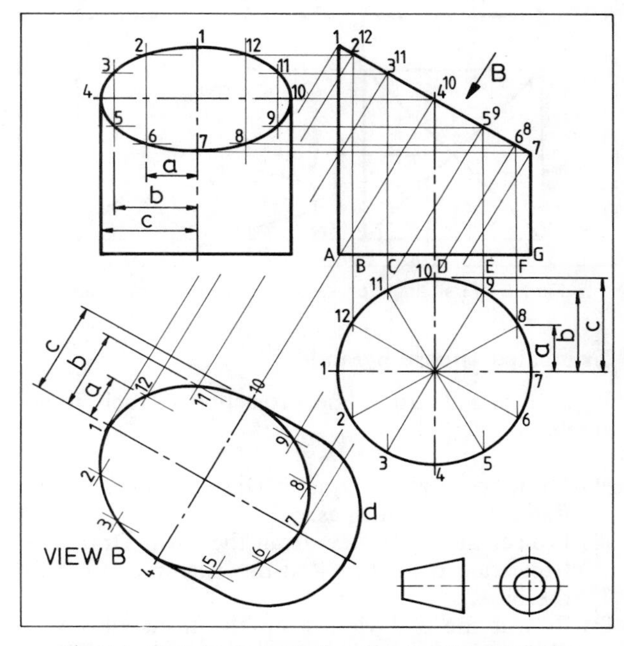

Fig.7.4 First Angle projection of a truncated cylinder including an auxiliary view

auxiliary view. Draw lines parallel to the centre line through the points so obtained. This will give the points 1 to 12 in the auxiliary view. Draw a fair curve through these points. This produces the true shape of the sloping face of the cylinder;
(d) the outline of the curve *d* in the auxiliary view is drawn in a manner similar to that employed in obtaining the true shape, but by taking projections from A to G in the front view.

Square pyramid

Fig. 7.5 is a First Angle projection.

(1) Draw the plan – a square with diagonals.
(2) Project the front view from the plan.
(3) Project the end view from the plan and front view via a 45° projection line.

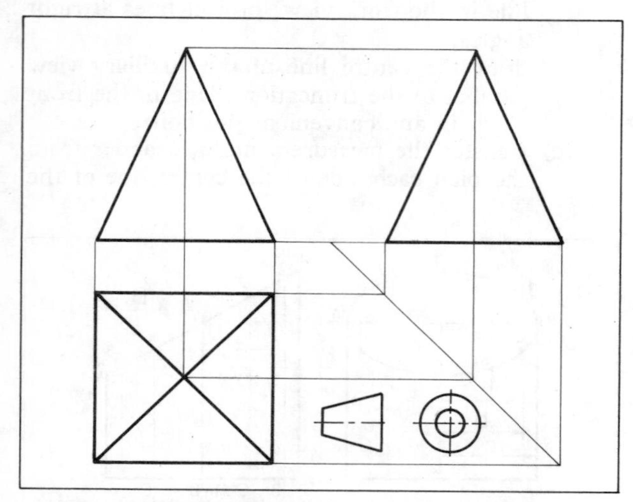

Fig.7.5 First Angle projection of a square pyramid

Truncated square pyramid

Fig. 7.6 is a Third Angle projection to include an auxiliary view.

(1) Draw the plan – a square. Draw its diagonals in fine construction lines.
(2) Project the front view from the plan. Draw the truncation plane line – in this example at 45° to the base.
(3) Project the end view from the front view and plan.
(4) Complete the plan by projecting from A and B in the front view to AA and BB. Draw the plan lines of the truncated face as shown.
(5) To draw the auxiliary view – VIEW C:
   (a) project from 1, 2 and 5 in the front view at right angles to the truncation line;
   (b) transfer the length 1–4 from the plan along one of the projection lines with a compass;
   (c) draw lines at right angles to the projection lines at 1 and 4 to give lines 1–2 and 3–4;
   (d) the point 5 can be found in VIEW C in a similar manner by transferring from the plan with a compass;
   (e) join points 1, 2, 3 and 4 to 5;
   (f) project from A and B in the front view to obtain AA and BB in VIEW C;
   (g) complete VIEW C as shown.

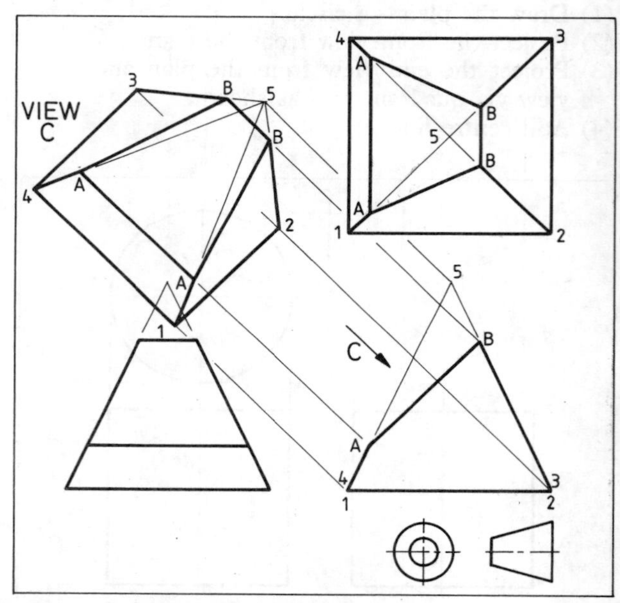

Fig.7.6 Third Angle projection of a truncated square pyramid including an auxiliary view

Truncated hexagonal pyramid

Fig. 7.7 is a First Angle projection to include an auxiliary view. The procedure for obtaining the four views shown follows similar lines to that described for Fig. 7.6.

Note

(1) Commence by drawing the outline of the plan – a regular hexagon.
(2) Project front, end and auxiliary views of the full hexagonal pyramid prior to its truncation.

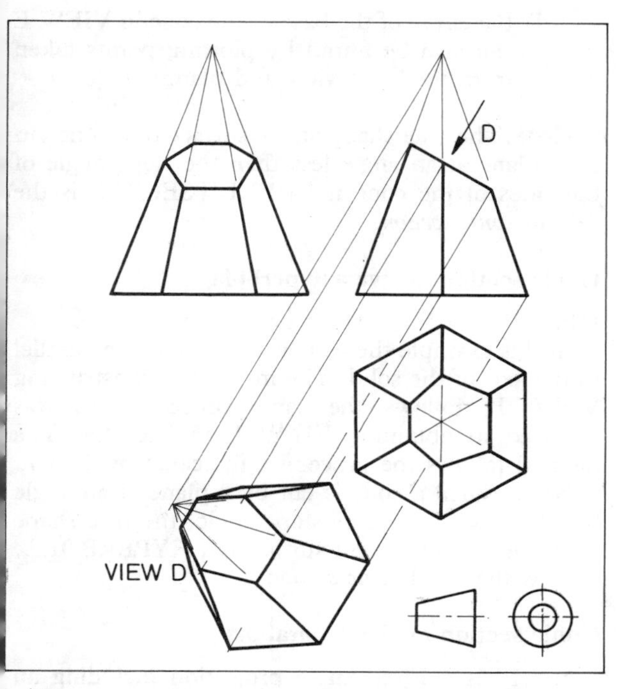

Fig.7.7 First Angle projection of a truncated hexagonal pyramid including an auxiliary view

Outlines of the truncated face can then be transferred between views.

Frustum of cone

Fig. 7.8 is a First Angle projection.

(1) Draw the outline of the plan of the cone prior to its upper part being cut off – a circle of base diameter.
(2) Project the front view and end view of the full cone.
(3) Add the cutting plane which will produce the frustum to front and end views.
(4) Project points 1 and 2 into the plan to give 3 and 4. The circle of radius A3 (or A4) completes the plan.

Note The *conic section* in this example is a CIRCLE.

Conic section to give an ellipse

Fig. 7.9 is a First Angle projection to include the auxiliary view EE.

(1) Draw plan, front view and end view of the full cone in that order.
(2) Add the truncation cutting plane to the front view – in this example at 45° to the base of the cone.
(3) Divide the plan outline circle into 12 equal parts by 30° and 60° lines through its centre.

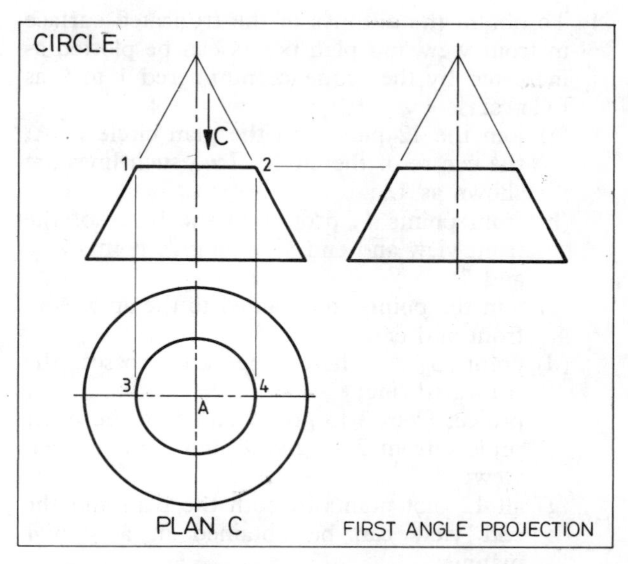

Fig.7.8 First Angle projection of frustum of a cone. Conic section showing a circle

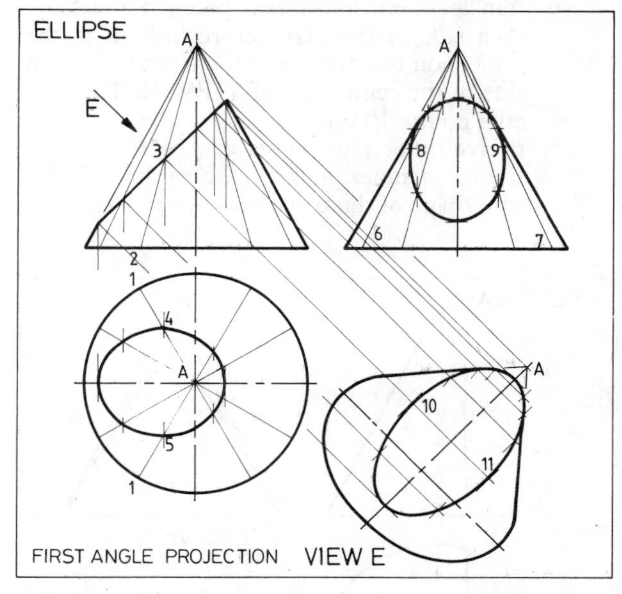

Fig.7.9 First Angle projection of a truncated cone. Conic section showing an ellipse

(4) To obtain the outlines of the truncated surface in front view and plan points can be plotted as indicated by the sequence numbered 1 to 9 as follows:
   (a) join the 12 points on the plan circle to A, the centre of the circle. Two such lines are shown as 1A;
   (b) from points 1, project to the bases of the front view and end view to give points 2, 6 and 7;
   (c) join the points so obtained to the apex A in front and end views;
   (d) point 3 is where line 2A crosses the truncated line;
   (e) project from 3 to give 4 and 5 in the plan;
   (f) project from 3 to give 8 and 9 in the end view;
   (g) all 12 plot points in both the plan and the end view can be obtained in a similar manner.
(5) To draw the auxiliary view – VIEW E:
   (a) draw the centre line of the auxiliary view;
   (b) transfer the distance that points 4 and 5 are each side of the plan centre line on to the projection line from 3 in the front view each side of the centre line of VIEW E. This will give points 10 and 11;
   (c) twelve other plot points can be found in a similar manner to give the outline of the true shape of the truncated face in VIEW E;
   (d) the curve of the base of the cone in VIEW E can also be found by plotting points taken from the front view and plan.

Note The true shape of the surface of a cone cut by a plane at an angle less than the slope angle of the sides of the cone is an ELLIPSE. This is the second *conic section*.

Conic section to give a hyperbola

Fig. 7.10 is a First Angle projection.

In this example the cone is cut by a plane parallel to the axis of the solid. The method of constructing VIEW H follows the same procedure as was followed in obtaining VIEW E in Fig. 7.9. The method follows the procedure indicated by 1 to 7.

Note When a cone is cut by a plane at an angle between its axis and its slope angle, the true shape of the outline of the cut surface is a HYPERBOLA. This is the third *conic section*.

Conic section to give a parabola

Fig. 7.11 is a First Angle projection including an auxiliary view, VIEW P. In this example the cone is cut by a plane parallel to the slope angle of the solid. The method of constructing VIEW P follows the same procedure as was used to obtain the outlines in Figs 7.9 and 7.10. The method follows the procedure indicated by 1 to 7. Note, however,

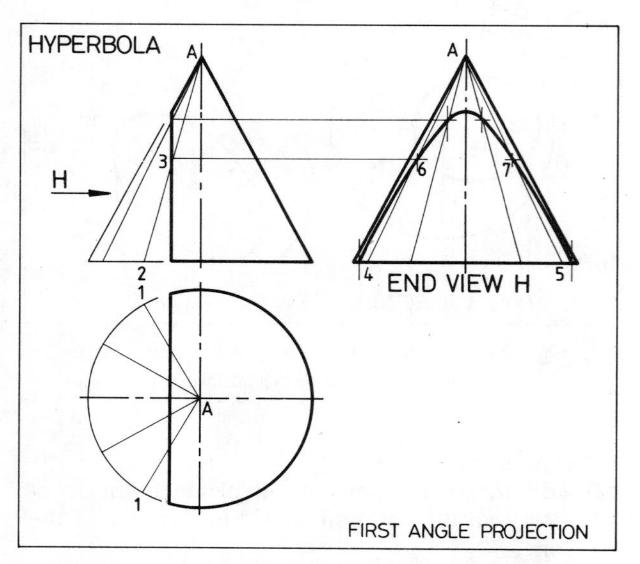

Fig.7.10 First Angle projection of a cone cut by a vertical plane. Conic section showing a hyperbola

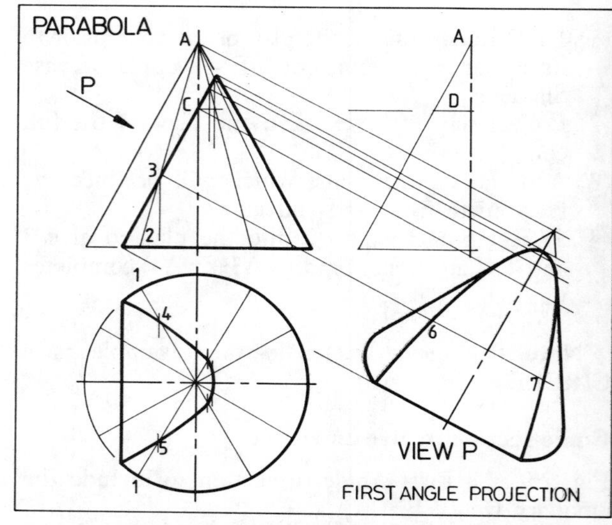

Fig.7.11 First Angle projection of a cone cut by a plane parallel to slope angle. Conic section showing a parabola

the length D obtained by projecting C on the front view centre line across a partial end view.

Note When a cone is cut by a plane at an angle the same as the slope angle of the cone, the true shape of the outline of the cut surface is a PARABOLA. This is the fourth *conic section*.

APPLICATIONS TO ORTHOGRAPHIC PROJECTIONS OF ENGINEERING COMPONENTS

Three examples of applications of the above methods of projections of geometrical solids to engineering drawing are given in Figs 7.12 to 7.14.

Projections of aluminium extrusion

The true shape of the face of an aluminium extrusion cut at an angle of 45° is given in Fig. 7.12. This example has been drawn in First Angle projection.

(1) A front view and plan of the length of extrusion is drawn.
(2) VIEW A is projected at right angles to the cut surface of the extrusion. Measurements across the auxiliary view are transferred with compasses from the plan.

Projections of a slide

The true shape of the sloping face of the slide in VIEW B of Fig. 7.13 was obtained by adopting the methods of projection described in Fig. 7.4 to find the outlines of the curves in VIEW B. This example has been drawn in Third Angle projection.

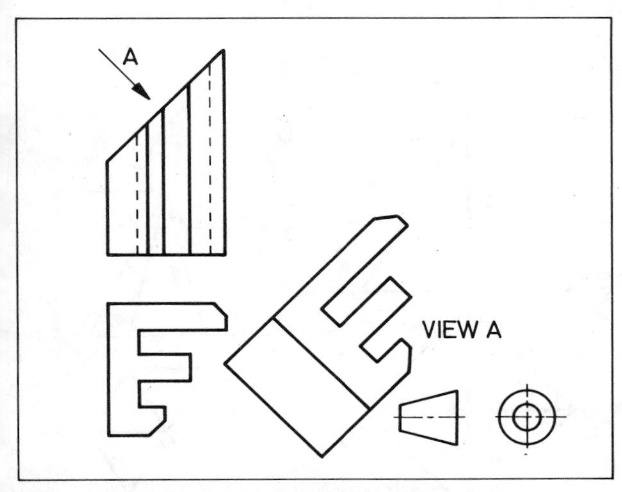

Fig.7.12 First Angle projection of an aluminium extrusion showing an auxiliary view

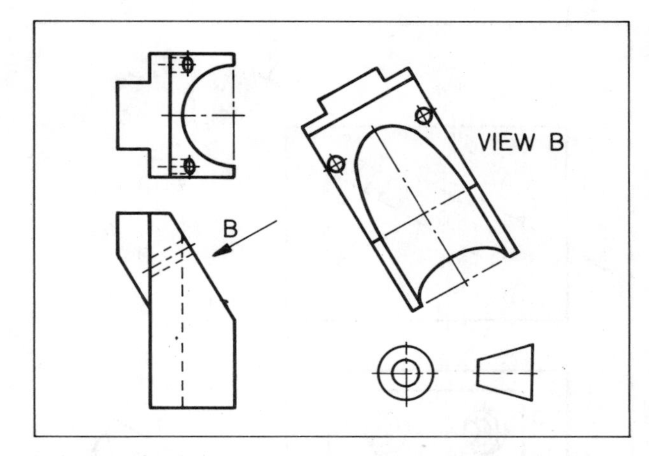

Fig.7.13 Third Angle projection of a slide including an auxiliary view

Auxiliary view including a section

Fig. 7.14 shows the method of constructing an auxiliary view applied to a sectional view in which the true shape of a surface in front of the cut of the section plane has been drawn. This example is in First Angle projection. Note the section plane line drawn across the front view and the label C–C applied to the resulting sectional view.

Exercises

Ten exercises follow which are designed to give the student practice in applying the methods described above. When working these exercises, use a scale of 1:1 (full size). All given dimensions are in millimetres.

(1) A pictorial drawing of a regular hexagonal prism is shown. Each of the sides of the hexagonal faces is 30 mm long and the prism is 50 mm high.
Draw a front view as seen in the direction of arrow F, an end view as seen in the direction of arrow E and a plan. Work in Third Angle projection.
(2) Copy the two given views, drawn in First Angle projection, of a truncated hexagonal prism. Add an end view as seen from E and an auxiliary view as seen from A.
(3) Copy the two given views of a truncated

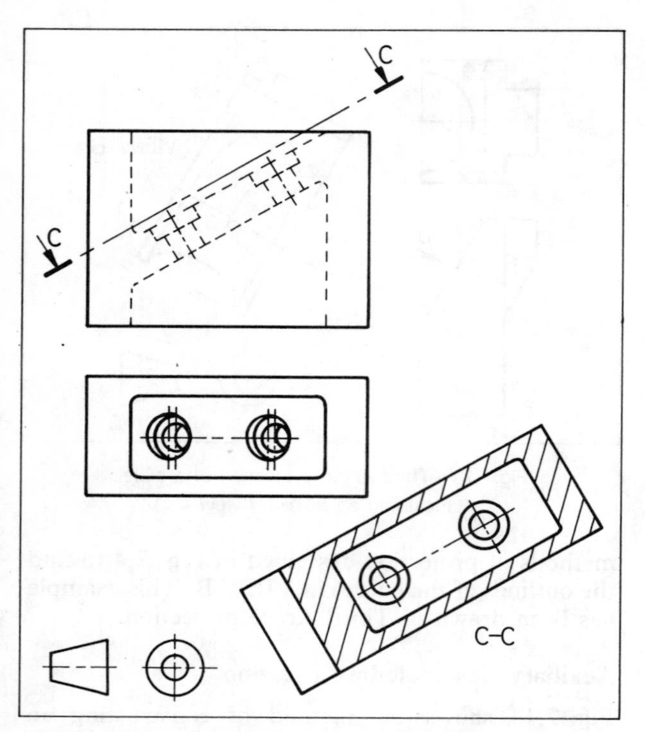

Fig.7.14 An orthographic projection which includes a sectional view showing the true shape of a sloping face

cylinder and add an end view as seen in the direction of arrow E. Work in Third Angle.
(4) Third Angle views of a square pyramid are given. Copy the two views. Add the sectional view A–A.
(5) Copy the two given views of a square pyramid and add the sectional view B–B.
(6) A front view and a plan of a hexagonal pyramid are given. The prism is to be cut by a cylindrical plane surface as indicated by the chain line of Ø60. Copy the front view, add a plan which includes the outline of the surface cut by the cylinder. Add an end view to include the cut surface.
(7) Copy the two given Third Angle views of a cone. Add the sectional view C–C. Include in the plan the outline of the area cut by the section plane C–C. Add an end view which includes the outline of the cut surface.
(8) The given drawing shows a right cylinder resting on a plane X–Y. Draw the given view, and in Third Angle projection, add the end view E and the plan P.
(9) Copy the two given views and add the auxiliary view as seen in the direction of the arrow D.
(10) Draw the two given views in Third Angle projection. Add the auxiliary view as seen in the direction of the arrow E.

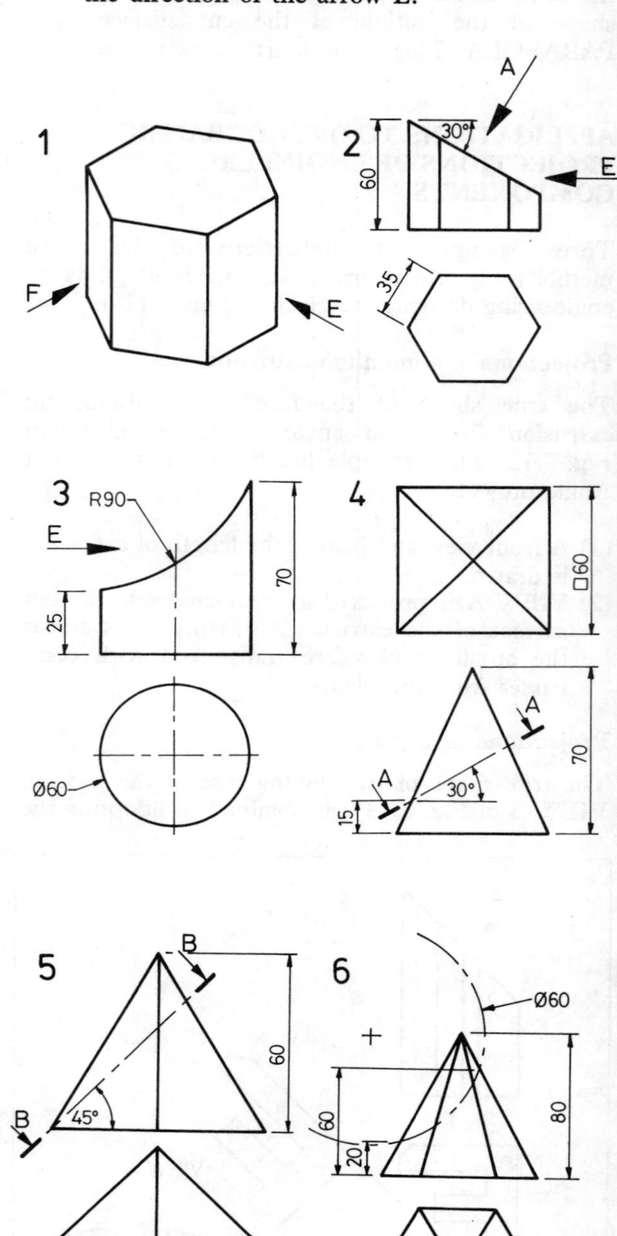

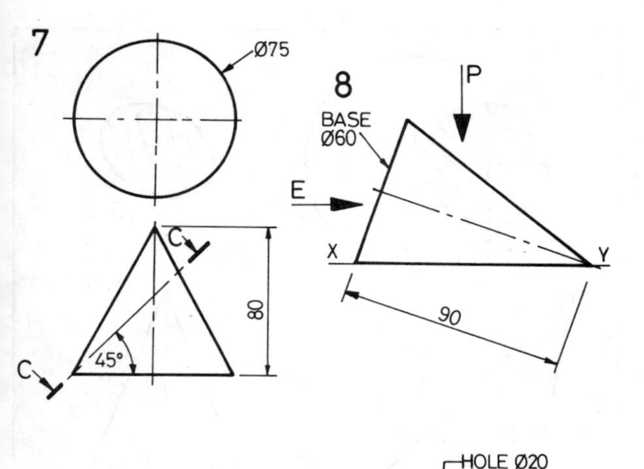

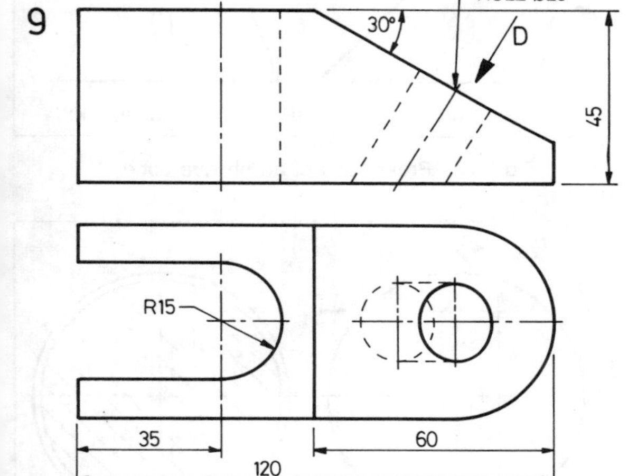

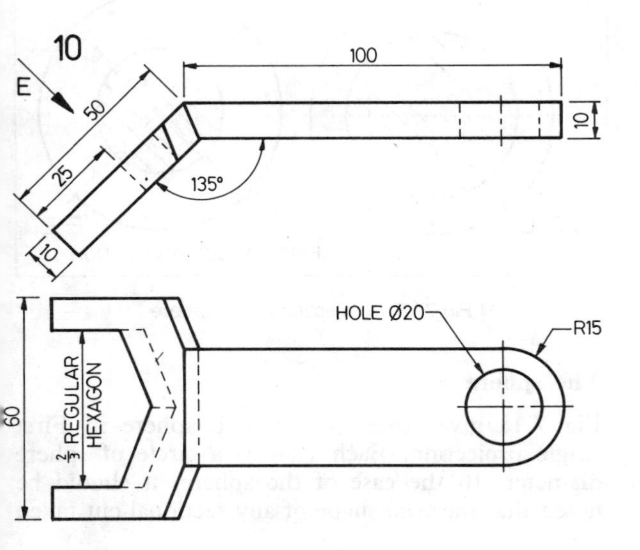

OBLIQUE SOLIDS

The axis of an oblique solid is at an angle other than 90° to its base. The axis slopes to one side as the solid stands on its base. Three examples of orthographic projections of simple oblique solids are shown below.

Oblique hexagonal pyramid

Fig. 7.15 is a First Angle projection. In this example the base of the oblique pyramid is a regular hexagon with its axis sloping at an angle of 58° to its base. To draw orthographic views of such a solid, proceed as follows:

(1) Draw the plan of the base – a regular hexagon.
(2) Project the vertices of the hexagonal base into the front view.
(3) Complete the front view.
(4) Project the apex of the solid from the front view into the plan.
(5) Complete the plan by drawing the sloping lines from the vertices of the hexagonal base to the pyramid's apex.
(6) Project the end view from the front view and plan.

Note In this example a sectional cut A–A taken at right angles to the axis produces an irregular hexagon.

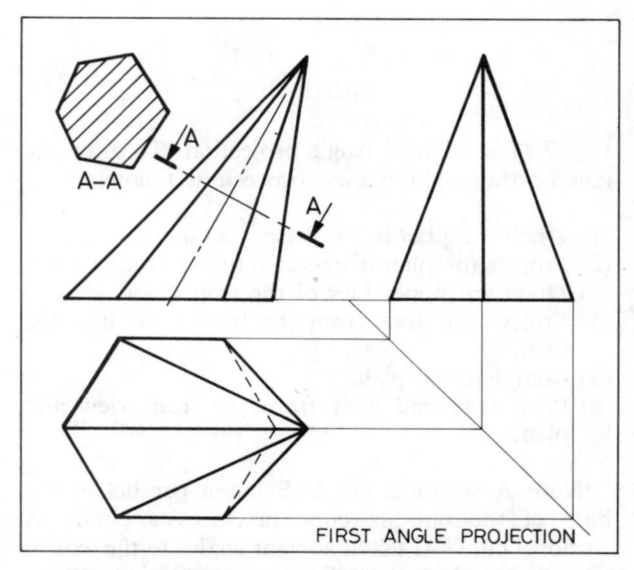

Fig.7.15 Projections of an oblique hexagonal pyramid

Oblique hexagonal pyramid – second example

Fig. 7.16 is a Third Angle projection. To draw the three views of this example proceed as for example 1 of Fig. 7.15 except that the views are in Third Angle.

Note The sectional cut B–B taken parallel to the base produces a regular hexagon.

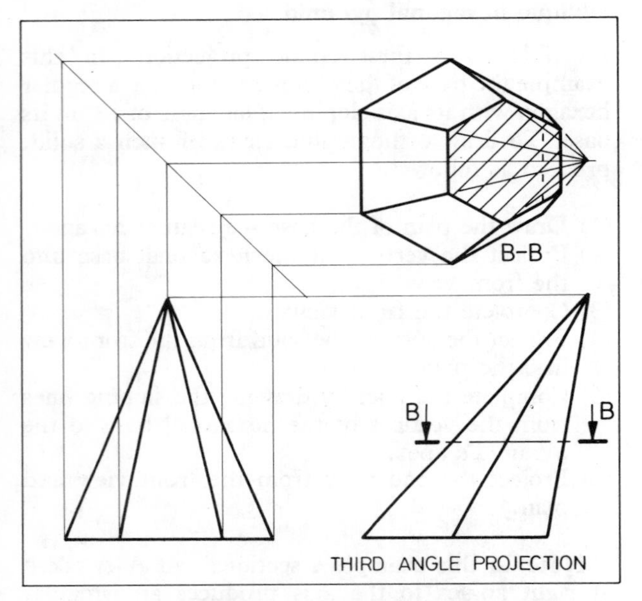

Fig.7.16 Projections of an oblique hexagonal pyramid including a sectional view

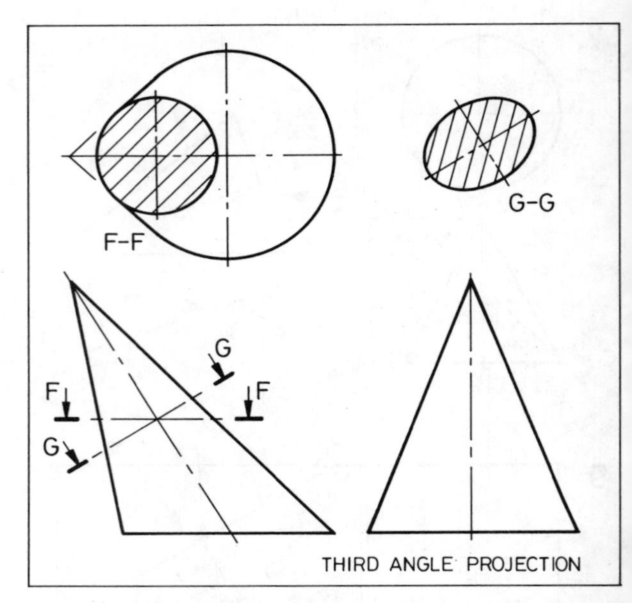

Fig.7.17 Projections of an oblique cone

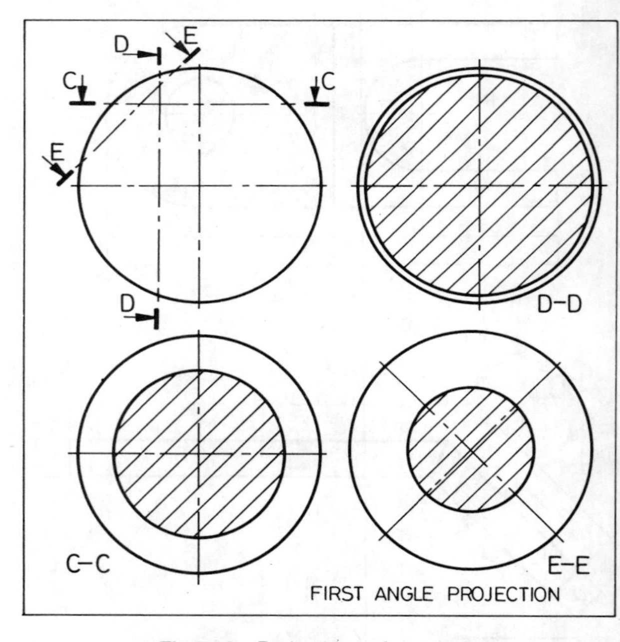

Fig.7.18 Projections of a sphere

Oblique cone

Fig. 7.17 is a Third Angle projection. To draw the given orthographic views, proceed as follows:

(1) Draw the plan of the base – a circle.
(2) Project the plan diameter into the front view.
(3) Draw the slope sides of the front view.
(4) Project the apex from the front view into the plan.
(5) Complete the plan.
(6) Project an end view from the front view and plan.

Note A sectional cut F–F taken parallel to the base of the oblique cone produces a circle. A sectional cut G–G taken at right angles to the axis of the cone produces an ellipse.

The sphere

Fig. 7.18 gives three views of a sphere in First Angle projection. Each view is a circle of sphere diameter. In the case of the sphere, it should be noted that the true shape of any sectional cut taken at any angle through the sphere, is a circle. Thus the true shapes produced by the sectional cuts C–C, D–D and E–E are all circles. The true shapes of all sectional cuts taken through the centre of a sphere are circles of sphere diameter, known as *great circles* of the sphere.

TRUE LENGTHS OF LINES

When describing the geometry of orthographic projection, many textbooks use the letters XY to describe the line of join between the vertical planes and the horizontal planes on to which projections are made. In the next few pages the practice of referring to the join line as XY is adopted here.

In Fig. 7.19 a pictorial drawing of a VP and an HP in a First Angle position is given. The line joining the VP and HP is labelled XY. A straight line is placed within the angle of the two planes, so that it lies at an angle to both the VP and the HP. Projections of the line as seen from the front and from above are drawn on to the VP and the HP. The reader may find value in referring to Fig. 7.19 when working the methods of finding the true lengths of lines which lie at angles to VP and HP.

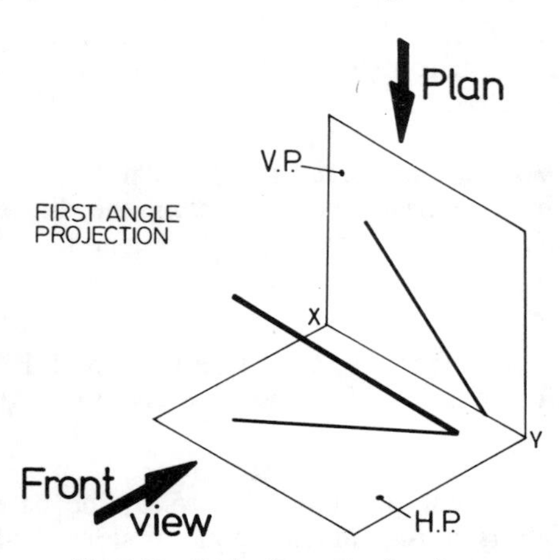

Fig.7.19 Projections of a line in space

To find the true length of a line Fig. 7.20

A front view and a plan of a line AB are given. To find the true length of AB:

(1) Draw B_1C parallel to XY.
(2) Set a compass to A_1B_1. With the compass centred at B_1 draw an arc to meet B_1C at C.
(3) Draw AT parallel to XY.

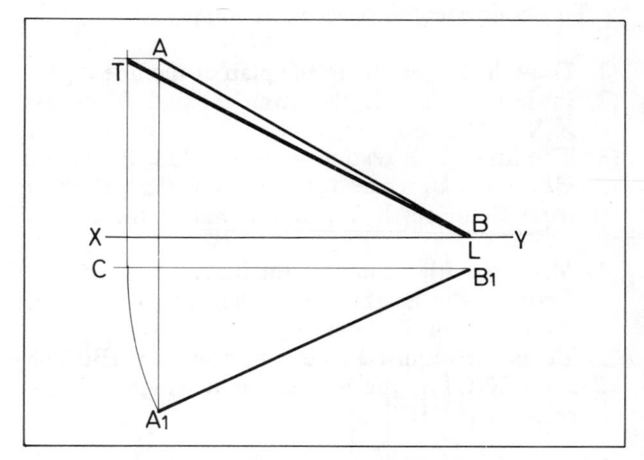

Fig.7.20 To find the *true* length of a line

(4) Project from C vertically to meet AT at T.
(5) TL is the required true length.

Second method Fig. 7.21

It may be more convenient to project a view as seen looking at *either* front view or plan of the line at right angles – to draw a new, or auxiliary view of the line. Adopting this method not only obtains the true length of the line but also gives the true angle at which the line rests in relation to the VP or the HP. If the view is as seen at right angles to the plan of the line, then the true angle of the line to the HP is found. If the view is as seen at right angles to the front view of the line, then the true angle of the line to the VP is found.

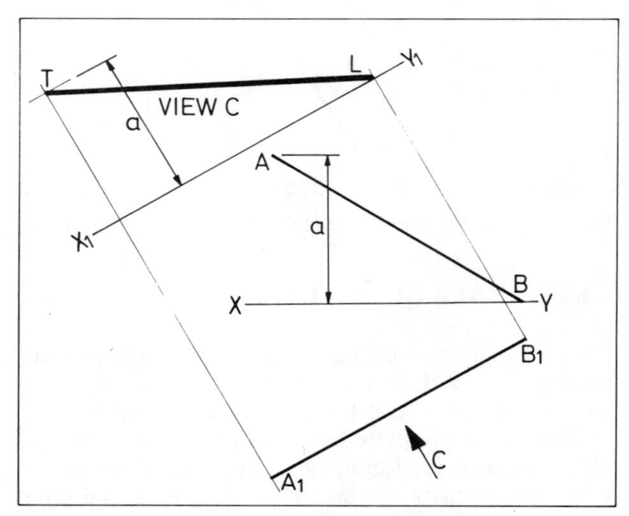

Fig.7.21 To find the *true* length of a line – second method

To obtain view C proceed as follows:

(1) Draw X_1Y_1 parallel to the plan of the line A_1B_1.
(2) Project at right angles from A_1 and B_1 across X_1Y_1.
(3) The line AB is resting with one end, B, on the HP. Thus L, where the perpendicular projector from B_1 meets X_1Y_1, is one end of the line in VIEW C.
(4) Measure with a compass the height a above XY. Transfer the height a with the compass to give the height of T above X_1Y_1.
(5) TL is the required true length of line AB. The angle X_1LT is the true angle at which the line rests on the HP.

Note The direction of viewing can be taken looking at the line from the opposite side – see Fig. 7.22. Thus looking in the direction of the arrow D gives the true length TL and the true angle to the VP of X_1LT.

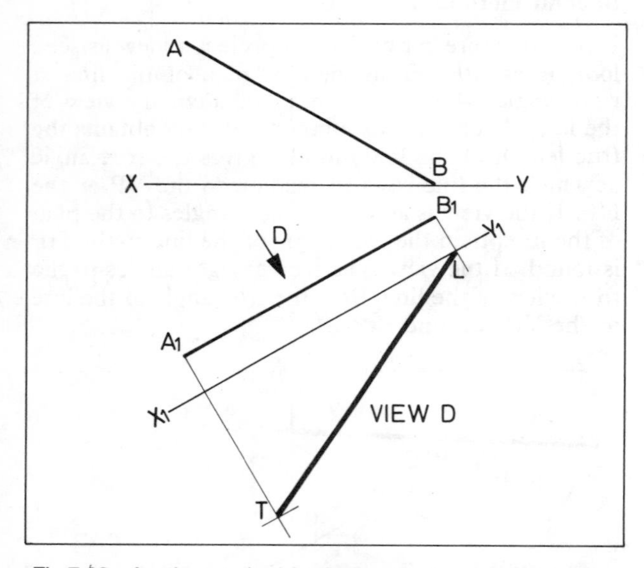

Fig.7.22 Another method for finding the *true* length of a line

TRUE SHAPE OF FLAT PLANES

Fig. 7.23 shows a triangular plate lying in space at an angle to both the VP and to the HP. A front view of the plate has been projected on to the VP and a plan of the plate has been projected on to the HP. Readers may find this illustration of value when considering the methods of finding the true shape of lamina from orthographic projections.

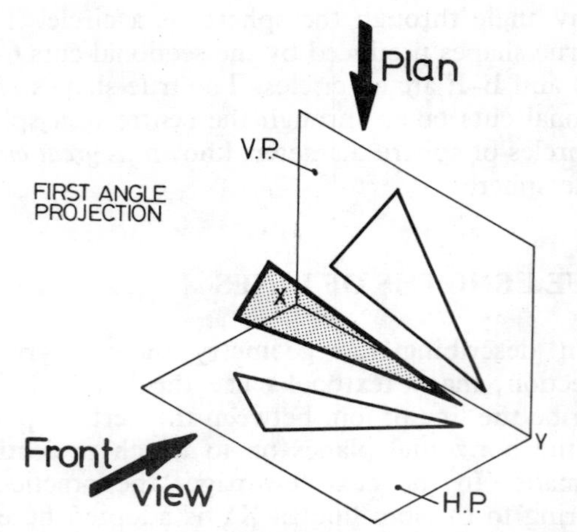

Fig.7.23 Projections of a triangular lamina in space

To find the true shape of a triangular lamina

Fig. 7.24 is a First Angle projection.
To find the true shape of the triangle *abc*:

(1) Find the true length of each of the sides *ab*, *bc* and *ca* of the triangle by the method shown by Figs 7.21 and 7.22.
(2) Having found the true lengths of each of the sides, the true shape of the triangle can now be constructed.

Note Any straight-sided polygon can be reduced to a number of triangles by drawing the diagonals through one of the vertices of the polygon.

Exercises

Draw the following exercises to a scale of 1:1 (full size). All the given drawings are in First Angle projection.

(1) A front view of an oblique solid, the base of which is a regular hexagon of sides 30 mm long, is shown. In Third Angle projection draw the given front view and add the two views looking in the directions E and P.
(2) Copy the given front view of an oblique cone. It stands on a base of Ø70 mm. Add the sectional views A–A and B–B.
(3) The given front view is of an oblique pyramid which stands on a base which is a regular octagon. Draw the given view and add the sectional view C–C.
(4) Draw the given front view of an oblique cone

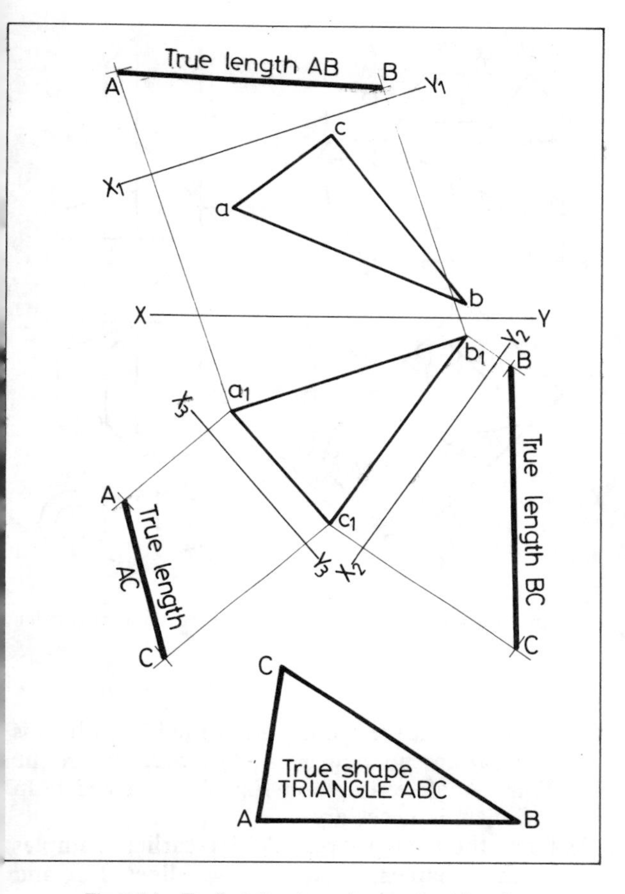

Fig.7.24 To find the *true* shape of a triangle

and add the sectional view D–D. Work in Third Angle projection.

(5) Two views of a line which slopes in space at angles to both the vertical and horizontal planes is shown. Find the true length of the line AB.

(6) Two straight lines AB and BC are joined at B. From the given front view and plan of the two lines find:
 (a) the true lengths AB and BC;
 (b) the true angle ABC.

(7) The triangle ABC with B resting against the vertical plane is lying in space at angles to both the VP and the HP. Find the true shape of the triangle and the angle at which it rests against the VP.

(8) A five-sided plate is shown in two views. Find the true shape of the plate.

Note As shown by 8a any straight-sided

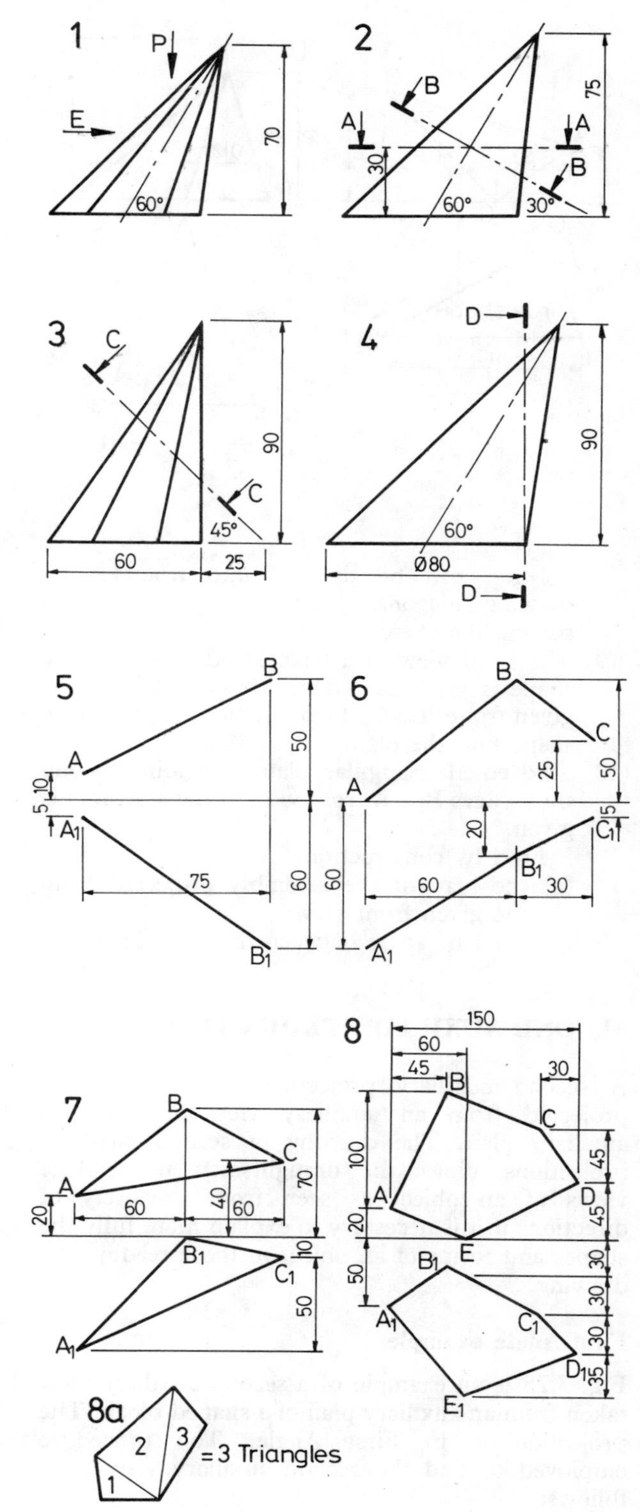

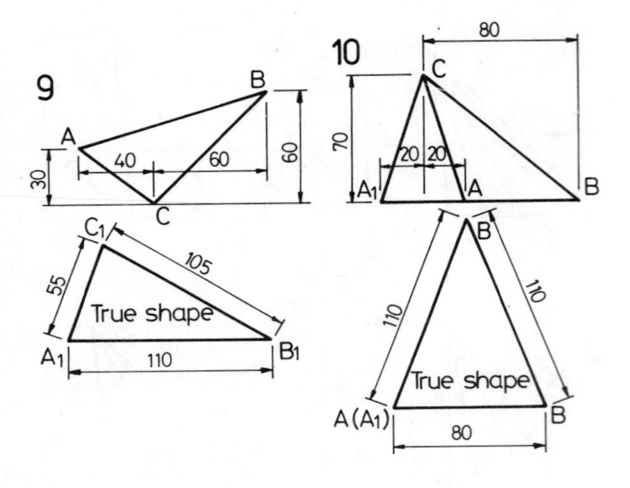

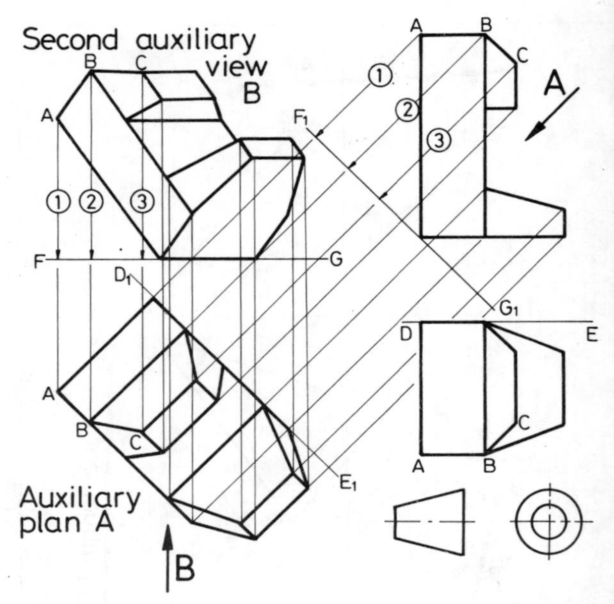

Fig.7.25 A second auxiliary view in a First Angle projection

polygon can be divided into triangles by drawing diagonals. This fact will help in solving the exercise.

(9) The front view of a triangle ABC whose true shape is given in $A_1B_1C_1$, is given. Copy the given front view and from it and the given true shape find the plan.

(10) Two equal triangular plates are joined along their edges BC. A front view of the assembly is given.
Find by construction:
(a) the plan of the assembly projected from the given front view;
(b) the true angle between the two plates.

SECOND AUXILIARY PROJECTION

A second auxiliary projection is one which is projected from an auxiliary view or from an auxiliary plan. The drawing of second auxiliary projections allows the draughtsman to produce views of an object as seen from a variety of directions if it is necessary to explain more fully the shapes and forms of an object to those reading the drawing.

First Angle example

Fig. 7.25 is an example of a second auxiliary view taken from an auxiliary plan of a shaped block. The projection is in First Angle. The procedure employed to find the second auxiliary view is as follows:

(1) Draw a front view and plan of the block. In this example an end view is not required, but see the Third Angle example in Fig. 7.26. in which an end view is necessary.
(2) Draw the auxiliary plan A. See earlier examples in this chapter. Note the two lines DE and D_1E_1 on which the plan and auxiliary plan are based. The positions of A, B and C below D_1E_1 in the auxiliary plan A have been measured from the positions of A, B and C below DE in the plan.
(3) Draw the base line FG on which the second auxiliary view B is based. FG is at right angles to the direction of viewing B.
(4) Draw the base line F_1G_1 touching the front view at right angles to the direction of viewing A.
(5) Project lines from points on the auxiliary plan A parallel to the direction of viewing B_1 to cross the base line FG.
(6) To obtain the distances at which the projected points from the auxiliary plan A lie above the base line FG, step off the distances which the respective points lie above F_1G_1. The encircled figures 1, 2 and 3 on front and second auxiliary views show three of these respective lengths.
(7) When all such points have been projected and plotted, the second auxiliary view B can be completed.

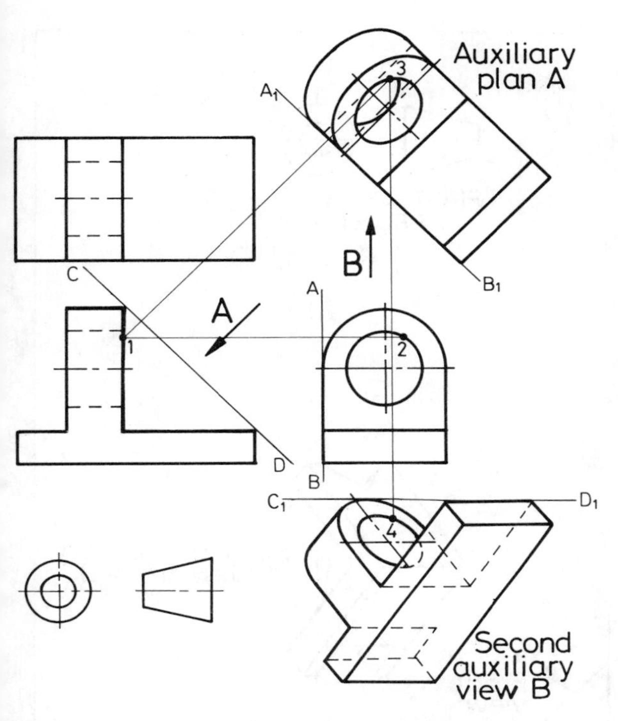

Fig.7.26 A second auxiliary view in a Third Angle projection

Third Angle example

A Third Angle example of a second auxiliary view is shown in Fig. 7.26. The procedure is as follows:

(1) Draw the front and end views and plan of the object.
(2) Project and draw the auxiliary plan A as seen in the direction of viewing A.
(3) Draw the base line CD touching the front view at right angles to the direction of viewing A.
(4) Draw the base line C_1D_1 on which the second auxiliary view B will be based, at right angles to the direction of viewing B.
(5) The projection and plotting of points in the second auxiliary view B now follows the same procedure as that given above for the First Angle example, Fig. 7.25, except that this example is in Third Angle projection.

For *all* plot points in the second auxiliary view B the procedure shown for plotting point 1 from the front view to the second auxiliary view can be followed. This is given by the sequence 1 to 4 as follows:

(a) Project from 1 in the front view to 2 in the end view.
(b) Project from 1 in the front view to the auxiliary plan A to obtain 3, which lies at the same perpendicular distance from A_1B_1 as does 2 from AB.
(c) Project from 3 across C_1D_1 in the second auxliary view B. The perpendicular distance that 4 is from C_1D_1 is the same as the perpendicular distance that 1 is from CD in the front view.
(d) When sufficient number of points have been plotted in the second auxiliary view B, the view can be completed.

Note

(1) In both examples given above, second auxiliary *views* have been drawn. Second auxiliary *plans* can be drawn in a similar manner projected from auxiliary views.
(2) In both examples above, the directions of viewing have been taken at 45° to both front view for the auxiliary plan and 45° to the auxiliary plan to obtain the second auxiliary view. Directions of viewing at any other angles can be taken using the same procedures as detailed above.

Fig. 7.27 is a First Angle orthographic projection of an object in which four second auxiliary views have been projected from four auxiliary plans. This drawing has been included here to show that the methods of second auxiliary projections can give a very detailed series of views of an object as seen in a variety of viewing directions.

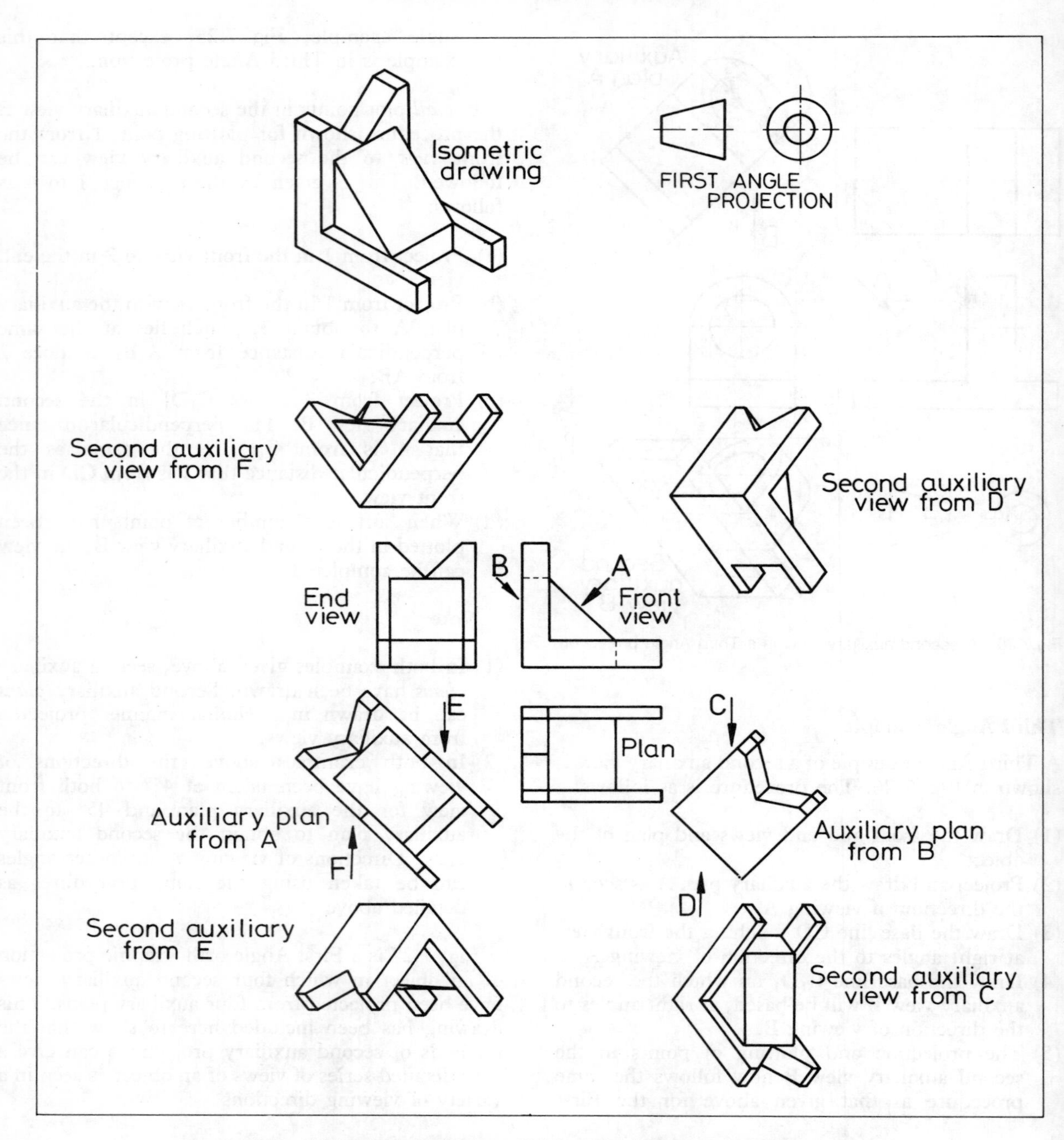

Fig.7.27 A First Angle projection which includes four second auxiliary views

8 Dimensioning

RULES FOR DIMENSIONING

Good dimensioning clearly defines the sizes, shape and location of the parts of a component described in an engineering drawing. Features such as lengths, diameters, angles and position should be completely and accurately described by the dimensions contained in a drawing. The following general rules apply to the dimensioning of engineering drawings.

(1) Dimensioning should be complete. It should be possible to produce a component from the reading of its drawing without the need to scale parts of the drawing or to make arithmetical calculations from the given dimensions, or to have to refer to other documents. There should be no need to deduce dimensions from others on a drawing.
(2) Dimensions should not be repeated. It may be necessary to add auxiliary dimensions (see Fig. 8.20) but only if such auxiliary dimensions serve a good purpose at some stage in production processes.
(3) A dimension without a tolerance cannot be considered as a practical possibility. However, the tolerance need not necessarily be placed with the dimension. Tolerances may appear elsewhere on a drawing sheet or may be defined elsewhere – e.g. by methods of production; by practices adopted within the firm producing the component.
(4) The selection of datum surfaces from which dimensions are taken should be considered with care. Incorrect selection of datum surfaces could result in the production of components of little functional value.

When placing dimensions on a drawing sheet the following conventions should be observed. Refer to Fig. 8.1.

(1) Dimension lines and their related projection lines are thin lines.

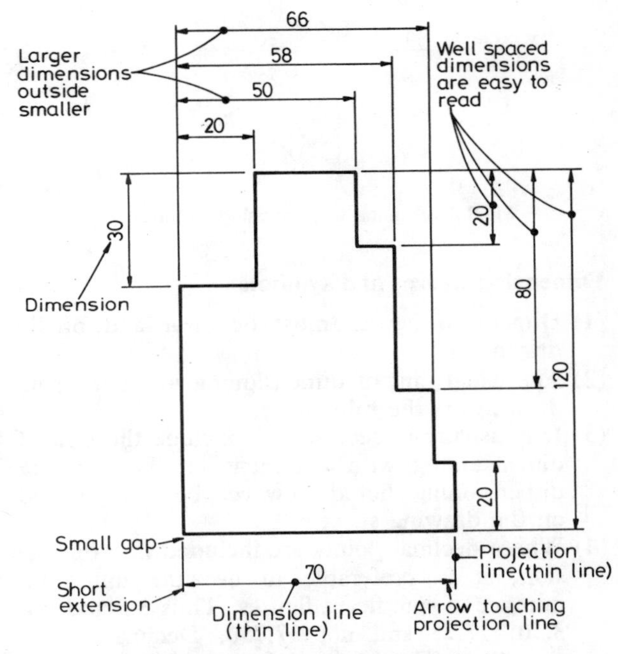

Fig.8.1 Methods of linear dimensioning

(2) Centre lines should not be used as dimension lines.
(3) Dimension lines and their related projection lines should, as far as is possible, be placed outside the view to which they refer.
(4) Dimensions should be adequately spaced for clarity.
(5) Larger dimensions should, as far as is possible, be placed outside smaller dimensions, to avoid projection lines crossing dimension lines.
(6) Dimension lines should not, as far as is possible, be broken.
(7) In general dimensions should be placed just above the dimension lines in such a position as to be read from the lower edge of the drawing sheet or from the right hand edge of the drawing sheet. When it is necessary to place dimensions at angles other than horizontally or

vertically, a guide to the positions of dimension lines and their related figures is given in Fig. 8.2. Note that it is advisable to avoid placing dimensions at angles within the areas shown shaded in Fig. 8.2.

(8) Avoid dimensioning to hidden detail lines.

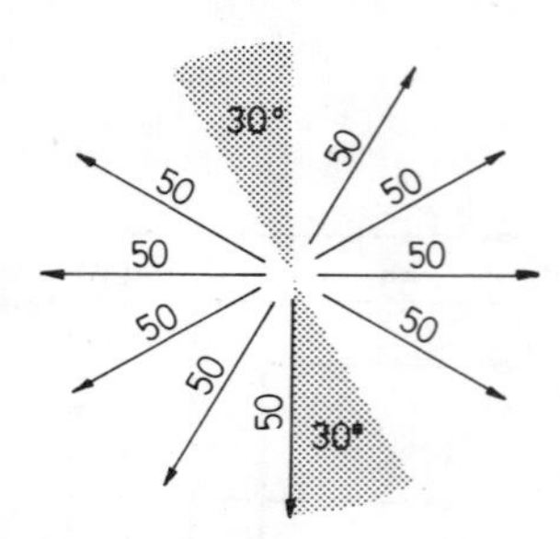

Fig.8.2 A guide to positioning dimensions

Dimension figures and symbols

(1) Dimension figures must be clear and boldly drawn.
(2) The usual unit of dimensioning in engineering drawings is the millimetre.
(3) It is usually unnecessary to include the unit of dimensioning with a dimension. The unit of dimensioning should, however, be clearly stated on the drawing sheet.
(4) Where decimal points are included in a dimension, it is preferable to use the minimum number of significant figures. Thus 3.5 and not 3.50; 17.75 and not 17.750. Decimal points should be drawn as full stops, although in drawings from countries outside the UK the use of a comma as a decimal point is common. If the dimension is less than unity a 0 should be placed in front of the decimal point. Thus 0.5 and not .5; 0.15 and not .15.
(5) Arrowheads should be dense and black.
(6) The following symbols related to dimensions should be placed in front of the figures to which they refer:
R – Radius
Ø – Diameter
□ – Square
SR – Sphere radius
SØ – Sphere diameter.
(7) Abbreviations such as CSK (countersunk), CBORE (counterbore) should also be placed in front of the figure of dimension to which they refer.
(8) When the unit of dimensioning is included with the figures of a dimension, the abbreviation for the unit is placed after the figures, with a gap between the figures and the abbreviation. Thus 25 mm; 3.375 m; 7 km.

Dimensions taken from points of intersection

As can be seen by reference to Fig. 8.1, small gaps should be left between the ends of projection lines and the points on the surface of the view to which they refer. If, however, the projection lines are to be taken to points on the surface of a view or to points outside the view, then the projection lines should pass through the points to which they refer. Fig. 8.3 gives an example of such dimensions. The reference points may be emphasized with small dots as shown in Fig. 8.4.

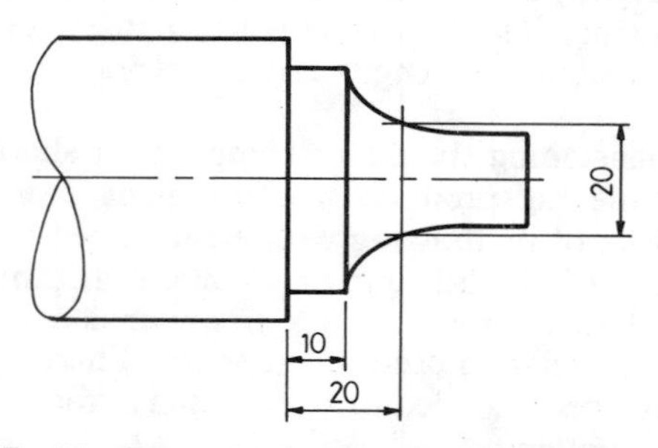

Fig.8.3 Dimensioning from points of intersection

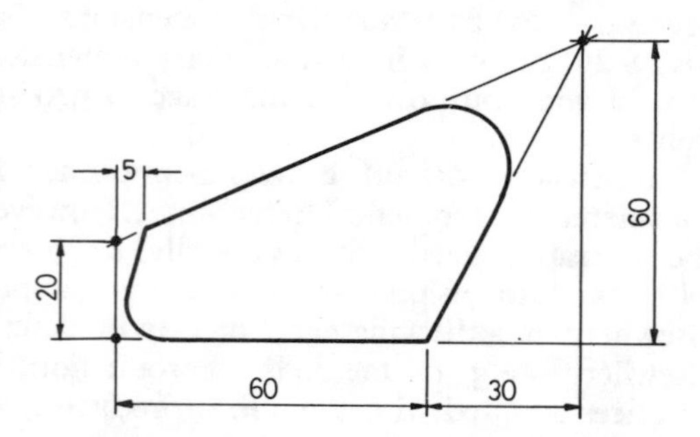

Fig.8.4 Dimensioning from intersecting lines

Small dimensions

When dimensions are small, the space within which the dimension can be placed is often of restricted size. Small dimensions can be shown by any one of the four methods shown in Fig. 8.5. When a series of small dimensions follow one another, the method of Fig. 8.6 can be adopted. The arrowheads on the projection lines are replaced with small dots.

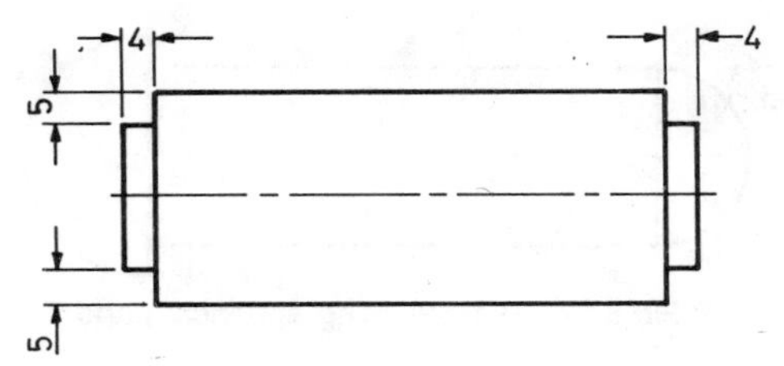

Fig.8.5 Small dimensions

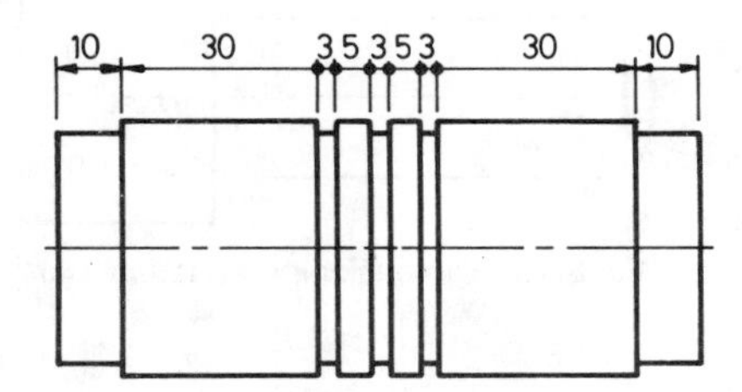

Fig.8.6 Small dimensions

Parallel dimensions taken from a common datum

Where a number of dimensions are to be taken from a common datum surface, one of the three methods of Fig. 8.7 may be adopted:

(1) A small circle defines the common origin on the projection line taken from the common datum surface. Dimensions are placed in line with a single dimension line.
(2) Each dimension is taken separately from the common datum origin.
(3) A small circle defines the common origin on the projection line from the datum surface. The dimensions are placed in line with the projection lines from the various surfaces to which the dimensions refer.

Dimensions of radius

The following rules should be observed when dimensioning radii:

(1) The dimensioning line should pass through the centre of the radius from which the arc was drawn.
(2) The dimension line should have only one arrow.
(3) The capital letter R should precede the dimension.

Fig. 8.8 gives examples of four different methods of dimensioning small radii.

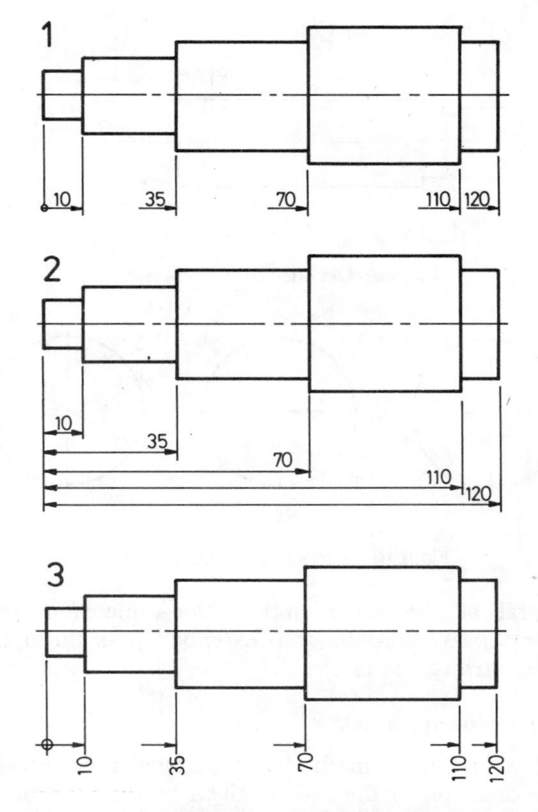

Fig.8.7 Parallel dimensions from a common datum

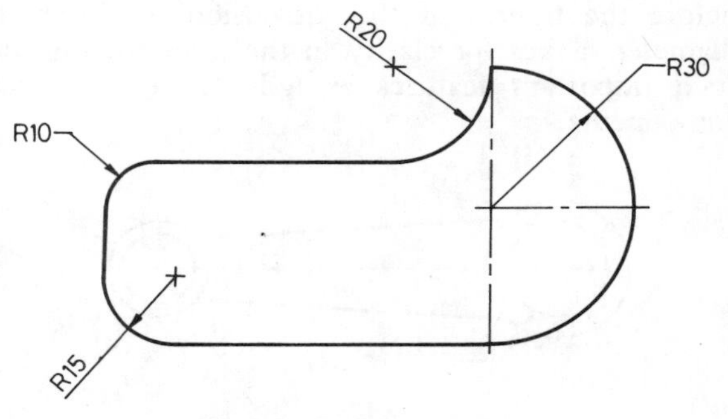

Fig.8.8 Radial dimensions

Dimensioning diameters

Figs 8.9 and 8.10 show methods of dimensioning the diameters of circles or of circular parts. In Fig. 8.9 the dimensions all give the diameter of the cylinders forming the component. Circles can be dimensioned by one of the methods indicated in Fig. 8.10. Unless dimensioned as shown by the

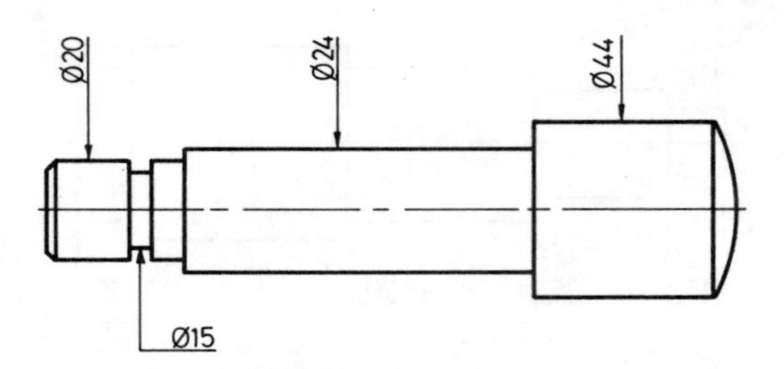

Fig.8.9 Dimensioning diameters

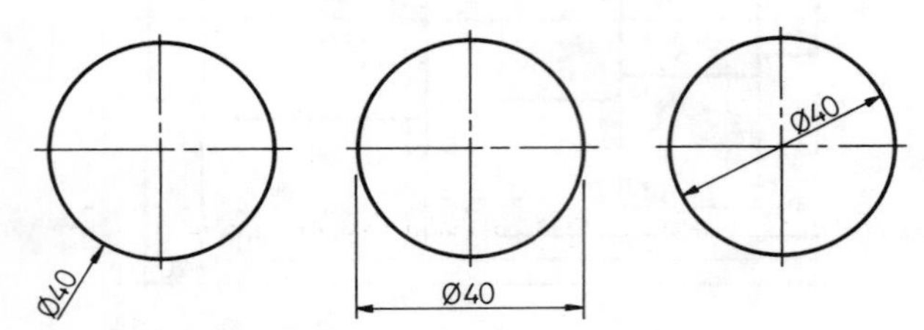

Fig.8.10 Dimensioning diameters

central of the three circles, the dimension line should pass through, or if extended pass through, the centre of the circle.

Dimensioning holes

Fig. 8.11 shows methods of dimensioning holes. The diameter of the hole is given by the symbol Ø and the word HOLE is printed in front of the symbol. Adoption of the word and the symbol before the figures of the dimension of the hole diameter makes for clarity in the dimensioning of such important features as holes in engineering components.

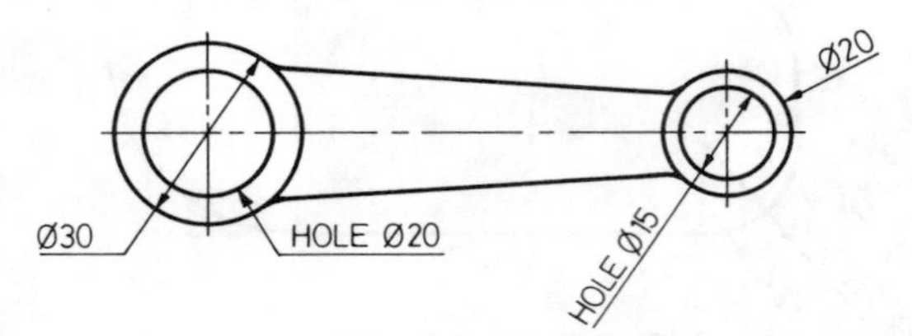

Fig.8.11 Dimensioning holes and circular parts

Spherical dimensions

Figs 8.12, 8.13 and 8.14 are examples which include the dimensions of spherical or part spherical details in engineering drawings. Note the common features in these three examples:

(1) The dimension lines pass through, or if extended would pass through, the centres of the spheres to which the dimensions refer.
(2) The capital letter S, denoting sphere, is followed by either R (radius) or Ø (diameter). Both symbols SR or SØ precede the dimension.

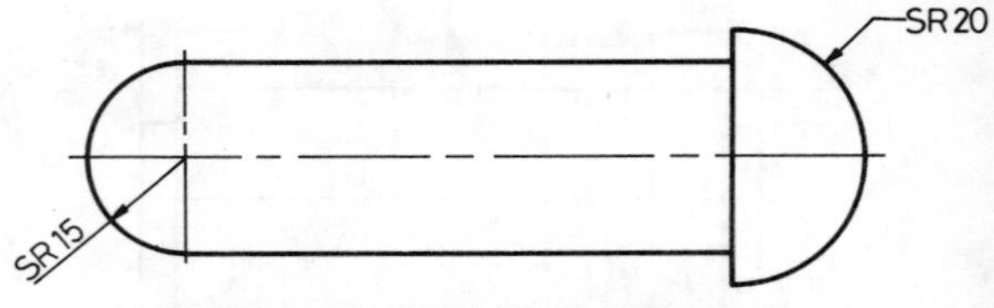

Fig.8.12 Dimensioning spherical parts

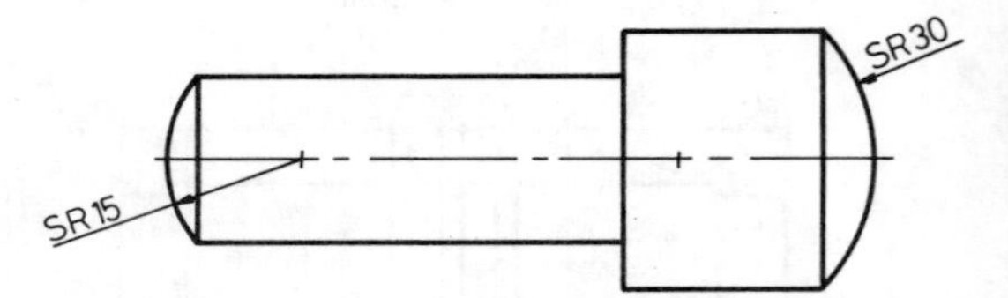

Fig.8.13 Dimensioning spherical parts

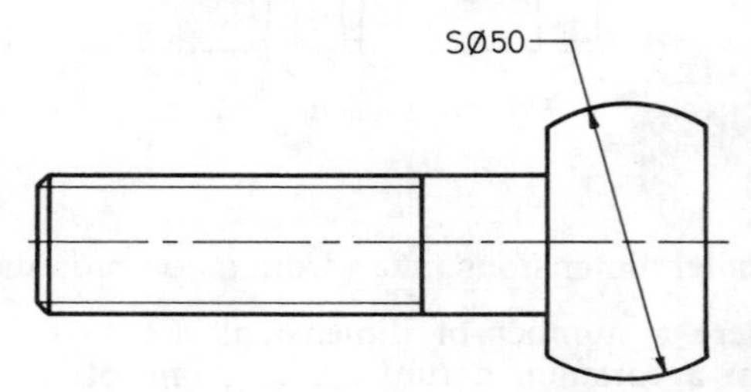

Fig.8.14 A spherical dimension

Dimensioning countersunk or counterbored holes

Fig. 8.15 shows examples of methods of dimensioning countersunk and counterbored holes. Note that the dimensioning of the two views in this drawing must not be taken as typical because the dimensioning of the two holes is given in the front view only to be repeated in the plan. This is not good practice in that dimensions should not be repeated on the same drawing. In this example, however, the two forms of dimensioning are given in order to show that *either* method is correct. Thus either the dimensioning as given for the front view *or* that given for the sectional plan view should have been included in the drawing.

Dimensioning chamfers and bevels

Fig. 8.16 illustrates two methods of dimensioning chamfers. In the two methods, both the angle and

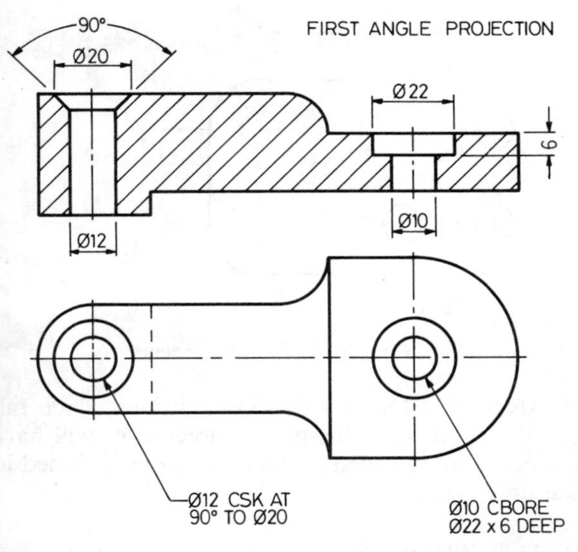

Fig.8.15 Dimensioning counterbored and countersunk holes

the depth of the chamfer are included in the dimensions. The abbreviation CHAM could have also been included, but in the two methods shown it is unnecessary to add the abbreviation because the dimensioning, position and shape of the chamfers are quite clear without the addition of the abbreviation in the dimension.

Dimensioning angles

Four methods for showing the size of angles as dimensions are shown in Fig. 8.17. The size of an angle can be shown either as a number of degrees or as degrees, minutes and seconds, the abbreviation being ° for degrees, ′ for minutes, ″ for seconds. A minute is $^1/_{60}$ of a degree and a second is $^1/_{60}$ of a minute. It is unusual to show measurements of angles in engineering drawings in radians.

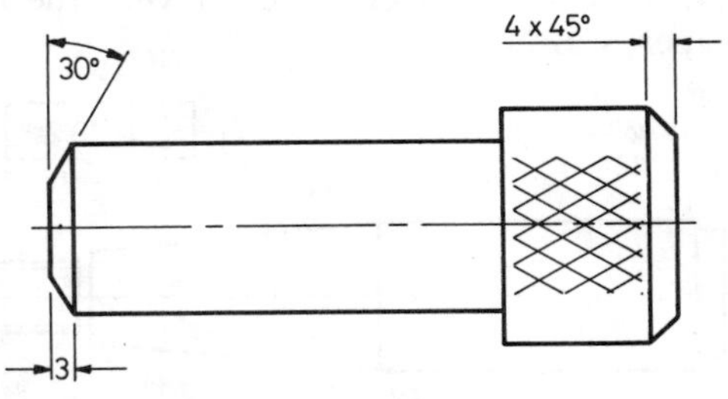

Fig.8.16 Dimensioning chamfers

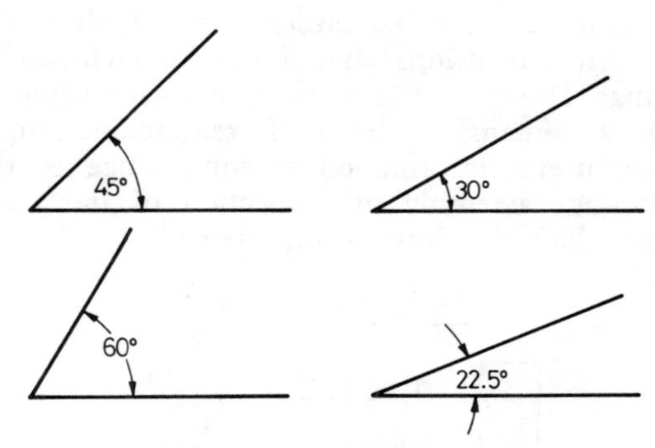

Fig.8.17 Dimensioning angles

The use of leaders

Leaders are added to drawings to indicate the name of the materials from which a part is made, or to give special instructions for any part of a drawing. In general leaders are thin lines and terminate:

(1) in an arrow if touching a line on a drawing;
(2) in a dot if touching a surface on a drawing;
(3) in neither an arrow nor a dot if finishing at another line.

Examples for each of these three terminations for leader lines are shown in the example given in Fig. 8.18.

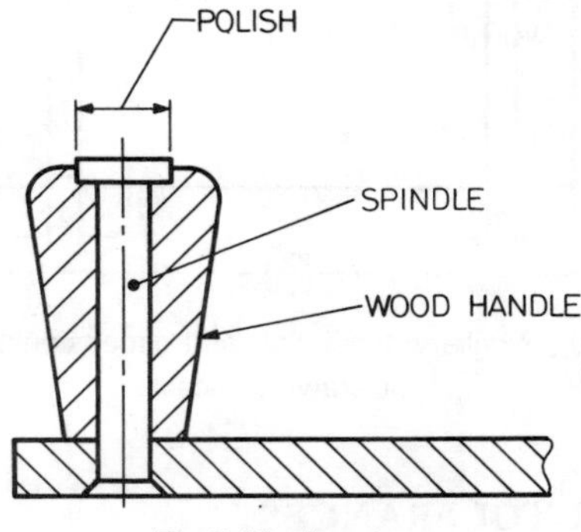

Fig.8.18 Leaders

Auxiliary dimensions

Occasions may arise when it is necessary to include an auxiliary dimension in a drawing. Two examples of such auxiliary dimensions are shown in Figs 8.19 and 8.20. An auxiliary dimension is printed within brackets. Note that in both the given examples, either the auxiliary dimension is redundant, or one of the other dimensions in each example is redundant. It was noted earlier (page 87) that such redundant dimensions should not be included in drawings. However, the occasion may arise when an auxiliary dimension, even if redundant, could provide useful information at some stage in the production, assembly or inspection of the component which the drawing represents.

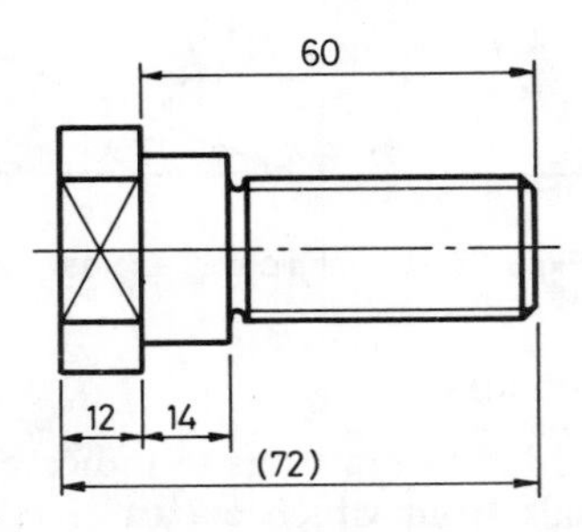

Fig.8.19 An auxiliary dimension

Dimensioning items not drawn to scale

Fig. 8.20 includes examples of parts which have not been drawn to the same scale as the main drawing. The dimensions of such parts are underlined with a thin line.

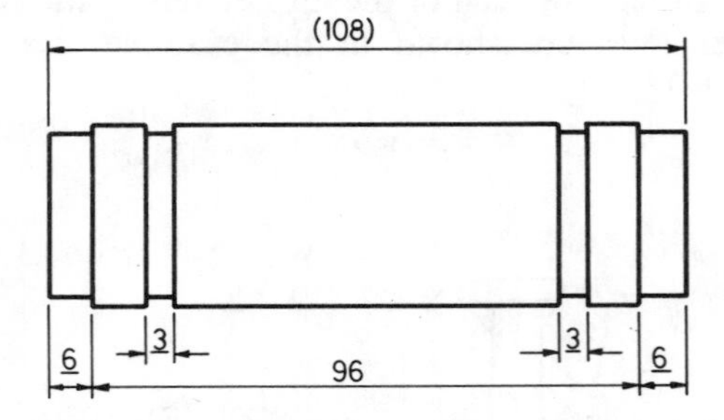

Fig.8.20 Auxiliary dimension and dimensioning items not drawn to scale

LINEAR TOLERANCES

As stated earlier (page 87), a dimension without a tolerance is, in engineering practice, a practical impossibility. The limits within which a linear dimension can be tolerated can be included with the dimension. Fig. 8.21 indicates methods of showing tolerances against dimensions. The method of tolerance dimensioning adopted depends partly on the use for which a component is intended. When a drawing includes a general statement such as TOLERANCES ± 0.5 mm UNLESS OTHER-

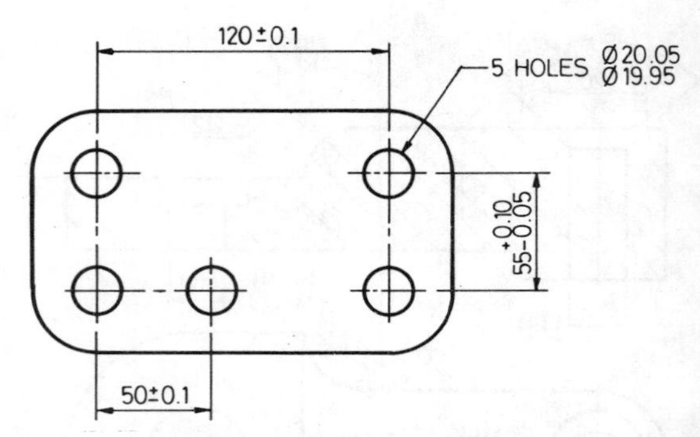

Fig.8.21 Linear tolerances

WISE STATED, only those dimensions which fall inside, or outside, this general tolerance, will have tolerance limits added to the dimensions included in the drawing.

Angular tolerances

Fig. 8.22 gives examples of methods of showing upper and lower limits of tolerance for the size of angles.

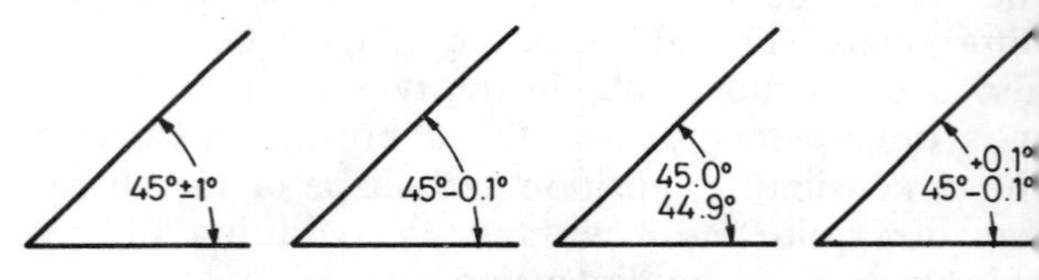

Fig.8.22 Angular tolerances

Dimensioning tapers

Tapers can be dimensioned in several ways (Figs 8.23 and 8.24). Some examples are:

(1) The diameter, or width, at both ends of the taper can be dimensioned, together with the length of the taper.
(2) The diameter, or width, at one end can be given together with the rate of taper.
(3) The diameter or width at a dimensioned position of the taper, together with the rate of taper, can be given.

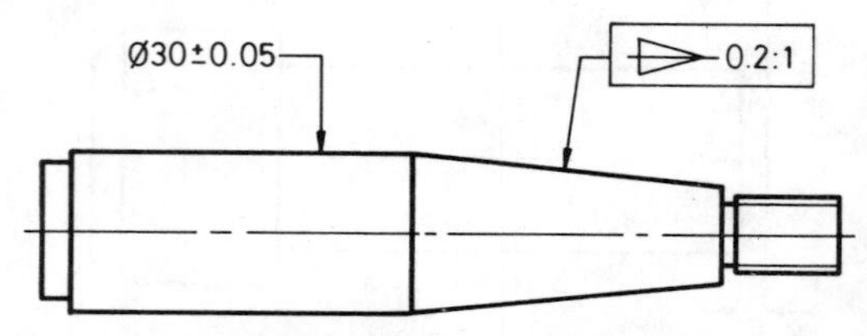

Fig.8.23 Dimensioning a taper

Fig. 8.23 and 8.24 give two examples showing the second and third of these three methods of dimensioning. Note the following in the two given views:

(1) The symbol for a taper.
(2) The slope of the taper given as a ratio of width:length.
(3) The rectangle surrounding the taper symbol and the taper ratio. The rectangle indicates that the tolerance on the diameter (or width) from which the taper is derived is applicable to any section taken perpendicularly to the length of the diameter.

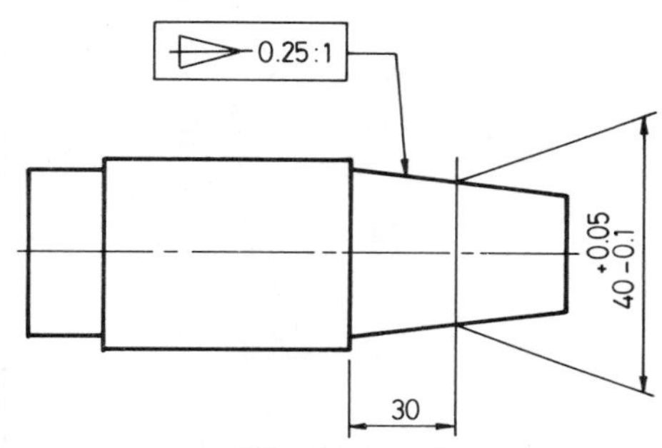

Fig.8.24 Dimensioning a taper

LIMITS AND FITS

It is not possible to machine a part in an engineering assembly to a precise and exact size. In order to overcome this problem in practice, parts are machined to permitted tolerances of size, the tolerances defining the upper and lower limits of sizes between which the part may be machined. The class of fit to which a part should be machined depends upon the function the part is designed to perform within an assembly. On drawings, tolerances of fit are indicated by including the permitted maximum and minimum sizes with the dimensions on the drawing, according to the class of fit required by the design. Such tolerances indicate the limits of a size of a fit between mating parts. BS4500: *ISO Limits and fits* defines a series of tolerances suitable for all classes of engineering work from coarse to fine.

Hole and Shaft Fig. 8.25

Hole

For the purpose of defining limits and fits here, a hole is taken to be the standard part of a fit on which a tolerance is based. This is because a hole is generally machined by drilling and/or reaming. However, it must be emphasized that some fits must necessarily depend upon a shaft-based system.

Shaft

A shaft can be regarded as a part which is machined or ground to give a required fit in a hole. However, in a shaft-based system, it would be the hole which would be machined to take the shaft.

Types of fit

A shaft may fit in a hole to give one of three types of fit.

A clearance fit

The shaft is smaller than the hole in which it fits, allowing the shaft to run or rotate within the hole. Typical clearance fits are found in all types of shaft bearings which allow the shaft to rotate within the bearing; all types of fit in which one part slides within another.

An interference fit

The shaft is larger in diameter than the hole in which it fits. Pressure or heat will be necessary to assist in ensuring the two parts will fit together. This type of fit usually results in a permanent assembly. Typical interference fits are involved in pressfit bushes; couplings shrunk on shafts after pre-heating.

A transition fit

A light interference type of fit which allows parts to be assembled with a minimum of pressure. This type of fit can also be released with a minimum of pressure. Typical examples of transition fits are required in such items as fasteners – keys, pins and parts fitted together for location purposes.

Note The question of limits and fits is concerned not only with holes and shafts, but also can be applied to parts of square section and also to the sizes of length, height and depth of parts. An item such as the fit of a key in its keyway will be dimensioned with tolerances of fit.

Fig. 8.26 Clearance fit

In practice there will be some *deviation* from the model definition of tolerance shown by Fig. 8.26 in

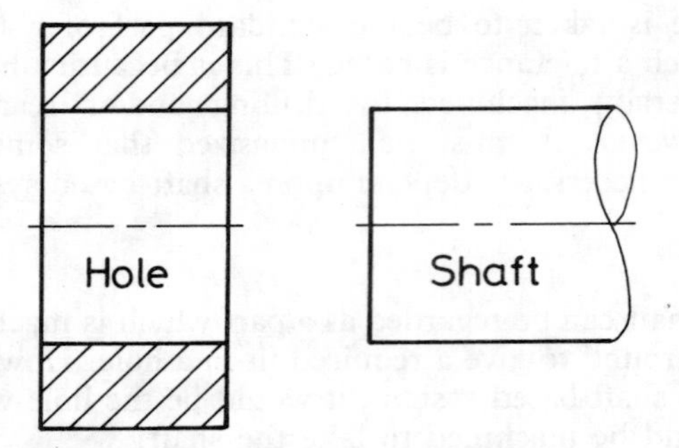

Fig.8.25 Hole and shaft

that the actual maximum and minimum diameters (sizes) obtained by measurement, will vary from their corresponding basic diameters (sizes). For a fuller description of this problem the reader is referred to BS4500: *Limits and fits dimensions on drawings*.

The reader will see dimensions on drawings defining limits and fits such as:

Ø40 + 0.05; Ø40 − 0.05; Ø40 $\begin{matrix} + 0.005 \\ - 0.05 \end{matrix}$

Ø70 H7/f7; Ø40 H8/f7

The last two dimensions are with reference to Data Sheet 4500A (*Selected ISO fits – hole basis*) from BS4500.

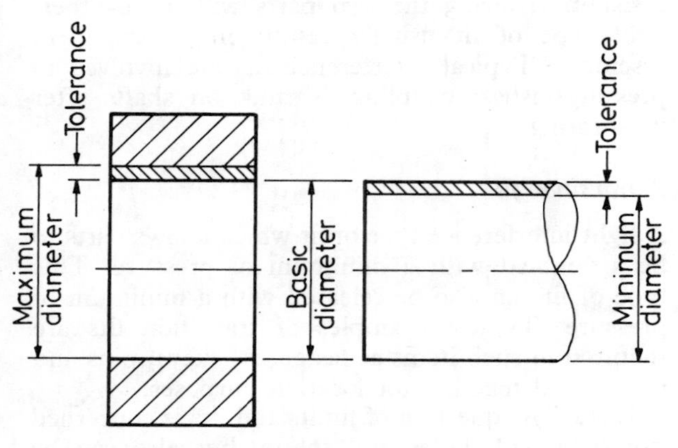

Fig.8.26 Hole-based fits tolerances

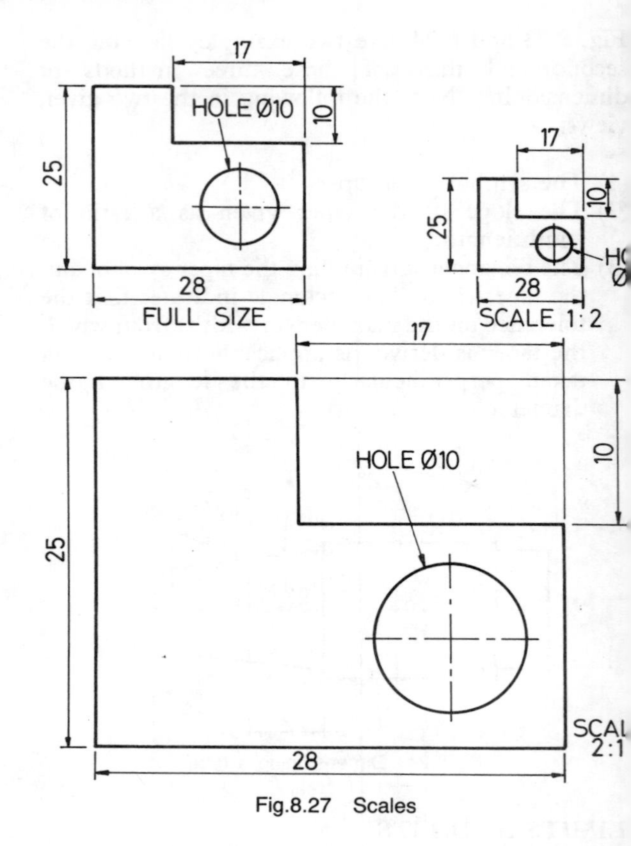

Fig.8.27 Scales

Scales for engineering drawings

In order to be able to include details of a large item on a drawing sheet it may be necessary to draw at a reduced scale. To ensure that details of a small component are clear, it may be necessary to draw at an enlarged scale.

The scale to which a drawing has been made must be clearly stated on the drawing sheet as a ratio. Common scales for engineering drawings are:

Reduced scales 1:2 1:5 1:10 1:20 1:50

Enlarged scales 2:1 5:1 10:1 20:1 50:1

Examples of a dimensioned item drawn to different scales are given in Fig. 8.27. Note that full size dimensions are added to a drawing irrespective of the scale to which it has been drawn.

9 Surface finish

In general, a sectional profile taken through any surface produced by an engineering production process will show two types of irregularity. The first, resulting from the method of machining adopted, is superimposed upon the second, which results from machine vibration or chatter or from the stresses resulting from any heat processes to which the machined component has been subjected. Fig. 9.1 shows, in an exaggerated form, these two general forms of surface irregularity resulting from production processes. The irregularities resulting from machining are superimposed upon the wave-like irregularities resulting from machine vibration or from heat processes.

Measurements of the depths of the irregularities of surfaces resulting from the production processes involved in engineering, are taken as an indication of the quality of the surface texture or surface roughness. The smaller the depths of the irregularities, the smoother is the surface. In practice the depths of the irregularities are measured with devices such as electrical integrating instruments, which give average readings of depth, taken over a number of consecutive sampling lengths of the surface being examined.

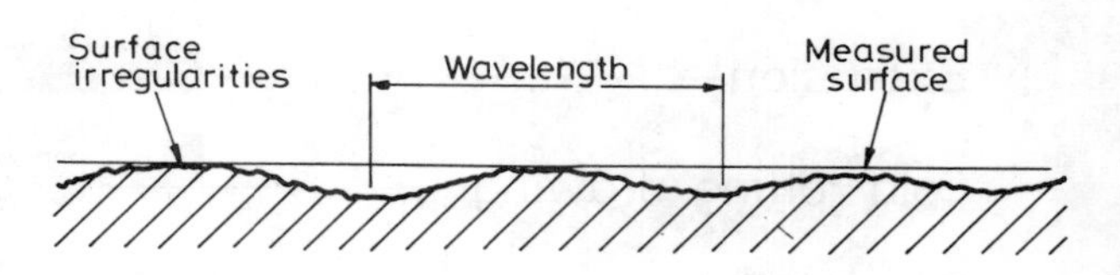

Fig.9.1 Surface irregularities from machining

μm		Microinches
50	N12	2000
25	N11	1000
12.5	N10	500
6.3	N9	250
3.2	N8	125
1.6	N7	63
0.8	N6	32
0.4	N5	16
0.2	N4	8
0.1	N3	4
0.05	N2	2
0.025	N1	1
0.0125		0.5

Fig.9.2 Preferred values of surface roughness

PREFERRED VALUE OF SURFACE ROUGHNESS

For the purpose of defining the limits of the qualities of surface roughness on drawings, a series of preferred values in micrometres is used to describe the averages of measurements of depth of the surface irregularities resulting from engineering processes. This series is given in Fig. 9.2. The symbol for a micrometre is μm. 1 μm is $^1/_{1\,000\,000}$ metre or $^1/_{1000}$ millimetre.

An N series of numbers can be used in place of the preferred micrometre values. The N series also relates to inch equivalents of the micrometre values. If drawings are to be placed between firms using different units of measurement, the adoption of N values reduces the confusion which may arise as to the precise values intended. The inch values in Fig. 9.2 are in microinches. 1 microinch = $^1/_{1\,000\,000}$ inch.

Surface roughness values produced by the more common engineering production processes are shown in the table Fig. 9.3. In Fig. 9.3 both N values and μm values are given at the extremes of the surface roughness values for each process. Thus sand casting can be expected to produce surfaces, the roughness of which lie between the values 50 μm and 6.3 μm and at the other extreme, lapping can be expected to produce surface finishes to values lying between 0.8 μm and 0.0125 μm of roughness.

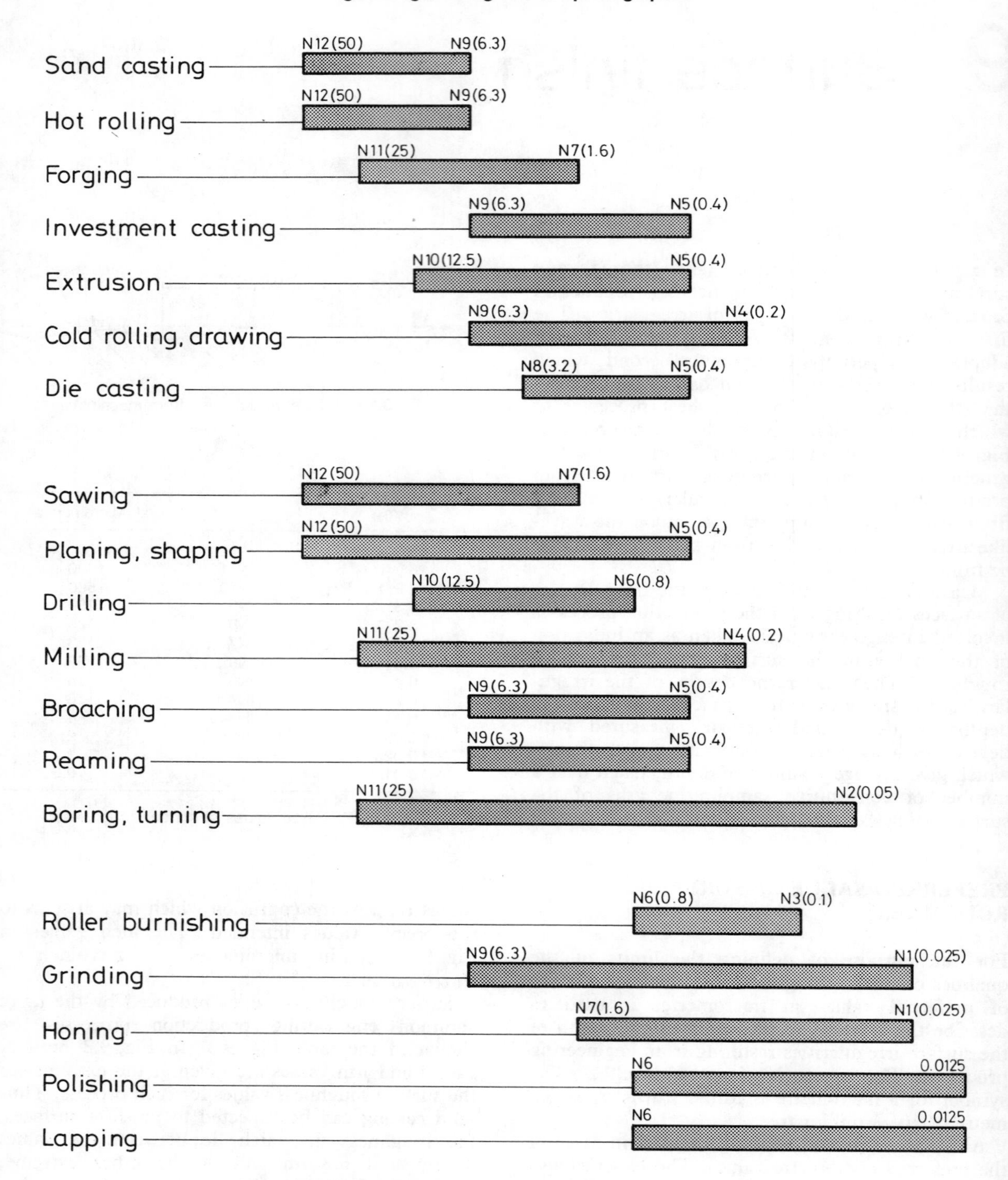

Fig.9.3 Surface roughness values from common production methods

British Standards machining symbol

Fig. 9.4 shows the basic British Standards symbol for indicating the surface roughness to which a part should be finished. On its own, without added roughness values or other added information, the symbol states that the surface to which it refers should be machined.

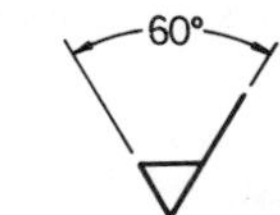

Fig.9.4 Machining symbol

When the symbol is included on a drawing as in Fig. 9.5, with the statement ALL OVER, this indicates that all surfaces of the component portrayed in the drawing should be machined, subject to any general tolerances stated on the drawing.

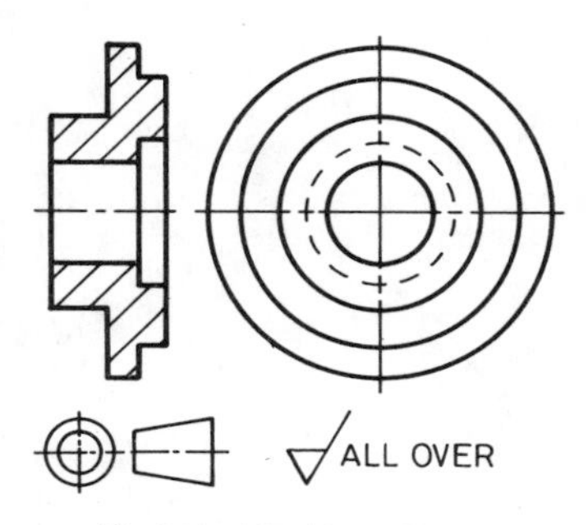

Fig.9.5 Machine all over

Surface roughness values placed above the machining symbol as in the examples given in Fig. 9.6 indicate that each of the surfaces should be machined to achieve the surface finish given by the roughness value. When a single value figure is included over a machining symbol, any value from zero to that given is acceptable. If the required surface roughness needs to fall between maximum and minimum values these must be expressed with the machining symbol with the maximum value placed above the minimum value. See Fig. 9.10.

Surface roughness μm figures may be replaced by N values as in the example given by Fig. 9.7. The surface rougness values may be replaced by lower case letters as in Fig. 9.8. If lower case letters are used in this manner, the meanings of the letters must be clearly stated elsewhere on the drawing.

When the surface is to be finished to a maximum permissible roughness value and it does not matter

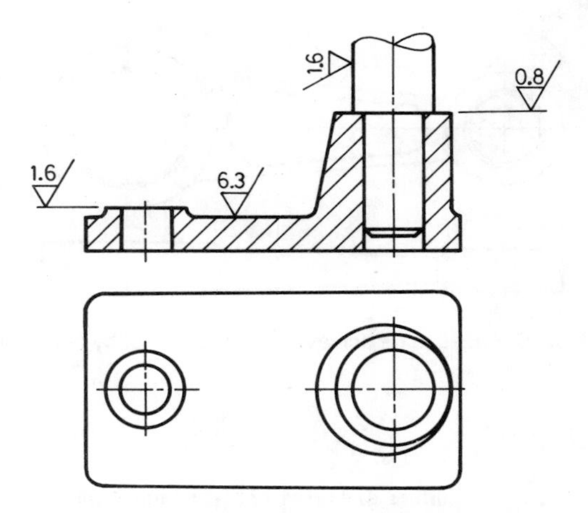

Fig.9.6 Applications of machining symbol

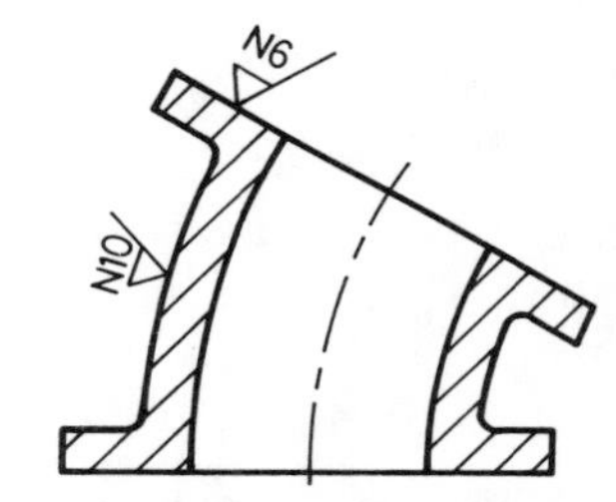

Fig.9.7 N numbers to replace μm values

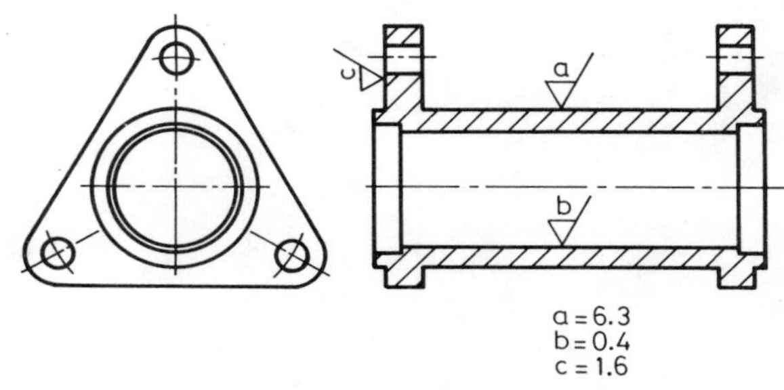

Fig.9.8 Letters replacing μm values

how the required finish is to be achieved, whether by machining or otherwise, the top line of the triangle in the machining symbol is not drawn. An example is given in Fig. 9.9. If a surface must *not* be machined the printed statement DO NOT MACHINE is added to one side of the machining symbol.

Fig. 9.10 gives four examples of machining symbols with added indications of surface roughness values. The meanings of each of the four examples are as follows:

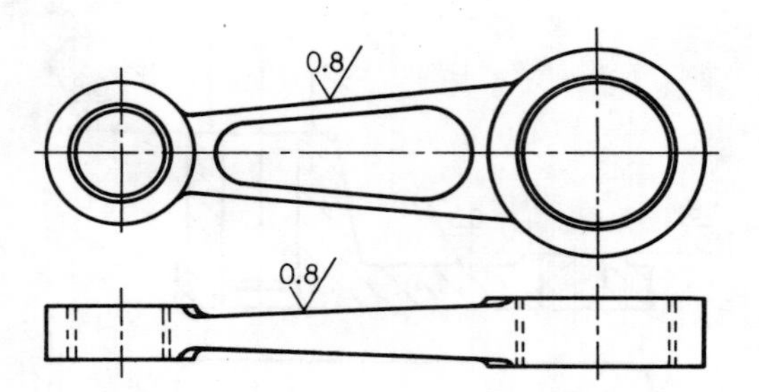

Fig.9.9 Surfaces to be achieved whether or not by machining

Fig.9.10 Further examples of machining symbols

(i) The circle enclosed within the walls of the machining symbol means that machining is *not* permitted to achieve the required surface roughness.
(ii) A surface roughness value lying between 1.6 μm and 3.2 μm is to be achieved without machining. Again, machining is not permissible.
(iii) Machined surface values must lie betwen N4 and N5.
(iv) Machined surface values must lie between *a* and *b*, with *a* values and *b* values clearly stated elsewhere on the drawing sheet.

10 Fastenings

The various parts of engineering assemblies are joined to each other by means of fastenings, either of a permanent or of a temporary nature. Conventional methods of drawing and indicating such fastenings have been devised and those who produce and use engineering drawings need to understand and be able to apply the conventions. Only the conventional methods of drawing the more common engineering fastenings are included here – bolts and studs, with associated nuts, washers and pins; keys; splines; rivets; welds.

SCREW THREADS

The helix

All screw threads are based upon the geometrical form known as a *helix*. A helix is the locus of a point traced on the surface of a cylinder as the cylinder rotates about its axis with constant angular velocity and the point travels with constant linear velocity parallel to the axis.

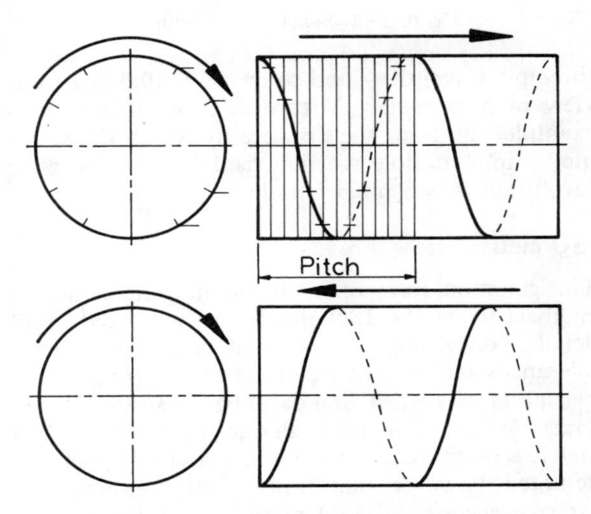

Fig.10.1 Right hand and left hand helices. Views drawn in First Angle projection

Fig. 10.1 shows front and end views of two cylinders drawn in First Angle orthographic projection, each with a simple line helix drawn on the surfaces of the cylinders. In the upper, *right hand* helix, as the cylinder moves with a clockwise rotation, the point tracing the helix moves from left to right. In the lower, *left hand* helix, as the cylinder moves with a clockwise rotation, the point moves from right to left. Fig. 10.2 shows front views of both right hand and left hand screw threads of V section.

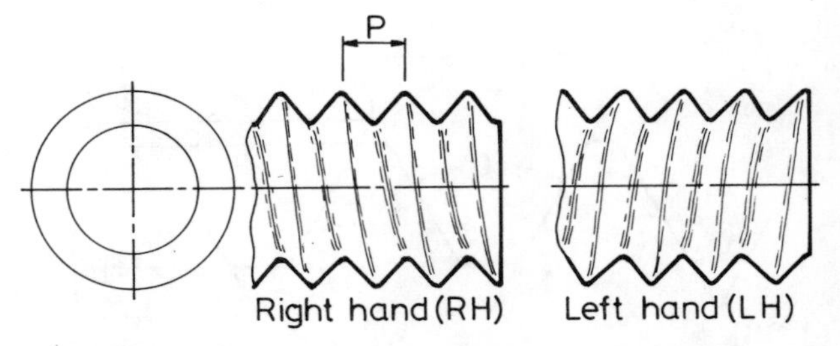

Fig.10.2 Right hand and left hand V screw threads

If a screwed part with a right hand thread is turned with a clockwise rotation into its screwed hole, the screwed part moves into the hole. If a screwed part with a left hand thread is turned clockwise into its screwed hole, the screwed part moves out of the hole. Right hand screws are much more common than are left hand screws.

The majority of all screwed parts found in engineering components have 'single-start' screw threads. Occasionally, however, 'two-start' (or twin-start) or other multiple 'start' screw threads will be more suitable. With a single-start screw thread, each complete rotation of the part containing the screw, takes the part into its screwed hole by a length equal to one pitch (P) of the screw. With a twin-start screw thread, each complete revolution of the screwed part into its screwed hole takes the part into the hole by a length equal to two pitches of the thread. With a triple-start thread, the distance a part moves into its screwed hole will be equal to

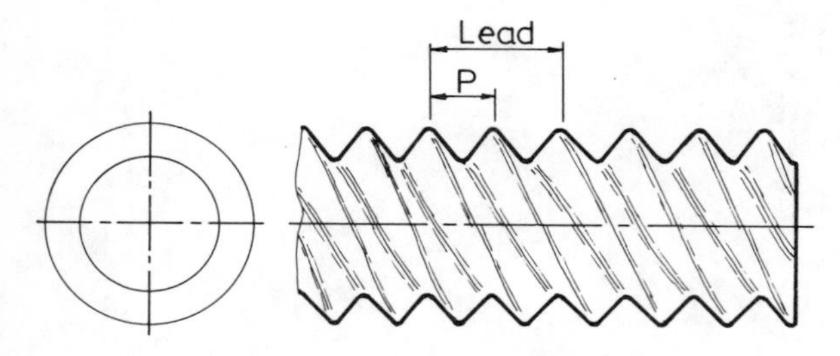

Fig.10.3 Twin-start V screw thread

three pitch lengths – and so on. Fig. 10.3 is a front view of a twin-start V thread. Note that in this example, the lead, the distance by which the screw moves into its hole when turned by one complete revolution is two pitch lengths.

ISO metric screw threads

The common form of V thread in general use in engineering is the ISO metric screw thread. Full details concerning screw diameters, pitch sizes, tolerances and fits can be found by referring to the two parts of British Standard BS3643: *ISO metric screw threads*. The basic design form of an ISO metric screw thread is shown in Fig. 10.4. It should be noted, however, that in practice the internal and external sections of ISO metric screw threads are modified slightly as indicated in the nut and bolt sections given in Fig. 10.5.

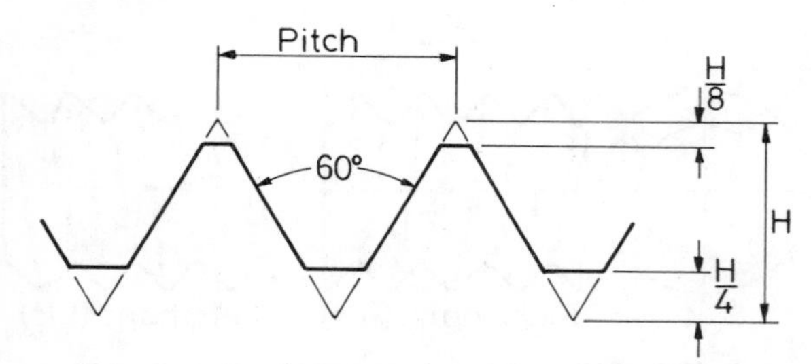

Fig.10.4 Basic ISO metric screw thread

In general, components carrying ISO metric screw threads are manufactured with either coarse pitch series threads or with fine pitch series threads. Coarse pitch series threads are suitable for the vast majority of engineering purposes where V section threads are appropriate. Coarse pitch series threads are usually designated with the prefix M, followed by a number indicating the external diameter of the thread in millimetres. When fine pitch series threads or other ISO metric threads are required,

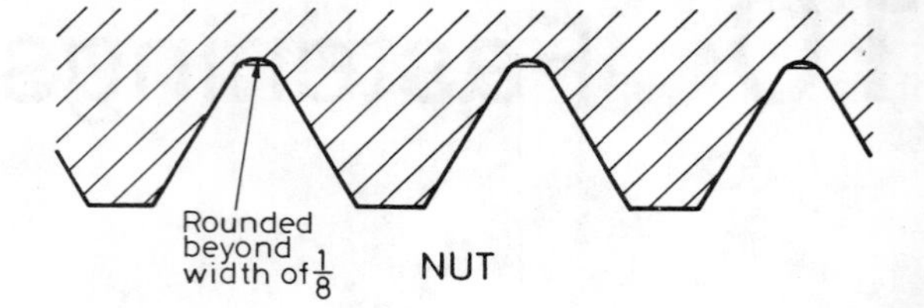

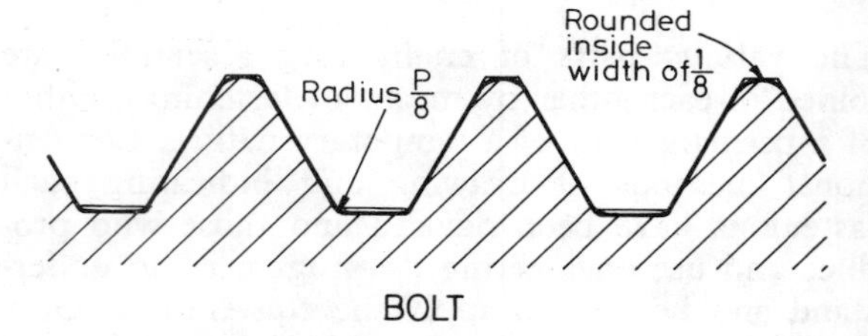

Fig.10.5 Internal and external ISO metric threads

this M designation is followed by the pitch of the thread in millimetres. Thus M10 indicates an ISO metric thread of 10 mm diameter with a coarse series pitch; M10 × 1.25 indicates an ISO metric thread of 10 mm diameter with a fine series pitch; M10 × 1.0 indicates an ISO metric thread with a pitch of 1 mm. In general, the absence of a pitch figure shows that a coarse series pitch thread is required. Details of tolerances of fit may be added to the thread designation numbers. For fuller details of such tolerance indications the student is advised to refer to BS3643.

Some selected typical coarse series and fine series diameter/pitch combinations are given below.

Thread diameter (mm)	Coarse series pitch (mm)	Fine series pitch (mm)
3	0.5	0.35
5	0.8	0.5
8	1.25	1.0
10	1.5	1.25
12	1.75	1.25
16	2.0	1.5
20	2.5	1.5
24	3.0	2.0
30	3.5	2.0

Other forms of screw threads

Many other forms of screw thread are in use in engineering. Among threads of a V form, the student will come across Unified threads with a 60° angle, Whitworth threads with a 55° angle (now largely superseded by the ISO metric form), British Association threads of 47.5° angle used mainly for instrument making. A form of thread devised to achieve maximum power transmission is the square thread shown in section in Fig. 10.6. Square threads are suitable for vice and cramp screws and in jacking mechanisms. Another thread, designed for such mechanisms as valve screws in gas and water supply systems, is the Acme thread, illustrated in a sectional view in Fig. 10.7.

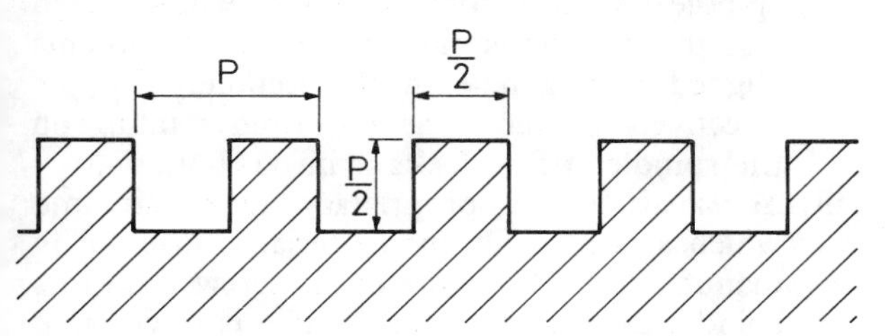

Fig.10.6 Square thread

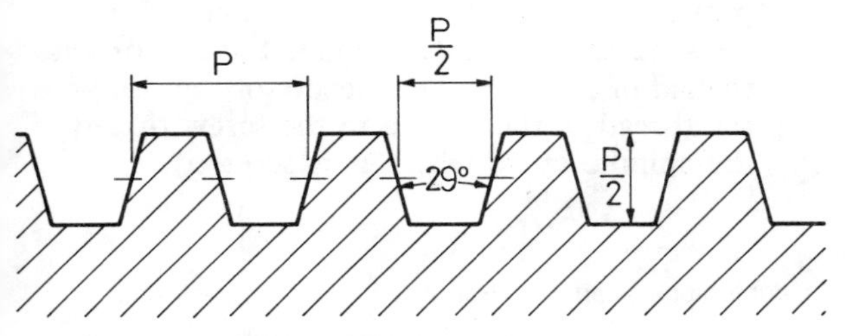

Fig.10.7 Acme thread

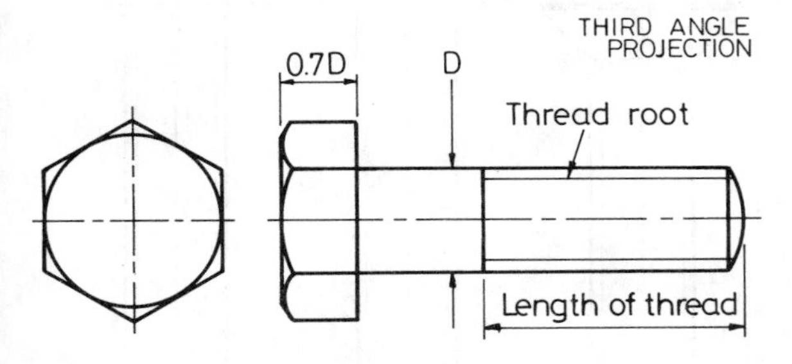

Fig.10.8 BS308: Conventional drawing of a hexagonal head bolt – Third Angle projection

NUTS AND BOLTS

Conventional drawing of hexagonal head bolt

Fig. 10.8 shows the conventional method of drawing a threaded component, in this example a hexagonal head bolt. Note the following:

(1) The threaded part is shown by thin lines drawn parallel to the diameter of the screwed portion of the component. The depth of thread indicated by the lines should approximate to the actual depth of the thread being shown.
(2) The length of the threaded portion terminates in a thick line drawn at right angles across the screw threads.

When drawing hexagonal headed bolts and hexagonal nuts the British Standards publication PD7300: *Nuts and bolts* suggests that the dimensions shown in Fig. 10.9 are appropriate.

Note

(1) The diameter of the bolt is *D*.
(2) The internal screw thread in the nut is indicated by a thin line circle with a break at one part.

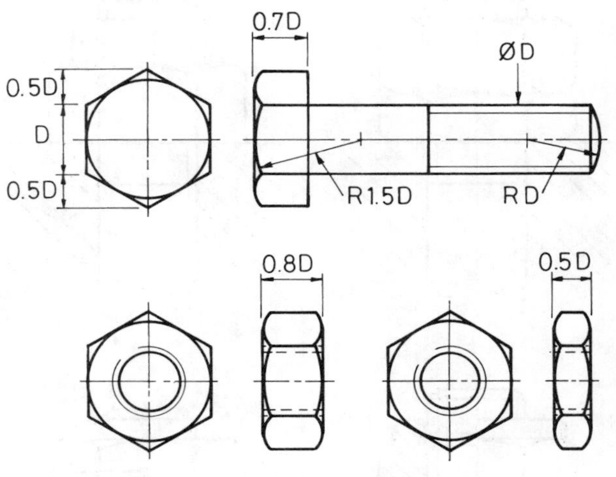

Fig.10.9 Dimensions suggested for drawing hexagonal headed bolts and hexagonal nuts – Third Angle projection

Other types of nuts and bolts

Two commonly used hexagonal nuts are illustrated in Third Angle projection in Fig. 10.10. Hexagonal nuts are chamfered at 30° as shown on either one, or both, faces. The chamfers assist in restricting any damage caused to the top and bottom hexagonal corners when the nuts are assembled on their screw threads.

Lock nuts

Many different types of lock nuts have been designed to ensure that nuts do not become loose under the working conditions to which assemblies

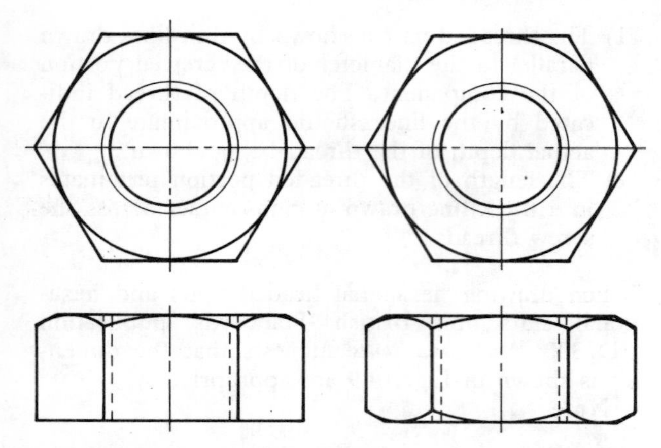

Fig.10.10 Third Angle projections of hexagonal nuts

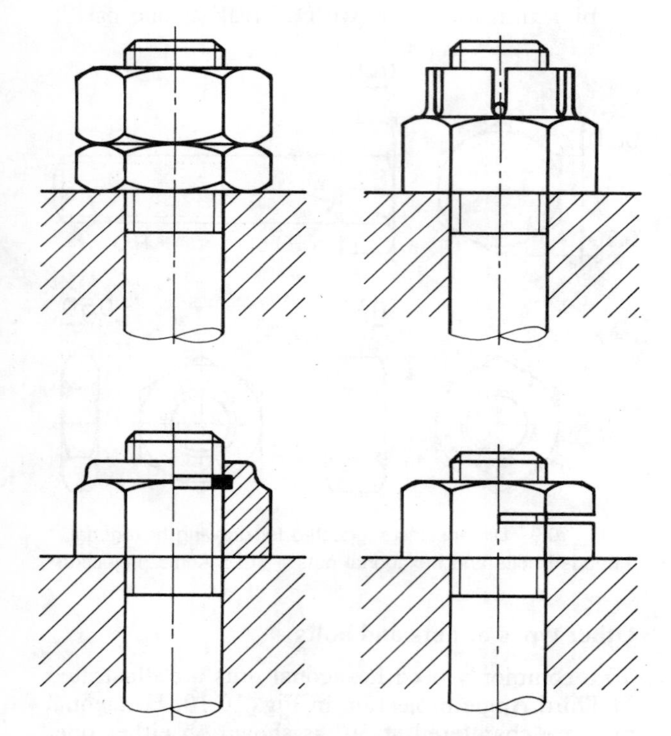

Fig.10.11 Examples of lock nuts
(i) lock nut (ii) Castle nut (iii) Simmond's nut (iv) nut with slot

may be subjected. Fig. 10.11 shows four examples of types of lock nuts.

(i) *Half nut* Half nuts are frequently employed as lock nuts. They should be placed under the full thickness nut to ensure that it is the thicker nut which takes any possible load placed on the assembly. The two nuts should be tightened against each other to prevent either from moving off the screwed thread to which they are attached.

(ii) *Castle nut* Used in conjunction with a pin (often a split pin), the pin being driven through one of the slots in the nut and through a hole in the threaded spindle on to which the nut is fitted. The nut is tightened on to the spindle and may then have to be unthreaded slightly to allow a slot in the nut to become aligned with a hole in the spindle. The pin effectively prevents the nut from rotating on the spindle and so locks it in position.

(iii) *Simmonds nut* A proprietary lock nut into which a ring of fibrous material is inserted in manufacture. When the nut is screwed on to a spindle the thread of the spindle is forced into the fibre ring and locks on to the fibre.

(iv) *Nut with slot* After this nut is tightened in position the slot is closed by either a hammer blow on the nut surface above the slot or with the aid of a punch. The closure of the slot jams the thread of the nut on to the screw thread of the spindle on to which it is screwed.

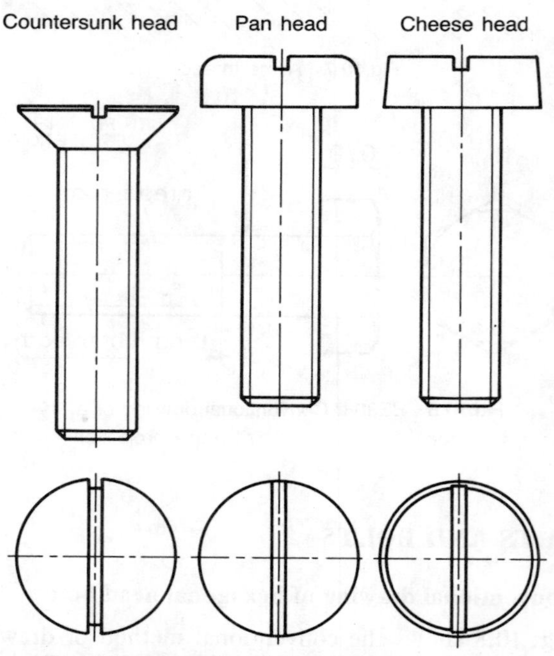

Fig.10.12 Examples of machine screws drawn in First Angle projection

Machine screws

Of the various machine screws manufactured, three are shown in First Angle projections in Fig. 10.12. A commonly accepted description of a 'bolt' which is screwed throughout the length of its diameter is to call it a 'screw'. Countersunk machine screws are fitted where it is necessary to finish an assembly with screw heads flush with the surface through which they are fitted. Pan head, cheese head and similar headed screws and bolts can be used where the head can be left proud of the surface through which they are fitted. When attaching thin sheet material to other parts with the aid of bolts or screws, it may be necessary to employ pan or cheese headed screws because the sheet material may be of insufficient thickness to allow countersink holes to be drilled through the material. Machine screws may have heads with slots cut in them to enable a traditional style screwdriver to fit in the slots, or may have heads with sockets cut centrally to receive hexagonal socket spanners or Pozidriv or Phillips screwdrivers.

Some hexagonal socket bolts and screws

Several examples of bolts and screws with hexagonal socket holes in their heads are shown in Fig. 10.13. The diagrams show a bolt with a diamond knurled head, a bolt with a countersunk head and three grub screws. Grub screws are shaped in various ways at their lower ends to ensure they grip on to spindles securely.

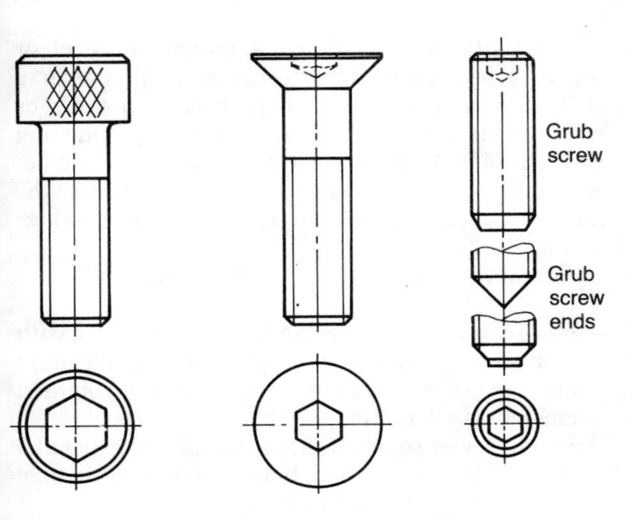

Fig.10.13 First Angle projections of hexagonal socket bolts and screws

Screwed studs

Another common screwed fastening device, for fitting parts of an assembly together, is the screwed stud. Although studs are manufactured in a vast range of different sizes of diameter and length, they all have common features as indicated in Fig. 10.14. The, usually shorter, metal end has a thread such that it makes a close fit in the screwed hole into which the stud is tightened. The, usually longer, nut end has a medium fit screw thread worked on its length. Between these screwed ends is a plain portion which fits into a hole in an assembly between metal and nut. When a nut is removed from a stud, the fact that it is being removed from a medium fit screw thread ensures that the close-fit screw in the metal end is not worked out of its hole.

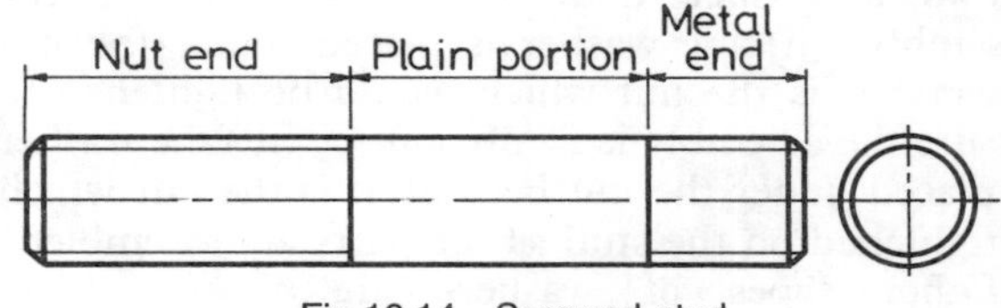

Fig.10.14 Screwed stud

WASHERS

As with nuts, bolts and studs, washers are manufactured in a large range of different types and sizes and from a variety of materials. The most common are plain or bevelled washers such as are illustrated in First Angle projections in Fig. 10.15. Plain washers are designed to be placed under bolt heads or nuts to prevent the heads or nuts damaging the surface of the part on to which they are being tightened. Thus when an assembly is fastened with

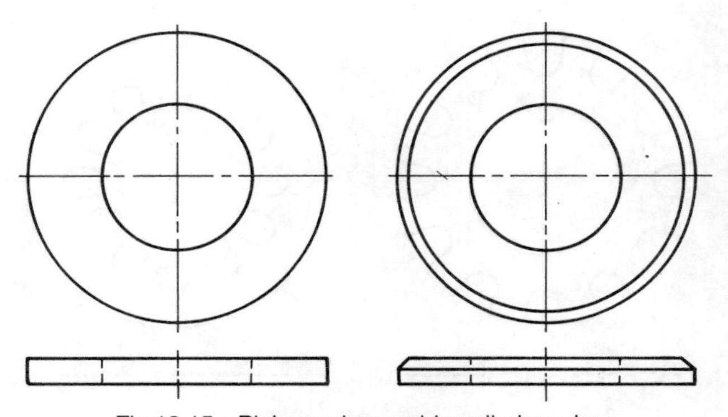

Fig.10.15 Plain washer and bevelled washer

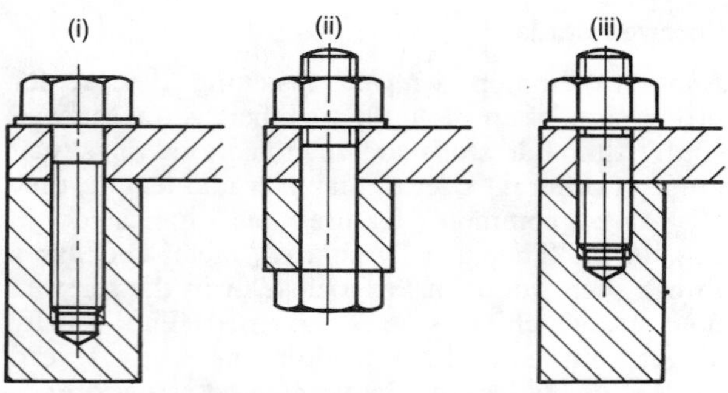

Fig.10.16 Examples of the use of washers

nuts, bolts or studs and a washer is included in the assembly, the washer is placed under that part of the fastening which is being turned to tighten the screwed parts in the assembly. This is illustrated in the three sectional drawings of Fig. 10.16. Thus (i) shows a washer under the bolt head of the assembly; (ii) the washer is placed under the nut because it is the nut which would be tightened to ensure the assembly is firmly joined; (iii) the washer is placed under the nut because it is the nut which is tightened on the stud as the parts are assembled.

Other types of washers are illustrated in Figs 10.17 and 10.18. Spring and toothed lock washers have the effect of acting as partial locking devices, the spring washers because they exert a slight tension between the screw head or nut and toothed washers because the teeth of the washers

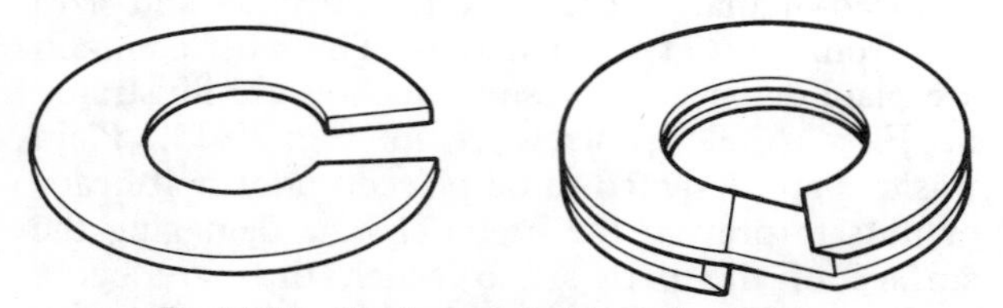

Fig.10.17 Single and double spring washers

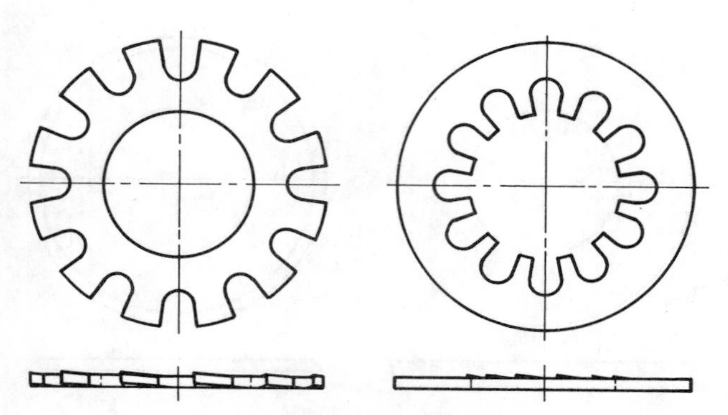

Fig.10.18 Toothed lock washers

tend to 'bite' into the surfaces of the head or nut of the screwed part assisting in preventing a head or nut working loose.

Circlips

Circlips are designed to fit into grooves machined inside holes or in the surfaces of spindles. Circlips are fitted into such grooves to prevent lateral movement of parts assembled in the holes or on the spidles. Circlips are usually made with two small holes cut into lugs each side of the clip opening. The holes are intended to receive the ends of round-nosed pliers when the clips are to be released from their grooves. Some circlips can only be released with the aid of purpose made tools. Fig. 10.19 shows two types of circlips. They are most often made from spring steel.

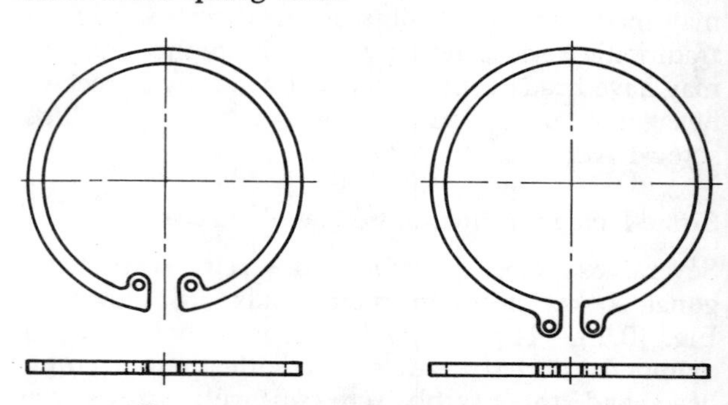

Fig.10.19 Internal and external circlips

KEYS

When fitting a gear wheel, a pulley, a wheel or other such circular parts firmly to a spindle or a shaft in such a manner that the part cannot slip or rotate on its spindle, keys can be inserted in mating slots cut in both the circular part and in the spindle. A number of different types of keys are made, the more common of which are shown in the drawings of Fig. 10.20.

The keys illustrated in Fig. 10.20 are:

- *Rectangular keys* of rectangular section and with parallel top and bottom edges. Rectangular keys may also be tapered from end to end, a common taper being 1 in 100.
- *Square key* of square section, usually with parallel top and bottom, although again square keys may be tapered at a slope of 1 in 100.
- *Woodruff key* of partly circular shape and fitted into a milled recess in the shaft.

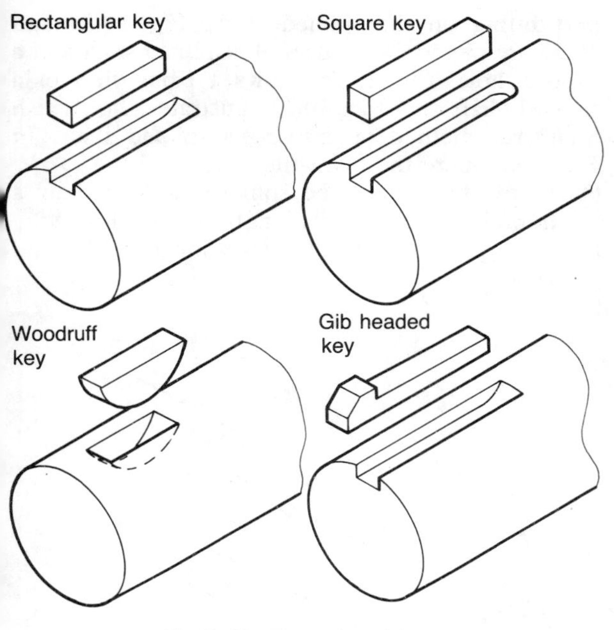

Fig.10.20 Examples of keys

– *Gib headed key* often tapered at 1 in 100. Double gib headed keys are also made with a head at each end. Double gib headed keys are parallel along the length of the key part of the fitting.

All keys and their keyways are designed to prevent rotational slipping between the parts in which they are inserted but, in some cases, keys and keyways can effectively be fitted to allow movement between the two parts along the direction of the axis of the spindle. Fig. 10.21 is a part sectional view taken through a pulley fitted to its spindle by means of a rectangular key. The key is fitted into keyways cut in both the hole of the pulley and in the surface of the spindle. The key effectively prevents rotation of the pulley on its shaft. Sideways or lateral movement of the pulley along the spindle will be prevented by the addition of a washer and nut on the screw thread at the right hand end of the spindle. Note the drawing convention shown in this sectional view – when a key is drawn in a sectional view, it should be shown as an outside view. Because this rule also applies to the spindle in this drawing, the area around the key and its keyways has been part sectioned (see page 00). This allows both the key and the spindle to be shown as outside views.

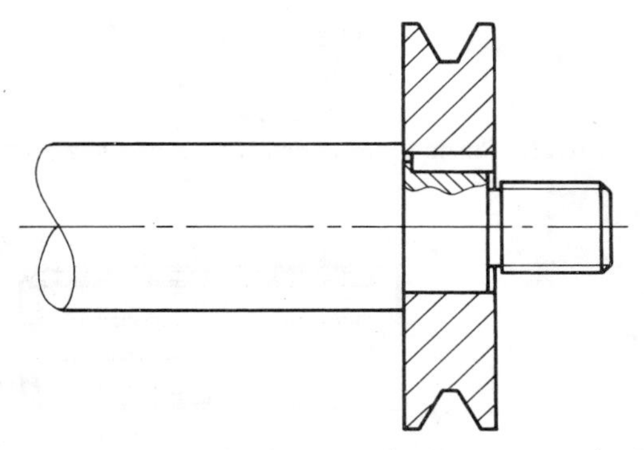

Fig.10.21 A pulley fixed to a shaft with a rectangular key

A second example of a drawing of a key within a sectional view is given by Fig. 10.22. In this example, a spur gear is fixed to a shaft by means of a Woodruff key. The gear can move lengthwise relative to the spindle until a washer and nut are fitted on the screw thread at the end of the spindle. The key effectively prevents rotational movement of the gear wheel on its shaft. Note again in this example the key and the spindle are shown by outside views within the sectional view by adoption of a part section.

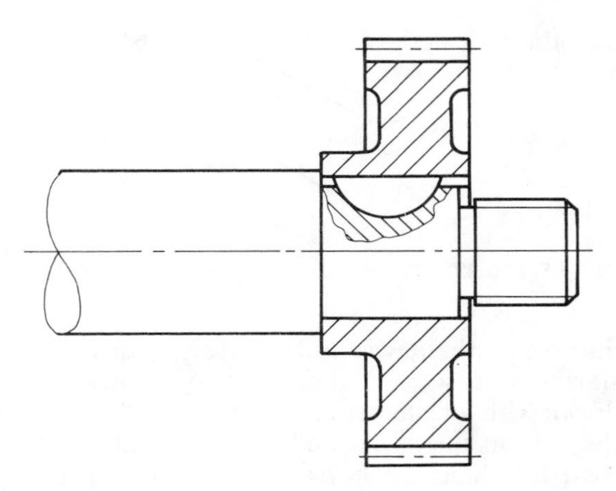

Fig.10.22 A spur gear fixed to a shaft with a Woodruff key

Drawing sizes for keys and keyways

When a key is to be shown in a view in an engineering drawing the dimensions indicated in Fig. 10.23 are suitable. These dimensions are not necessarily the dimensions of the actual keys and keyways which will be used in manufacture, but clearly show the position and shape of the keys. Thus when drawing a rectangular key the rectangular dimension for drawing purposes can be $D/4$ times $D/6$ where D is the diameter of the spindle

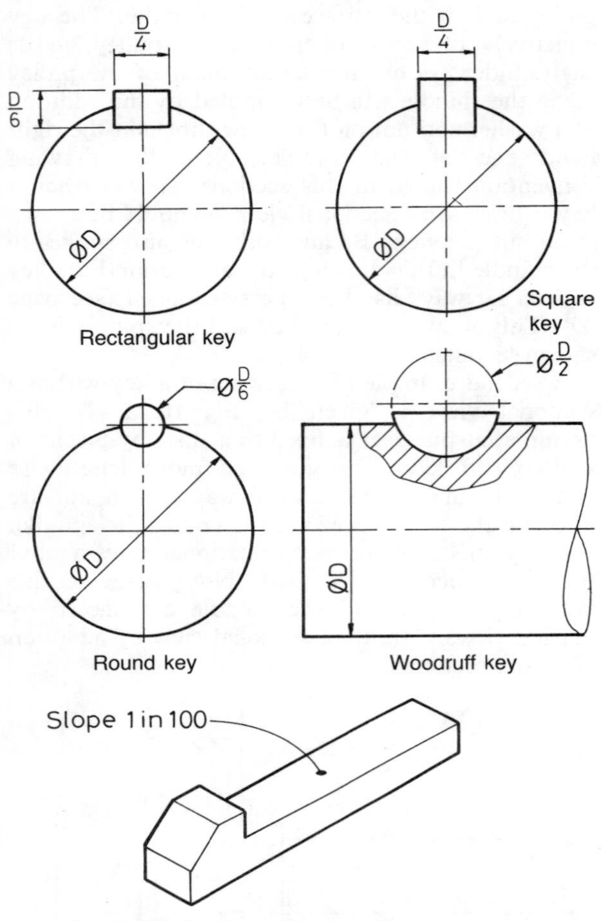

Fig.10.23 Drawing sizes for keys and keyways

into which the key is to be fitted. A square key is shown by a square of sides *D*/4. A round key is drawn with a diameter of *D*/6 and with the centre of the key on the surface of the circle indicating the shaft in which the keyway is cut. Woodruff keys can be shown by part circles of a diameter of *D*/2. Note that in a Woodruff key, the key is less than semi-circular in shape.

SPLINES

When a design requires that a part such as a gear wheel must not rotate on its shaft, yet must be able to move freely along the shaft parallel to the shaft's axis, then the shaft can be splined. A series of grooves is cut around the circumference of the shaft to mate in matching grooves cut in the hole in the part fitting on the splined shaft. Figs 10.24 and 10.25 are pictorial drawings of a splined shaft and a splined hole. Fig. 10.26 shows a front view of a splined shaft and Fig. 10.27 illustrates the British Standards method of drawing a splined shaft. In Fig. 10.27 note the following:

(1) In the front view the spline is indicated by a thin chain line and its length is dimensioned.
(2) Only part of the spline is shown in the end view.

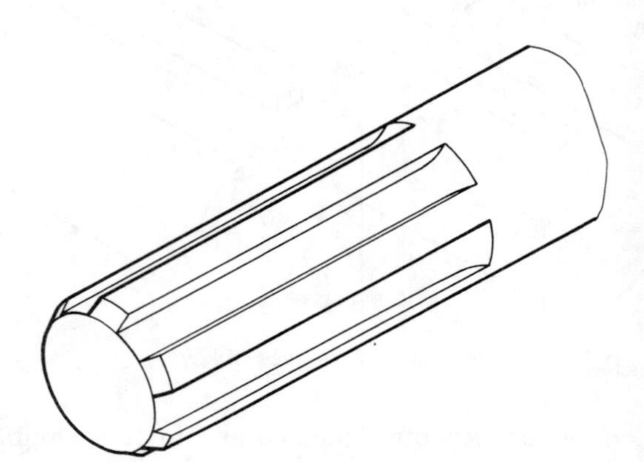

Fig.10.24 A spline on a shaft

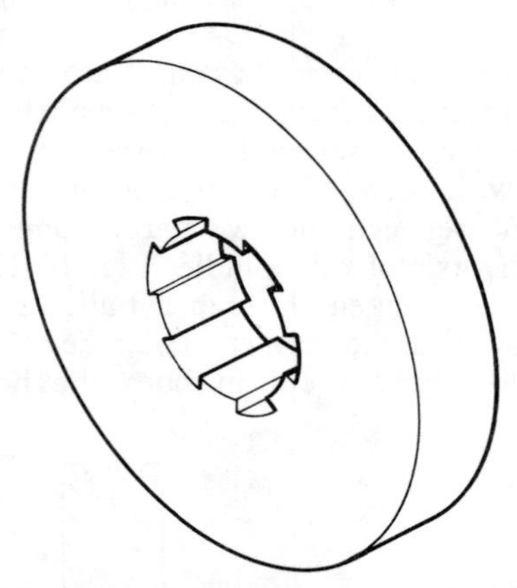

Fig.10.25 Splined hole in which a splined shaft fits

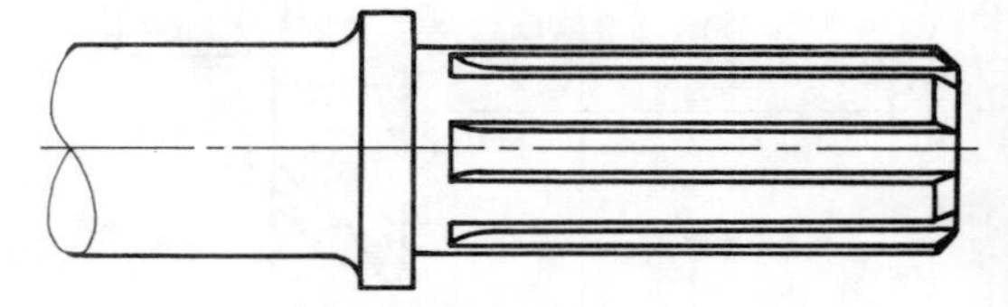

Fig.10.26 Front view of a splined shaft

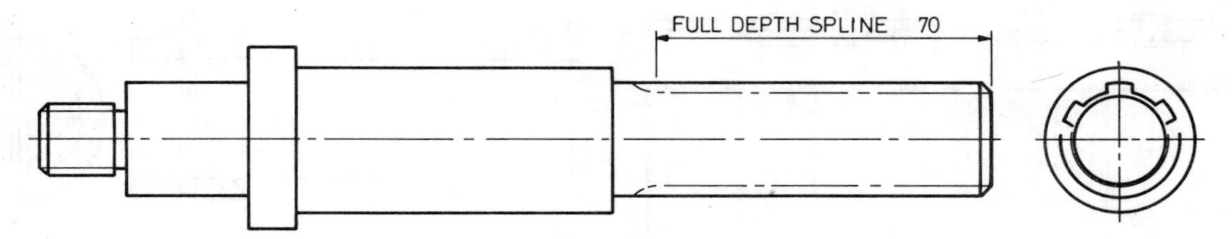

Fig.10.27 Third Angle projection showing BS convention for a spline

RIVETS

Joints held by rivets form permanent fastenings which cannot be easily separated. When it becomes necessary to repair or maintain a part held to another by rivets, the rivets can be drilled out. A riveted joint, however, is unlike one made with screwed fastenings in that it cannot be easily unfastened once the joint has been made, in the same way for example that a nut can be removed from a bolt to unfasten a joint.

Rivets are manufactured in a wide range of sizes, of different types and made from a variety of materials. The three most common types of solid rivet used in engineering practice are shown in the drawings of Fig. 10.28. Countersunk head rivets are used when flush faces are required on both sides of a riveted joint; round head rivets are suitable where countersinking is not practicable for some reason, and where the heads will not form an obstruction; flat head rivets are generally for forming joints between sheets of thin materials. Many other forms of rivets are made, some of which are designed for joining thin materials such as plastics, leathers, fibre sheet, plywoods. A common form of rivet is the blind rivet such as POP rivets, which are designed to be used in joints to which access is only possible from one side, or where access is generally difficult. Blind rivets can only be fastened with the aid of hand or power operated tools, specifically designed for fastening the rivets. Generally blind rivets are placed into the holes in which they are to be fixed and the tool grips the end of, and pulls through, a mandrel running through a hole in the centre of the rivet. The end of the mandrel expands the other end of the rivet to fix the joint and the mandrel is either pulled right through the rivet or breaks at a weakened point at a pre-determined pressure from the tool.

Fig. 10.29 shows sectional views through three riveted joints. Note that rivets are drawn as outside views where they occur in sectional drawings. The three drawings show:

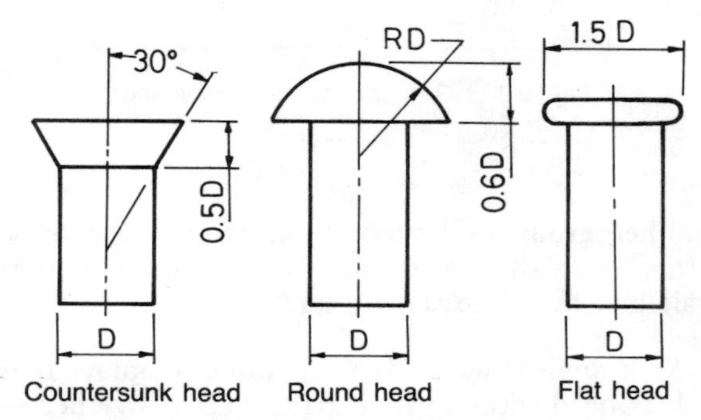

Fig.10.28 Common types of rivets

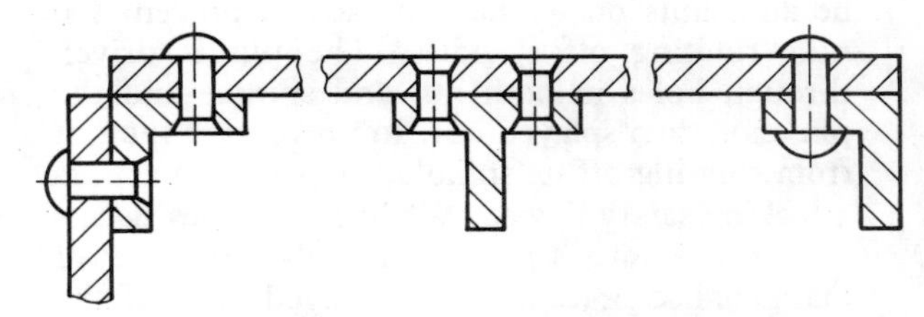

Fig.10.29 Examples of riveting

(1) round head rivets which have been fixed by hammering the ends into countersunk holes;
(2) countersunk rivets with ends fixed in countersunk holes;
(3) round head rivets fixed by hammering the ends to a round head shape with the aid of some form of rivet 'set' tool.

Fig. 10.30 shows two joints made between sheets of thin material with flat head rivets. That on the right is known as a *single riveted tap joint*. That on the left is a *single riveted butt joint with a cover plate*. Note that it is not necessary to draw the circles of all the rivets in a plan view; the centres of the rivets being indicated by crosses.

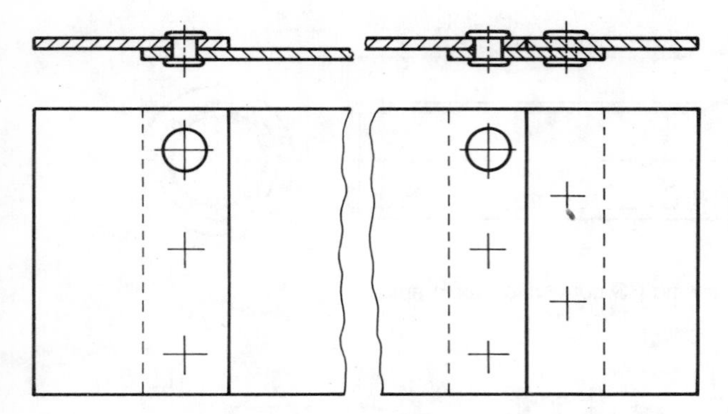

Fig.10.30 Further examples of riveting

Pins

Another group of temporary fastenings are those formed with the aid of pins. Of the variety of pins available, three are shown here.

1. *Split pins* (Fig. 10.31) are often employed as locking devices to hold parts firmly together in order to prevent them from slipping or from rotating apart. A common use for split pins is for holding nuts on to their threads to prevent the nuts rotating off spindles. The pin is driven through holes in both nut and spindle and the pin ends then splayed out. In preventing the nut from rotating off its spindle, the split pin acts as a locking/safety device. When it becomes necessary to remove the nut, for the purpose of maintenance or repair, the splayed ends of the pin are lifted, the pin is pulled from its hole with the aid of a pair of pliers and the nut can then be easily removed from its thread. Note that when drawing a pin within a sectional view, the pin is described as an outside view.
2. *Taper pins* (Fig. 10.32) are driven into tapered holes drilled through both parts of the assembly in which they are fitted. When driven fully home, taper pins form a tight fastening locating one part of the assembly relative to another. They can be quickly released by driving the pin in the opposite direction with the aid of hammers and/or punches.
3. *Cotter pins* are wedge shaped pins formed by working a tapered flat along one side of the pin. A sectional view through a typical cotter pin assembly is given in Fig. 10.33. As the nut on the end of the cotter is tightened, so the flat on the side of the pin jams more tightly against a fiat worked on the spindle to which the part holding the cotter is fastened. One of the most common examples of cotter pins held assemblies is that used to secure gear wheels and pedal levers to the bottom axles of bicycles.

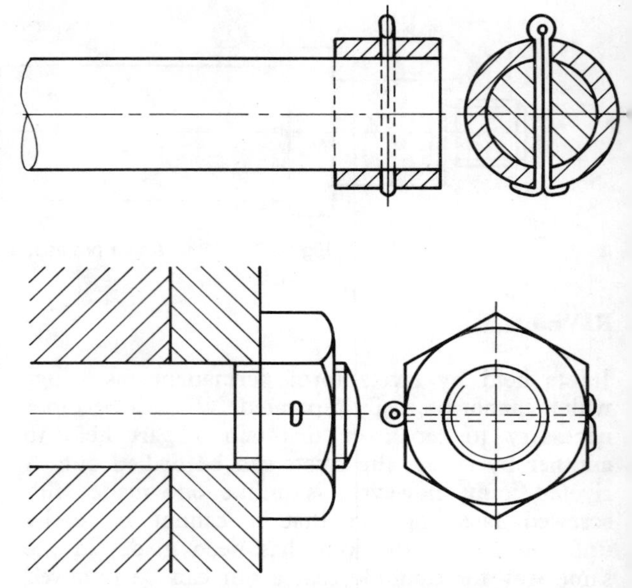

Fig.10.31 Examples of the use of split pins – Third Angle projections

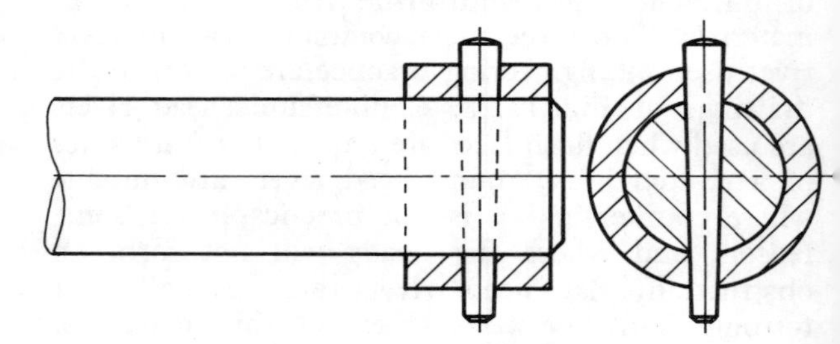

Fig.10.32 Example of the use of a taper pin

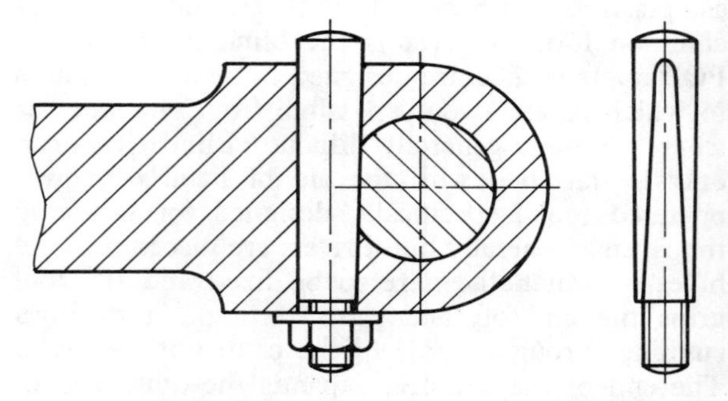

Fig.10.33 Example of a the use of a cotter pin

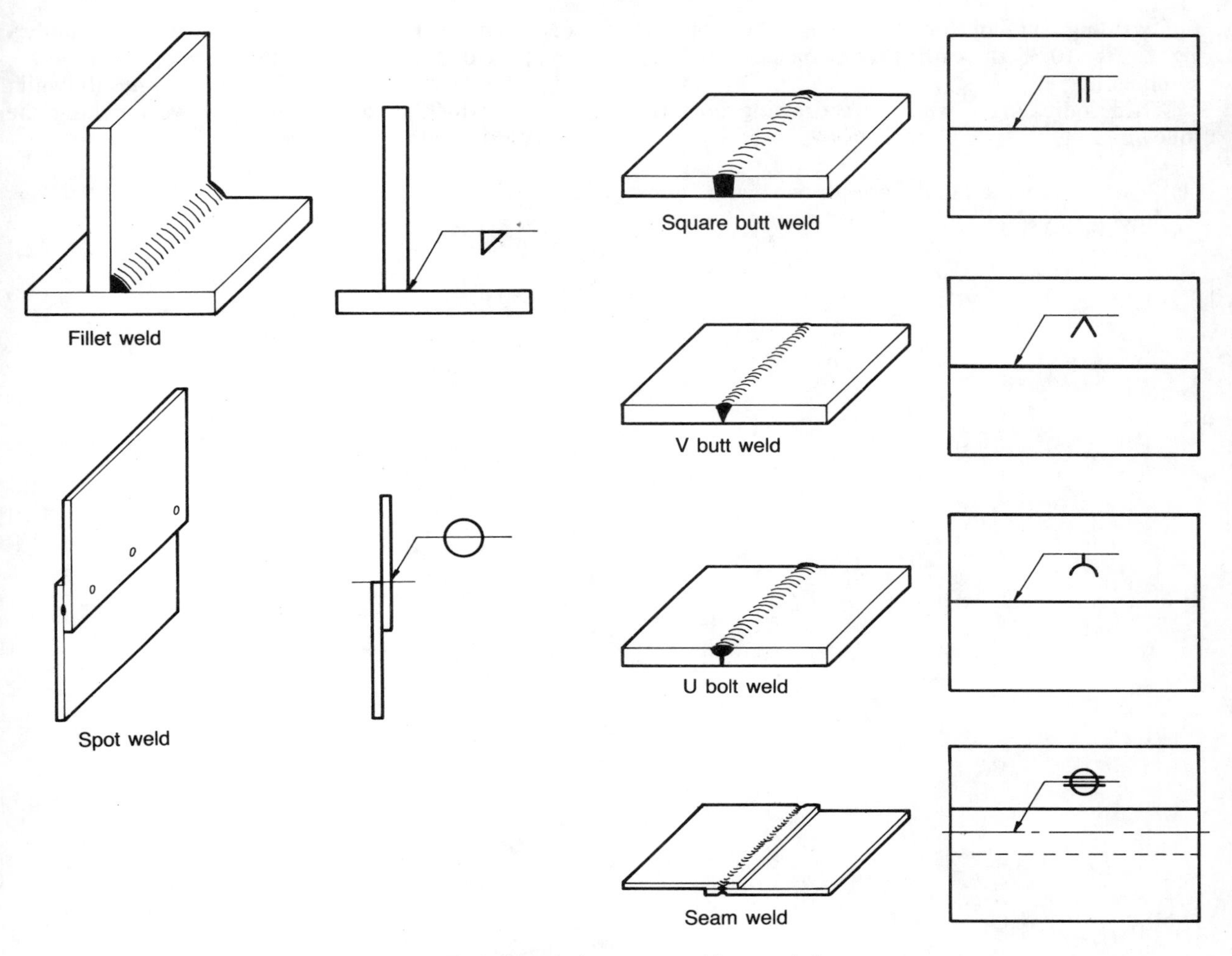

Fig.10.34 Examples of elementary welding symbols

WELDED JOINTS

Parts held together by means of a welded joint are permanently assembled. Properly made welded joints are as strong as the materials in which they have been made. It is far beyond the scope of this book to discuss the number and variety of different forms of welds. When a welded joint needs to be shown in an engineering drawing, it is best indicated by means of the appropriate British Standards symbol taken from BS499: *Specification for symbols for welding*. Fig. 10.34 shows some of the more common welded joints together with the BS symbol representing the welds. Pictorial drawings of the common welds are given on the left and

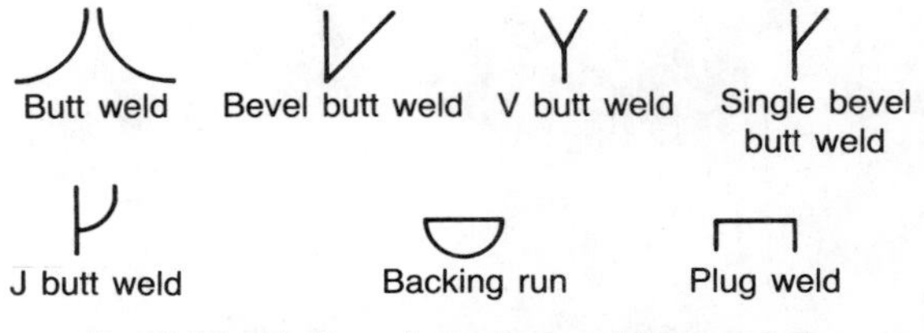

Fig.10.35 Further elementary welding symbols

the welding symbol for the welds given on the right. Fig. 10.35 shows further elementary welding symbols.

When indicating a weld on a drawing note the following:

(1) The welding symbols are drawn with thick lines.
(2) Thin reference lines are drawn either under, over or through the symbols.
(3) The reference lines end with thin lines drawn at 60° which in turn end in arrows touching the weld position.

11 Geometrical tolerances

INTRODUCTION

As has been seen in Chapter 8, tolerances may be applied to dimensions of length and to dimensions such as radii, diameters and angles. Although linear tolerances define upper and lower limits of size for any such particular dimension, they do not define the possible variations of features such as the geometrical shape and form of a dimensioned object. The limits of features such as straightness, flatness, perpendicularity or circularity are not fully defined by toleranced linear dimensions.

As can be seen from Fig. 11.1(a) it would normally be assumed, from the dimensions of the given shape, that it is a rectangle of overall dimensions of 100 mm × 25 mm, with a tolerance of ± 0.05 mm on each dimension. However, the shape could be re-drawn to the outline given by Fig. 11.1(b) and the dimensions could still be acceptable. This is because the given dimensions have not stipulated details concerning the straightness of the 100 mm sides of the shape, nor indeed the perpendicularity of the short sides to the long sides. Thus any of the measurements A, B, C, D, etc., in Fig. 11.1(b) taken parallel to the 25 mm dimension line could all be 25 mm ± 0.05 mm. The problem of straightness and perpendicularity has, of course, been exaggerated in Fig. 11.1(b), but even very small variations in straightness could render an object manufactured to dimensions given only linear tolerances, to be unsuitable for its function. Similar problems concerning the correct dimensional definition of geometrical shape and form can arise with regard to features such as circularity, cylindricity, parallelism and the like. The methods of dimensioning to geometrical tolerances assist in clearly defining the limits of straightness, flatness, circularity and other geometrical shapes and forms. These methods describe the limits of deviation of a feature from ideal geometrical shapes and forms. They are also used to indicate the limits of tolerance of the geometrical location or orientation of features such as holes in an object. A full description of the methods of applying geometrical tolerances will be found in BS308: Part 3. Only an outline of the methods is given here.

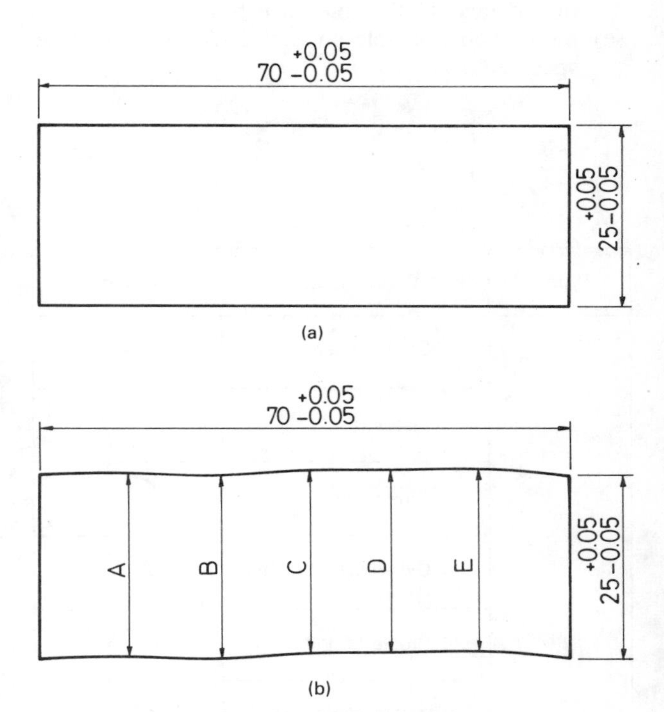

Fig.11.1 Deviations in straightness

SYMBOLS

Fig. 11.2 is a list of symbols for identifying the *characteristic* to which geometrical tolerances are applied.

Fig. 11.3 lists additional symbols required to indicate the feature and the characteristics to which part of an object the tolerance should be applied.

Fig. 11.4 shows a number of *tolerance frames*.

Tolerance frames are divided into two or more boxes in which the following details are given:

(a) the symbol for the characteristic to which the tolerance refers;
(b) the tolerance value of the *linear* dimension;
(c) the letter or letters identifying the datum on the object being dimensioned;
(d) notes relating to the toleranced features may be placed near to the tolerance frame;
(e) more than one tolerance characteristic may be specified.

Type	Characteristics	Symbol
Form	Straightness	—
	Flatness	▱
	Circularity	○
	Cylindricity	⌭
	Profile of line	⌒
	Profile of surface	⌓
Attitude	Parallelism	//
	Perpendicularity	⊥
	Angularity	∠
Location	Position	⌖
	Concentricity	◎
	Symmetry	⌯

Fig.11.2 Characteristics symbols

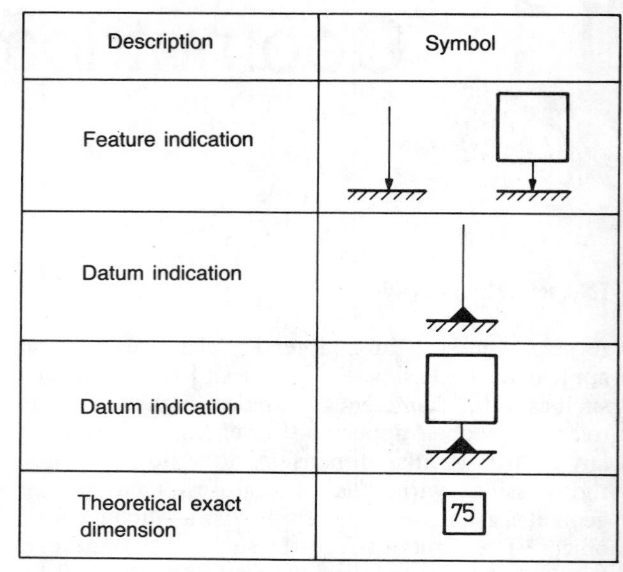

Description	Symbol
Feature indication	
Datum indication	
Datum indication	
Theoretical exact dimension	75

Fig.11.3 Additional symbols

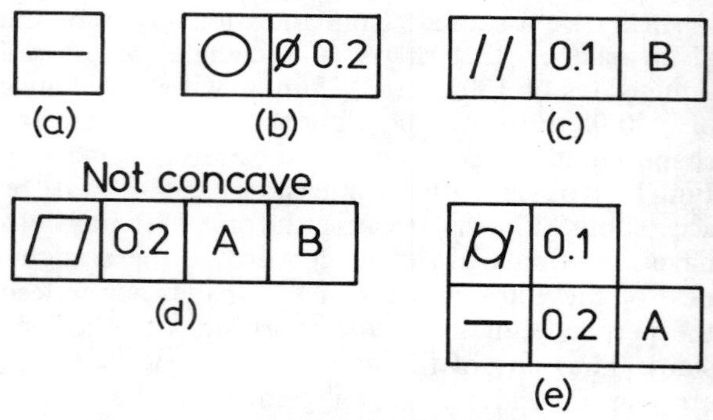

Fig.11.4 Tolerance frames

APPLICATIONS OF GEOMETRICAL TOLERANCES

Eleven examples are given in the drawings of Figs 11.5 to 11.23.

Example 1 (Fig. 11.5)

When the tolerance is shown as an extension of a dimension line, it refers to the axis of the feature.

Example 2 (Fig. 11.6)

When the tolerance is shown as referring to an axis, the tolerance refers to all items along that axis. Note

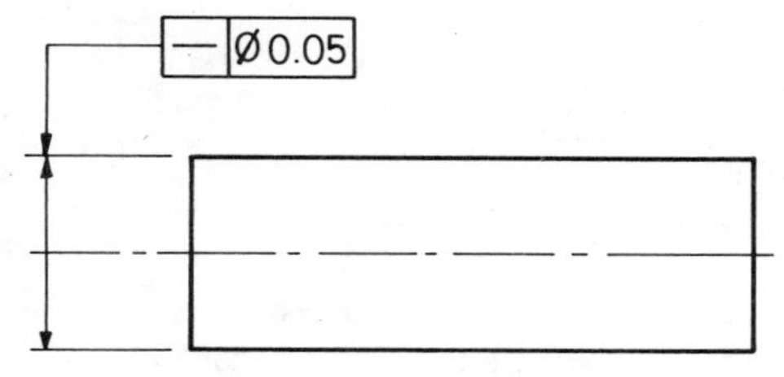

Fig.11.5 Example 1

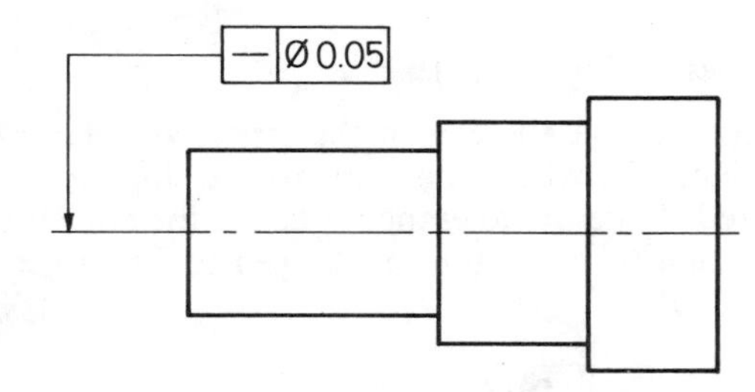

Fig.11.6 Example 2

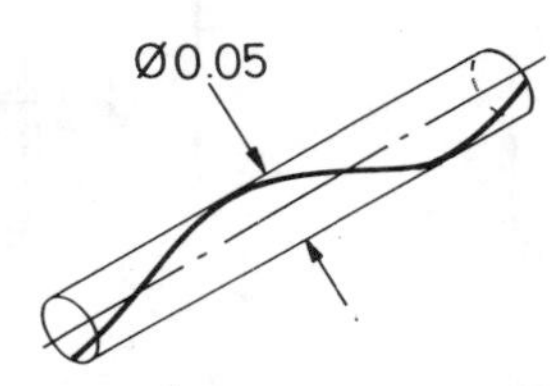

Fig.11.7 Tolerance zone for Examples 1 and 2

that the Ø0.05 tolerance in both examples applies to the line contained within a cylinder of axis length and of a diameter of 0.005 – Fig. 11.7.

Example 3 (Fig. 11.8)

The tolerance for the diameter of the given cylinder lies within a zone of concentric circles whose *radii* are separated by 0.03 mm as shown by Fig. 11.9.

Example 4 (Fig. 11.10)

The surface to which the tolerance symbols refer should be machined so that the surface can be contained within two flat planes 0.04 mm apart as indicated in Fig. 11.11.

Example 5 (Fig. 11.12)

The cylinder to which the tolerance refers must be finished so that the bounds of the cylinder lie between two concentric cylinders whose *radii* differ

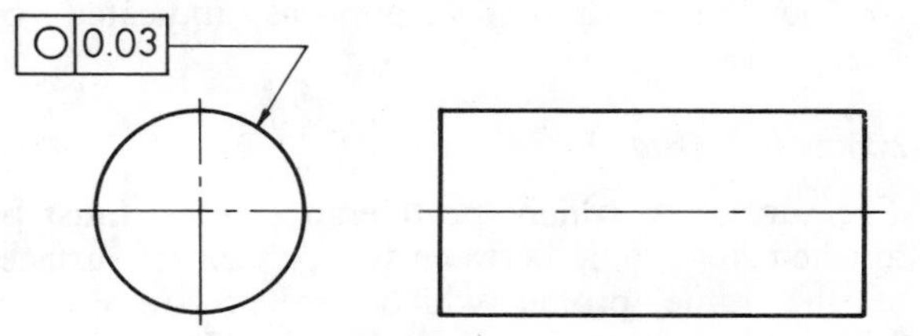

Fig.11.8 Example 3

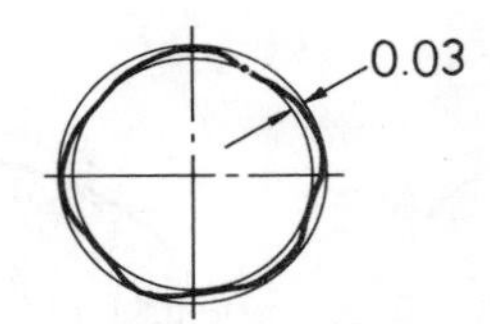

Fig.11.9 Tolerance zone for Example 3

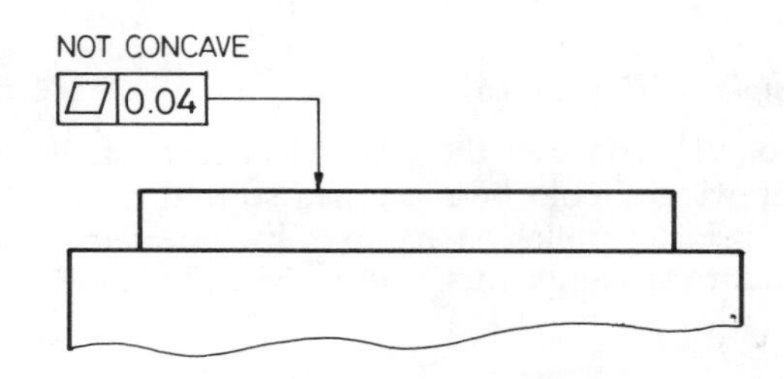

Fig.11.10 Example 4

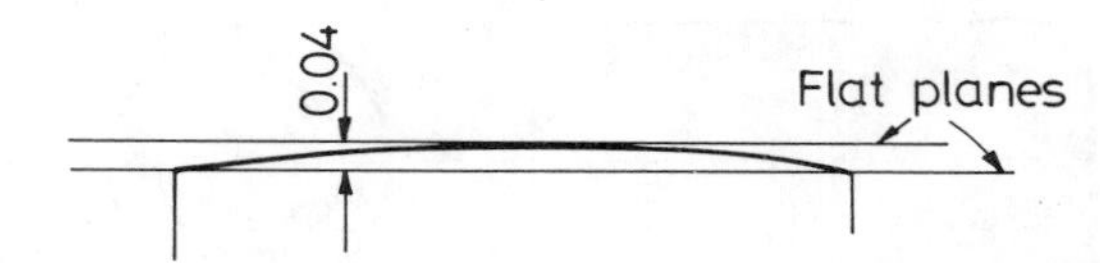

Fig.11.11 Tolerance zone for Example 4

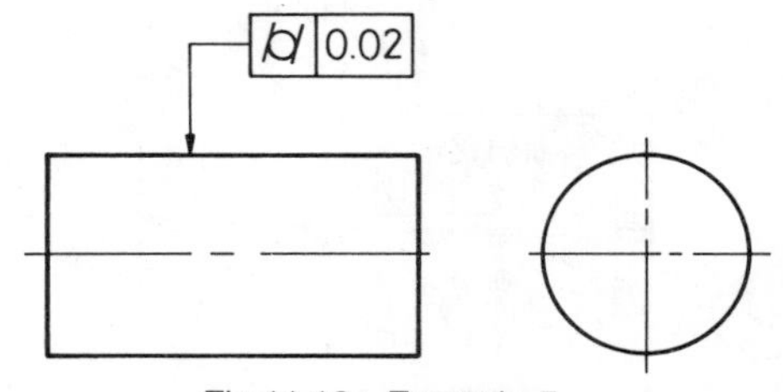

Fig.11.12 Example 5

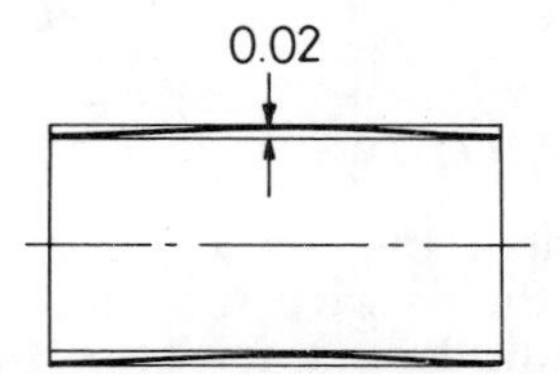

Fig.11.13 Tolerance zone for Example 5

by no more than 0.02 mm as indicated by Fig. 11.13.

Example 6 (Fig. 11.14)

The surface to which the tolerance refers must be finished so as to lie between two concentric surfaces of the same profile which are no more than 0.05 mm apart as shown by Fig. 11.15.

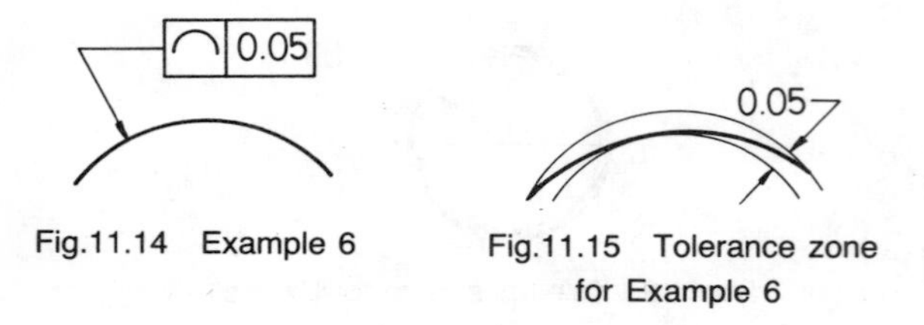

Fig.11.14 Example 6

Fig.11.15 Tolerance zone for Example 6

Example 7 (Fig. 11.16)

The outer surface of the cylindrical form shown in the drawing should be machined so that it deviates from being parallel to its axis by no more than 0.04 mm throughout its length. See Fig. 11.17.

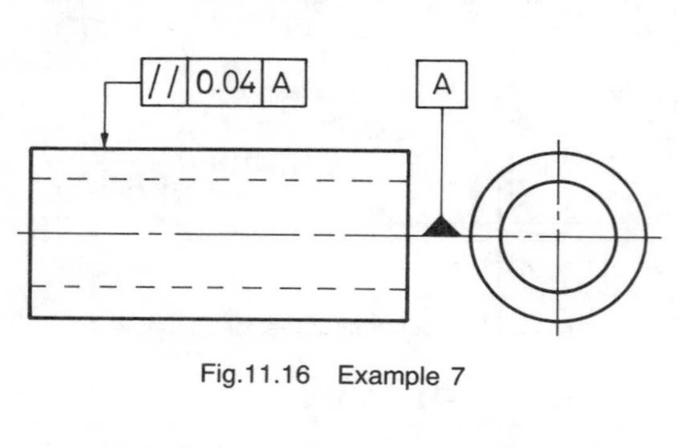

Fig.11.16 Example 7

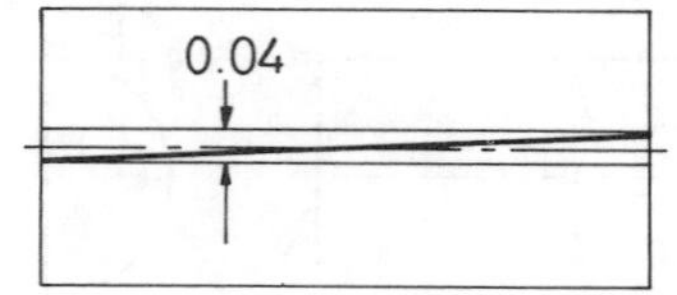

Fig.11.17 Tolerance zone for Example 7

Example 8 (Fig. 11.18)

In this example the vertical part of the form portrayed by the drawing should not deviate from being perpendicular to its base by more than 0.04 mm throughout its height. See Fig. 11.19.

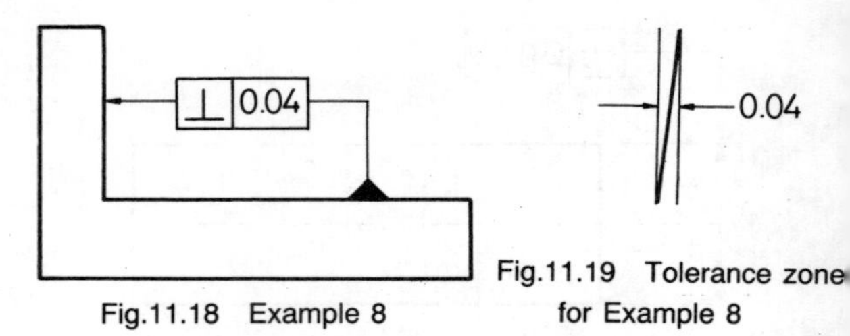

Fig.11.18 Example 8

Fig.11.19 Tolerance zone for Example 8

Example 9 (Fig. 11.20)

In this example the axis of the form has been taken as a datum to which the angle of the sloping face is referred. Note the tolerance zone for the angled face in relation to the datum of the centre line given by Fig. 11.21.

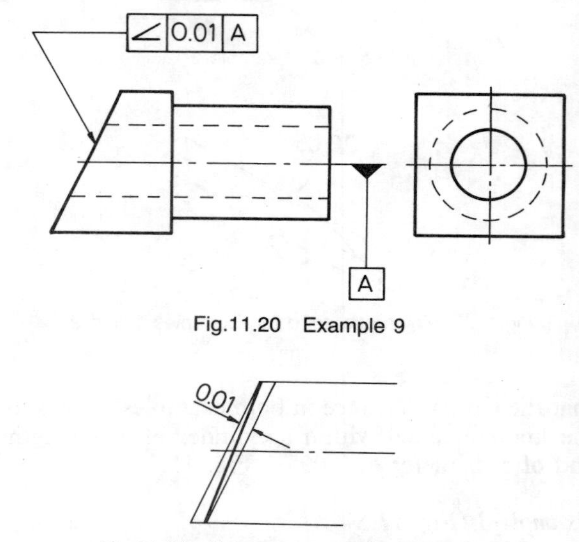

Fig.11.20 Example 9

Fig.11.21 Tolerance zone for Example 9

Example 10 (Fig. 11.22)

The position of the hole is given by the two theoretically exact dimensions of 50 and 25. Their theoretical exactness is indicated by their being enclosed within boxes. The centre of the hole is toleranced so that it lies within the tolerance zone formed by a cylinder of Ø0.01 whose centre is 25 mm and 50 mm from the datum edges A and B respectively. The reason for the tolerance zone being a cylinder is due to the fact that the length of the cylinder is the same as the thickness of the material in which the hole is to be bored.

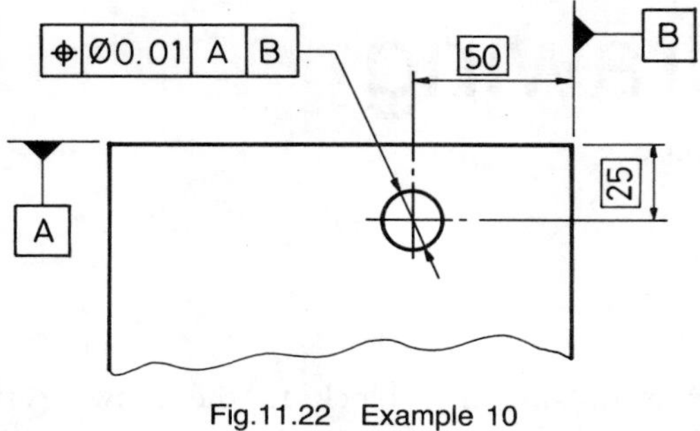

Fig.11.22 Example 10

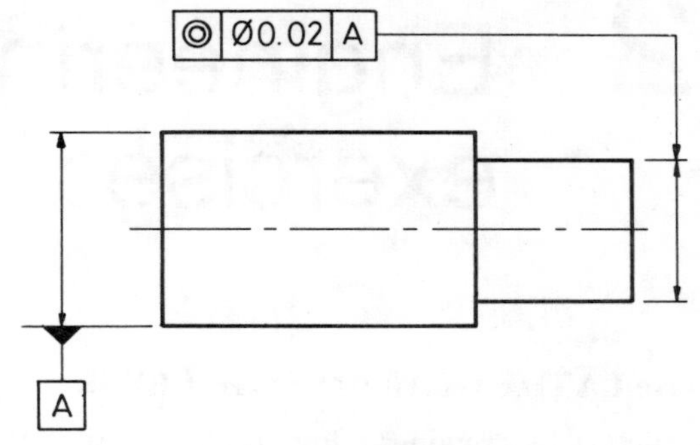

Fig.11.23 Example 11

Example 11 (Fig. 11.23)

This tolerance indicates that the diameter of the small end of the object must be concentric with the diameter of the large end within a tolerance zone formed by two circles with a common centre and where radii differ by no more than 0.02 mm.

12 Engineering drawing exercises

Exercise LATHE GEAR CHANGE LEVER

The pictorial drawing, Fig. 12.1, shows the assembled parts of a GEAR CHANGE LEVER from an engineering lathe. Details of the parts of the assembly are shown in Fig. 12.2.

Using an A3 sheet of drawing paper and working in either First or Third Angle orthographic projection to a scale of 1:1 (full size) draw the following views of the *assembled* GEAR CHANGE LEVER.

(1) A front view.
(2) A sectional plan, on the cutting plane indicated by A–A.
(3) An end view as seen from the right of the front view.
(4) An end view as seen from the left of the front view.

Add a suitable title block to the drawing sheet which includes all information relevant to the assembly drawing.

Exercise

Make the following pictorial drawings of the parts from the details given in the drawings on page 117.

(1) A freehand drawing, approximately full size, of Part 1 (Gear bracket).
(2) A cabinet drawing of Part 1 drawn to scale 1:1.
(3) An isometric drawing, scale 1:1, of Part 2 (Gear handle).

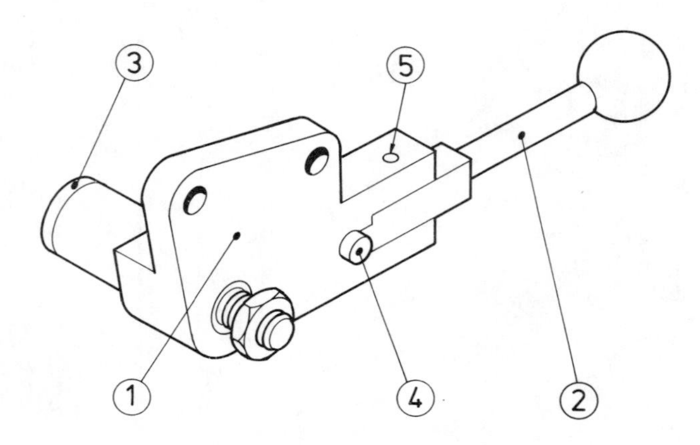

Fig. 12.1

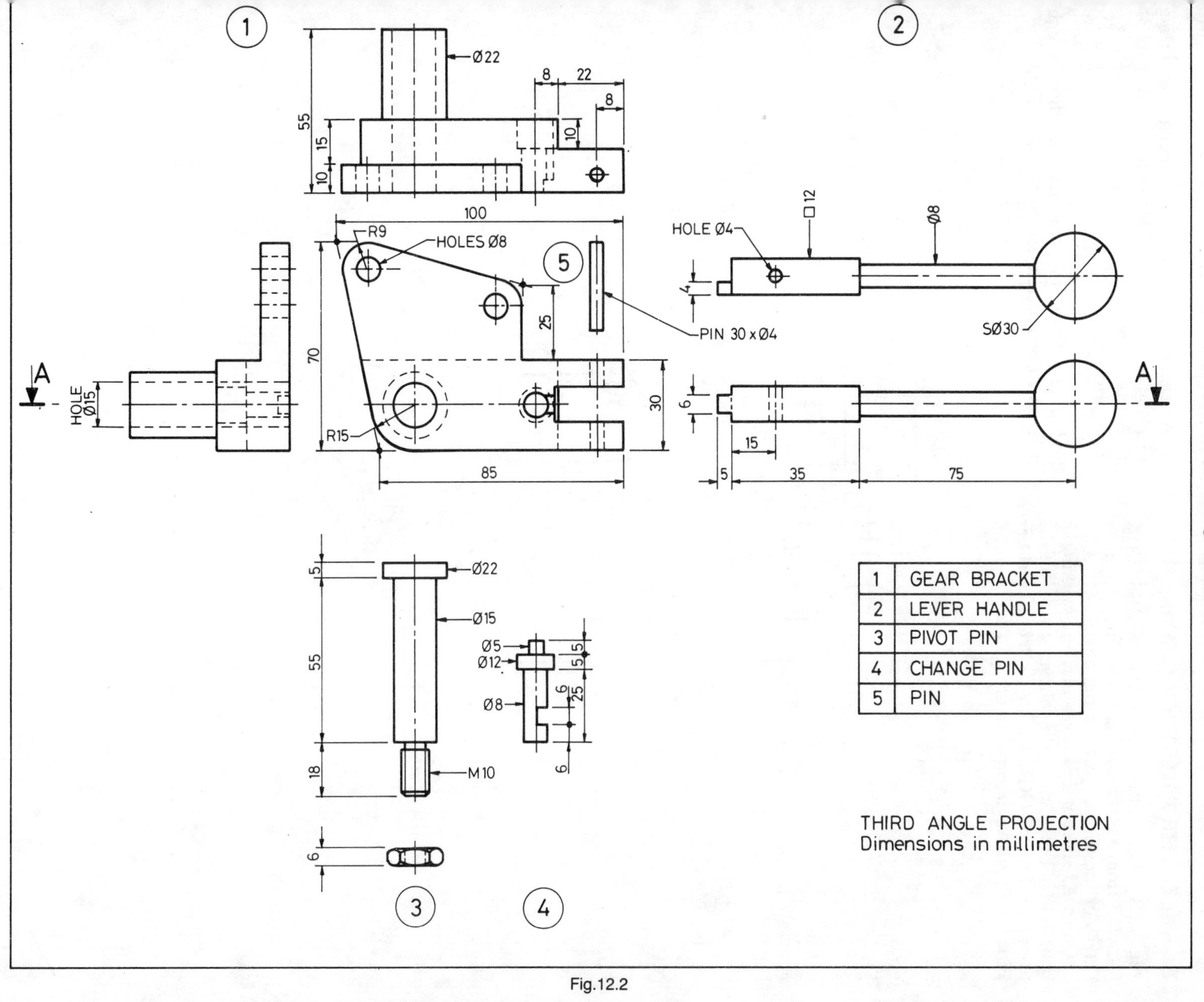
1
2
Ø22
55
15
10
8
22
8
10
100
R9
HOLES Ø8
5
70
25
PIN 30 x Ø4
HOLE Ø4
□ 12
Ø8
4
SØ30
A
A
HOLE Ø15
30
R15
85
6
15
5
35
75
5
Ø22
Ø15
55
Ø5
Ø12
5
5
6
25
Ø8
18
M10
6
6
3
4
1 GEAR BRACKET
2 LEVER HANDLE
3 PIVOT PIN
4 CHANGE PIN
5 PIN
THIRD ANGLE PROJECTION
Dimensions in millimetres

Fig.12.2

Exercise LATHE TAILSTOCK CLAMP

Fig. 12.3 shows the assembled TAILSTOCK CLAMP from a screw-cutting lathe. Fig. 12.4 gives details of the various parts of the device.

On an A3 sheet of drawing paper, and working to scale 1:1 (full size), draw the following views of the *assembled* TAILSTOCK CLAMP. Work in either First or Third Angle projection.

(1) A sectional end view taken along the cutting plane and in the direction indicated on Part 3.
(2) A front view.
(3) A plan.

Add a title block to your drawing sheet which includes all details relevant to the assembly.

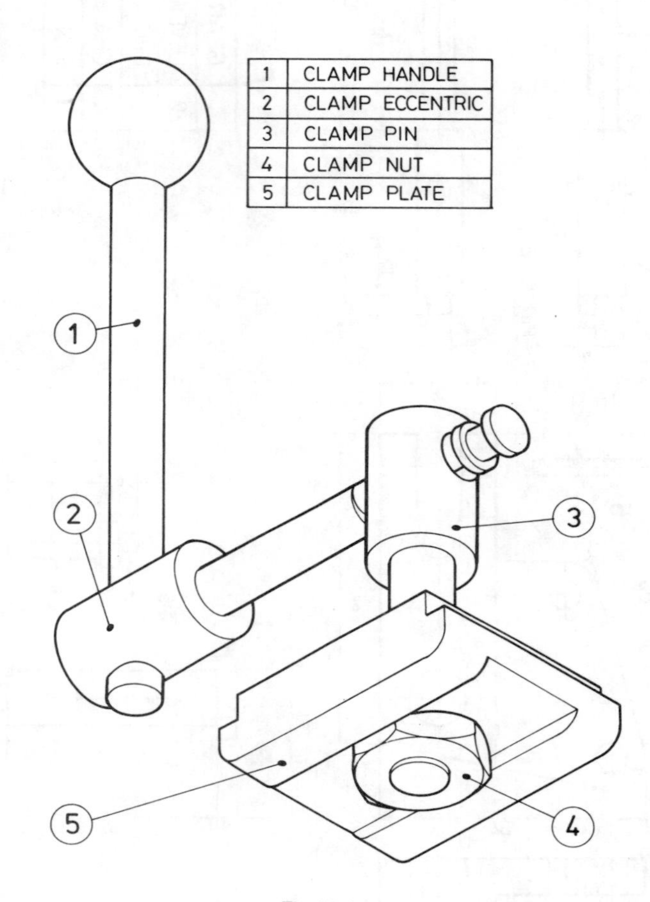

Fig.12.3

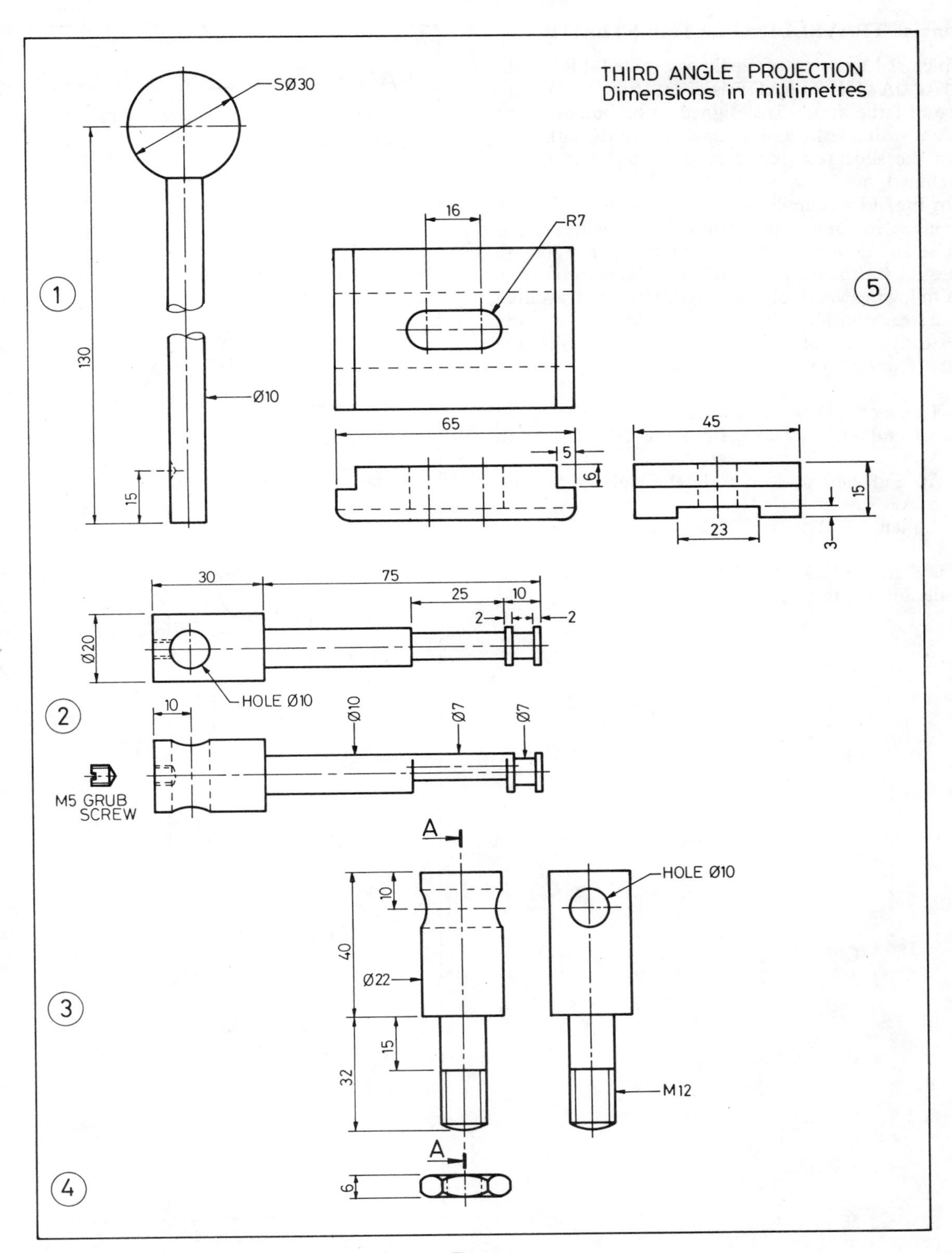
THIRD ANGLE PROJECTION
Dimensions in millimetres
SØ30
130
Ø10
15
16
R7
65
5
6
45
15
23
3
30
75
25
10
2
2
Ø20
HOLE Ø10
10
Ø10
Ø7
Ø7
M5 GRUB SCREW
A
10
40
Ø22
15
32
HOLE Ø10
M12
A
6
1
2
3
4
5

Fig.12.4

Exercise TRAVELLING LATHE STEADY

A pictorial drawing of partly assembled TRAVELLING LATHE STEADY is given (Fig. 12.5). This type of lathe steady is designed to be bolted to the slide rest of a lathe and so travel along the lathe bed with the slide rest as the material being turned is machined.

In Fig. 12.6, details of the parts of the STEADY are given in First Angle projection drawings.

Use an A3 size sheet of drawing paper. Work to scale 1:1 (full size). Draw in Third Angle projection the following views of the ASSEMBLED travelling lathe steady with the Parts 6 in a position as if ready to steady work of 15 mm diameter and with the bolts (Parts 5) set fully into their holes:

(1) The sectional front view A–A.
(2) An end view as seen from the left of Section A–A.
(3) An end view as seen from the right of Section A–A.
(4) A plan.

Add a title block plus all relevant instructional details for assembling the parts.

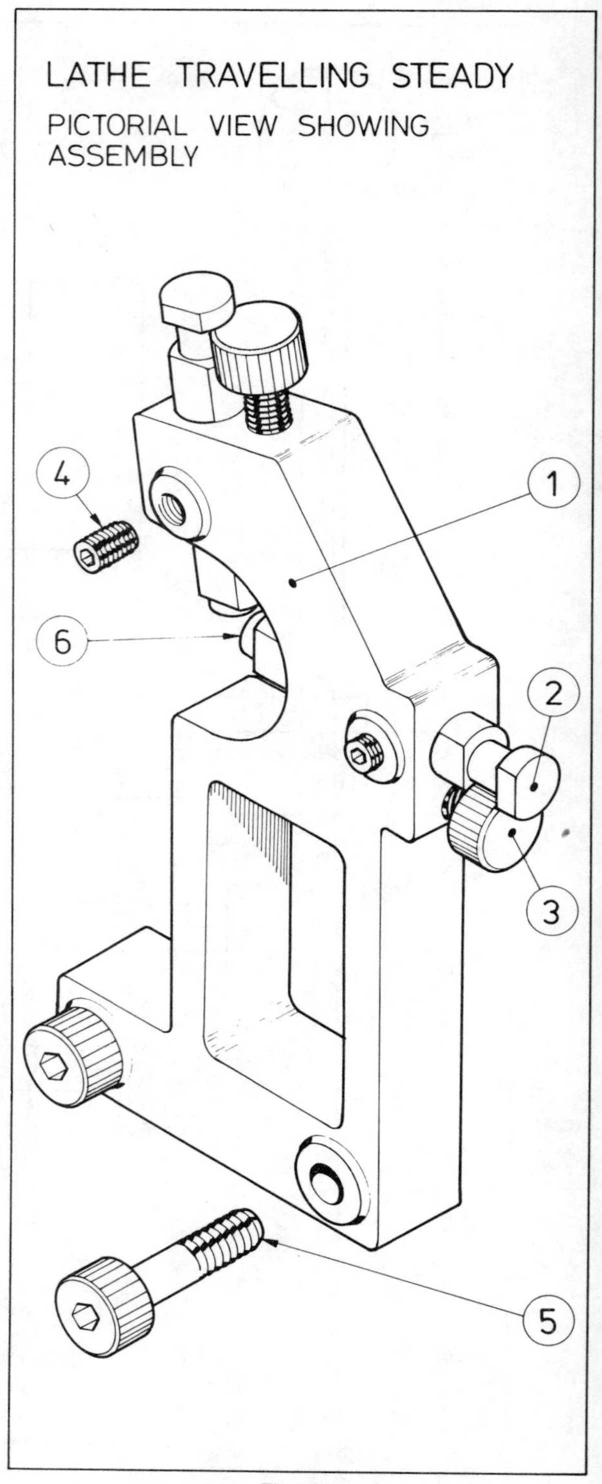

Fig.12.5

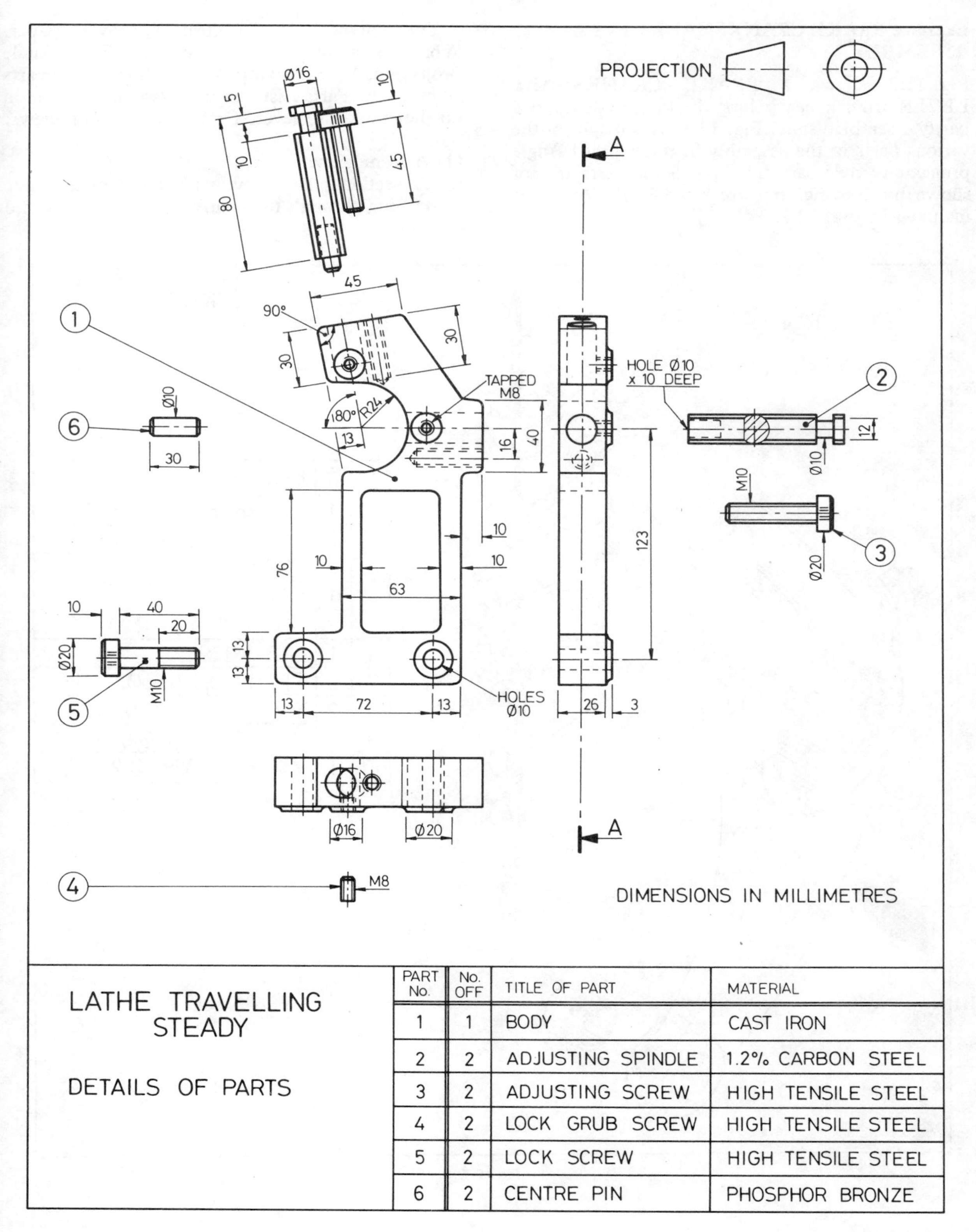

PART No.	No. OFF	TITLE OF PART	MATERIAL
1	1	BODY	CAST IRON
2	2	ADJUSTING SPINDLE	1.2% CARBON STEEL
3	2	ADJUSTING SCREW	HIGH TENSILE STEEL
4	2	LOCK GRUB SCREW	HIGH TENSILE STEEL
5	2	LOCK SCREW	HIGH TENSILE STEEL
6	2	CENTRE PIN	PHOSPHOR BRONZE

Fig.12.6

Exercise BRAKE CRANKSHAFT LEVER ASSEMBLY

Fig. 12.7 shows a BRAKE CRANKSHAFT LEVER from a heavy lorry braking system, in a partly assembled state. Fig. 12.8 gives details of the various parts of the assembly in three Third Angle projection single-part drawings. Some parts are not shown by drawings but are listed in the parts list included in Fig. 12.7.

You will need an A3 sheet of drawing paper. Work to a scale of 1:2 and in First Angle projection. Your drawings should show all the parts given in the Parts List in a fully assembled position on the crankshaft lever. Draw the following views:

(1) A front view.
(2) A sectional end view with the section plane cutting through the centre of the two fork end

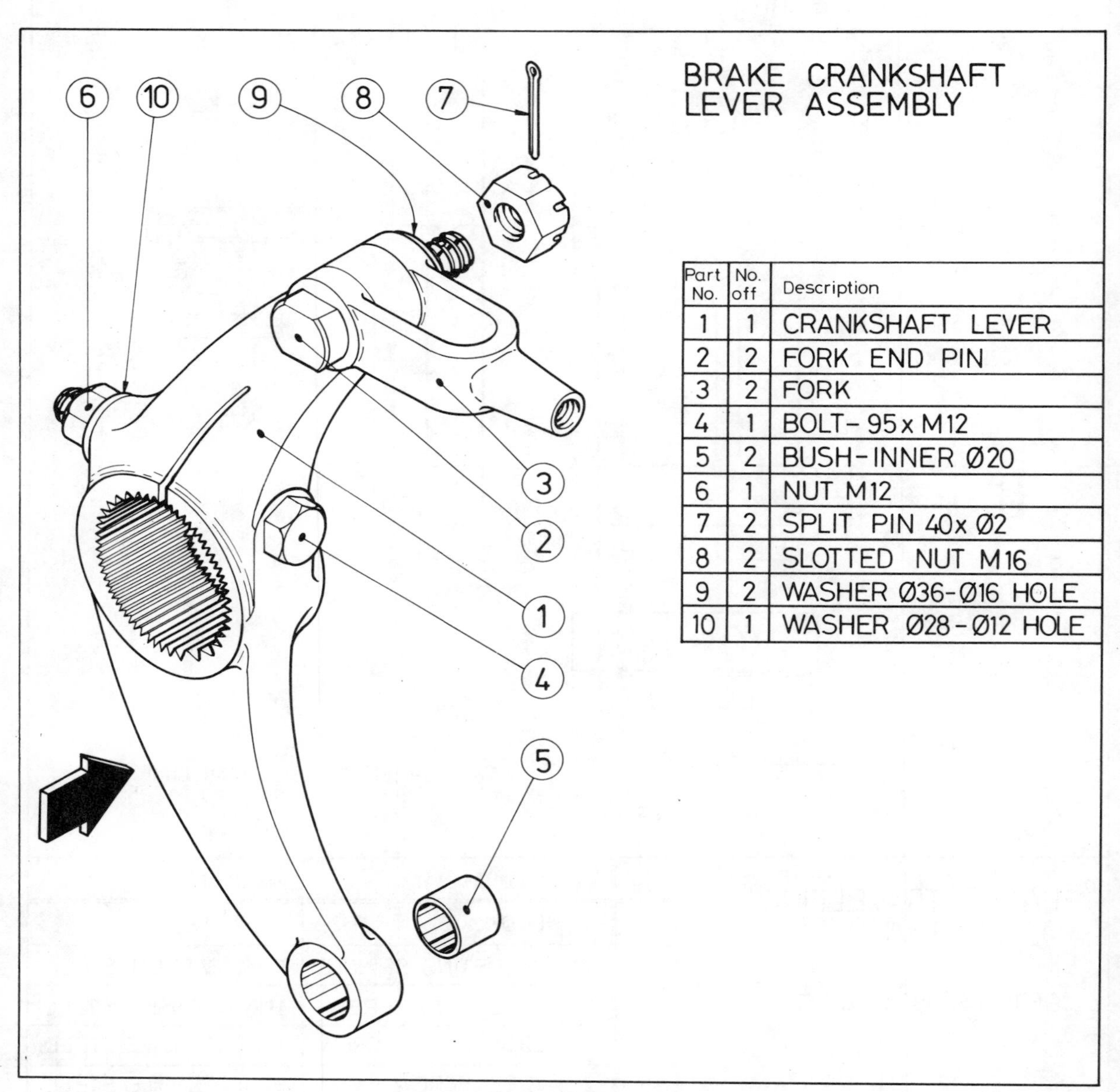

Part No.	No. off	Description
1	1	CRANKSHAFT LEVER
2	2	FORK END PIN
3	2	FORK
4	1	BOLT- 95 x M12
5	2	BUSH-INNER Ø20
6	1	NUT M12
7	2	SPLIT PIN 40x Ø2
8	2	SLOTTED NUT M16
9	2	WASHER Ø36-Ø16 HOLE
10	1	WASHER Ø28 - Ø12 HOLE

Fig.12.7

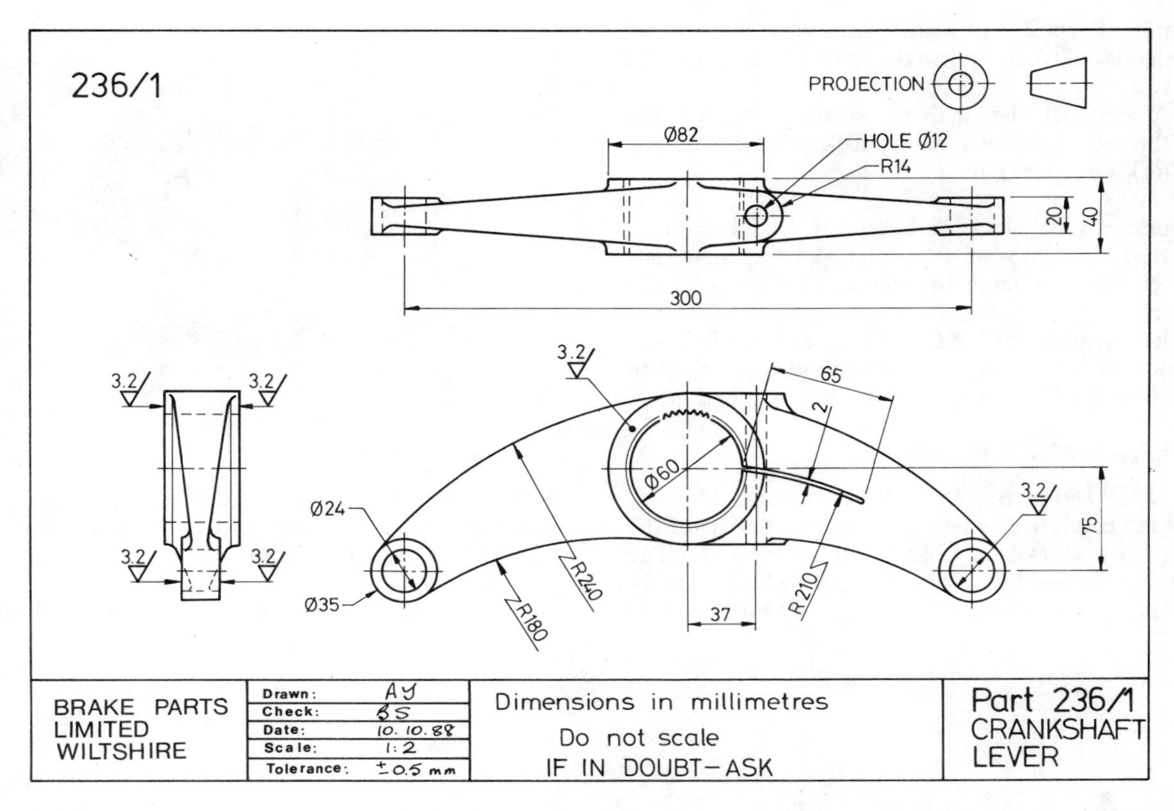
236/1
PROJECTION
Ø82
HOLE Ø12
R14
20
40
300
3.2
65
2
Ø60
Ø24
Ø35
R240
R180
R210
37
75
BRAKE PARTS LIMITED WILTSHIRE
Drawn: AY
Check: BS
Date: 10.10.88
Scale: 1:2
Tolerance: ±0.5 mm
Dimensions in millimetres
Do not scale
IF IN DOUBT-ASK
Part 236/1
CRANKSHAFT LEVER

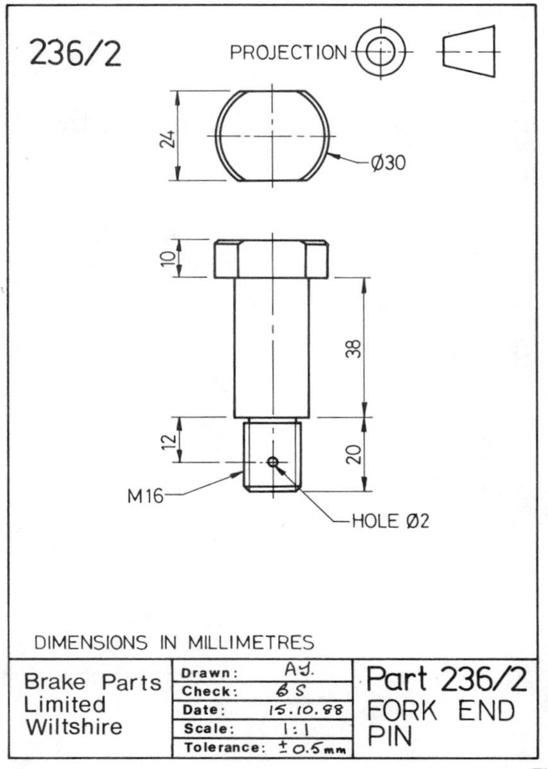
236/2
PROJECTION
24
Ø30
10
38
12
20
M16
HOLE Ø2
DIMENSIONS IN MILLIMETRES
Brake Parts Limited Wiltshire
Drawn: AY.
Check: BS
Date: 15.10.88
Scale: 1:1
Tolerance: ±0.5mm
Part 236/2
FORK END PIN

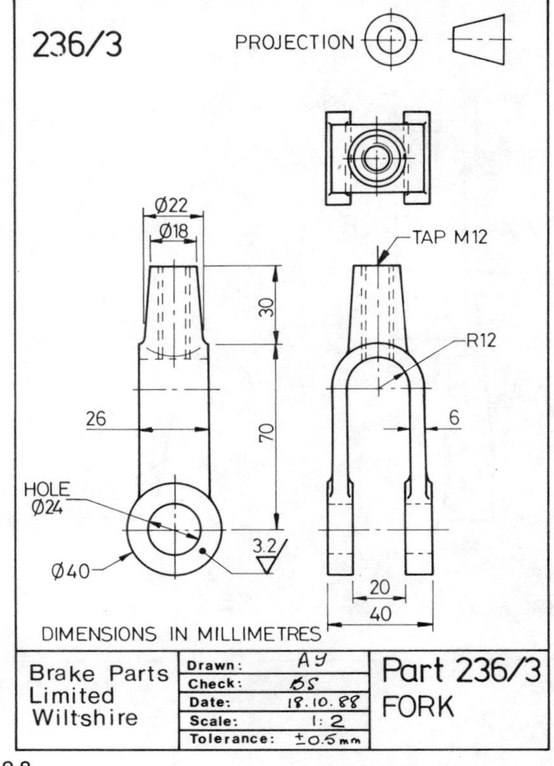
236/3
PROJECTION
Ø22
Ø18
TAP M12
30
R12
26
70
6
HOLE Ø24
Ø40
3.2
20
40
DIMENSIONS IN MILLIMETRES
Brake Parts Limited Wiltshire
Drawn: AY
Check: BS
Date: 18.10.88
Scale: 1:2
Tolerance: ±0.5mm
Part 236/3
FORK

Fig.12.8

pins (Parts 2) and looking in a direction so that details of the crankshaft lever (Part 1) can be seen.
(3) A sectional plan with the section plane cutting through the centre of the fork (Part 3) and the fork end pin (Part 2).

Include a title block and a parts list. Include a materials list in your parts list showing materials you consider suitable for the various parts of the assembly.

The serrations of the 60 mm diameter hole in the crankshaft lever (Part 1) should be dimensioned to give details of how they should be machined.

Exercise WATER PUMP

Fig. 12.9 shows a water pump from a domestic washing machine. Details of the various parts of the pump are shown in Figs 12.10 and 12.11. The pump is driven by a friction wheel which engages on a patterned rubber ring fitting over Part 5 of the pump. This rubber ring is not included in the detail drawings given on page 125 and should not be included in the drawing produced as an answer to this exercise.

Draw, scale 2:1 (twice full size), a sectional view

Fig.12.9

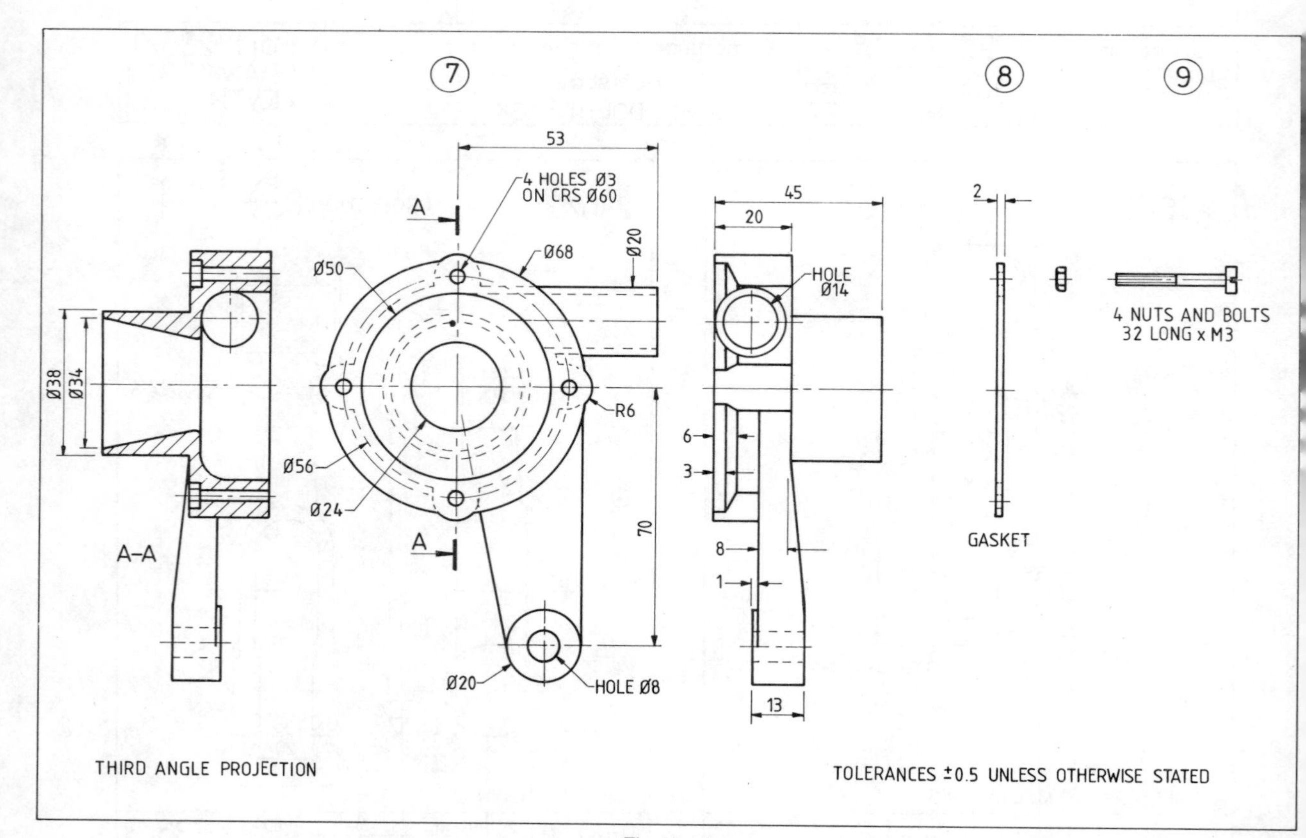

Fig.12.10

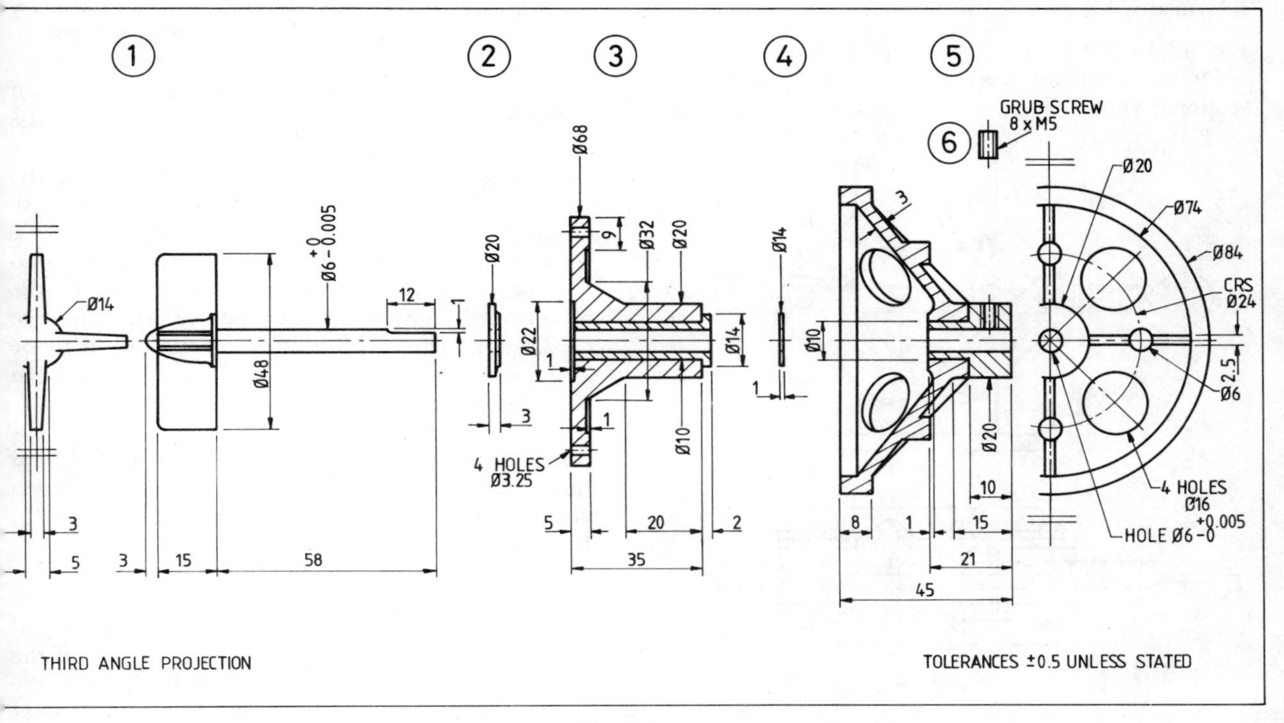

Fig.12.11

taken centrally through the *assembled* water pump.

Note Parts 1, 2, 3, 4 and 5 are assembled together and held by Part 6. This sub-assembly is then held in Part 7, with a gasket between Parts 3 and 7, by four nuts and bolts (Parts 9).

Exercise TURNING ATTACHMENT

Part of a SPHERE TURNING ATTACHMENT is shown (Fig. 12.12) in two views in Third Angle projection. The assembly consists of the following parts:

- Part 1 Tool retaining bolt
- Part 2 Tool post
- Part 3 Tool ring
- Part 4 Tool base
- Part 5 Nut, bolt and washer
- Part 6 Inset.

Make freehand sketches, drawn to a suitable scale, showing each part separately.

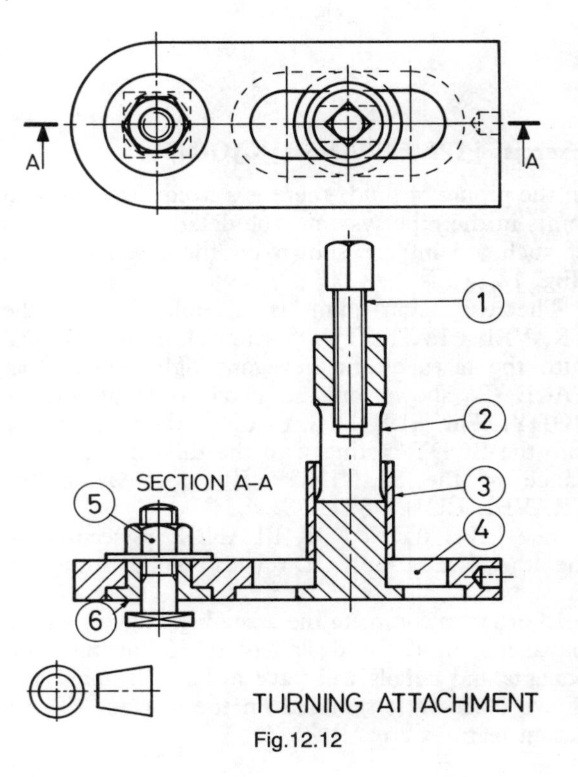

Fig.12.12

Exercise CAR JACK

Fig. 12.13 is a front view and plan of a car jack.

Draw, freehand and to a suitable size, the sectional view S–S.

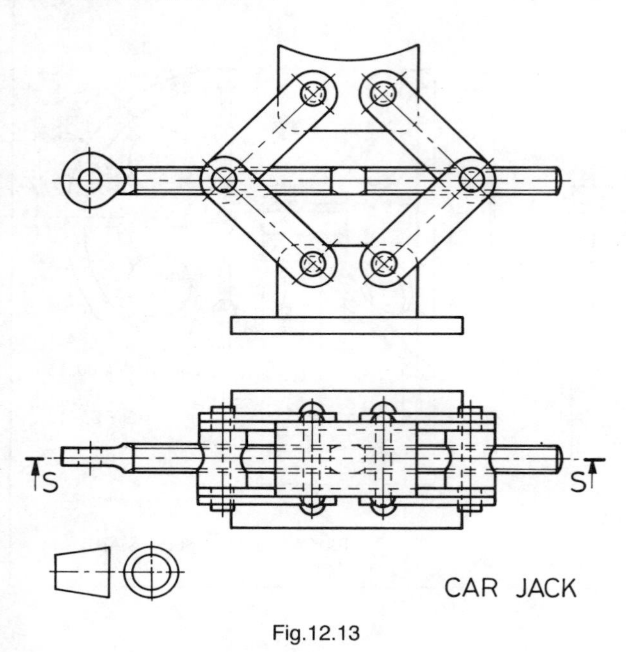

Fig.12.13

Exercise PIPE EXPANSION JOINT

In the piping of fluids there is a need for expansion joints in the pipe system. The detailed components of such a joint are shown on the given drawing (Fig. 12.14).

The expansion joint is assembled with the TRAVEL LIMIT STUDS screwed into the BODY with the faces of the hexagons tightened against FACE 'B' shown on the detail drawing of the BODY. The SLIDING PIPE is then assembled into the BODY casting with the three holes in the flange of the SLIDING PIPE located on the TRAVEL LIMIT STUDS.

The PIPE ADAPTOR FLANGE is secured to the other face of the BODY with bolts or studs and nuts.

In order to complete the assembly drawing of the expansion joint, the design of the following components and details will have to be considered and shown correctly assembled on the drawing. These design features are:

(1) A means of sealing the sliding pipe in the body of the joint so that it can slide in or out to accommodate expansion but prevent leakage. The seal arrangement should be capable of adjustment to take up wear or leakage while the joint is in use.
(2) A method of sealing between the faces of the welded pipe flange and body faces, when these are bolted together.
(3) That the travel limit studs require threaded items which can be adjusted to limit the outward movement of the sliding pipe to 25 mm. These threaded items also need to be locked against vibration once they have been adjusted.

Dimensions not given may be estimated and minor modifications may be made to the given components to accommodate the additional items designed.

Answer the following questions:

(1) Draw FULL SIZE, in either First or Third Angle projection, the following views of the assembled components and indicate, on the drawing, the method of projection used. (**Note** The sliding pipe must be shown in its fully contracted position, with flange face 'A', shown on the sliding pipe drawing and flange face 'B', shown on the body drawing, positioned 75 mm apart.)
   (a) A sectional elevation on the plane X–X, shown on the detail drawing of the sliding pipe.
   (b) An outside plan view projected from view (a) and looking in the direction of arrow 'R', shown on the detail drawing of the sliding pipe.
   (c) An end elevation looking in the direction of the arrow 'S', shown on the detailed drawing of the sliding pipe. The top half is to be shown in section on the plane Y–Y, shown on the same detail drawing.

(Cambridge)

Exercise PNEUMATIC RIVETING GUN

The body shell of a vessel is fabricated using an aluminium section and a wood substitute as a laminate. They are first bonded together and then riveted using the double rivets as shown in Fig. 12.16 and Fig. 12.17.

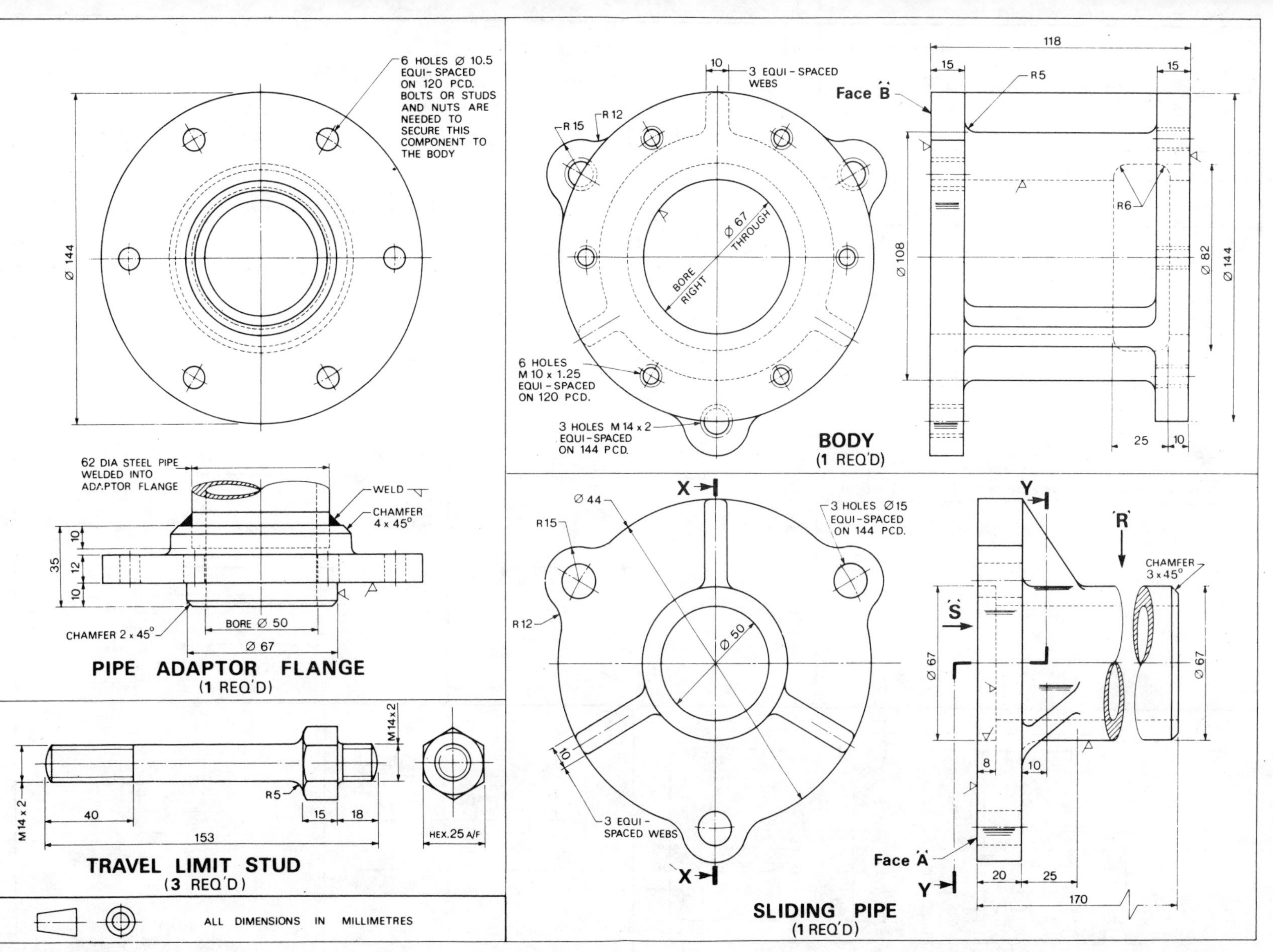
6 HOLES Ø 10.5 EQUI-SPACED ON 120 PCD. BOLTS OR STUDS AND NUTS ARE NEEDED TO SECURE THIS COMPONENT TO THE BODY
Ø 144
62 DIA STEEL PIPE WELDED INTO ADAPTOR FLANGE
WELD
CHAMFER 4 x 45°
CHAMFER 2 x 45°
BORE Ø 50
Ø 67
35
10
12
10
PIPE ADAPTOR FLANGE
(1 REQ'D)
M14 x 2
R5
40
15
18
153
HEX.25 A/F
TRAVEL LIMIT STUD
(3 REQ'D)
ALL DIMENSIONS IN MILLIMETRES
10
3 EQUI-SPACED WEBS
R 15
R 12
Ø 67 THROUGH
BORE RIGHT
6 HOLES M 10 x 1.25 EQUI-SPACED ON 120 PCD.
3 HOLES M 14 x 2 EQUI-SPACED ON 144 PCD.
BODY
(1 REQ'D)
118
15
15
Face 'B'
R5
R6
Ø 108
Ø 82
Ø 144
25
10
X
Ø 44
R15
R12
3 HOLES Ø15 EQUI-SPACED ON 144 PCD.
Ø 50
10
3 EQUI-SPACED WEBS
Y
'R'
CHAMFER 3 x 45°
'S'
Ø 67
Ø 67
8
10
Face 'A'
20
25
170
SLIDING PIPE
(1 REQ'D)

Fig.12.14

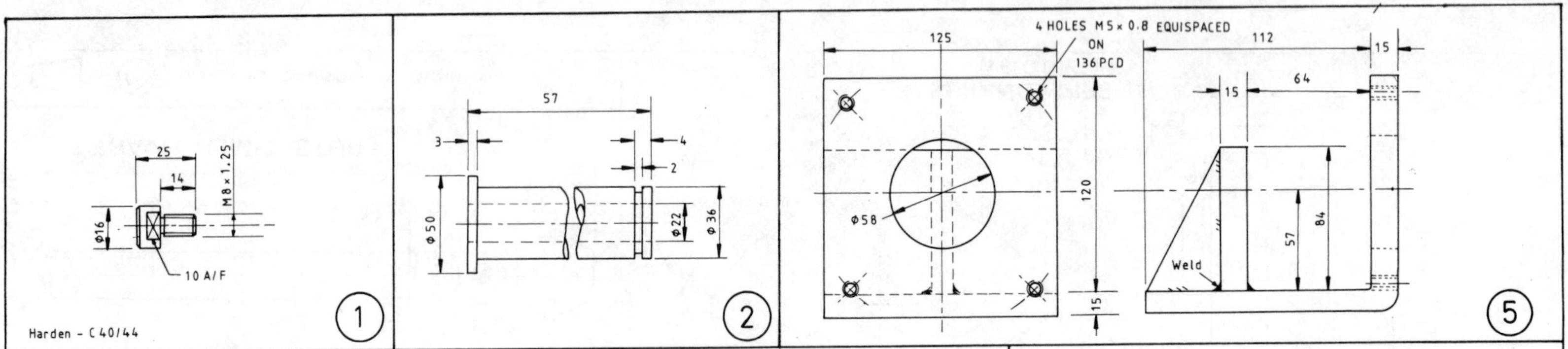

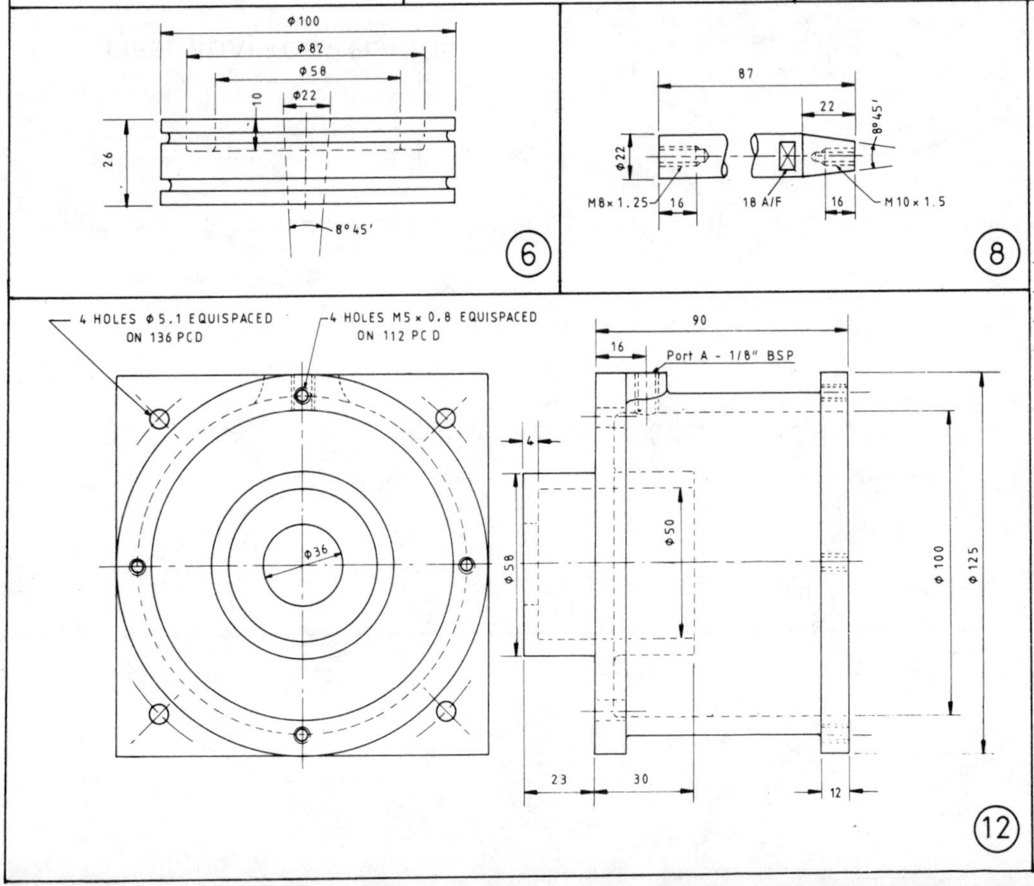

Harden - C40/44

4 HOLES M5 × 0.8 EQUISPACED ON 136 PCD

4 HOLES ϕ5.1 EQUISPACED ON 136 PCD

4 HOLES M5 × 0.8 EQUISPACED ON 112 PCD

Port A - 1/8" BSP

Detail	No.	Mat.	Component	* Not shown
14	8		Bolts M5×0·8×20 long (nuts not required)	*
13	1	Alum D2	Cylinder Cover	*
12	1	Alum D2	Cylinder	
11	1		Compression Spring, 70 mean dia	*
10	1		Washer Ø10	*
9	1		Set Bolt M10×1·5×15 long	*
8	1	EN 8	Piston Rod	
7	2		'O' Rings, for Ø100	*
6	1	Alum D6	Piston	
5	1	EN 8	Anvil	
4	1		Circlip, external for Ø36	*
3	1		Compression Spring, 43 mean dia	*
2	1	EN 8	Outer-Rivet Retaining Bush	
1	1	EN 13	Punch	

PNEUMATIC RIVETING GUN

All dimensions in millimetres.

Fig 12.15

The components shown on the detail drawing are the main parts of a pneumatic riveting gun which has been designed to rivet the two parts of the rivets together when they are in position in the laminate. The components are assembled in the following manner:

The hardened steel punch (1) is screwed into the piston rod (8) and the piston (6) is secured to the other end of the piston rod and fixed in position by the set-bolt (9) and washer (10). The cylinder (12) is bolted to the anvil (5). The outer-rivet retaining bush (2), with its spring (3), is pushed into the hole in the cylinder so that its end with the circlip groove projects outside the cylinder. The circlip (4) when fitted into the groove prevents the bush from being ejected by its spring into the cylinder. The spring (11) is placed over the spigot inside the cylinder and the piston assembly is now fitted into the outer-rivet retaining bush with the piston fitting into the cylinder. The cylinder cover (13) when bolted in position prevents the piston assembly from being ejected by the spring (11).

In operation, the two parts of the rivet are first placed in position in the hole in the laminate by hand (see Fig. 12.16). The anvil, with the assembled cylinder, is then arranged to straddle the laminate and assembled rivet, with the leg of the anvil held against the head of the inner-rivet and with the outer-rivet retaining bush adjacent to the head of the outer-rivet.

When operating the gun, compressed air is fed into the cylinder sequentially by an air sequence valve. This first allows air into port A (in the cylinder), then after a brief period, into a port in the cylinder cover while simultaneously exhausting through port A. Air is then automatically exhausted from both ports. When the air enters port A, the outer-rivet retaining bush is thrust, against the influence of the spring, to ensure that the outer-rivet is fully entered into the hole in the laminate. The reaction ensures that the inner-rivet is held securely against the outer-rivet, thus pinching the two parts of the rivet and the two parts of the laminate together. When air enters the cylinder cover port, the main piston assembly is driven at speed down the cylinder, so that the punch performs the riveting operation on the inner-rivet.

(a) Draw, full size, a sectional elevation of the assembled riveting gun showing the piston and bush in the fully actuated positions, i.e. at the instant when riveting has been achieved.

Note Dimensions which have been omitted should be decided for yourself. Most of the parts marked with an asterisk are standard *bought-out* components and use accepted conventions for showing these wherever possible. The cylinder cover (13), however, has to be designed as part of the requirements of part (b).

(b) The design of the anvil (5), as shown, does not provide for location on the head of the inner-rivet, neither does it allow for wear at this position.

(i) Prepare a modification for this part of the anvil which will provide good location on the head of the rivet and facilitate easy replacement when worn.

(ii) Design and decide the dimensions of the cylinder cover (13).

Note Ideas for these two parts should be explored by the use of freehand sketches, but final decisions for both should be incorporated into your solution to part (a).

(Welsh)

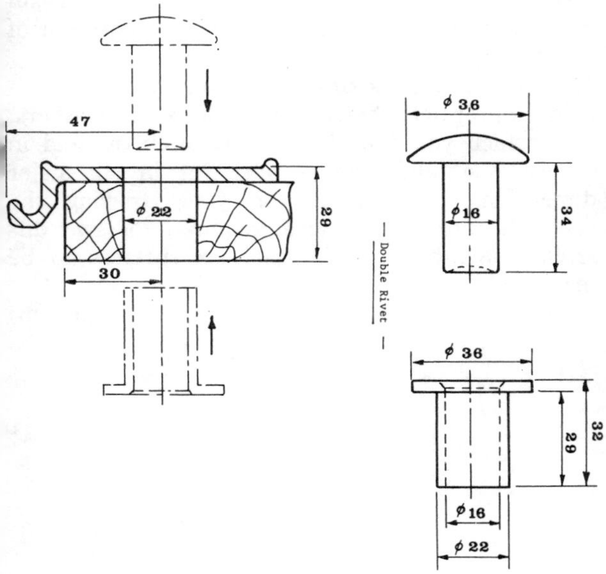

47
ϕ 22
29
30
— Double Rivet —
ϕ 3,6
ϕ 16
34
ϕ 36
29
32
ϕ 16
ϕ 22

Fig.12.16

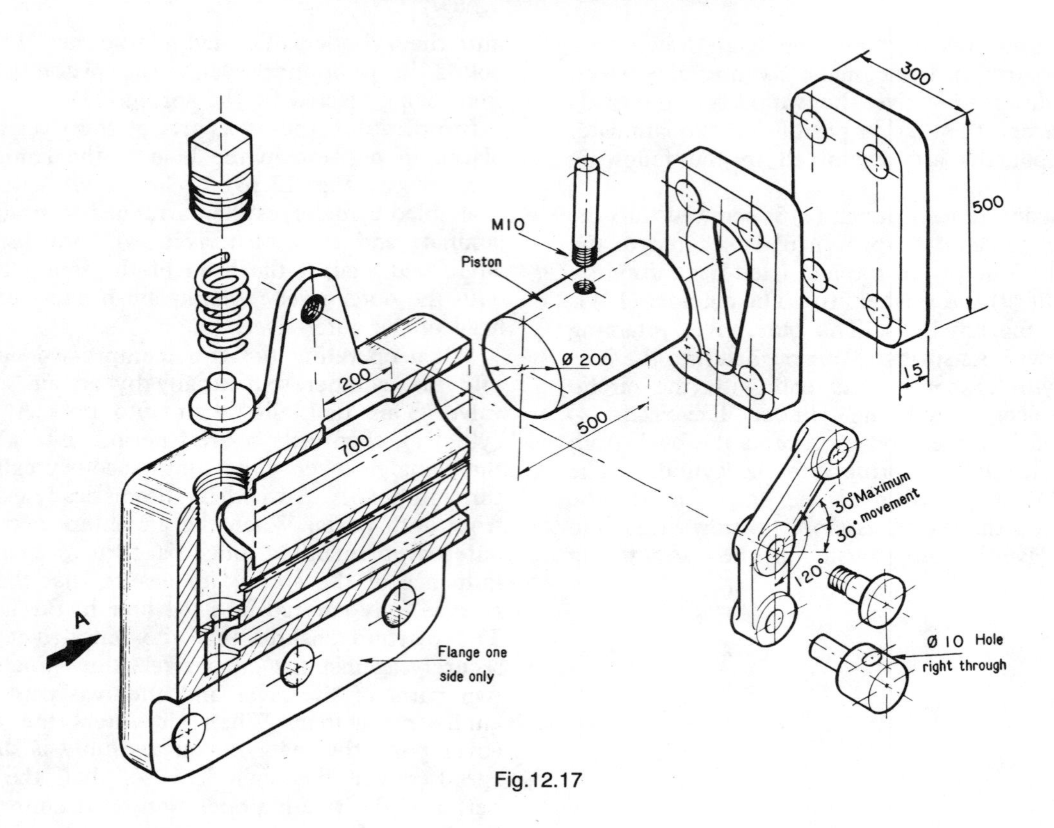

Fig.12.17

Exercise OIL DAMPED SHOCK ABSORBER

The given drawing (Fig. 12.17) shows an exploded, sectioned, isometric sketch of the parts which make up a lever-action, oil-damped shock absorber.

Assuming that the main dimensions are as shown in the sketch, draw the following views of the fully assembled shock absorber in Third Angle projection:

(i) an elevation, with hidden detail, looking in the direction of arrow A,

(ii) a half sectional view looking from the left of (i) showing the top half of the shock absorber sectioned – the sectional plane being along the centreline of the piston,

(iii) a sectioned view looking from below (ii), again the sectional plane being along the centreline of the piston,

(iv) an elevation looking down on (ii).

Add appropriate bolts, studs, gaskets, washers, etc., which you consider to have been omitted in order to simplify the sketch. Put in six major dimensions and indicate on your drawing the probable form of tolerance required for two different moving parts. Indicate six surfaces to be machined.

(London)

Exercise FEED MECHANISM FOR A SHAPING MACHINE

Fig. 12.18 show details of a ratchet feed mechanism for a shaping machine, which is assembled as follows:

The graduated collar, detail 1, is fed onto the ratchet shaft, detail 2, so that face R abuts face S. The graduated collar is held in position on the ratchet shaft by the retaining screw, detail 3, which is screwed into the graduated collar and locates in the 5 mm diameter × 2 mm deep hole in the ratchet shaft. The sleeve, detail 4, is fed on to the ratchet shaft until it abuts the graduated collar.

The compression spring, detail 5, is fed along the 8 mm diameter portion of the ratchet pawl, detail 6, until it makes contact with the 20 mm diameter face. The 8 mm diameter shaft portion of the ratchet pawl together with the compression spring is fed into the 20 mm diameter hole in the ratchet body, detail 7, the compression spring locating in the 16 mm diameter counterbore hole and the 8 mm diameter shaft portion of the ratchet pawl protruding through the 8 mm diameter hole in the ratchet body. The ratchet pawl and compression spring is compressed and then the ratchet knob, detail 8, is fed on to the 8 mm diameter portion of the ratchet pawl. A 3 mm diameter pin (not drawn) locates the ratchet knob on the ratchet pawl, the 8 mm × 5 mm tongue on the ratchet knob seating in the 8 mm × 6 mm slot in the ratchet body.

This sub-assembly is fed on to the ratchet shaft and the 42 mm diameter bore in the ratchet body is fed along the 42 mm diameter of the sleeve until face T abuts face U on the graduated collar.

A spring washer (not drawn) is fed along the 10 mm diameter portion to the bolt head of the drive link bolt, detail 9, the drive link bolt being passed through the 10 mm hole and screwed into the M8 × 1 tapped hole in the ratchet body.

The ratchet wheel, detail 10, is fed along the 24 mm diameter portion of the ratchet shaft, until face V abuts face W on the ratchet body, the driving face on the ratchet pawl locating in one of the 4 mm wide × 2 mm deep grooves in the ratchet wheel.

The shear pin, detail 11, designed to shear if the mechanism is overloaded, is inserted into the 6 mm diameter × 9 mm deep counterbore in the ratchet wheel. The ratchet drive collar, detail 12, is fed on to the 24 mm diameter portion of the ratchet shaft until it abuts the ratchet wheel, the protruding portion of the shear pin locating in the 6 mm diameter hole in the ratchet drive collar. The taper pin, detail 13, locks the ratchet drive collar on the ratchet shaft.

With the ratchet feed mechanism fully assembled and showing the ratchet pawl in a position which will allow the ratchet wheel and ratchet shaft to move anti-clockwise when viewed in the direction of arrow B, draw full size in third angle projection, the following views, omitting hidden detail:

(a) (i) a sectional elevation taken on the cutting plane X–X,
(ii) a complete elevation looking in the direction of arrow B.

(b) Add to the drawing:
a standard machining symbol, on surface R, indicating a surface texture of 6.3; the title; standard projection symbol required for the drawing and the recommended method of indicating the scale used.

(AEB 1984)

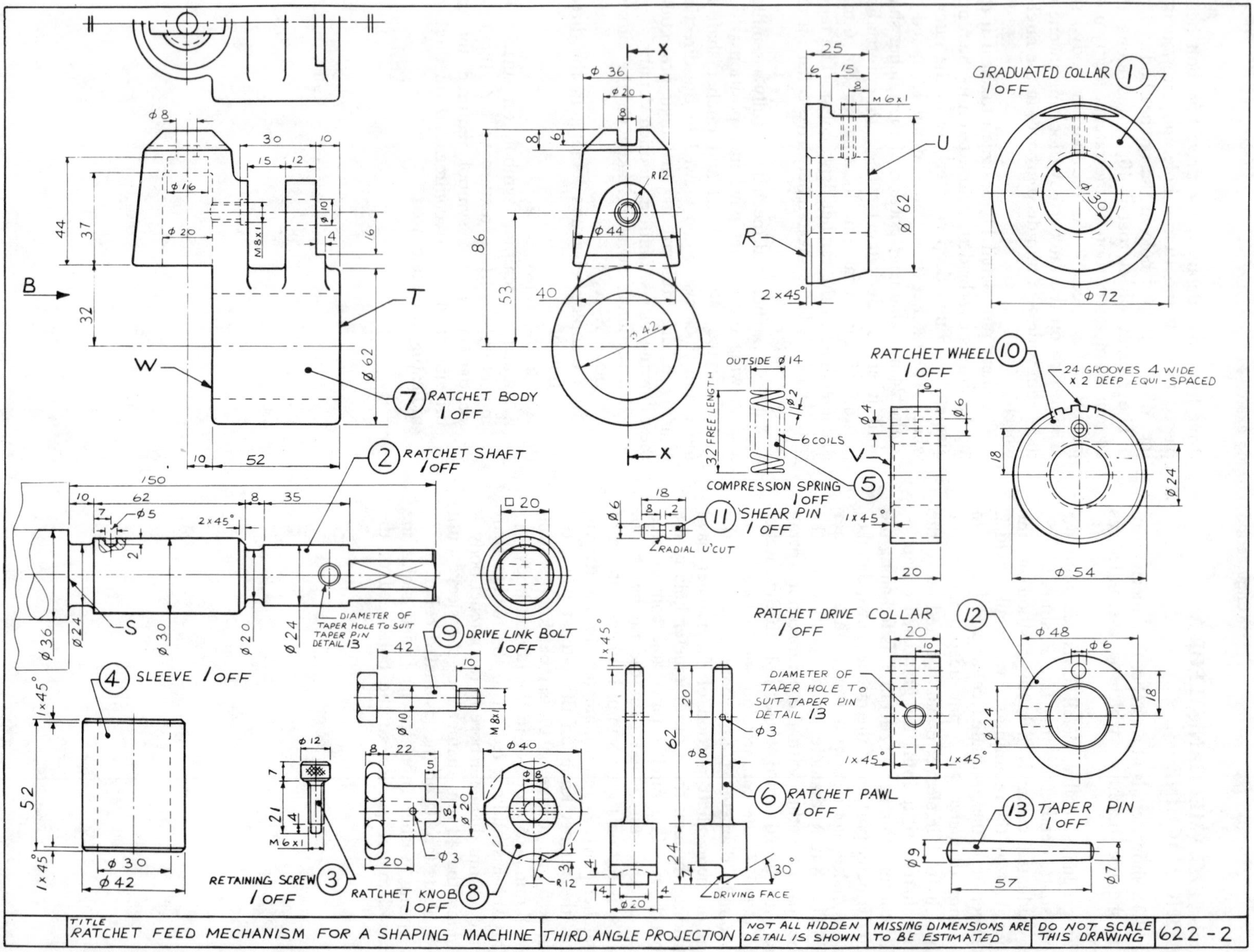
GRADUATED COLLAR 1 1 OFF
RATCHET SHAFT 2 1 OFF
RETAINING SCREW 3 1 OFF
SLEEVE 4 1 OFF
COMPRESSION SPRING 5 1 OFF
RATCHET PAWL 6 1 OFF
RATCHET BODY 7 1 OFF
RATCHET KNOB 8 1 OFF
DRIVE LINK BOLT 9 1 OFF
RATCHET WHEEL 10 1 OFF
SHEAR PIN 11 1 OFF
RATCHET DRIVE COLLAR 12 1 OFF
TAPER PIN 13 1 OFF
24 GROOVES 4 WIDE x 2 DEEP EQUI-SPACED
DIAMETER OF TAPER HOLE TO SUIT TAPER PIN DETAIL 13
OUTSIDE Φ14
32 FREE LENGTH
6 COILS
RADIAL 'U' CUT
DRIVING FACE
TITLE RATCHET FEED MECHANISM FOR A SHAPING MACHINE
THIRD ANGLE PROJECTION
NOT ALL HIDDEN DETAIL IS SHOWN
MISSING DIMENSIONS ARE TO BE ESTIMATED
DO NOT SCALE THIS DRAWING
622 - 2

Fig.12.18

13 Graphs and charts

INTRODUCTION

Data and information expressed in the form of a series of numbers are very difficult to evaluate or to analyse for significant trends or for overall properties. If the data can be translated into a suitable graphical form (into a *graph*) the general relationships are much easier to understand. With the aid of a graph overall trends of one variable component in a series of data as compared with others can be clearly seen. Graphs, however, are not a good medium for the provision of precise information relating to data. Depending upon the scale adopted, graphs may provide adequate accuracy for many tasks, but if precise quantities are required, these must be obtained from the original data from which the graph was constructed. For this reason, original data should be provided with a graph.

The term *chart* is frequently used as having the same meaning as the word *graph*. However, it is more usual to consider a chart as a means of representing sequential or spatial relationships in symbolic or diagrammatic form. A map is an example of a chart in which terrain and features are represented by special symbols.

TWO-DIMENSIONAL GRAPHS

Linear co-ordinate graphs

Linear co-ordinate graphs are the most common form of graph to represent changes between two variables. They are plotted from points on a grid using two measurements called co-ordinates. The horizontal line represents one variable and is called the x axis (or *abscissa*). The vertical line represents the other variable and is called the y axis (or *ordinate*). Fig. 13.1 shows a typical graph of this type. This graph represents the output powers for three hydraulic pumps in terms of changing pressures. Each of the three curves is distinguished from the others by means of distinct symbols, e.g. a

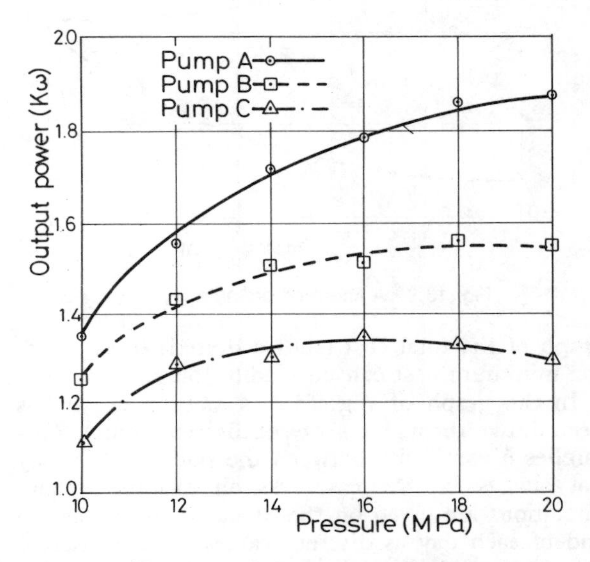

Fig. 13.1 A linear co-ordinate graph

circle, square or cross and by different types of lines, e.g. full, dotted and dashed. Note that the tests carried out as indicated by the graphs are at discrete pressures as represented by the symbols, the points are joined by smooth curves. These curves imply that it should be possible to find the pressure and power relationship at points other than those tested from the graph, by estimation (or *interpolation*). As is shown by Fig. 13.1, it is good practice to terminate the curve either side of the symbol to allow greater accuracy when reading at that point.

It is possible to employ graphs to determine information which may be difficult to determine mathematically. Fig. 13.2 shows the drop in the resale value of a machine tool and the cost of maintenance over a number of years. Because the cost of maintenance rises with the age of the machine, there is a minimum total cost at a particular age. This can be found by summing the ordinate values of the two curves to produce a

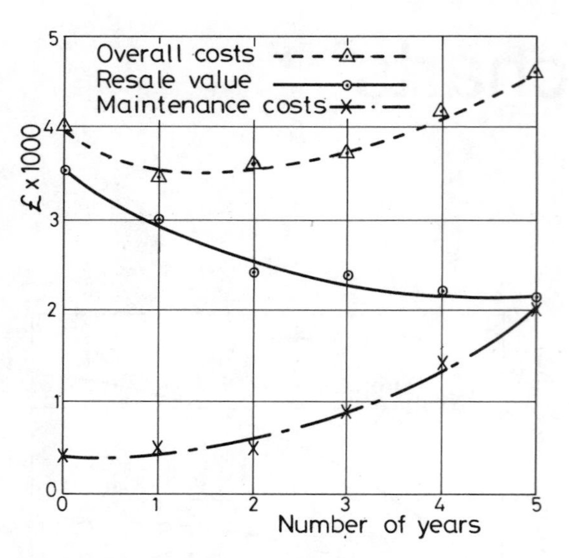

Fig. 13.2 A linear co-ordinate graph

graph of the total cost (shown dotted) from which the minimum cost can be readily found.

In the graph of Fig. 13.2, a smooth curve has been drawn through a series of discrete points. This implies a continuity between the points. This may not always be the case. As an example, share quotations are given on the Stock Exchange at the end of each day as discrete values. These discrete values are usually joined together each day by straight line segments as shown in Fig. 13.3. It would not be appropriate to join the points by a smooth curve, because a smooth curve would imply a continuity in between the daily readings, which in fact is not present. The reason for joining the points with straight lines is to emphasize an overall trend.

The interpretation of graphs must be carried out with care, because the choice of scale, origin and the data used can produce a misleading impression. Fig. 13.4(a) shows a graph prepared by the sales department of a machine tool company giving the results of its sales campaign in a favourable light. The Managing Director, however, had the results plotted on a new range of time and a new scale (Fig. 13.4(b)). The resulting graph displayed a much less impressive sales campaign.

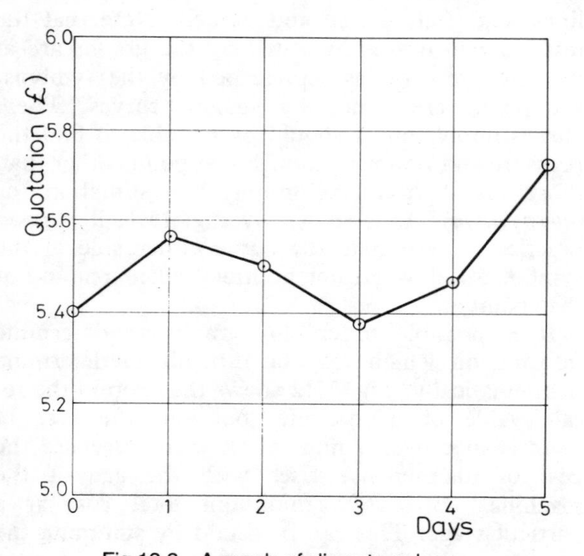

Fig.13.3 A graph of discrete values

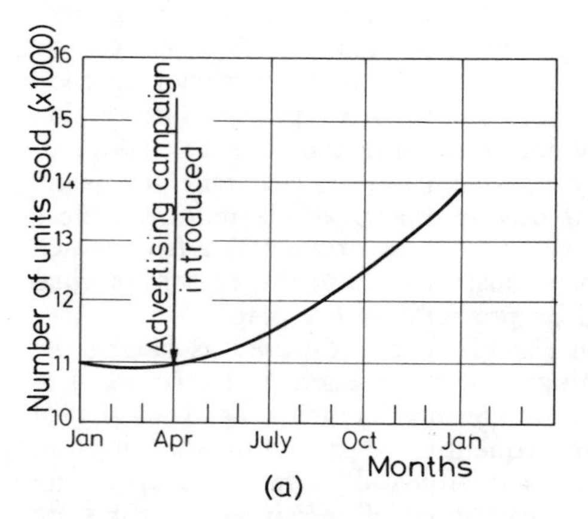

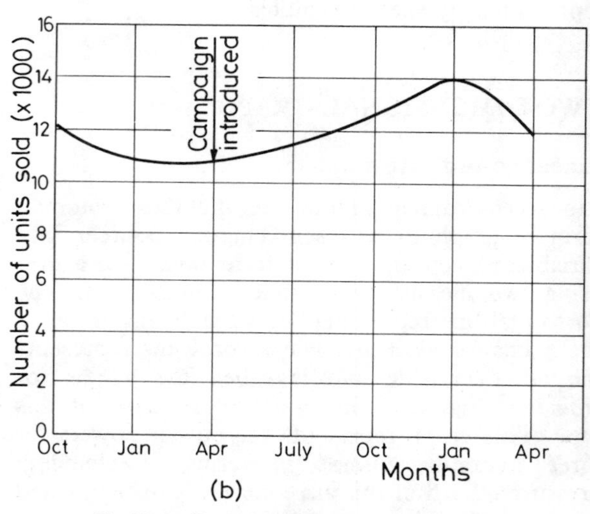

Fig.13.4 Two viewpoints of the same data

Straight line graphs

A point P can be represented by its x and y co-ordinates as $P(x,y)$. Similarly a straight line can be described by two points lying on the graph as $P_1(x_1y_1)$, $P_2(x_2y_2)$. The generalized equation for a straight line is:

$$y = mx + c$$

where m = the tangent of the angle between the line and the horizontal, i.e. the *slope* of the line

and c = the intercept of the line with the y axis at $x = 0$

If an experiment is conducted in which data are produced and plotted as points which lie more or less on a straight line, then the equation of that line can be found from the above slope/intercept formula, as shown by Fig. 13.5. In this example it is necessary to project back from the end of the line to intersect with the y axis to give $c = 10$. The slope is found from:

$$m = \frac{\Delta y}{\Delta x} = \frac{50 - 20}{4 - 1} = 10$$

Therefore the equation for the line is:

$$y = 10x + 10$$

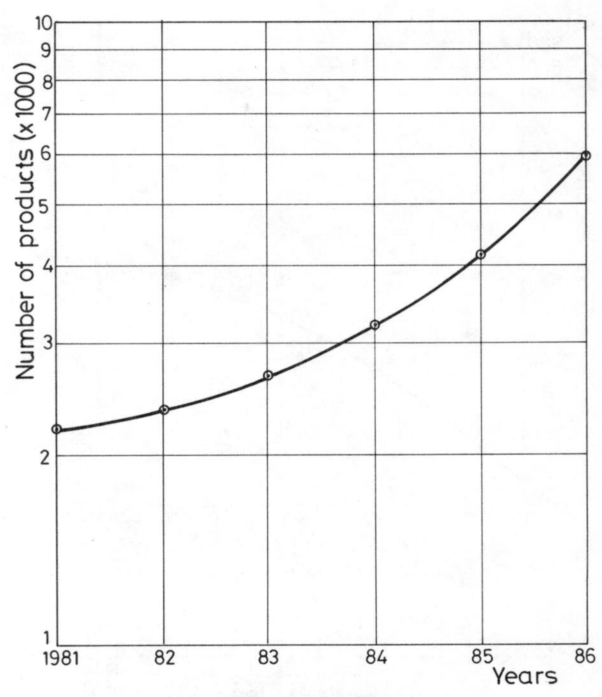

Fig.13.6 Semi-log graph

Non-linear Co-ordinate graphs

In engineering it is not unusual to find that a variable changes in an approximately logarithmic (or *log*) manner with respect to another. In such cases, it is appropriate to use a *semi-log* graph as shown in Fig. 13.6. This shows the growth in sales of a product over a number of years. The y axis, representing the number of products sold, is to a log scale. The x axis, representing the year of sales, is to a linear scale. Semi-log graphs are very good for showing the relative rate of change. When both variables change in an approximately logarithmic way, a *log/log* plot is used, an example being given by Fig. 13.7. This graph shows the variation of wind tunnel velocity against the distance from the wind tunnel wall.

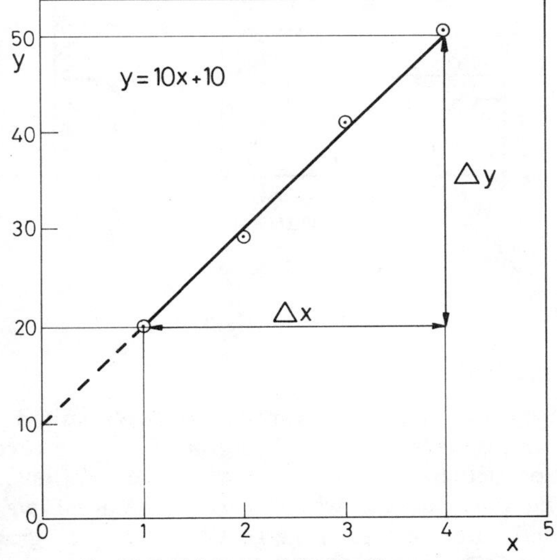

Fig.13.5 Method of finding the equation of a straight line graph

If the variables vary in an exactly logarithmic manner the log/log plot will be a straight line. This is much easier to interpret than the curve resulting from plotting in linear co-ordinates. The equation of a log/log relationship is of the form:

$$y = cx^m$$

This can be expressed by taking logarithms of both sides as:

$$\log y = \log c + m \log x$$

This is the equation for a straight line in which the slope is m and the intercept is $\log c$, provided the axes are plotted as $\log x/\log y$. However, since $\log 1 = 0$, the intercept with the y axis must be taken at $x = 1$.

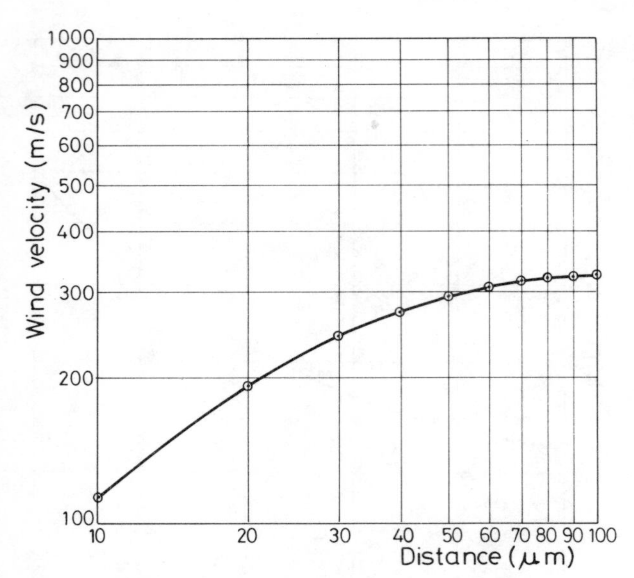

Fig. 13.7 A log/log graph

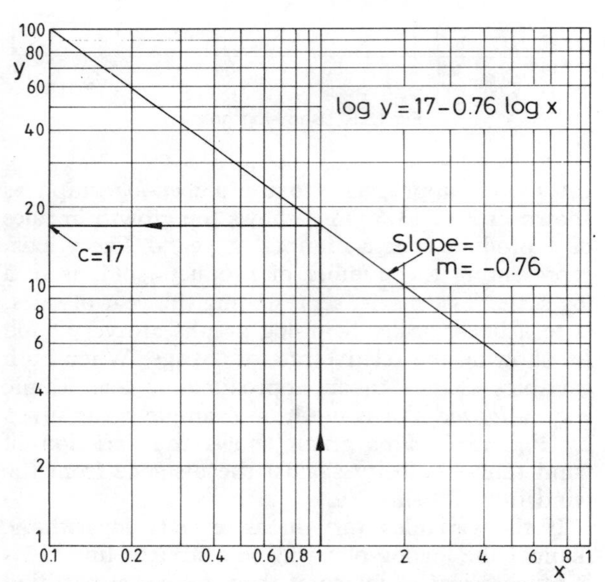

Fig.13.8 Graph of a straight line on a log/log plot

Fig. 13.8 shows a log/log plot. Since the slope of the graph is downwards, the value of m is negative, i.e.

$$m = \frac{\Delta \log y}{\Delta \log x} = \frac{\log 5 - \log 100}{\log 5 - \log 0.1}$$
$$= \frac{0.7 - 2.0}{0.7 - (-1)} = \frac{-1.3}{1.7}$$
$$= -0.76$$

Note Since m is a slope, it may be evaluated by measuring directly from the graph. For this any horizontal or vertical scale of measurement may be taken as long as it is the same, e.g.:

$$m = \frac{-7.6 \text{ cm}}{10 \text{ cm}} = -0.76 \text{ as before}$$

The intercept at $x = 1.0$ is in the middle of the plot. Hence $c = 17$ and the equation of the line is:

$$\log y = 17 - 0.76 \log x$$

Bar graphs

Bar graphs provide an effective method of displaying discrete entities for comparison when there is no sense of continuity between entities. Fig. 13.9 shows a comparison of the production of a factory for three distinct periods. Not only is the total production shown in this bar graph, but also how the product mix varies as a proportion of total production. Showing the values as a percentage of the total often gives a better comparison between adjacent bars than using number values.

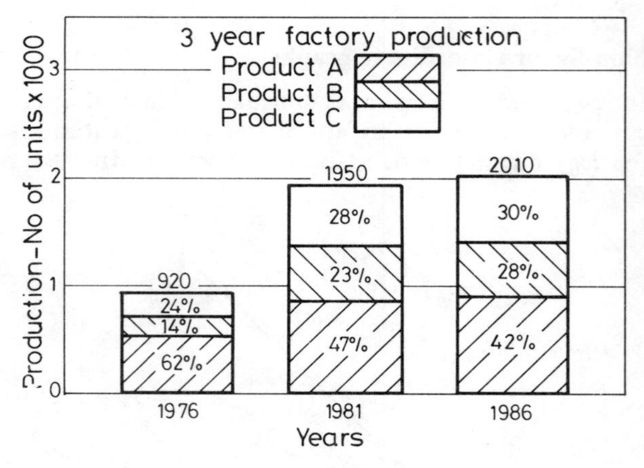

Fig.13.9 A bar graph

Pie graphs

Pie graphs, like bar graphs, are well suited to showing discrete entities. Pie graphs are, however, also particularly good for showing the relationship of the parts to the whole – how the total *pie* is divided into parts. Fig. 13.10 is a pie graph showing the distribution of personnel in a company given the following data:

Personnel	No. of employees	% of total	Angle in degrees
Unskilled	510	48	173°
Skilled	120	12	43°
Research	83	8	29°
Administration	275	27	97°
Other	42	5	18°
Totals	1030	100	360°

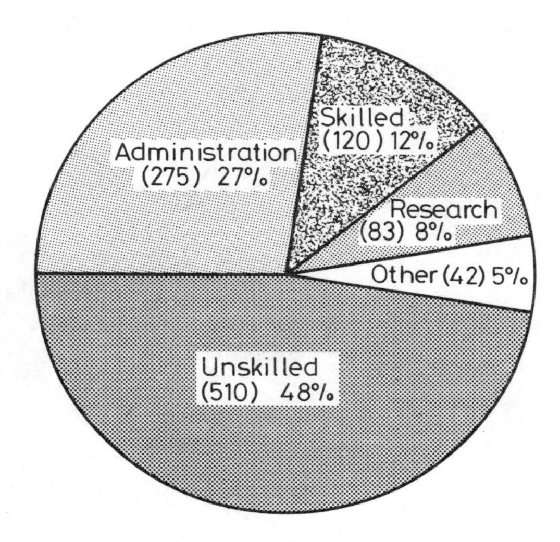

Fig.13.10 A pie graph

The total of 1030 employees is represented by the full circle of 360°. Because it is the relative proportions which are of interest here, it is best to find first the individual percentages of the total and then find these as a proportion of the full circle. Pie graphs give no information graphically about absolute numbers and thus it is advisable to write them on the pie graph, to avoid the loss of valuable information. Note that the pie graph of Fig. 13.10 is set out so that the smaller arc segments are horizontal in order to facilitate lettering. Pie graphs are most effective when the number of variables to be displayed is small. It is possible to use the diameter of the pie to represent, in proportion, the total quantity being displayed. Thus if the data shown in Fig. 13.10 were to be shown for three separate years, to indicate changes in total personnel employed, three separate pie graphs could be drawn, the diameters of which represent in proportion to their diameters, the total number of personnel for each of the three years.

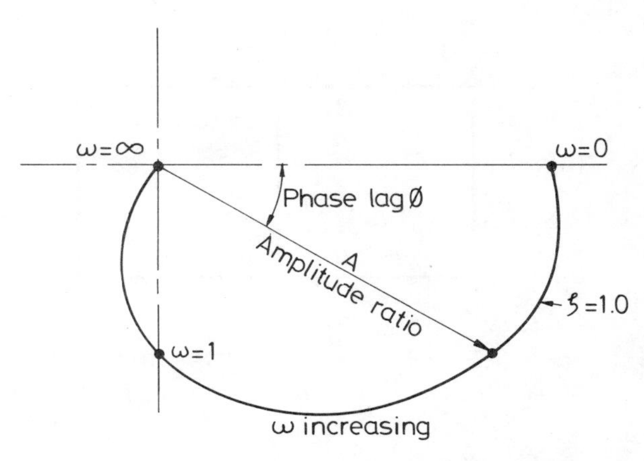

Fig.13.11 Closed loop polar plot of an electric control system

Polar graphs

In contrast to Cartesian axis graphs, polar graphs use polar co-ordinates, whose variables are plotted as a change in radius and angle. Fig. 13.11 shows a plot of the electrical response of the electrical control system illustrated by Fig. 13.12. The relative amplitude of an output displacement x is compared with an input displacement y to form an amplitude ratio A. The magnitude of A is shown as a radial value on the polar plot. The value of A is a *modulus*, i.e. an absolute magnitude independent of sign, written as $/A/$. If the input signal varies in a sinusoidal manner, the difference in phase between sinusoid input signal (x) and the resultant sinusoid output signal (y), is shown as an angle (ϕ). The values of the disturbing frequency (ω) of the input signal are also plotted along the response curve for each modulus of amplitude ratio $/A/$ and phase angle ϕ. This type of polar plot is commonly used in electrical control systems and is called a closed loop polar plot.

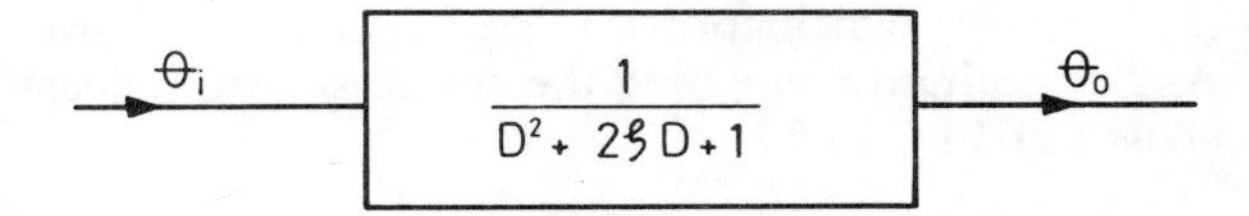

Fig.13.12 Electrical control system figured in Fig.13.11

REPRESENTATION OF A 2-D PLANE

In the same way as a line may be represented by its end points, a plane may be represented by its boundary lines. Thus the object shown in

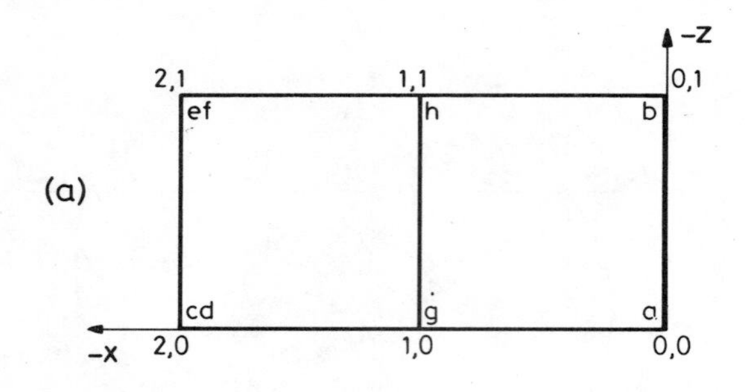

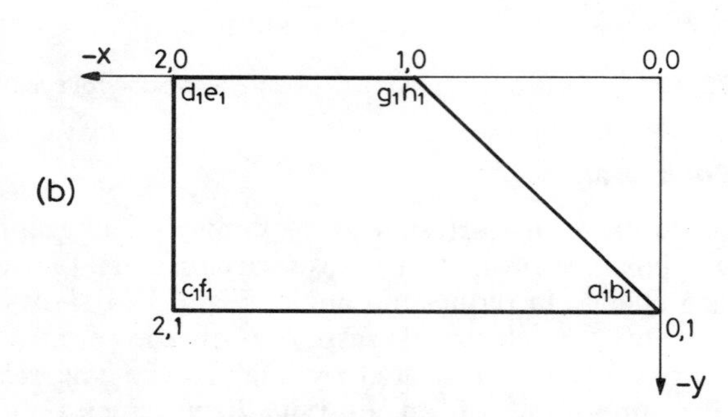

Fig.13.13 Front view and plan of an object represented as a graph

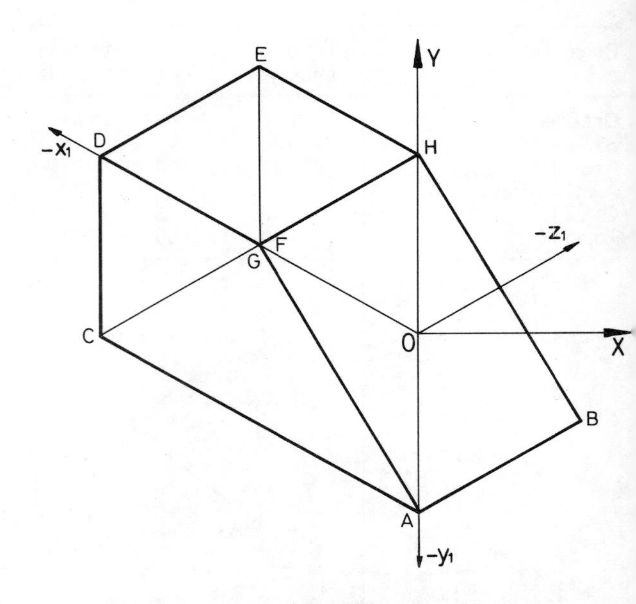

Fig.13.14 Third Angle quadrant containing object shown in Fig.13.13

Fig. 13.13(b) can be represented by its graphical co-ordinates. The front view, in Third Angle projection, can be thought of as a graph in the $-x$, $-y$ plane. Similarly the plan view shown in Fig. 13.13(a) can be thought of as another graph in the $-x$, $-z$ plane. This leads to the concept of a series of 2-D graphs which can be inter-related to form a 3-D object. This is the basis of much of the calculation used in computer graphics to represent objects. The plan and front views of Fig. 13.13 are related together as a pair of planes $(0, -x, -z)$ and $(0, -x, -y)$ which form the concept of the Third Angle quadrant containing the wedge shaped object shown in Fig. 13.14.

THREE-DIMENSIONAL GRAPHS

The two 2-D graphs shown in Fig. 13.13 can be thought of as *mapped* on to an isometric view as in Fig. 13.14. The axes of the object $(-x_1, -y_1, -z_1)$ are here mapped on to the OXY plane which can be thought of as representing the axes of a graph for a plotter or graphics display screen.

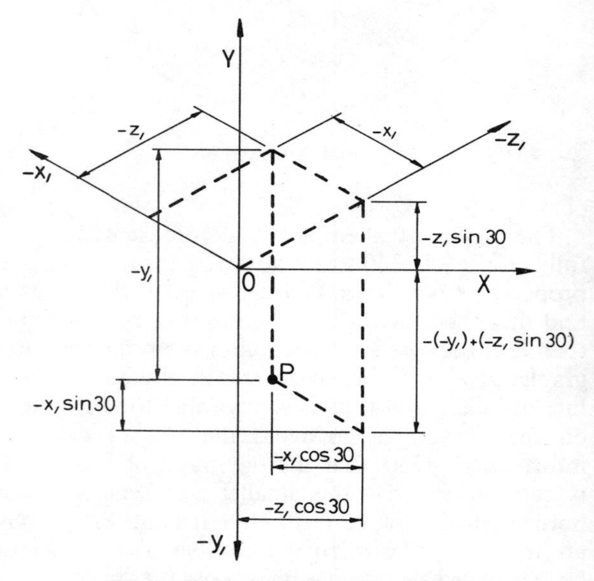

Fig.13.15 Co-ordinates of a point P transformed into the isometric plant

Fig. 13.15 shows the co-ordinates of a point P transformed into the isometric plane OXY. From Fig. 13.15 these isometric co-ordinates can be related to co-ordinates on the block by the equations

Corner point	x_1	y_1	z_1	$x_1 - z_1$	$-(x_1 + z_1)$	$-0.5(x_1 + z_1)$	X $0.866(x_1 - z_1)$	Y $y_1 - 0.5(x_1 + z_1)$
A	0	−1	0	0	0	0	0	−1
B	0	−1	−1	1	1	0.5	0.866	−0.5
C	−2	−1	0	−2	2	1	−1.732	0
D	−2	0	0	−2	2	1	−1.732	1
E	−2	0	−1	−1	3	1.5	−0.866	1.5
F	−2	−1	−1	−1	3	1.5	−0.866	0.5
G	−1	0	0	−1	1	0.5	−0.866	0.5
H	−1	0	−1	0	2	1	0	1

$$\begin{aligned} Px &= -z_1 \cos 30° - (-x_1 \cos 30°) \\ &= 0.866(x_1 - z_1) \\ \text{and } Py &= -(-y_1) + (-z_1 \sin 30°) + (-x_1 \sin 30°) \\ &= -0.5(x_1 + z_1) + y_1 \end{aligned}$$

If these two equations are used to find the transformed equations of all points on the block whose plan and front views are given in Fig. 13.13, then the isometric view of the block can be constructed. It is best in this instance to use a table for calculating the co-ordinates.

When these X and Y values are set off as calculated, the result is the wedge shaped block shown in Fig. 13.14. It is possible to adjust the origin of the xy plane by appropriate adjustments of the co-ordinates, e.g. the origin of the 0x and 0y could have been plotted at A by adding 1 to the Y values. If necessary all the co-ordinate values could be multipled by the isometric scale of 0.816 to produce a correctly scaled isometric drawing.

The above process of transforming the $x_1y_1z_1$ co-ordinates mathematically into XY graph co-ordinates seems complex compared to the normal graphical methods given in Chapter 6 which are more intuitive. The reason for including the mathematical explanation for the construction of the isometric view is that these calculations are required by a computer to generate the co-ordinates for points to be displayed on a graphics screen.

3-D line co-ordinate graphs

A 3-D line co-ordinate graph allows the representation of three inter-related variables together in one view. Fig. 13.16 shows the growth of a factory in terms of a number of employees, size of site and number of years. Because of the nature of the plot the number of years is represented along the $-z$ axis. This 3-D graph could be represented by a pair of separate 2-D graphs showing, e.g. site area (as ordinate)/year (abscissa) and employees (ordinate)/

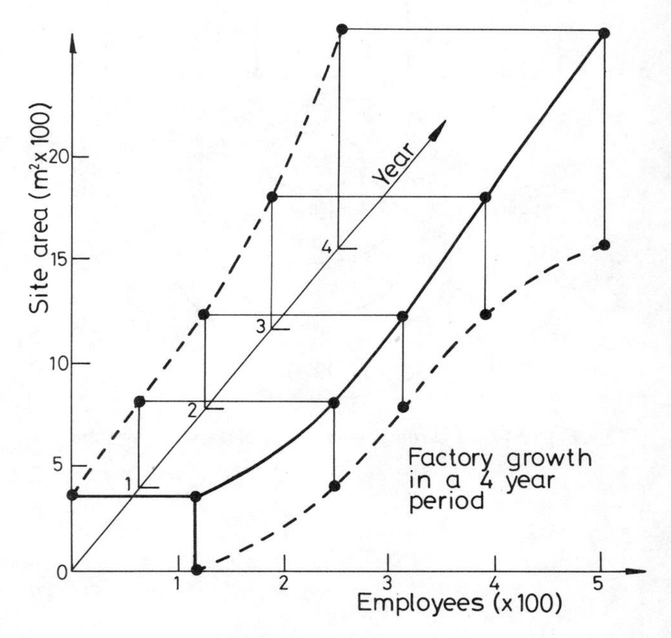

Fig.13.16 A 3-D graph

year (abscissa). These two 2-D graphs would allow intermediate values to be interpolated more accurately than when using the 3-D graph. However, the pictorial impact of the inter-related variables would be diminished. The relationship between a greater number than three variables can be expressed by using a series of 2-D and 3-D graphs to inter-relate them.

3-D bar and pie graphs

These are frequently drawn for visual impact, as shown by Fig. 13.17(a) and (b). While the third variable dimension could, in theory, be used to represent a third variable, in practice this is unusual.

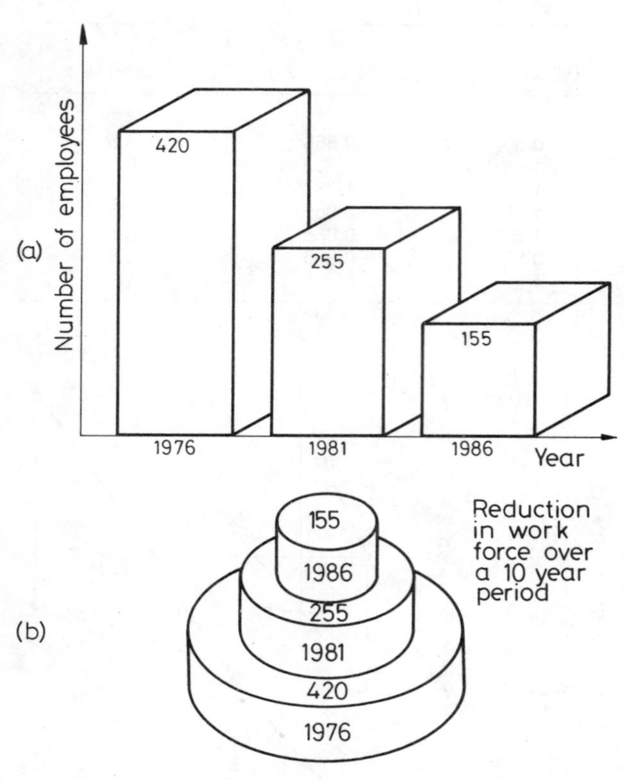

Fig.13.17 3-D representation of bar and pie graphs

CHARTS

Organization charts

The organization of a group of people within a company can be represented in a chart as shown in Fig. 13.18, which depicts the organizational structure of a design team. The chart shows the way in which the personnel in the lower blocks are responsible to the personnel in the higher blocks, each in turn responsible to the Chief Design Engineer who is in overall charge. The chart shows the paths of communication between personnel. Blocks placed at the same level imply that personnel shown in these blocks have a similar level of responsibility and authority.

Flow charts

Flow charts are used for describing a sequence of events or actions and are of value for planning purposes. Specific symbols are associated with particular parts of flow charts as described in the British Standard BS4058: *Specification for processing flow chart symbols, rules and conventions*. Fig. 13.19 shows a selection of the symbols from BS4058 which are in most common use, together with their function.

Flow charts are being increasingly used because they can assist in the planning of sequences of operations for computer programming. Each action or event may give rise to several lines of coding. Fig. 13.20 shows a typical computer flow chart for the sequence of events needed to produce the

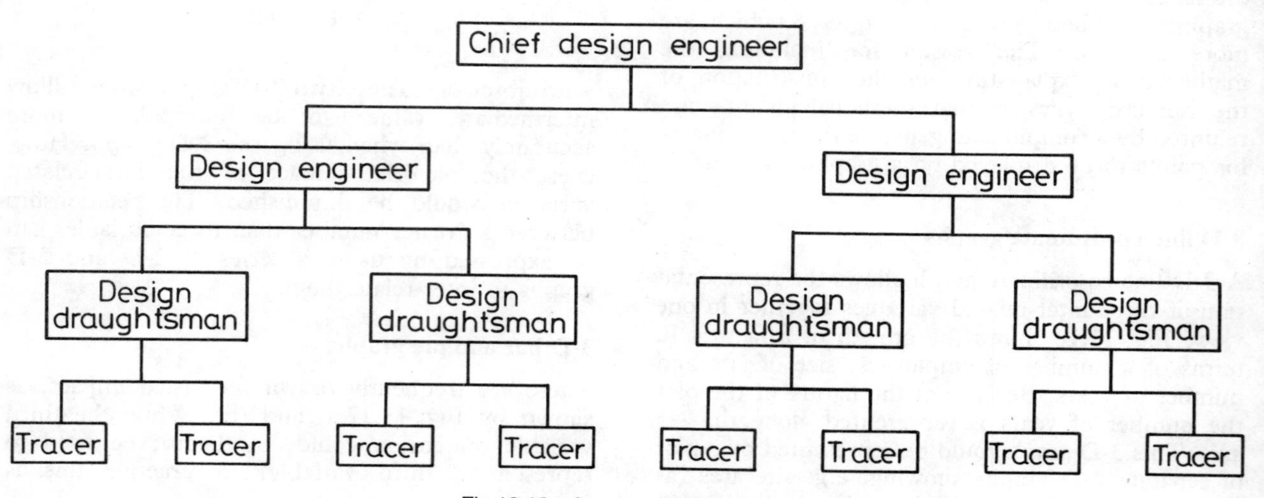

Fig.13.18 An organization chart

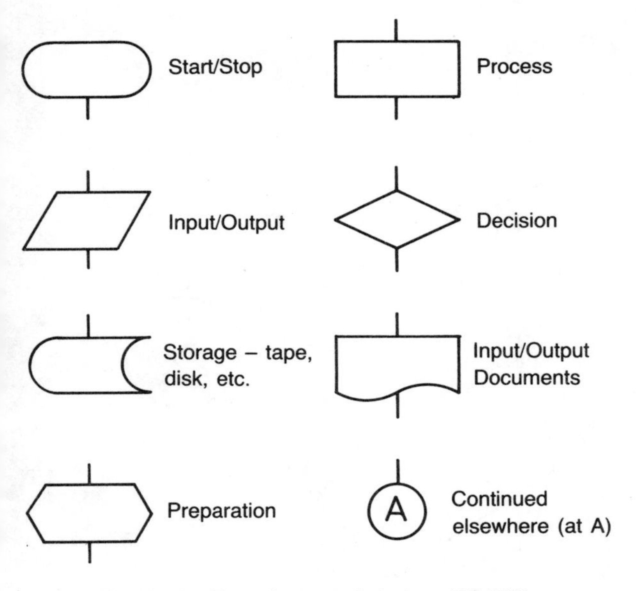

Fig.13.19 Flow chart symbols from BS4058

computer program employed for drawing the three squares given in program 2 of Chapter 15 (page 168). The program has a *start* point, after which data is entered. Then follows a *preparation* phase before the process of actually drawing the square. Having drawn the square, a *decision* phase follows, i.e. have three squares been drawn? If so the program *branches* to a *stop* phase. If three squares have not been drawn the program branches to a *no* route, followed by a modification to the preparation phase by incrementing the counter and moving to a new offset position. The program then takes a *return* loop to recommence the process of drawing another square. The general direction of flow for the sequence of operations is from the top to the bottom and from left to right. Return loops are shown branching off to the left. The difficulty with flow charts is that the detail to be included at each process can vary a great deal. In most computer programs the amount of detail required will depend upon the computer language and the hardware which is to be used, as well as the job which is to be performed by the program.

Critical path charts

Critical path charts are another form of chart frequently used by engineering managers as an organizational chart concerned with the time required to produce a series of events. A critical

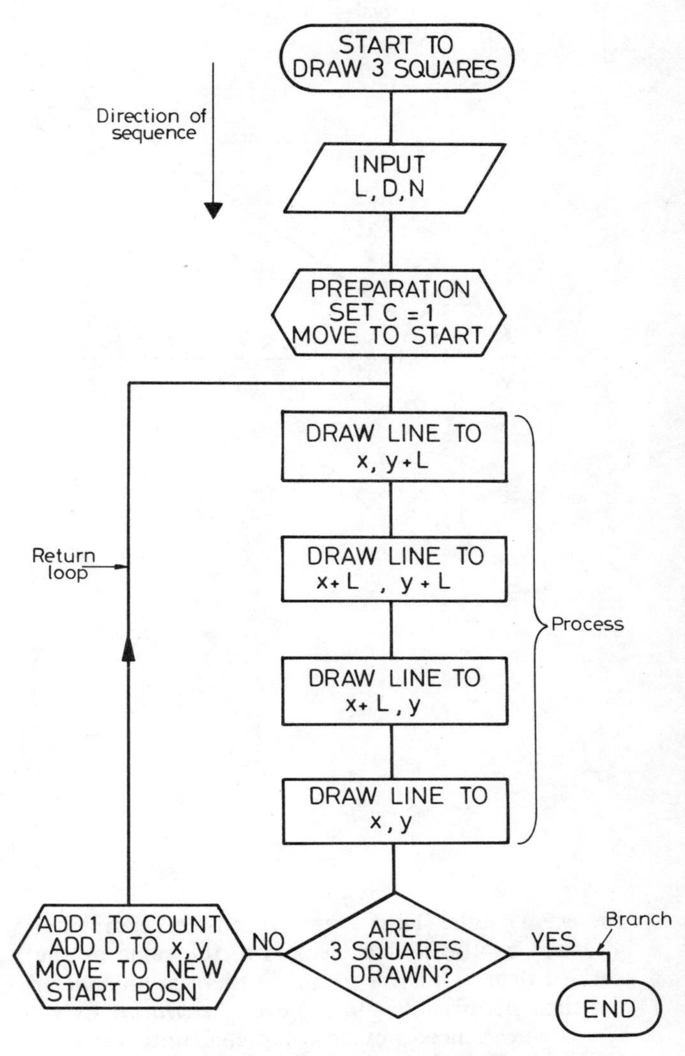

Fig.13.20 Computer flow chart for drawing three squares

path chart is a form of network. An example of such a chart is given by Fig. 13.21, which shows the production process in which an assembly comprising three parts, A, B and C, is produced. Each part requires to be machined before assembly. Each event shown as a circle on the chart is associated with a time which has elapsed since the job started, placed just above the event circles.

The earliest completion time for process ⑥ is thus seen to be 6 weeks in this example. The time taken between processes is placed on the line joining the events. Working back from the final event ⑥, the latest possible time is placed under

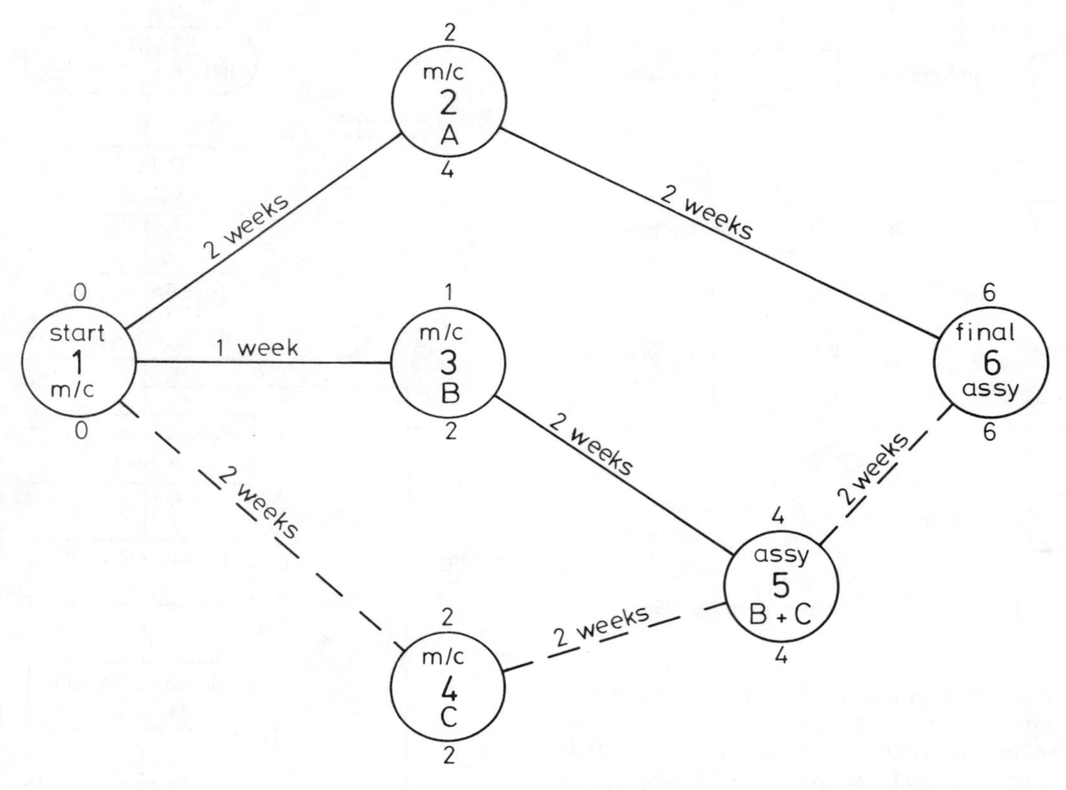

Fig.13.21 A critical path chart

the event circle. Thus event ⑤ must be completed at latest by the fourth week, i.e. the same as the earliest date. Thus for event ⑤ there is no *float* in the time permissible and the event is *critical*. Event ②, however, need not be completed until week 4, i.e. event ② has two weeks float and is not critical.

A *critical* path is defined as the longest overall route (shown dotted) between start and finish. This controls the overall production time and indicates those processes which would be the most rewarding to those efforts made to reduce times, or which should be started earlier than the other activities.

NOMOGRAPHS

A *nomograph*, *nomogram* or *number chart* is an arrangement of calibrated graphical scales to permit the conversion of values from one scale to another or the solving of an unknown from a mathematical or an empirical relationship.

Concurrent scales

Concurrent scales are the most common form of nomograph in which one value can be rapidly converted into another. Any relationship of the type A = B + C can be converted into a concurrent scale. Fig. 13.22 is an example in the form of a Fahrenheit/Celsius temperature conversion, where $°F = (9/5)°C + 32°$. The construction of the chart involves setting down the two scales so that the position and length of each scale coincide. Thus in the given example, the Celsius scale is set off to a suitable length from 0 to 100. Using the conversion equation, the corresponding end points for the Fahrenheit scale, i.e. 32 and 212, can be found: 180

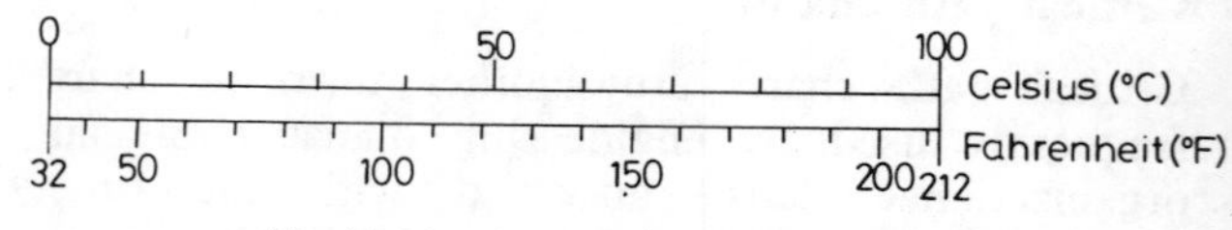

Fig.13.22 A concurrent scales chart

divisions between these two end points are then set off using the method of linear scaling outlined in Chapter 3.

Parallel scale alignment nomographs

A common form of nomograph, known as the parallel scale alignment graph, is one in which a straight line is drawn between two values and intersects with a third value as shown in Fig. 13.23. This shows linear scales for A and B with a third scale C which graphically represents the relationship A + B = C. Drawing a straight line between A and B intersects C to obtain the appropriate value which satisfies the equation. Fig. 13.24 shows the relationship A − B = C graphically, where the scale for B is in the reverse direction to that for A, giving the negative sign. While it is quite easy to read an existing nomograph, the creation of an original one can become somewhat complex. Let us assume that a new nomograph is to be created to represent A + 3B = 4C, where A lies between 0 and 12; B lies between 0 and 8 and hence C must lie between 0 and 9. First the two outer scales representing A and B to a suitable scale are drawn any distance apart (Fig. 13.25(a)). The end values of C are now found by joining the ends of A and B together as seen in Fig. 13.25(a). Two sets of A and B are now chosen which give the same value of C, e.g. when A = 0 and B = 8, C = 6; and when A = 12 and B = 4, C = 6. The two straight lines connecting these points on A and B are then drawn (Fig. 13.25(b)). This fixes the location of C as parallel to A and B and passing through the intersection at C = 6. Since the values for C = 0, 6 and 9 are now positioned it is quite straightforward to set off the linear scale for C as shown by Fig. 13.25(c).

In addition to linear scales, nomographs may be constructed using logarithmic scales, since if:

$$A = B.C$$

then $\log A = \log B + \log C$

and so the log nomograph scale can be constructed using the summation process as above. In this example log graph paper will aid in setting off scales equivalent to A, B and C to suitable lengths.

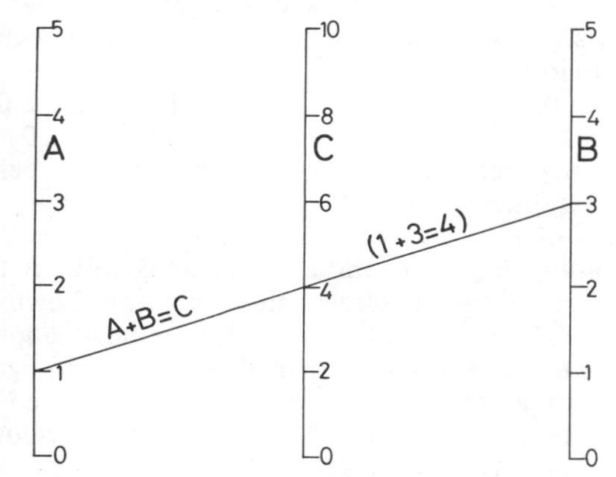

Fig.13.23 A nomograph for the relationship A + B = C

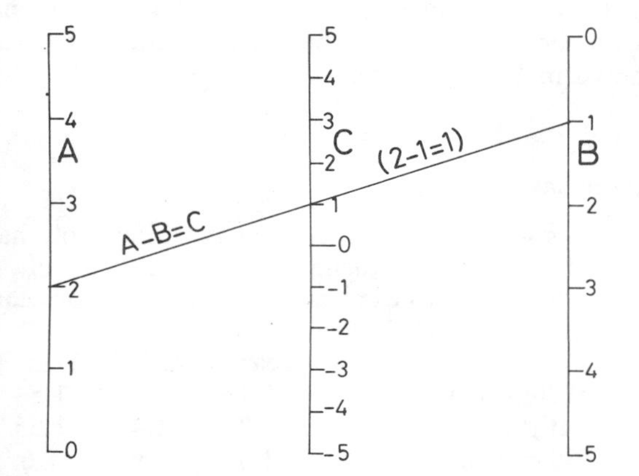

Fig.13.24 A nomograph for the relationship A − B = C

N or Z nomographs

It is possible to construct a nomograph to represent the relationship C = A/B using linear scales. Fig. 13.26 is an example where OA = 5, OB = 15. The outer scales of the N are linear functional scales. The diagonal line containing values of C is drawn from A = 0 to B = 0. Since the function is C = A/B, the scales for A and for B are in opposite directions. If a parallel scale were used, the outer legs would have to be to a logarithmic scale.

A more complex form of N graph can be constructed for equations of the form:

$$C = \frac{A + 3}{B + 5}$$

where A lies from 0 to 7; B lies from 0 to 15, as shown in Fig. 13.27.

First draw the end scales A and B to a suitable scale. These are then appropriately extended so as to position correctly the diagonal line (Fig. 13.27(a)). The maximum and minimum values of A and B are joined to find the extremities of C. The position of the diagonal is found by locating the positions where the functions A + 3 = 0 (i.e. A = −3) and B + 5 = 0 (i.e. B = −5) are satisfied.

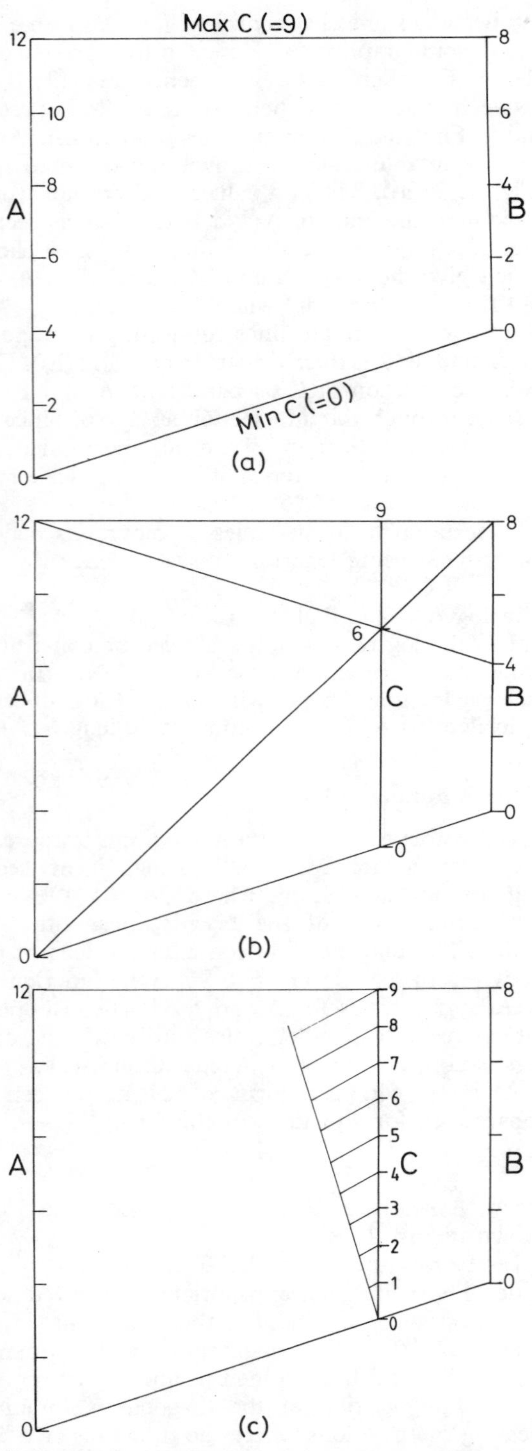

Fig. 13.25 Construction of a nomograph representing the relationship A + 3B = 4C

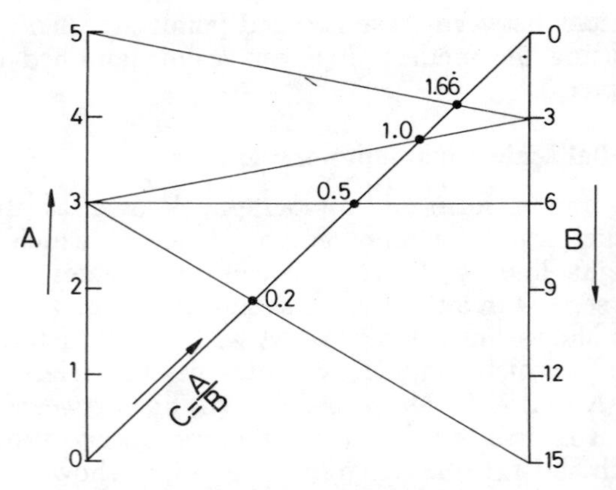

Fig. 13.26 N-nomograph for the relationship C = A/B

In order to divide the diagonal to the appropriate scale, it is now necessary to select the upper limit of the outer scales, e.g. A = 7, and substitute this in the given equation. This calculates a number of values for B for the given values of C, as shown in the following table:

C	0.5	0.6	0.7	0.8	0.9	1.0	1.5	2.0
B	15.0	11.7	9.3	7.5	6.1	5.0	1.7	0

Note that because it is the scale for C which is being formed, increments of C are used with intermediate values of B.

Joining A = 7 to these values of B will cut the diagonal at the required values of C as shown in Fig. 13.27(b). The same procedure is now adopted using the maximum value of B (i.e. 15), and again calculating the values of A which are required to give the desired values of C as in the table below:

C	0.1	0.2	0.3	0.4	0.5
A	0	1.0	3.0	5.0	7.0

Values of B = 15 are now joined to the calculated values of A to intersect with the diagonal to find again the remainder of the desired values of C, as shown in Fig. 13.27(c).

Exercises

(1) A company manufacturing machine tools has the following turnover (in millions of £ sterling) for sales of machines in three consecutive years:

	Year 1	Year 2	Year 3
Milling machines	1.1	1.4	1.8
Lathes	1.3	1.4	1.55
Pillar drills	2.3	1.9	1.6

Create a 3-D bar graph to show the sales of

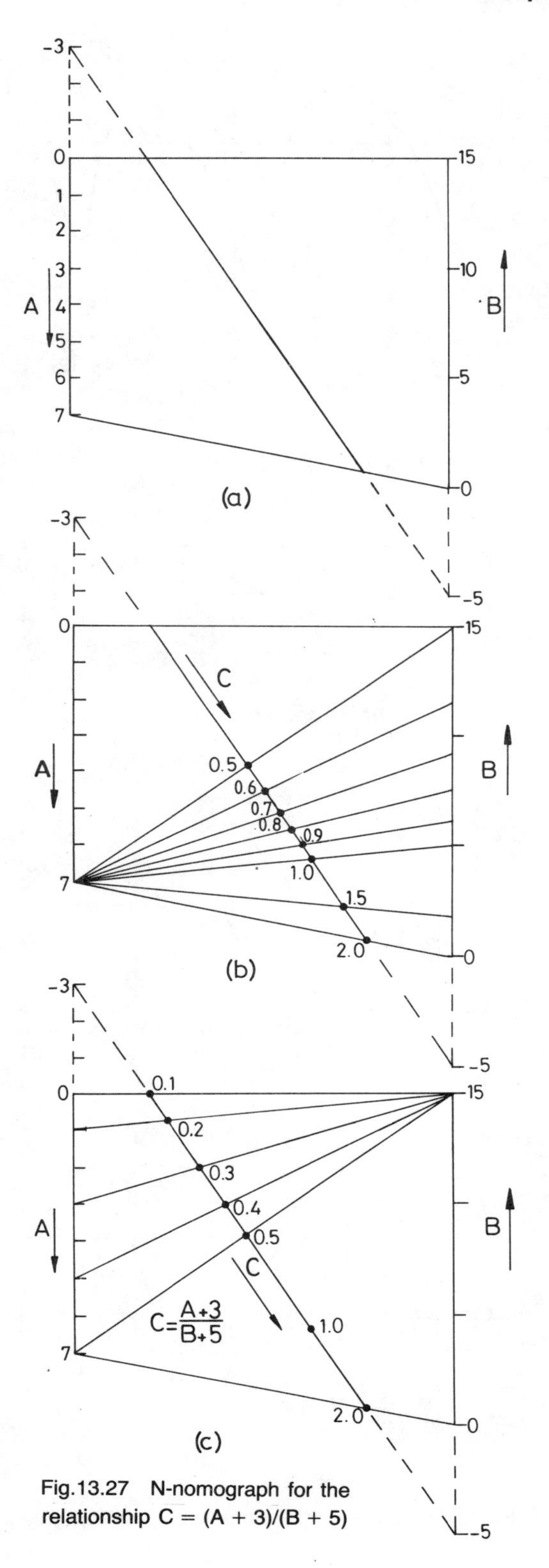

Fig.13.27 N-nomograph for the relationship C = (A + 3)/(B + 5)

machine tools over the three years as relative percentages.

(2) Use the data given in Exercise 1 to create a 3-D pie graph showing the relative proportion of sales each year and the relative magnitude each year.

(3) The following data show the compressibility of hydraulic oil for various temperatures and for various pressures:

Compression (% reduction in volume)	0	1.9	3.5	4.9	6.0	7.0
Temperature (°F)	50	100	150	200	250	300
Pressure ($N/m^2 \times 10^6$)	0	5	10	15	20	25

(a) Draw a series of 2-D linear co-ordinate graphs to represent all combinations of the various relationships.

(b) Create a single 3-D linear co-ordinate graph to demonstrate how each variable is inter-related.

(4) The following data show the cost per unit of producing a hand tool together with the warehouse costs of storage of each part:

No. of parts ($\times 10^6$)	2	4	6	8	10
Costs per part (£) manufacture	3	2	1.25	0.75	0.5
Costs per part (£) warehousing	0.25	0.5	0.9	1.4	2.0

Find, graphically, the number of units to minimize the total cost per part.

(5) Use the following data to draw a polar plot of the illumination levels under a lamp for various angles to the vertical. The zero degrees position is directly under the lamp and the illumination level is symmetrical about the vertical.

Angle to vertical	0°	10°	20°	30°	40°	50°	60°	70°
Illumination level (lumens)	7000	8000	9000	11000	10000	7000	4000	0

Use the plot to determine the maximum illumination level and its angle to the vertical.

(6) A closed loop polar diagram (see Fig. 13.11) is to be drawn for an electrical control system. The polar plot shows the amplitude ratio

$$|A| = \frac{|\text{output amplitude } A_2|}{|\text{input amplitude } A_1|}$$

plotted as a radius and a phase lag, angle ϕ,

shown as an angle gradually increasing from zero at the positive x axis. The disturbance frequency ω (expressed in radians per second) is shown as a series of points along the plot. The disturbance frequency ω can be found from:

ω (radians per second) $= 2\pi \times$ frequency (in hertz)

Use the data given below to draw the closed loop polar diagram.

Frequency (f) Hz	5	6	8	10	12	14	16	32
$/A/$	1.16	1.35	1.7	2.3	2.1	1.4	0.55	0.7
ϕ	25	35	50	75	130	155	180	235

(7) (a) The graphs of Fig. 13.28 show the lower limb motions during a walking cycle. Use the information given in the graphs to devise data for a new drawing which shows a *stick figure* showing the thigh, lower leg and foot as single lines walking on the spot, i.e. centred about the hip displacement origin. Fig. 13.29 shows a start for the required figure, drawn at the moment of heel contact.

(b) Repeat the plot of the stick figure walking on the spot, this time using the heel as the fixed datum. Assume:

(i) The thigh and lower leg length are both 500 mm.

(ii) The foot can be represented by two lines of 100 mm and 140 mm long at a fixed inclusive angle of 55°. The zero angle for ankle bending is at 35° to the lower leg.

(iii) A complete stride cycle is to be drawn, i.e. from 0 to 100% of the cycle in 1/5 cycle intervals.

(8) A 3-D line A, B has the following co-ordinates in millimetres:

	x	y	z
A	20	40	40
B	80	60	80

Use the 2-D projections of the line to find graphically the equation of the line in the form $ax + by + cz + d = 0$.

(9) A 3-D figure has the following corner co-ordinates in millimetres:

	x	y	z
A	0	0	0
B	40	20	0
C	0	40	0
D	20	20	40

Use the co-ordinates to construct the plan and

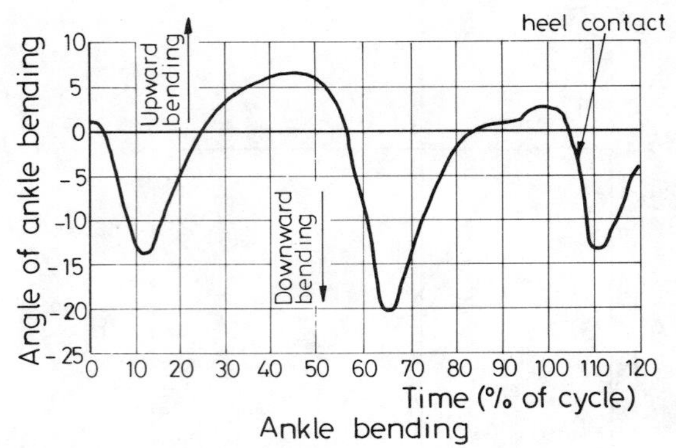

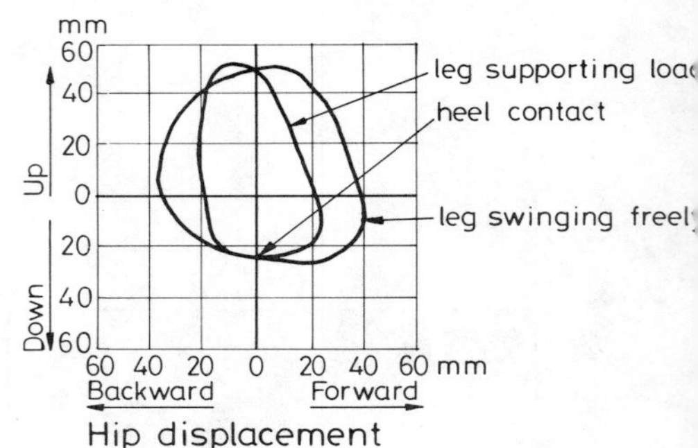

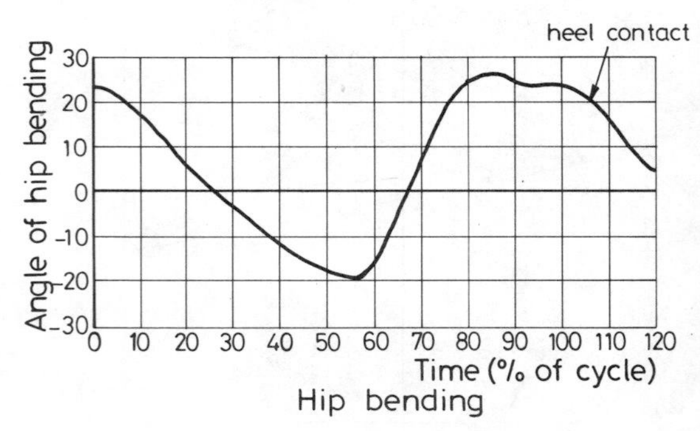

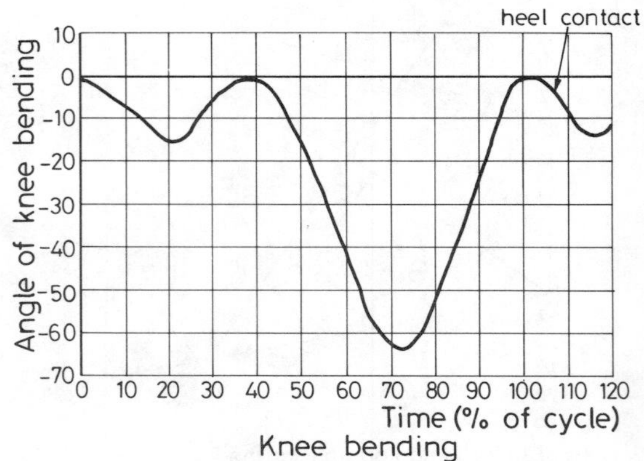

Fig.13.28 Lower limb motions during a walking cycle

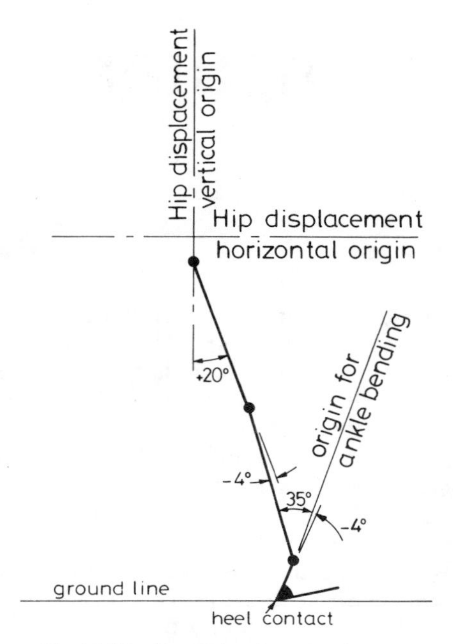

Fig.13.29 Example of a stick figure to represent a walking cycle

front and end views in First Angle projection.

(10) Use the co-ordinates given in Exercise 9 to calculate the isometric co-ordinates of the figure and then draw its isometric view. Show the face ABD nearest the origin.

(11) Draw an organization chart for a manufacturing company. The sales manager, works manager, chief engineer and treasurer are all responsible to the managing director and each has his own group of departments. The works manager has under him a production manager, a maintenance manager and a purchasing manager. The production manager has four foremen, each in charge of ten work people and is also in charge of the tool and die shop (three work people) and the inspection department (five work people). The purchasing manager is responsible for the stores department (a foreman and three work people) and a shipping/packing department (a foreman and two work people). The maintenance manager has a foreman and three work people under him.

(12) Create a critical path chart for the following machining and assembly activities in the production of a motor car engine.

After placing an order, the engine block is machined (2 hours), deburred and spare holes plugged and sealed (0.6 hour), painted and baked (1 hour). At the time of the order the four pistons are also machined (0.4 hour each), deburred (0.25 hour each), piston and oil control rings assembled together (0.1 hour each). The pistons are then assembled on to the four connecting rods (0.2 hour each). The four connecting rod and piston sub-assemblies are then placed into the engine block (0.1 hour each).

After the order is placed, the engine cylinder head is also machined (0.6 hour), deburred (0.1 hour), painted and baked (1 hour). The cylinder head is then connected to the assembled block using a gasket (0.05 hour) and eight screws tightened down (0.1 hour).

Indicate the critical activities and show the limiting time for an engine to be produced.

(13) Draw a concurrent scale which can be used to find the area A of a circle ($A = \pi R^2$) where R varies between 1 and 100 mm.

(14) Using semi-log graph paper as an aid, construct a semi-log scale nomogram for the equation:

$$z = xy^2$$

where x varies from 1 to 100 and y varies from 1 to 10.

(15) Construct an N nomogram to evaluate the equation:

$$z = \frac{x - 2}{y + 2}$$

where x varies from 0 to 8
and y varies from 0 to 16.

(16) Prepare a flow chart for the process of replacing a light bulb in a ceiling lamp. Remember to include such processes as bringing a step ladder and the new bulb, checking the bulb, etc.

(17) Prepare a flow chart for the process of replacing a motor car spark plug. Remember to include such activities as opening the car bonnet, bringing tools, collecting and visually checking the new spark plug, etc.

(18) Prepare a flow chart for the process of drawing a circle using a computer as shown in the program given in Chapter 15 (page 174).

14 Introduction to computer graphics

THE RELATIONSHIP OF COMPUTER GRAPHICS AND COMPUTER AIDED DESIGN

We have already seen in the introduction of Chapter 1 that Computer Graphics is at the heart of Computer Aided Design (CAD) and of Computer Aided Manufacture (CAM). There is much confusion about the use of the term CAD because for many years computer graphics systems were purely concerned with draughting and so the term CAD has mistakenly been used in some texts to mean 'Computer Aided Draughting'. In this text, CAD is taken to refer to the application of computers in the whole design process. This includes such activities as representing a model of the three-dimensional geometry of an object in the computer, displaying it on a graphics screen and producing dimensioned workshop drawings. A variety of computer programs can also be added to analyse the object to find, for example, how the part deforms under load; what stresses result and what would be an optimal shape. In addition, data about standard parts, e.g. bearings, nuts, bolts, keys and pins can be held in the computer so that scaled views of the parts can be added to an assembly drawing and additional information made available about such features as its properties, price and availability, all of which will be of vital interest to the designer. The geometry of any component can be held in the computer as a 'data base' which can be used to interact with other computer programs, thus giving the whole range of design and manufacture activities shown in Fig. 14.1. The figure shows that at the heart of an integrated CAD/CAM facility lies the graphics display screen. Through interaction with the display screen, data about the geometry of the object can be stored in the computer by using various views of the object. Once this geometry 'data base' has been passed to the computer, it can be accessed not only for all the purposes of computer aided design but for aiding in the manufacture of the object, and also for archiving (e.g. in producing 'hard copy' engineering drawings and for sales brochures). Many of the CAD activities are concerned with analysis such as finding critical stress levels by 'Finite Element' techniques. These activities will require the use of further computer programs but they will all use the same geometric data as a basis for the particular analysis. Similarly a knowledge of the product geometry can be used to control machine tools used in manufacturing the object, e.g. so that a computer numerical controlled lathe can produce turned objects. Thus it is the ability to link the design and manufacture activities using a common computer generated 'data base' that is going to revolutionize the whole manufacturing industry. We are in the early days of this revolution and, up to now, relatively few firms have fully implemented the whole range of CAD/CAM activities. However, even when companies have introduced graphics as only a simple draughting system, it is usually intended that they will eventually introduce full computer modelling of the product and then gradually add computer aided manufacture facilities.

THE EVOLUTION OF CAD – THE CHANGE FROM 2-D TO 3-D

The process of modelling, in a computer, a complex engineering component in three dimensions is difficult. It requires both sophisticated computer programs and special computer hardware for the graphical display systems. It is only in recent years that these facilities have been available at a reasonable price. Previously, the great majority of computer graphics available were for two-dimensional (2-D) draughting in which individual views are drawn on a display screen, but there is no facility for representing the three-dimensional (3-D) nature of a part. Features, such as which lines should be drawn as hidden detail, require the intervention of a draughtsman to put in the

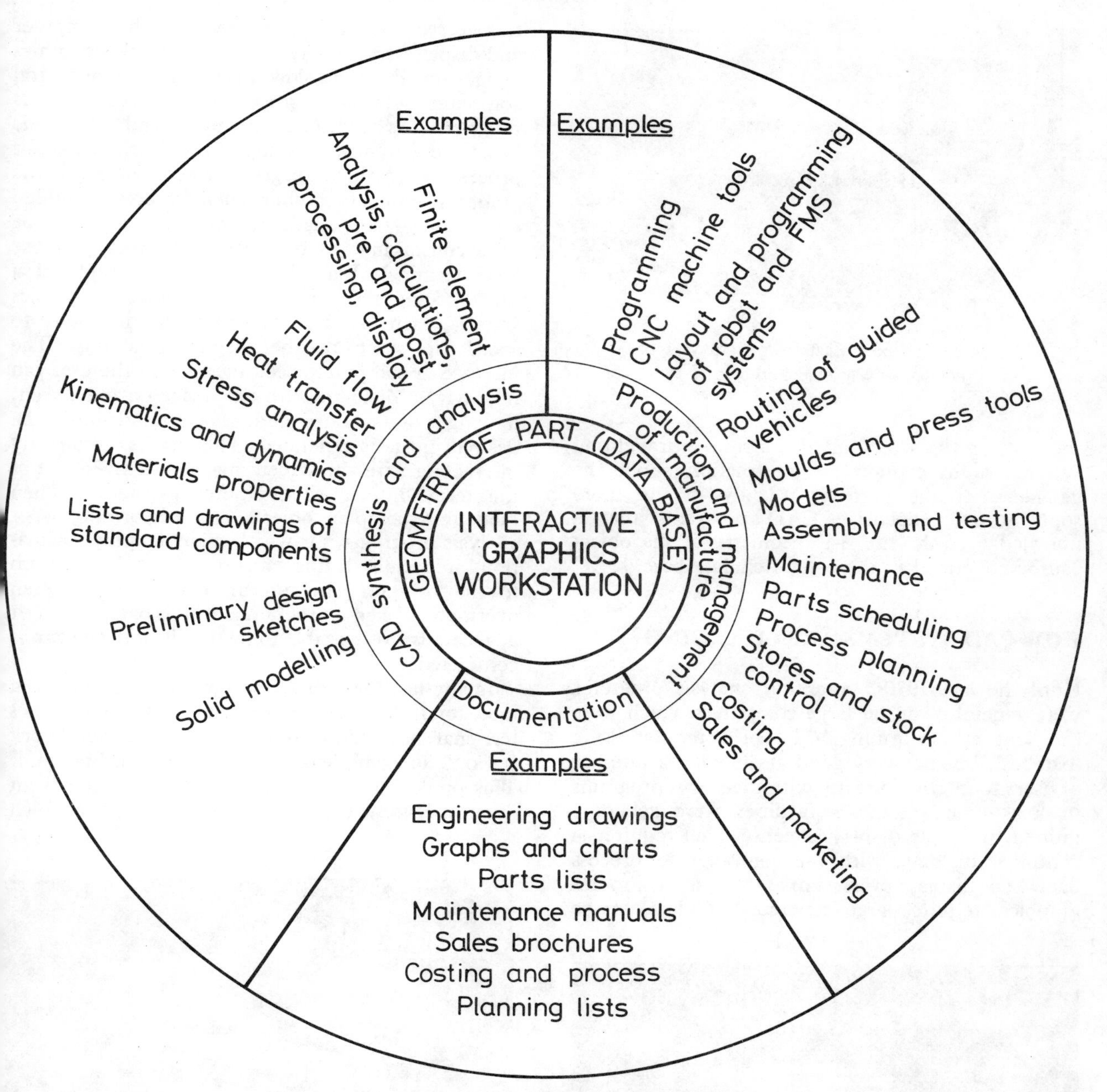

Fig.14.1 The central role of graphics in CAD/CAM

appropriate dashed lines. An example of the output from a popular system of this type, which is often used in education, is shown in Fig. 14.2. Many of the cheaper microcomputer-based systems contain only 2-D draughting systems with this level of complexity. These systems display the views of an object on a graphics screen in just the same way as an engineering drawing on paper. However, because each point and line are held in computer memory, changes to the drawing can be easily carried out without having to re-enter all the data by hand. Only those lines which are to be modified need be re-entered and all the rest can then be automatically regenerated on the screen. However,

Fig.14.2 Robocom 'Bitstik' – general view of equipment with object on screen

the lines on the screen in such a simple draughting system would contain no information about the geometry of the part. It is only in the more sophisticated, expensive CAD programs that a knowledge of the full 3-D geometry of the object can be contained in the computer data base.

HOW CAD SYSTEMS ARE CHANGING

Until the late 1970s, computer analysis programs were generally run on large computers which were excellent at performing a lot of computation in 'batches', but not very good at allowing a number of users to interact directly with their own programs in 'real time'. Graphics facilities were generally limited to simple display screens which required a continual dialogue with the computer to process data. To display even simple objects, computer graphics require large amounts of data to be transferred back and forth between the computer and display screen. The display of complex graphics images was therefore slow, particularly if the central computer was also processing a large analysis program. As computer memory and electronic hardware get cheaper, some of the 'intelligence' for processing graphics images has been added to the graphics terminals to allow such features as hidden line removal and shading, both of which can be time consuming, to be performed quickly at the local terminal. Fig. 14.3 shows an example of a central computer which hosts a number of graphics screens, each of which has additional hardware to speed up some of the display functions. The increase in computer speed means that the user can now have a dialogue with the image on the screen, moving points, lines and text around until the desired image is generated. This process of directly interacting with the screen images has given rise to the term 'interactive computer graphics'. When modelling complex objects and performing large analysis programs, for which many lengthy calculations are required, it is usual to submit the program to the computer to run in 'batch' mode, often overnight. When a program is run in batch mode, it is generally not possible to modify it until the run is completed.

In the last few years, the process of transferring more and more computer power to the graphics terminal has culminated in the 'intelligent work station', an example of which is shown in Fig. 14.4. This process has been brought about by the advent of cheaper miniaturized computing hardware which

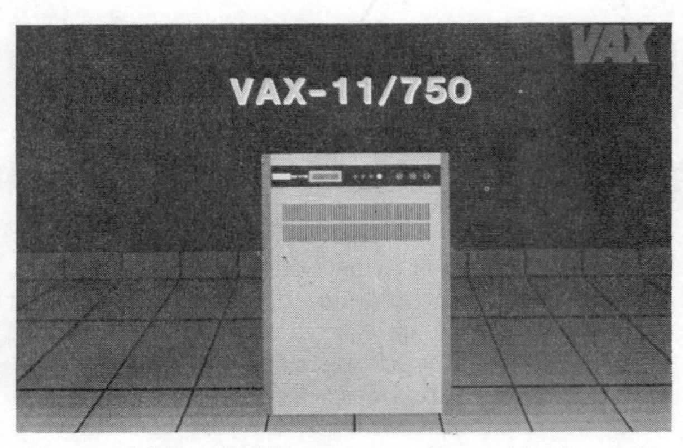

Fig.14.3 DEC VAX 750 computer with graphics terminals

Fig.14.4 Tektronix intelligent graphics work station

allows both the computer memory and the computer disk, which stores programs, to be sited alongside the graphics display screen to provide a self-contained CAD work station. Several work stations can be linked, or 'networked', together to allow information to be interchanged between them. There is also the possibility of linking each work station to a large computer which has a huge memory and Central Processing Unit (CPU) for processing very large computer analysis programs.

The advent of these facilities has allowed industry to have access to a whole range of CAD systems at a reasonable price. The integration of these systems has meant that CAD can now be very cost effective for industry. While in the past it was difficult for many industries to justify the expense of graphics displays and computing facilities in order to be available solely as draughting facilities, the integration of design and manufacture has resulted in a rapid growth of CAD in industry in recent years. The change in this area has been so rapid that there are still many people who mistakenly describe the area of computer graphics as 'just draughting' and have failed to see its true potential.

AN OVERVIEW OF A TYPICAL CAD FACILITY

A typical configuration of a large-scale industrial CAD system is shown in Fig. 14.5. A number of 'intelligent work stations' are shown networked together and connected to a very large Central Processor Unit (CPU) which can be used to process large programs. These larger programs, and applications data, can be stored on a central 'fixed head' disk storage system which can quickly access a vast amount of stored information. Magnetic tape is also frequently used as an additional storage 'back-up' in case of disk failure. Output devices can be connected to the large CPU, e.g. expensive plotters of A0 size which can produce drawings in 'batch' mode without tying up a work station terminal so that it cannot be used during the slow process of plotting drawings. Similarly expensive input devices can be centrally located so that they can transfer information to the computers. An example of this is a digitizer which can be used to input information about the x and y co-ordinates of existing engineering drawings, maps or printed circuit layouts.

Each of the intelligent work stations contains a computer and display screen. The computer also has associated with it a local storage facility in the form of a 'floppy' disk, smaller and much slower than the expensive central facility. The computer has sufficient memory to run both the graphics programs and the applications programs. The local computer is in turn connected to a number of display screens and keyboards. Each display has additional graphics 'processors' consisting of a variety of electronic devices which speed up the display process. Each display screen has associated with it a number of devices which enable information to be input to the computer, e.g. 'tablet', 'mouse', 'joystick', 'light pen'. These are described later in this chapter in the section on hardware. The work station also has at least one local system which allows information to be output from the computer as 'hard copy', e.g. a small plotter and printer.

The type of large-scale CAD system described here is very expensive and beyond the finances of many colleges and small firms. A central computer connected to three work stations, each of which has three display screens, would cost around £1 million including CAD software. However, a more limited single work station and display screen, without central facility could be purchased for around £100 000, with a limited modelling and draughting package.

The type of simple CAD facility that can be found in many small firms and colleges is shown in Fig. 14.6. This has a small microcomputer-based system with a supplementary memory and keyboard. An additional medium quality display screen is also provided together with a floppy disk drive. A 'tablet' is used for inputting information and a supplementary screen for displaying numbers and characters. Such a system, together with software, could be provided for around £12 000 with small printer and plotter, but would have very limited three-dimensional modelling capability. However, as the costs of both computer memory and displays fall, the capabilities of these small systems will soon rise to equal those provided by today's small intelligent work station.

HARDWARE FOR INTERACTIVE GRAPHICAL SYSTEMS

The term 'hardware' is used to cover all those pieces of equipment which are used to implement computer programs. The computer programs themselves are referred to as 'software' and are con-

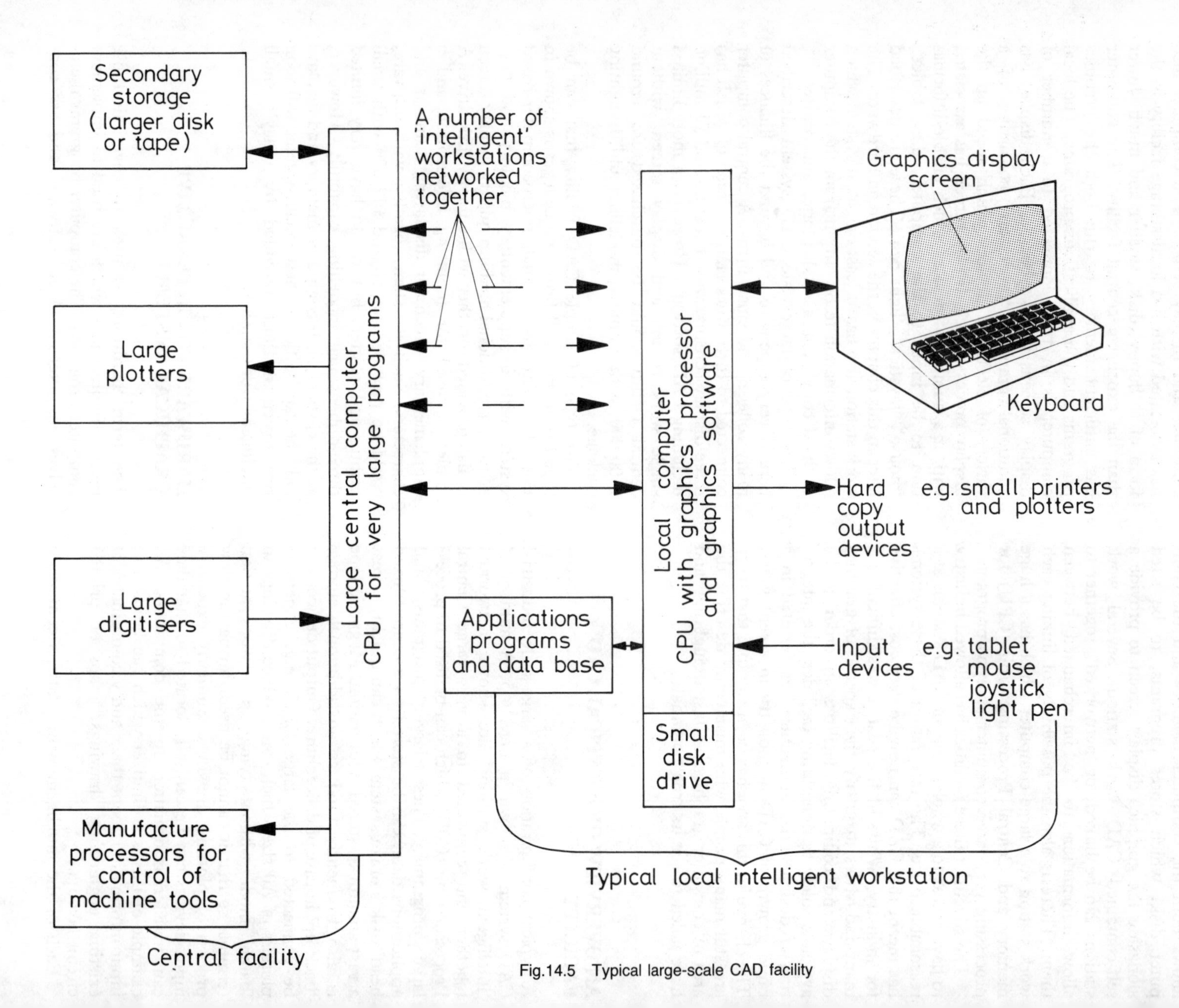

Fig.14.5 Typical large-scale CAD facility

Fig.14.6 'AutoCAD' draughting system

sidered in detail in Chapter 15. A third term 'firmware' has recently been introduced to cover those software instructions which have been implemented in electronic hardware, usually to enable increased speed of computation.

The division into hardware and software reflects the way that most companies organize their responsibilities, and it is now very rare to find a company which not only manufactures hardware but also originates software. A manufacturer, for example, of intelligent work stations, will enter into an arrangement with a number of software suppliers who will adapt their software to the requirements of his particular CAD equipment. Thus there are often a number of draughting and modelling programs available which will run on a particular CAD hardware system. Because the majority of CAD users are more interested in the application of software to a number of problems than they are in the hardware that drives the system, most users will approach the software company initially. The software company will then recommend a particular hardware system and generally take responsibility for seeing that the hardware and software will operate well together and perform to the customer requirements.

The term 'hardware' includes the computer with its memory and Central Processing Unit (CPU), the means of storing programs on disk or magnetic tape, the display screens, various devices for inputting instructions to the computer, e.g. keyboards, digitizers, tablets, etc., and the output devices which can give 'hard copy', e.g. plotters and printers.

The computer

Depending on the complexity of the CAD system, the computer required may range from a small microcomputer with a memory size typically ranging from 64 K bytes to 512 K bytes, through an intelligent work station (½ M byte to 10 M bytes) to a larger stand-alone 'main frame' machine (10 M byte to 30 M byte). Each byte consists of 8 bits. A bit is a binary number which can be 'on' (represented by a '1' in memory) or 'off' (represented by '0'). In addition to variations in size of memory, computer instructions are given in different 'word' lengths. A small microcomputer usually has a word length of 8 bits, the majority of earlier large computers have a word length of 16 bits, while the latest designs have word lengths of 32 bits. The word length affects the power and speed of instructions. A 16 bit word can be used to represent a large number to a certain precision which is expressed by the number of places after the decimal point. To obtain improved accuracy, or 'double precision', two 16 bit words would be required. However, if a computer with a 32 bit word is used, the same high precision can be obtained in a single word. This gives advantages in speed of processing. Since CAD graphics work requires both large numbers and high precision, 32 bit computers in modern work stations give considerable speed advantages.

Secondary storage media

Although a computer stores programs in its memory, when the computer is switched off, the program in its memory will be lost. In order to ensure that a program can be used on a subsequent occasion, it must be transferred from the computer's memory into a secondary storage medium to enable it to be loaded back into the computer when required. A further reason for needing such a storage medium is that most graphics application packages are too long to be totally stored in a computer's memory and will need to be loaded in and out of the memory while the program is running. The most common secondary storage is on disks.

Disks

The disks are coated with a magnetic oxide and revolve at very high speed. Magnetic sensors are tracked radially across the surface of the disk to 'read' the binary information which is coded magnetically in specific locations, or 'sectors', on the disk. The read and record head rides so closely above the disk surface that any dust or smoke particles will cause damage to the disk or the heads. For this reason cleanliness is essential and, on larger installations, a filtered air conditioning system is advisable to improve hardware reliability. There are three types of disk commonly available; floppy, cartridge and fixed head.

Floppy disks (Fig. 14.7)

These are small thin disks of flexible mylar, typically 89, 133 or 205 mm diameter. They store up to 0.5 M byte information and cost around £2 each and so each user can have several copies containing his own programs.

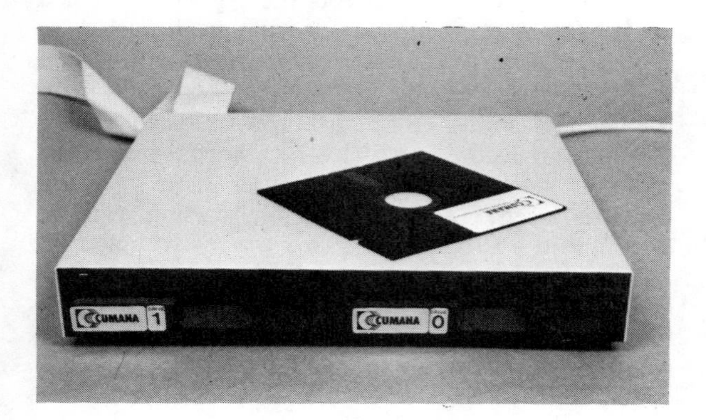

Fig.14.7 Floppy disks and disk drive

A disk cartridge (Fig. 14.8)

This is a more elaborate device which consists of a magnetic oxide coated disk of plastic, typically 1.5 mm thick by 375 mm diameter. The disk is mounted in bearings which are placed in the casing of the cartridge. Typically, the cartridge can store 10 Mb of information but costs around £50 each and so a user would generally store most of his working programs on a single disk cartridge.

Fixed head disks

Fixed head disks are generally used in large systems to store vast amounts of information (10 Mb up to 500 Mb) in a single fixed unit attached to a work station. Precision bearings in a fully sealed unit enable the disks to be rotated very rapidly and so ensure an improved time to access information.

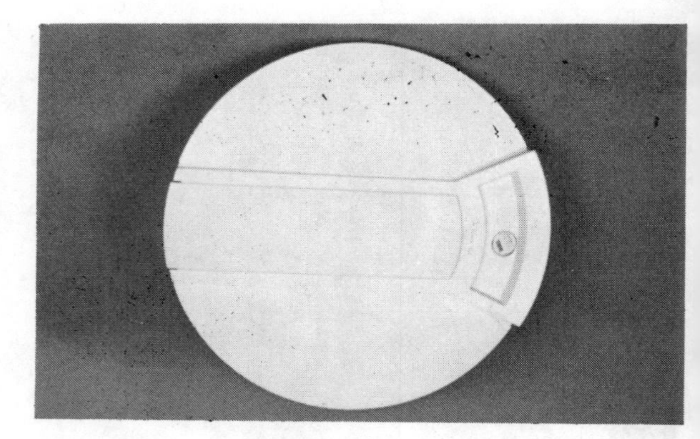

Fig.14.8 Cartridge disk

Smaller, cheaper fixed disk drives (called *Winchesters*) are often used in smaller CAD work stations.

Magnetic tape

An alternative secondary storage medium is magnetic tape. Magnetic tapes are much cheaper than disks. However, because a tape has to be unwound serially to find a particular piece of information, accessing data is much slower than when using disks (typically 200 times longer). Magnetic tape is therefore used in all but the very cheapest systems as a means of 'archiving', i.e. storing programs and data which are seldom needed and when storing on valuable disk space is not justified. Magnetic tapes are often used as 'back-up' storage in case the programs on disks become 'corrupted', i.e. destroyed or distorted in such a way that they are no longer a correct record of the program or data.

GRAPHICS DISPLAY SCREENS

At the heart of the CAD system is the graphical display screen or graphics unit. Its quality is important to the operator because it will be a big factor in how easy it is to use the CAD system. The basis of all currently used screens is the *cathode ray* tube (CRT) that is found in the home TV set. Fig. 14.9 shows the elements of a cathode ray tube. An electron gun produces a stream of electrons which accelerate towards a phosphor coated screen. On the way, the electron stream passes through a focusing system which converges the electrons to a point at the screen. The electrons are deflected to a particular location on the screen by vertical and horizontal magnetic deflection plates. Where the

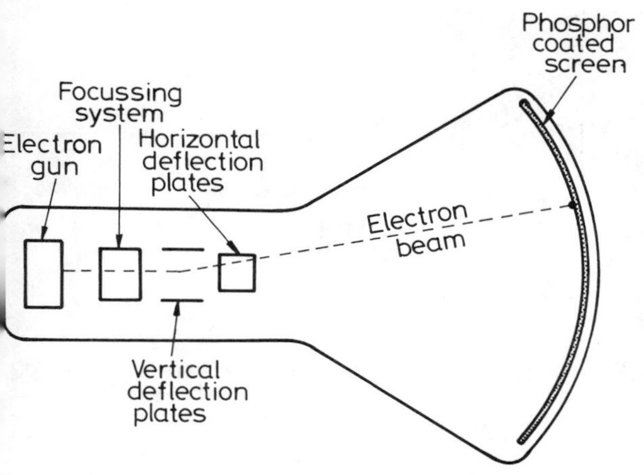

Fig.14.9 Basic operation of cathode ray tube

electrons hit the screen, the phosphor coating glows as a visible spot of light. Since the image quickly decays it has to be continually refreshed. Provided the refresh rate is greater than around 30 times a second, the image will not appear to flicker. On some displays the intensity of the image can be varied to give a *grey-tone scale* of a number of levels from white through to black, so that a picture can be generated rather like a half-tone photograph.

Colour can also be generated on a CAD screen, just as in domestic TV, as shown in Fig. 14.10. To generate colour, the cathode ray tube contains three electron guns, giving red, blue or green signals. The phosphor screen is coated with red, blue and green dots, arranged in thousands of triangular patterns. A *shadow mask* of fine holes is placed in front of the phosphor screen. The three guns shine

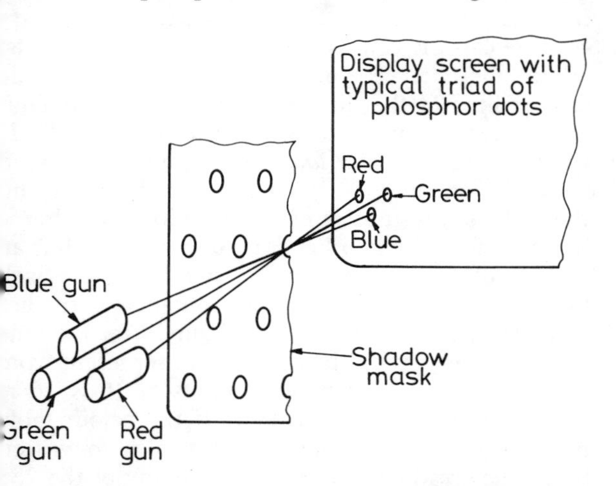

Fig.14.10 Basic operation of colour cathode ray tube

light through the holes in the mask illuminating some of the dots on the screen. The holes in the mask are spaced so that only those dots which are the same colour as the gun will be lit. The intensity of each beam is also variable, so that when seen from a distance, each triad of spots merges together and takes on a particular colour, depending on how strongly each of the red, blue and green spots is being excited.

Although, as we shall see later, a colour display requires more computing memory than monochrome, the quality in terms of the number of points displayed (or *resolution*), may be lower to achieve the same level of ability to discriminate easily between adjacent lines on the screen.

It is a point of some controversy currently as to whether a high resolution monochrome or a similarly priced medium resolution colour display should be used for computer graphics. Monochrome displays are generally recommended for 2-D draughting work, while the more complex 3-D solid modelling of components benefits from the use of different colours for adjacent features. Colour is particularly useful where objects overlap and it would otherwise be difficult to determine which line was which using a monochrome display.

Three main types of display are in common use: raster scan, direct beam refresh and storage tube.

Raster scan

This type of display is being increasingly employed. Fig. 14.11 shows the concept in which an electron beam traces a zig-zag pattern across the screen similar to that on a TV screen. However, a TV set uses an analogue signal, while a computer graphics screen uses a digital signal provided by the computer, which can be either on or off. As shown in Fig. 14.11 the beam starts at the top left hand corner and traverses from left to right of the screen. At the right hand end of the screen the beam moves back along the dotted path to the left hand end and

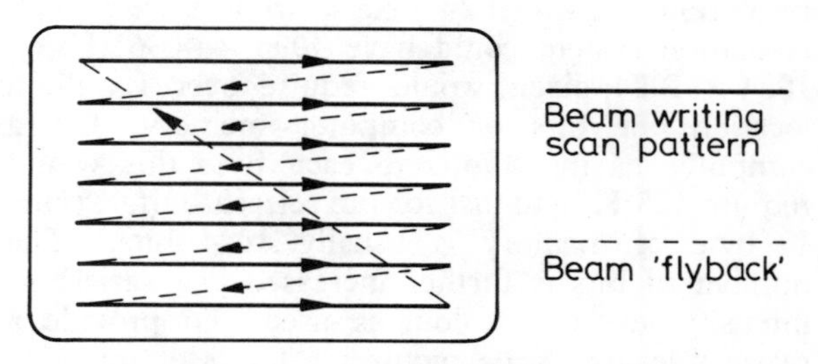

Fig.14.11 A raster scan display screen

starts to refresh the next line. This process continues until the bottom right corner of the screen is reached, when the beam flies back to the top left corner to start all over again. As the beam traverses along the line the computer continually turns the beam off or on to create the desired picture. The greater the number of points on the screen, the better is the quality (or 'resolution') of the picture.

A low resolution professional CAD screen has typically 256 lines of information and 312 addressable points on each line. Such a resolution would, however, be considered quite high on a home microcomputer system. The 312 × 256 matrix creates over 79 000 bits of information corresponding to the number of picture elements or *pixels*, each of which can either be turned on or off. Each pixel is stored in a special location in the memory and is scanned through every 1/30th or 1/60th second. When the screen is refreshed at this rate (greater than around 1/25th second) the persistence of vision of the eye causes the image to appear steady and without flicker. Each pixel is stored in the computer in such a way that the screen is 'mapped' successively into the computer memory with a memory location for each pixel in the *xy* plane of the screen. Each of the memory locations will contain either a '1' if the pixel is to be turned on, or a '0' if the pixel is to remain dark. Each time the raster scans across the screen from top to bottom, it consults every location in the mapped memory to decide which pixels should be turned 'on' to create the required picture. Fig. 14.12 shows the memory, called a *frame* (or *refresh*) buffer, in relation to a diagrammatic representation of a screen. Larger CAD systems have a separate frame buffer memory for mapping the pixels which can give faster access than a normal microprocessor memory, leading to very rapid refresh rates. These systems are known as *bit mapped* displays.

Medium resolution displays for industrial CAD systems have around 512 × 512 pixels; a high resolution 1024 × 1024 pixels; while a very high resolution system could have 4096 × 4096. Using 1024 × 1024 pixels would require over 1 million locations or bits of computer memory. On a computer having 8 bits to each byte this would require 128 K byte just for the refresh buffer. (One K byte of memory is usually 1024 bits.) The number of bits is further increased if a variety of intensity levels or colour is used. To provide a reasonable grey scale picture, 8 levels of intensity are generally needed which require 3 bits per pixel

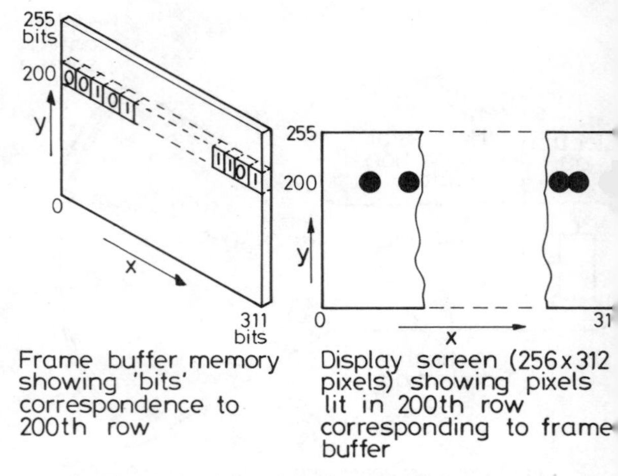

Fig.14.12 A frame buffer and display screen

– 3 binary bits are needed to represent the 8 levels because we can show decimal '0' by the binary number 000; decimal '1' by binary 001; and so on through to decimal '7' represented as a binary number by the 3 binary bits 111. Applying colour shading is more complex because each shade requires three guns, red, blue and green. If, as is common in a professional CAD system, 16 levels of shade for each colour are used, then the number 16 will require 4 binary bits for each gun. Thus for the three guns, each pixel will need a 12 bit word to define the 16 levels for red, blue and green. A typical arrangement is shown in Fig. 14.13. Here every pixel represented in the frame buffer requires not just the 0 or 1 (off or on) shown in Fig. 14.12, but a number of binary bits capable of differentiating a range of colours for each pixel. The 8 binary bits are capable of giving up to 256 separate levels. While these levels could be fed straight to the colour guns of the display screen this would limit the range of colours to 256. Instead, larger CAD systems use a colour *table* (or colour *map*) as an additional memory between the refresh buffer and the cathode ray tube guns. The 8 bits in the frame buffer now give a number from 0 to 255 which is an *address* of a location in the colour table. Each location in the colour table contains a further memory of 12 bits; 4 for the red gun, 4 for the blue and 4 for the green. Since 4 bits can represent from 0 to 15 hues, the 3 guns can represent 16 × 16 × 16 = 4096 variations in colour. If the colour table memory can be not only read but also re-written (i.e. it has read/write memory) then any of the 256 locations in the colour table can be reprogrammed to show any of the 4096 colours. The display screen can show any of 256 colours at one time which may be selected from a *palette* of 4096.

An alternative method of organizing the refresh buffer is to use the number of bits per pixel to represent differentiated display screens or *planes* that can be superimposed, one over the other. Thus in the example of Fig. 14.13, two planes, each of 4 bits could be represented by the same 8 bits per pixel. The two screens could then be used to aid animation. As a simple example a clock, including the minute and hour hand, could be shown on one screen while the second hand on its own could be shown on the overlapping screen. The first screen with all its detail need only be updated every minute, while the second hand, on its own, can be updated on its screen after every second. These 'multiple-plane bit-mapped' displays require a great deal of memory.

Costs of computer memory have fallen dramatically in recent years. This, together with the fact that raster CAD systems benefit from similar components to those in TV sets (and thus benefit from the cheaper costs of large-scale manufacture), has recently resulted in raster screens being the most popular type of CAD display. Even when a great deal of information is displayed the image does not flicker because the refresh rate is fast and constant. Also it is easy for a part of the picture to be selectively erased or changed.

Directed beam refresh displays

These are also called *stroke writing*, 'vector writing' or 'line drawing' refresh displays. In this system only the line segments, making up the image, are generated in turn by the directed beam. Curves are approximated by a number of straight line segments. Fig. 14.14 shows a typical sequence. After the image is drawn, the picture is refreshed by repeating the sequence. Thus the more detailed the image, the longer it is before the next refresh. Since the eye has a persistence of vision lasting around 1/25 s, if the refresh frequency is less than around 30 Hz the image flickers and is unpleasant to view. Refresh displays only require memory locations for the end points of a line in terms of the *x* and *y* coordinates on the screen. Thus for fairly simple objects, the size of memory required is much smaller than for a raster display, and is consequently cheaper. This refresh display preceded the design of raster scan displays, but because the cost of memory has fallen so dramatically in recent years, raster scan is now the preferred system.

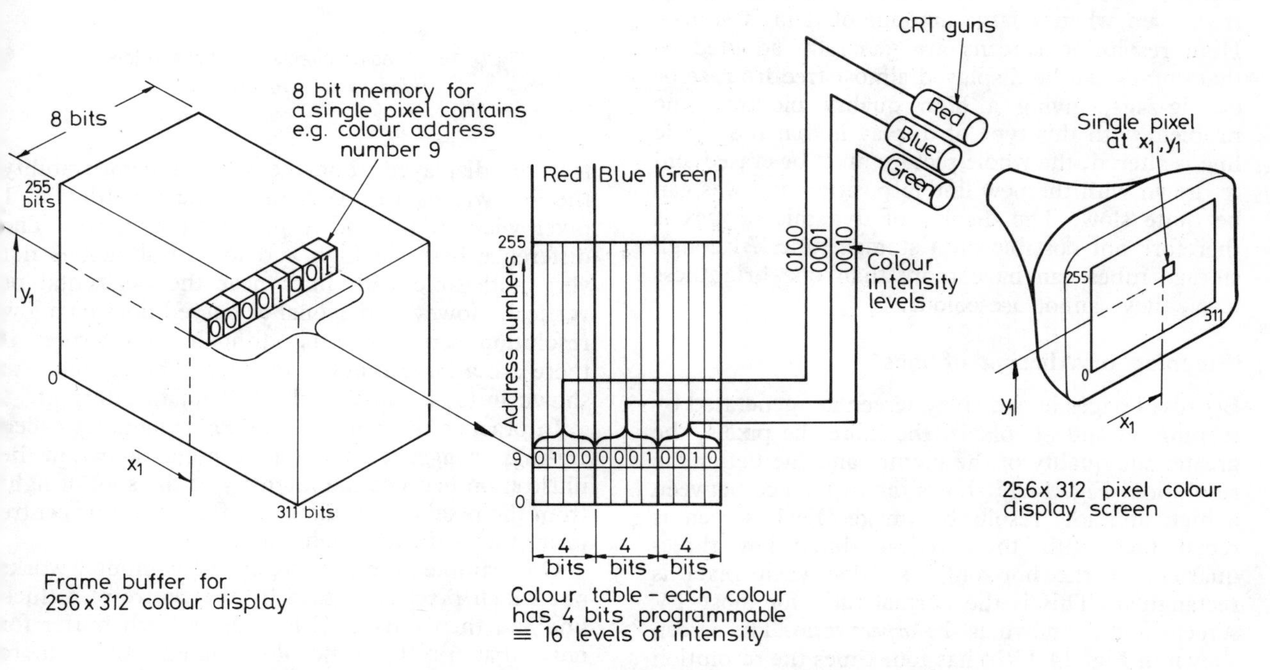

Fig.14.13 Organization of a programmable colour display screen

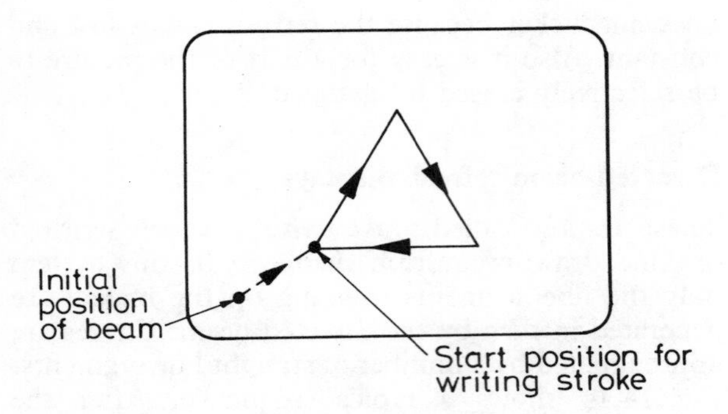

Fig.14.14 A directed beam refresh display

'Direct view' storage tube

This system uses vector writing, from one co-ordinate to another, just as in a directed beam refresh display, but the use of a long-persistent phosphor on the screen prevents the need for the screen to be continually refreshed. An additional electron gun, called a *flood gun*, is used in the cathode ray tube to create a *fog* of electrons which keep the phosphor elements glowing once they have been illuminated by the stroke writing electron beam. Thus, once the picture is drawn and stored on the screen, it does not need to be refreshed until a change is required. The screen is therefore flicker free, even when a large amount of data is stored. High resolution screens are generally adopted so that curves can be displayed almost free from steps or zig-zags, giving a high quality picture. The problem with this type of display is that if a single line is altered, the whole picture must be erased and re-drawn with the new line in position and this can be quite slow. The display of dynamic images is therefore not possible on a storage tube. Although storage tubes can have more than one brightness level, they cannot use colour.

'Stepping' or 'Aliasing' of lines

Because images on a display screen are generated by turning on and off pixels, the more the pixels, the greater the quality of the picture and the better the resolution. Fig. 14.15 shows the difference between a high and low resolution image. Each screen is rectangular with the vertical dimension three-quarters of the horizontal so that each pixel is rectangular. This is the normal ratio for most TV screens and is known as the *aspect* ratio. The screen shown in Fig. 14.15(b) has four times the resolution of that shown in Fig. 14.15(a) but each has similar

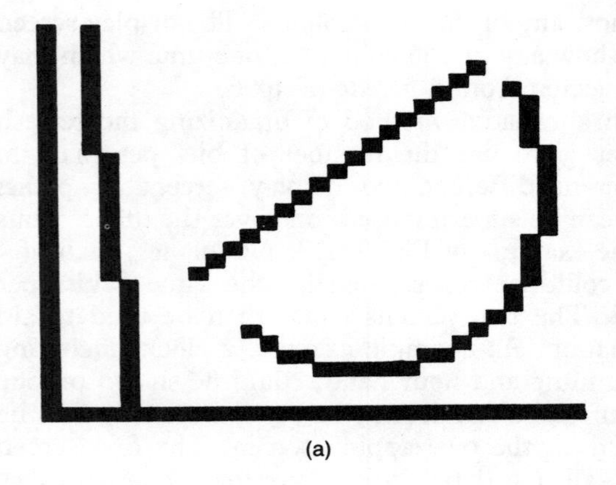
(a)

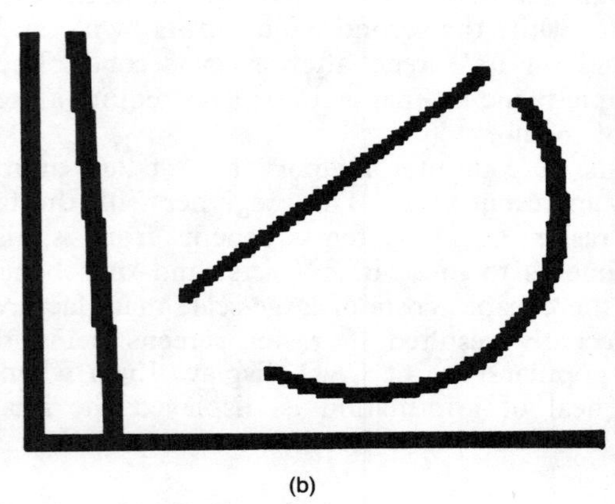
(b)

Fig.14.15 Aliasing effects on high and low resolution screens

features displayed. For the sake of comparability the line widths are the same physical width, i.e. 1 pixel wide in (a) and 4 pixels wide in (b). The difference between high and low resolution is not very noticeable with lines near the horizontal or vertical. However, diagonal or curved lines on a low resolution screen can be difficult to interpret if there are a large number of lines. The circular arc shown in (a) is particularly difficult to interpret.

In practice the steps or *aliasing* (sometimes called *zig-zags* or *jaggies*) are not as severe as shown in the illustration because the intensity of the spot of light from the pixel causes light to diffuse from its centre to overlap with its neighbours.

On a simple graphics screen, the computer works out which pixel is crossed by the centre of a thick line and then puts a '1' into the refresh buffer for only that pixel to be illuminated. In a more expensive system, the stepping effect can be

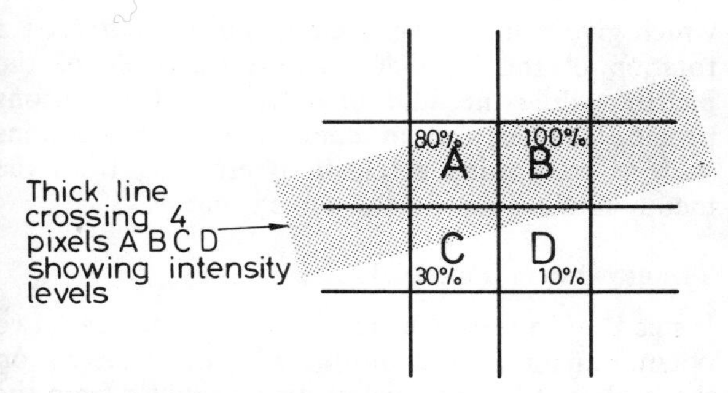

Fig.14.16 An anti-aliasing technique

minimized by looking at the pixels adjacent to the centre of a thick line in a technique called *anti-aliasing*. This concept is shown in Fig. 14.16 where part of a thick line crossed 4 pixels A, B, C, D. Pixel B is totally covered by the line and is fully lit. Pixel C is only one-third covered by the line and would, on a cheap graphics system, not be lit. An anti-aliasing technique would, however, illuminate pixel C but with an intensity only one-third that of B. Similarly A would have 80% of the intensity of B, while D has 10% of the intensity of B. The effect is that the edges of the line become diffused, lose their 'step' and are easier to interpret. However, the line also becomes less crisp. Anti-aliasing requires more memory and therefore requires more time and cost to generate a particular image. Each pixel would require several levels of intensity to be mapped, but the overall result is only one level of intensity for the line as a whole. Special anti-aliasing electronic hardware is being introduced to reduce costs, but at the present time it is still cheaper to minimize the *step* problem by opting for a high resolution screen. 'Stroke' generated screens have the added disadvantage that anti-aliasing requires a much larger number of pixels to be accessed, increasing the overall refresh time and promoting flicker.

Alpha numeric displays

In order to display images on the screen it is usual to select what you require from a *menu*. This is the name given to a list containing the type of lines, views, scales, etc., which can be chosen. While the menu could be part of a *tablet* on the desk in front of the screen, it is often more convenient for it to be part of the display screen. Frequently the *menu* is displayed along the edge or bottom of the graphics screen and a cursor used to point at whichever instruction is required. Fig. 14.17 shows a typical

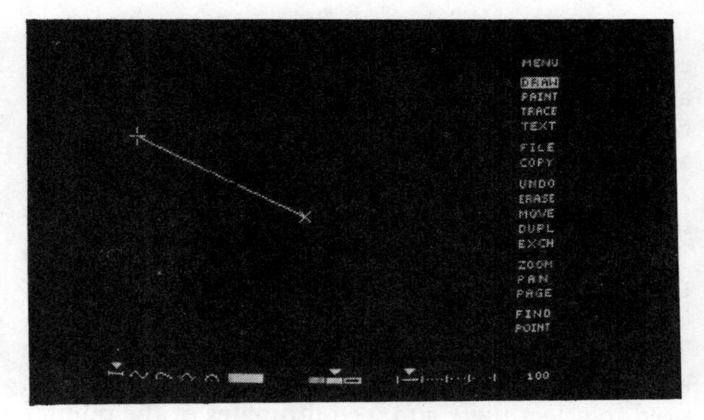

Fig.14.17 A graphics 'menu' on a display screen

arrangement. A number of menus can be listed on the screen, one replacing another so that a large number of instructions can be accessed. While it is convenient to view the menu on the screen alongside the picture to which it refers, the graphics area is thereby reduced. On large systems it is therefore usual to have a separate display screen for instructions. Since only letters and numbers are required, this is called an *alpha-numeric* screen and is often referred to as a *visual display unit* (VDU).

INPUT SYSTEMS

In order to use the graphics programs which have been loaded into the computer from disk or magnetic tape, it is necessary to interact with the programs by inputting data on to the display screen to build up views of an object. To get this information into the computer via the graphics display screen, some type of input device is needed.

On very simple graphics systems the computer keyboard is used by the operator to input data. By typing, e.g. Line $(x_1, y_1)(x_2, y_2)$ it is possible to use a simple program to draw a line from a point x_1y_1 to x_2y_2 whose co-ordinates can be specified. This type of system is slow and tedious for complex drawings and other, easier, methods are used to input data and commands on a professional CAD system. However, the ability to type in co-ordinates on a keyboard, with whatever degree of precision is required, makes this a preferred method when a high degree of accuracy is necessary.

One of the most common input systems uses a menu of drawing commands as discussed under 'Alpha numeric displays'. The advantage of this system is that it is possible to have a hierarchy of menus nested one inside the other. Thus selecting, e.g. the instruction 'draw' on one menu will automatically cause the next menu to be displayed containing a list of features to be drawn, e.g. lines, arcs, circles, etc. Selecting one of these could then access another menu from which the type of line or its co-ordinates can be selected.

To select an instruction it is necessary to point to the menu command, typically by having some control over the *x* and *y* co-ordinates of a pointer. To confirm that this is the desired location, a separate button can then be pressed. The devices used to select the *x* and *y* co-ordinates of the pointer work from a continuously varying electric signal (or *analogue* signal) which has to be converted inside the computer into a digital (binary) signal. This process is carried out by a piece of electronic hardware called an *analogue to digital converter* (A/D converter). The movement of the pointer on the display screen can be controlled by any one of the following devices.

Joystick or paddle Fig. 14.18

Essentially a joystick consists of two electrical potentiometers, one controlling the *x* co-ordinates and the other the *y* co-ordinate, which position the pointer anywhere on the screen. The pointer (or *cursor*) is often displayed as a flashing point or cross. A button on top of the joystick is used to confirm that this is the required point, whose co-ordinates are then entered into the computer.

Fig. 14.18 shows a more complex joystick controller, used on the 'Bitstick' CAD system. In addition to the usual horizontal and vertical motions which give *x* and *y* displacements of the cursor, a *z* rotation of the joystick controls the scale of the picture, while the additional L, R and T buttons provide, single and in combination, instructions such as confirming a selection, escaping from the menu, totally clearing the screen, etc.

Fig.14.18 'Bitstik' joystick controller

Thumbwheels Fig. 14.19

Instead of a joystick it is possible to use two potentiometers, fixed mutually at right angles on the keyboard so that they protrude slightly from the surface. Each thumbwheel controls respectively the *x* and *y* motions of the cursor. One of the keyboard buttons, usually the space bar, is used to confirm the menu selection.

A variation of this device called a *trackerball* consists of a trapped ball with just the surface protruding. The ball drives a pair of potentiometers on the underside. This has the advantage that diagonal motions of the trackerball adjust the two potentiometers simultaneously, making it easier to use than thumbwheels.

Fig.14.19 Keyboard cursor control

Mouse Fig. 14.20

This is a small block with a roller ball underneath which drives two potentiometers, placed mutually at right angles, to record the *x* and *y* motions of the mouse on the table. Wires from the mouse feed the signals to the computer. The mouse is free to move across the table in front of the user and does not have to be associated with any specific area on the table. The advantage of a mouse over a thumbwheel system is that, like the trackerball, diagonal movements of the mouse result in diagonal movements of the cursor on the screen. This is easier to control

Fig.14.20 A 'mouse' input system

than driving the thumbwheel x and y potentiometers separately.

GRAPHICS TABLET SYSTEMS Fig. 14.21

The graphics tablet is a board that can be placed on the table in front of a display screen so that it acts as a mimic of the screen area. Selecting a position on the tablet provides a signal to the computer so that the cursor is driven to a corresponding position on the display screen. The advantage of this approach is that the tablet can have its whole surface covered with menu instructions while leaving the screen free for drawing pictures. The disadvantage of the tablet system is that you have to look down at the tablet and up at the screen alternately and so it is easy to lose your place on the menu. Also, successive menus have to be overlaid by physically fixing separate menu sheets on to the tablet. The tablets x and y co-ordinates are

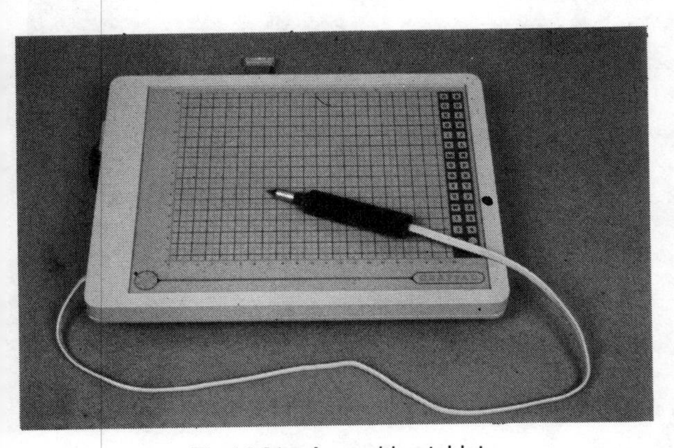

Fig.14.21 A graphics tablet

represented as analogue values and so an A/D converter is required. A variety of methods can be used to obtain the x and y locations on the tablet. The following is a list of common systems.

Pantograph Fig. 14.22

This is like a small draughting machine with two jointed links, which is clamped to the tablet at one end and a pointer moved over the board at the other. Potentiometers clamped to the joints can be calibrated, using a simple trigonometric program in the computer, to give the x and y co-ordinates of the pointer in terms of the angles θ and ϕ. Pantograph systems need very precise potentiometers to obtain even average accuracy of the pointer and so are only used for cheaper CAD systems.

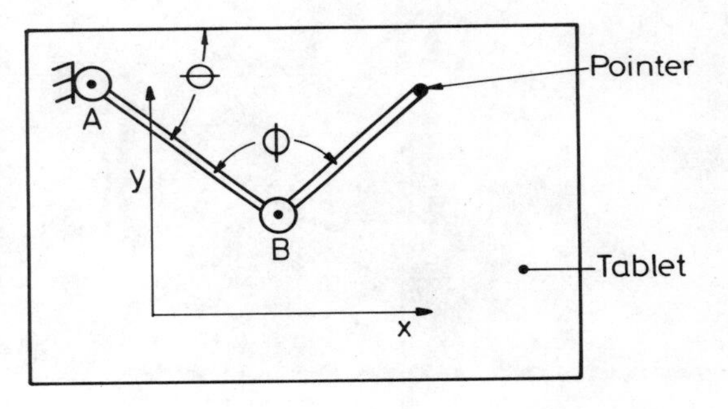

Fig.14.22 A pantograph input device. Potentiometers at A and B measure angles ϕ and θ as pointer is moved over tablet. A program converts these angles into x, y co-ordinates

Stylus and puck Fig. 14.23

In this device the pen-like *stylus* is used to point at a location on the tablet. Wires are buried under the tablet surface and create a magnetic field that is sensed by a receiver built into the stylus. On quality systems it is possible to resolve positions to better than 100 μm. An additional switch on the stylus confirms the position. The *puck* is similar to the stylus but uses a magnifying glass for accuracy. A cheaper version of the tablet uses two wires looped back and forth across the tablet surface so that they cross at right angles. The wires are held slightly apart by semi-conducting foil. Touching the surface with an ordinary pen presses the two wires together, altering the resistance of each so that the contact point can be approximately located.

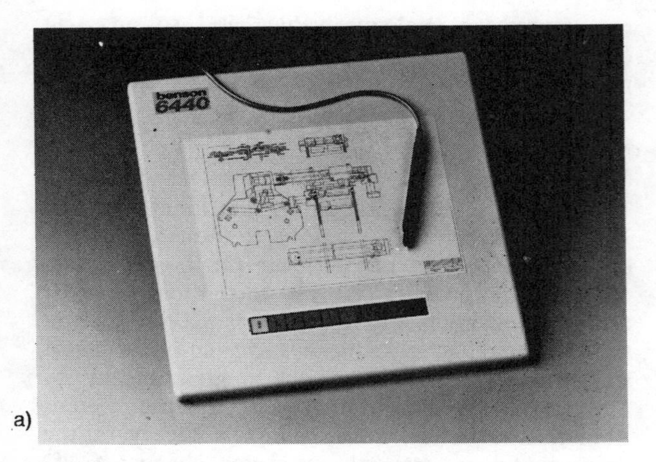

(a)

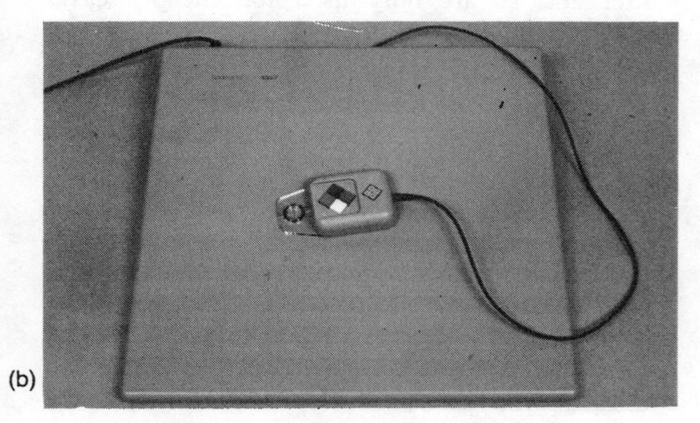

(b)

Fig.14.23 (a) stylus input device
(b) A puck input device

Light pen Fig. 14.24

This is a small pen-sized device with a light-sensitive diode in its tip. It is connected to the computer by a cable. If the pen is pointed at a glowing spot on the screen, the diode can detect this and pass a signal to the computer. Since the beam refreshes at a constant rate, the time for the refresh beam to traverse from the screen origin to the light pen can be used to give the address of the pixels and hence determine which feature is being displayed. Similarly the pen can be used to point at a cursor so movement of the pen causes the cursor to be dragged with it and be re-positioned. However, the speed at which the cursor can be dragged is limited by the refresh rate and the area scanned by the pen. Thus it is easy for the pen to lose track of the cursor. The illumination level of the screen and the angle at which the pen contacts

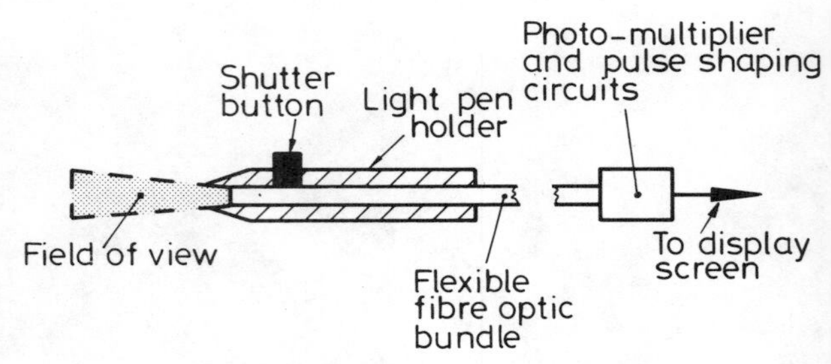

Fig.14.24 A light pen input device

the screen are both critical to successful use of the pen. Also, where two features are adjacent to each other, it is easy to 'pick' the wrong one. For all these reasons, light pens are being replaced by the tablet as the preferred system for inputting data.

Digitizers Fig. 14.25

The small tablet and stylus detailed above can also be used to input data from existing drawings as well as the menu commands previously described. Because the *x* and *y* co-ordinates of a position on the tablet are captured using the stylus, the stylus can be used to trace over a drawing and input lines to the computer as a series of vectors stored in digital form. When used in this way the tablet is described as a *digitizing* tablet. Professional digitizers tend to be expensive, large systems capable of reading drawings up to A0 size with great accuracy. To input data, a *puck*, consisting of a glass lens with

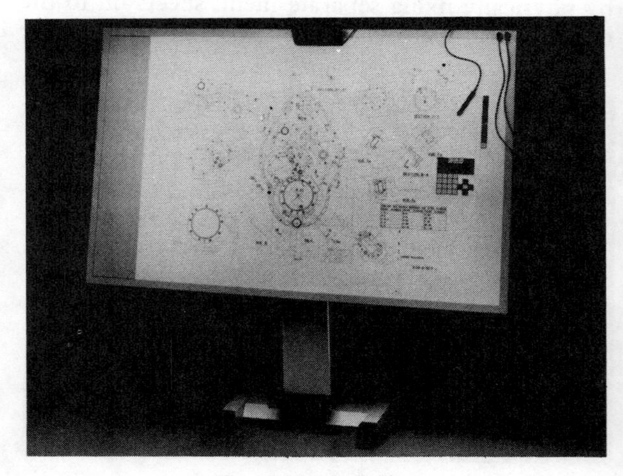

Fig.14.25 A digitizer

cross hairs, is passed over the existing drawing by hand. Each time the cross hairs are positioned over a point, its co-ordinates can be stored in the computer by pressing a button alongside the cross hairs. Additional text and features such as arrowheads are added from a keyboard.

Using a digitizer in this manner to store existing drawings is a lengthy process requiring extensive checking to ensure that the computerized drawing is free of errors. The data held in the computer by digitizing will only be a record of the drawing and will not represent the geometry of the object. To provide a solid model from such data would require a very expensive system and considerable further user input to define the product geometry. For these reasons it is not thought worth while to input existing drawings into a CAD base, unless they are part of a product range that is expected to have a long life and require frequent modifications. Most companies are content to implement CAD only for their new products.

The introduction of automatic line following systems, or *auto-vectorizers*, has helped to automate the process of digitizing. An auto-vectorizer employs a vision system which detects the contrast of ink lines on paper and will then track along the line automatically entering points as it moves. Special software ensures that raster style data for each pixel is converted to a series of vectors while the drawing is being scanned. This results in much smaller memory storage. At this stage, the image will consist of a series of often wavy lines, representing vectors and text, together with the smudges and folds of the paper. To improve the quality and remove unwanted features separate graphics *structuring* software is necessary. This enables the user to point to features which should be represented by straight lines and have them automatically straightened to their average line positions and entered into the computer as single vectors represented by their end points, instead of being entered as thousands of small vectors. Similarly the text and circular arcs can be regenerated from their vector representation and stored as separate hardware text characters or as *primitives* in which, for circles, only centres and radii are stored. Not only does this clean up the quality of text and arcs, but their representation by hardware as distinct entities or *primitives* requires a smaller memory than if stored as a large number of vectors. Even using such automatic digitizing techniques, however, digitizing of existing drawings remains a lengthy and costly process.

OUTPUT SYSTEMS

In addition to displaying drawings on a graphics screen, it is often necessary to have a permanent record or *hard copy* of a drawing. One form of hard copy is in the form of a photograph taken directly from the screen and either enlarged for display or miniaturized as a *microfiche* for filing as a record of the drawing. Microfiche filing, while useful for the storage of a large number of drawings in a small space, not only requires miniaturizing systems for producing the microfiches, but also requires special enlargers for viewing the drawings. Despite this microfiche is becoming a common form of keeping records in industry, not only of computer graphics, but also of conventionally produced engineering drawings.

The commonest form of hard copy still remains ink on paper. A number of devices are available for transferring the data from a computer on to paper.

Printers

The traditional method of producing hard copy from a computer is by using a printer for both text and graphs. It is also possible to produce simple graphics hard copy from a printer. Because a printer prints in a series of dots, the resulting graphics will not be of as high a quality as hard copy from a plotter. The results are adequate for a reasonable representation of what is seen on the screen in a process known as a *screen dump*. In this process every pixel on the screen is mapped on to the printer by a binary 1 when a dot is printed, or as a 0 when a dot is blank.

Dot matrix printers Fig. 14.26

These are the most common form of printer in particular for use on small CAD systems. The text quality is not as good as that obtained from a typewriter, but the print rate is considerably faster. Dot matrix printers operate by impacting a character on to a carbon ribbon which in turn prints on the paper in the same way in which typewriters print. Unlike the typewriters, however, which use a ready formed letterpress print character, a dot matrix printer sets up the appropriate characters as and when they are required. The printer head consists of a vertical row of nine pins which can move independently so that dots are printed as the head traverses the paper, to build up characters in

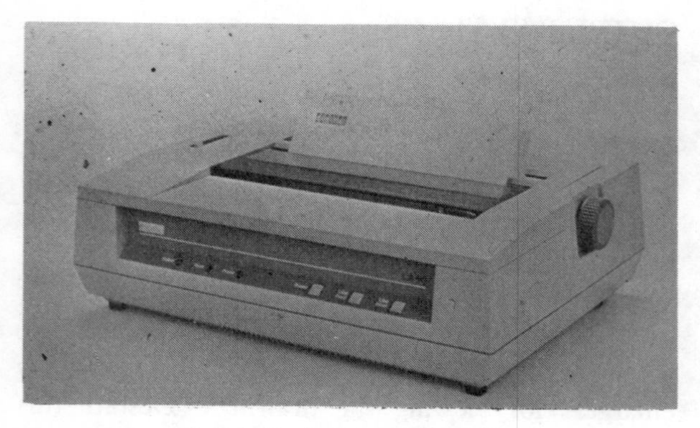

Fig.14.26 A dot matrix printer

much the same way as pixels on a raster screen. The appropriate pins forming the character are selected by the computer and pushed out by a number of tiny solenoids to strike the ribbon in the correct sequence as the head moves over the page. Typically, each character consists of a matrix of dots, 7 high by 5 wide. Because of the similarity between the dot matrix and the screen pixels, the program for a graphics screen dump is relatively simple. A limited range of colours can be added by using a printer with a series of rapidly moving coloured ink ribbons, but such devices are expensive.

The quality of text can be improved to that of a typewriter by printing each letter twice, with the dots offset by a fraction of a millimetre on the second pass. This blurs the crisp image of the dots slightly, but improves the overall quality of the print, so that it appears similar to that of a typewriter. This is known as *near letter quality* (NLQ).

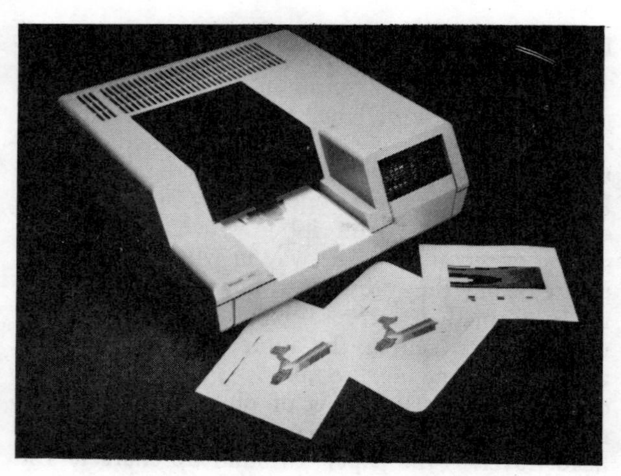

Fig.14.27 An ink jet printer

Ink jet printers Fig. 14.27

These are similar to dot matrix printers except that each dot is formed from a tiny jet of ink squirted through a hole and not by striking through a ribbon. Different coloured fast drying inks can be used. The blending together of different coloured dots gives a good range of colours.

Electrostatic printers

Electrostatic printers are fitted with an array of fine nibs that form electrostatically charged dots on the surface of the paper. Toner is placed on the charged surface and adheres to the dots to form the images. The image is then baked on by heating. Electrostatic printers produce quick monochrome copy.

Plotters Fig. 14.28

Small *x*, *y* plotters have been in use for a long time for drawing graphs, but plotters working to the same principles can be used for producing high quality engineering drawings. The paper is held on a flat bed either by suction or by electrostatic attraction. An *x* motion is given to a vertical bar that moves along the length of the bed. A pen moves on a separate carriage up and down the vertical bar to produce an independent motion. By driving the two motions in this manner, the pen can reach any position on the paper fixed to the flat bed. The direct current motors driving the plotter axes require analogue signals and thus a *digital-to-analogue* (D/A) converter is necessary to transform the digital signals from the computer to suit the analogue motors. The up and down motion of the pen is controlled by a solenoid determining when a

Fig.14.28 A flat bed plotter

line is to be drawn or a space is to occur. An alternative arrangement is to employ a stepper motor to drive the x and y motions, in which case a D/A converter is not necessary, because the computer digital signals can pulse the motors directly.

Large versions of x, y plotters of A0 size, but also up to E size, are used in industry for the production of quality engineering drawings. These are known as *flat bed* plotters and have an accuracy of about 0.1 mm.

Drum plotter Fig. 14.29

A pen moves backwards and forwards along a bar placed along the length of a drum to form the y motion. Paper is wound around the drum and the drum rotated to give the x motion. Because the paper is wound around the drum, virtually unlimited lengths of drawings can be produced. Different widths of pen and colours of inks may be inserted by the operator, or a group of pens may be held in a rack and be automatically selected when a different width or colour of line is required by the computer program.

Turtle Fig. 14.30

Turtle is the name given to a free-moving plotting device which can move around a flat surface. It is attached to the computer by a long lead. The turtle has a pen fixed to its underside which can be raised and lowered. The wheels can be incrementally driven by signals from the computer. Commands are relatively simple, but must be programmed in an exact sequence. A typical series of instructions would be: pen up; forward 100 mm; rotate 90°; forward 100 mm; pen down; forward 75 mm; rotate 120°; forward 75 mm; rotate 120°; forward 75 mm; pen up; stop. This sequence would position the turtle at a starting position $x = 100$, $y = 100$ and then draw an equilateral triangle of 75 mm side length. Although slow, a turtle can be quite accurate and provides an inexpensive means of producing drawings for low-cost CAD systems.

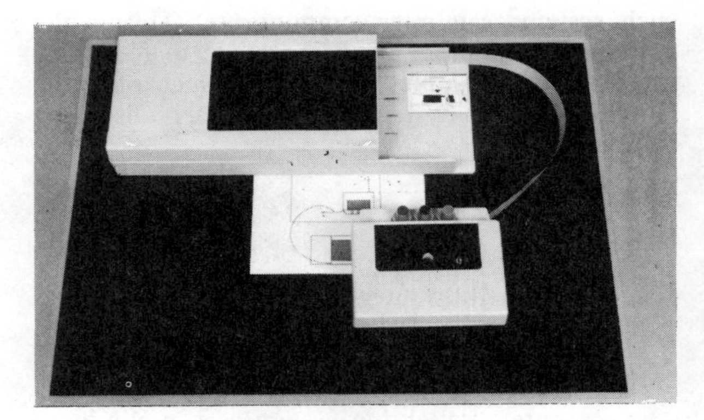

Fig.14.30 Turtle

Fig.14.29 A drum plotter

Note The need for hard copy of engineering drawings is largely an interim stage in the implementation of CAD. In those industries where CAD/CAM is well advanced, with a sufficient number of graphics terminals in both design offices and factory, hard copy is not needed. This is because all the data required can be accessed directly from graphics terminals. The automotive manufacturer British Leyland, for example, has announced the paperless factory in which all traditional drawing boards are replaced by graphics screens and all drawings in the factory viewed on display screens. However, the implications of this approach are that small sub-contractors supplying components to the main company, should also have their product drawings stored on CAD systems. This would not be a problem if the sub-contractors could afford to install a large CAD system similar to that installed in the main company to enable the two systems to communicate directly. However, the sub-contractors need only install a low-cost CAD system and it is unusual for such systems to be able to communicate directly with the larger systems. A series of internationally agreed standards are required for both hardware and software before such systems can inter-communicate. This is the reason why attempts are being made to formulate international graphics standards such as the Graphics Kernel System (GKS). This is discussed in Chapter 15.

Exercises

(1) Why is a fully integrated CAD system useful for more than draughting? Justify the cost in comparison with a 2-D draughting system.

(2) A small company wishes to introduce a computer draughting system as a preliminary to eventually introducing a wide range of CAD activity. What type of system would you recommend for the first purchase so that its capability could be gradually expanded?

(3) It is proposed to purchase a large central computer, together with a number of *dumb* graphics terminals (i.e. having no additional graphic processors) for the full range of CAD activity. Discuss the advantages and disadvantages of this type of system.

(4) A CAD system comprises a number of intelligent work stations linked to a large central computer as shown in Fig. 14.5.
(a) Distinguish between the role of the CPU in the central computer from that of the intelligent work stations.
(b) Contrast the role of the central magnetic tape facility with that of the work station's floppy disks.

(5) Why is it that although simple computer draughting systems have a small CPU memory and 8 bit word structure, for larger CAD systems considerable memory and a 32 bit word structure is usually necessary.

(6) What are the functions of secondary storage systems for CAD? Distinguish between their relative merits.

(7) A small company wishes to purchase a number of raster displays for computer draughting and solid modelling. Discuss the benefits of using colour or monochrome displays and high or low resolution screens.

(8) A raster scan monochrome 256 × 256 display is to be used for CAD. An image is to be displayed in which the central 4 pixels are turned *on*. These are surrounded by a band, 2 pixels wide, which is *off*. These in turn are surrounded by a further band, 2 pixels wide, which is turned *on*.
(a) Sketch the frame buffer for such a display indicating the bit pattern in the central region.
(b) How many bytes are needed for such a display?

(9) The screen in Exercise 8 is now a colour display in which 4 bits per pixel are used for addressing a colour map having 9 bits per address. In addition there are 2 bit planes used for animation.
(a) Sketch the arrangement of frame buffer, colour maps and screen.
(b) How many shades of colour can be represented on the screen?
(c) Calculate the new memory requirements for the display.

(10) Discuss the relative merits of raster scan, line drawing refresh and storage tube displays.

(11) A series of concentric circles, each represented by 32 facets is to be displayed on a vector refresh display. If the average time per vector is 30 microseconds, how many flicker-free circles can be displayed?

(12) A 128 × 128 raster display has a line 1 pixel wide drawn diagonally across the centre of the screen at 30° to the horizontal.
(a) Show the aliasing effect on the screen's central 16 pixels.
(b) If the anti-aliasing techniques were used, indicate the percentage brightness for the central 16 pixels.
(c) If the brightness level, including on and off were controlled by only 2 bits, draw the new anti-aliased screen image.

(13) Contrast the uses of a mouse on its own with that of a mouse used with a tablet. Why is a mouse superior to a pair of thumbwheels on a keyboard for most applications? When are the thumbwheels preferable?

(14) Why do most input systems have at least one switch associated with them?

(15) Why are companies generally not digitizing their existent drawings on paper?

(16) Auto-vectorizers generally store primitives and their attributes rather than digitized vectors. Why is this?

(17) A small company with a cheaper CAD installation may well use an ink jet printer as a screen dump, rather than use, say, a drawing plotter. Why is this? What disadvantages would it have compared with a drawing plotter?

(18) Why is it that plotters and printers are likely to disappear from use in the long term? What problems must first be overcome?

15 Computer graphics software

AN INTRODUCTION TO BASIC ASPECTS OF PROGRAMMING

Before discussing concepts specifically concerned with graphics software and how graphics programs operate, it is necessary to consider some of the more general concepts concerned in all programming.

LANGUAGES

As discussed in Chapter 14, a program (or algorithm) is a sequence of instructions which are carried out sequentially by the computer hardware. Chapter 14 also explained how the computer memory consists of a series of binary *bits* which are programmed to be either ON or OFF. Bits are combined together in groups to form instructions called a *machine code*. A machine code numbering system can present difficulties to the newcomer because it is based not on a decimal notation (i.e. to the base 10), but on a hexadecimal notation (i.e. to the base 16). A hexadecimal notation is used because it is convenient to store numbers in groups of four binary bits (e.g. 1111) which can represent 16 numbers from 0 to 15. The 16 numbers of the hexadecimal system are represented from 0 to 9, then the letters A, B, C, D, E and F represent 10 to 15. In order to ensure that everyone knows that a hexadecimal system is being employed, a prefix or suffix is used with the number. A number of alternatives are used. In the BBC micro, a prefix *&* is used, i.e. *&A24* represents in hexadecimal, the decimal number:

$$10(16)^2 + 2(16)^1 + 4(16)^0 = 2596.$$

Other commonly used hexadecimal formats are $A24; A24H; $A24_{16}$

It is usual to talk of the size of computer memory in groups of 8 bits, known as a *byte* (from the expression *by eight*), e.g. 64K. However, a 64K memory does not represent 64 000 bytes because in computer terminology K does not refer to 1000 but to 1024 (i.e. the binary number 100 00000000). Thus a 64K memory will give:

$$64 \times 1024 \times 8 = 524\,288 \text{ bits of memory.}$$

The term for half a byte, representing 4 bits is a *nybble*. Thus, although it was shown in Chapter 14 that a *word* varies in size depending upon the computer being used, a bit, byte and nybble are all fixed in size.

If a complex program were written as a series of instructions in *machine* code, it would be carried out very speedily and efficiently by the computer. This is because machine code is based in binary bits and the computer works on binary bits. However, the overall program would be very lengthy to write and would be difficult to understand. The next highest level of coding in which it is possible to write long programs is in a language called *assembler*. Assembler programs also run in the computer speedily and efficiently. Assembler statements consist of instructions such as LDA#2 (load a temporary memory store or *accumulator* with the number 2); STA &1FF (take the contents of the accumulator and store them in a memory address whose location is hex1FF). From assembler programs both instructions and data can be automatically translated or *compiled* by the computer into the hexadecimal machine code form. The assembler program is known as the *source code*, while the compiled form is called the *object code*. Although assembler is very efficient, it is still cumbersome to write and to understand and is known as a *low level* language.

For complex programs it is usual to write in a *high level* language. The language called BASIC (Beginners All-purpose Symbolic Instruction Code) is one of the most easily understood high level languages because it contains a number of English style statements. It is frequently used in schools and colleges for the more simple types of computer graphics. The following illustrates a simple BASIC program for drawing a square.

```
 10 REM. PROG 1. THIS PROGRAM
    DRAWS A SQUARE
 20 X = 200
 30 Y = 250
 40 L = 50
 50 MOVE X,Y
 60 DRAW X,Y+L
 70 DRAW X+L,Y+L
 80 DRAW X+L,Y
 90 DRAW X,Y
100 END
```

Each line of the program is numbered. The REM statement is not acted upon. It is a remark to aid the understanding of the program. Lines 20 to 40 provide the *data* for the program, with lines 20 and 30 stating the *x* and *y* co-ordinates, referred to the screen origin in absolute co-ordinates. Line 40 states the required length of the sides of the square. Line 50 moves the cursor to the start point for drawing the square. Lines 60 to 90 draw the square of side length L in a clockwise direction, starting with the vertical line. Line 100 ends the program.

Typing RUN into the computer keyboard would result in the BASIC program being compiled into object code while running and the square would then be drawn on the display screen. To modify the size of the square, it would only be necessary to change L in line 40. The square could be positioned anywhere on the screen by changing the values of *x* and *y* in lines 20 and 30. The strength of BASIC is

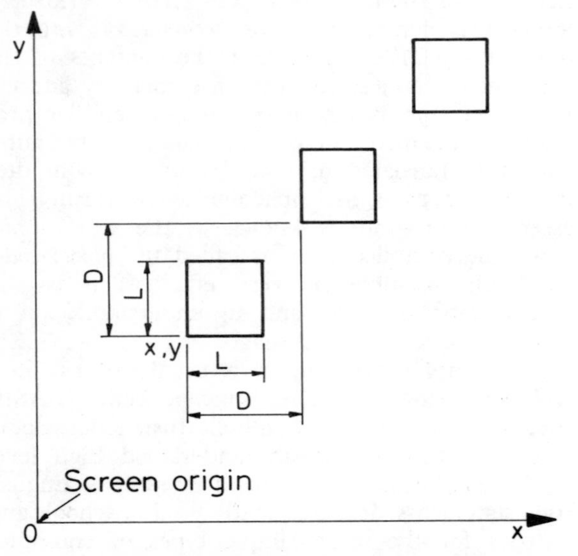

Fig. 15.1 3 squares resulting from Program 2, drawn together with axes and dimensions

that it is easy to use, e.g. to set up conditional logic statements using commands such as IF . . . THEN . . . . This instruction could allow the sequence of commands being executed to branch off into a side loop until a particular condition is met, when the program could once again continue its sequence. This type of conditional logic has already been discussed in Chapter 13 on flow charts. The effect of introducing conditional logic can be seen in an amplification of the previous program for drawing a square to one in which three squares are drawn offset from the first as shown in Fig. 15.1. The BASIC program is as follows:

```
 10 REM. PROG 2. THIS PROGRAM
    DRAWS 3 SQUARES
 20 X = 200
 30 Y = 250
 40 L = 50
 50 D = 100
 60 N = 3
 70 C = 1
 80 MOVE X,Y
 90 DRAW X,Y+L
100 DRAW X+L,Y+L
110 DRAW X+L,Y
120 DRAW X,Y
130 IF C = N THEN END
140 C = C+1
150 X = X+D
160 Y = Y+D
170 GOTO 80
180 END
```

Program 2 uses program 1 to draw the square as before but, in addition, uses a count 'C' which is set to 1 initially in line 70. Having drawn the square in lines 80 to 120, line 130 then checks the count to see if C = N (i.e. 3). If it does then the program ends. If it does not, then line 140 is carried out and the count C is incremented by 1. The values of X and Y are then incremented by a displacement value D before the program returns to line 80 to draw a new square. This process is then repeated a third time, so that now C = N and hence in line 130 the program ends.

The structure of program 2 is now rather awkward and could be tidied up to become easier to follow. Because program 2 uses the simple routine of program 1 to draw a square over and over again, it would be easier if we called program 1 as a separate '*procedure*'. The BBC microcomputer is an example of a system which has a powerful procedure routine. Program 3 shows how program 2 would appear on a BBC micro using a procedure called 'PROCSQUARE' to draw the square which can be separately defined at lines 90 to 150. The use of the 'procedure' makes the program easier to follow. Because program 3 is designed for use on a BBC micro, the resolution and colours available on the screen must first be defined by line 15. Mode 1 defines a graphics screen mode in which the screen has a resolution of 320 pixels horizontally by 256 vertically and four colours are available for each pixel. If programs 1 and 2 are also to be run on the BBC micro, then the programs will each require the additional line: 15 MODE 1

```
 10 REM. PROG 3. USING PROCEDURES
 15 MODE 1
 20 X = 200: Y = 250: L = 50: D = 100:
    N = 3
 30 FOR C = 1 TO N
 40 PROCSQUARE
 50 X = X+D
 60 Y = Y+D
 70 NEXT C
 80 END
 90 DEF PROCSQUARE
100 MOVE X,Y
110 DRAW X,Y+L
120 DRAW X+L,Y+L
130 DRAW X+L,Y
140 DRAW X,Y
150 ENDPROC
```

Line 20 gives a string of data. Lines 30 and 70 control the number of repetitions of drawing the square. Line 40 calls for a specific procedure called PROCSQUARE which is defined in lines 90 to 150.

While BASIC, like other high level languages, is easy to write and understand, it is quite slow to run because the compiled version will usually contain a large number of redundant statements. If it is necessary for small sections of the program to run quickly, e.g. for a dynamic display, then it is quite usual to have that section written in assembler code and called up from the main BASIC program.

Another popular high level language called FORTRAN is slightly more removed from everyday English than BASIC. However, it is much more suitable for calculating mathematical formulae. Since complex drawings involve many calculations, a large number of the professional CAD systems were programmed in FORTRAN. FORTRAN statements do not require line numbers and are thus easily distinguished from BASIC. FORTRAN source statements must be compiled into object code as a separate activity prior to running the program. This makes 'editing' the program into its final form a little more tedious but improves the time required for the computer to execute the program.

Other high level languages which are becoming popular for complex graphics programs are called 'C' and 'PASCAL'. These have a highly structured approach which is well suited to graphics programming because there are often a number of *nested* routines which are placed one inside another and have many different *branch* and *return* loops. The structure which is imposed by these languages makes it less likely that the programmer will have a loop return to the wrong location. This could be a condition which would not show up for some time until, when the particular branch is called, the program fails to do what was intended, often with disconcerting results whose cause can be difficult to locate and remedy.

FILING SYSTEMS

Because graphics software is lengthy, particularly when the applications data is also included, it is often necessary to have sections of programs transferred from disk into the computer memory and then back to the disk again repeatedly. Indeed in smaller microcomputer-based systems, a different floppy disk is used to hold each part of the program. The following separate *files* are used in many smaller graphics systems.

Graphics system software

This file will contain most of the standard software required to prepare a particular drawing and will include routines for drawing lines, arcs, circles, etc., in different colours and line types, to a variety of scales, etc. This is usually loaded into the computer memory. The additional software that is required is in the form of a *Read Only Memory* (ROM) chip. This is a dedicated microchip which will allow those routines which are used most frequently to run much more quickly than if they were programmed in software. The ROM chip can only be read from and cannot be re-programmed by writing new programs to it. To be able to change the program using software, a chip known as *Random Access Memory* (RAM) is needed.

The working file

In order to build up a picture of a drawing, it is necessary to use the graphics system software to create a series of lines which are stored in a working file (or *work page*) which is held in the computer memory. By referring to a series of *menu* commands, it is possible to move the cursor around the work page on the screen, draw lines of several types and colours, delete any part of the drawing, etc., in order to build up the final version of your drawing on the work page.

Library files

Having created the required drawings, it is possible to store them on a separate disk called a library file. Most small CAD systems allow the user to store a number of pictures in separate library files. In this way a series of simple drawings can be filed separately and then called up to be combined to form a more complex drawing on the work page, which can in turn be filed in the library. In this way drawings of considerable complexity can be gradually built up. It is usually possible to display the library files as pictures on the display screen because they are stored in the file as scaled down images. This allows the user to identify quickly the various files without having to remember what name they are filed under. Having finally completed a drawing, it is possible to then store it on a separate *archive* disk which is used only for finished drawings.

A 'buffer' disk

During the process of producing the finalized drawing of a work page, particularly on the smaller micro-based CAD systems, occasions will arise when the computer memory is too small to contain both the full system software and the work page contents. In this instance a *buffer* disk is employed as a temporary storage to swop programs backwards and forwards as a drawing is being compiled.

PRINCIPLES OF GRAPHICS SOFTWARE CO-ORDINATE SYSTEMS

In order to represent 2-D (two-dimensional) objects, the graphics screen can be used quite simply to represent the two axes of the object employing the vertical screen direction as the y axis and the horizontal direction as the x axis. Difficulties arise when defining 3-D (three-dimensional) objects which require a third z axis because of a number of conventions. The most common convention adopted in texts on geometry is known as the *right hand Cartesian co-ordinate axis system*. This is illustrated in Fig. 15.2. In this system the x and y axes are as in the 2-D system and the positive z axis is shown as if coming out of the paper. Thus a point in 3-D space is defined by the Cartesian co-ordinate dimensions $x_1y_1z_1$.

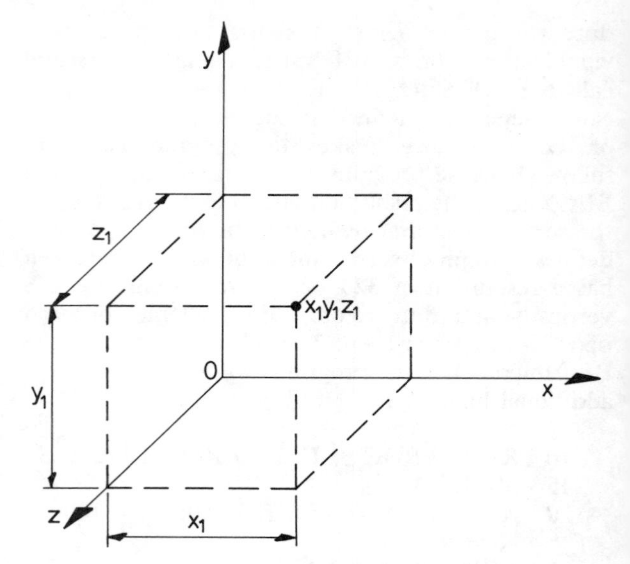

Fig.15.2 Positive axes in a right hand Cartesian co-ordinate system

If the point is rotated, say about the $0z$ axis, the positive angle is conventionally taken as counter-clockwise. Thus moving the point from $x_1y_1z_1$ to $x_2y_2z_2$ will produce the result as shown in Fig. 15.3 when viewed along $z0$. An alternative way of viewing the rotation is to think of the point as fixed with reference to a *world* co-ordinate system, while the axes are rotated. The result would be as shown in Fig. 15.4 in which the axes are moved through a clockwise angle θ. This concept can arouse confusion because some texts use a convention of moving the object with reference to a fixed set of axes, others employ a convention of moving the axes with reference to the fixed object.

Further confusion can arise because some texts describe a left hand set of Cartesian angles as indicated by Fig. 15.5. This method is favoured in some texts where it is thought to be more 'natural' for the depth of the object (along the z axis) to recede away from the observer into the plane of the

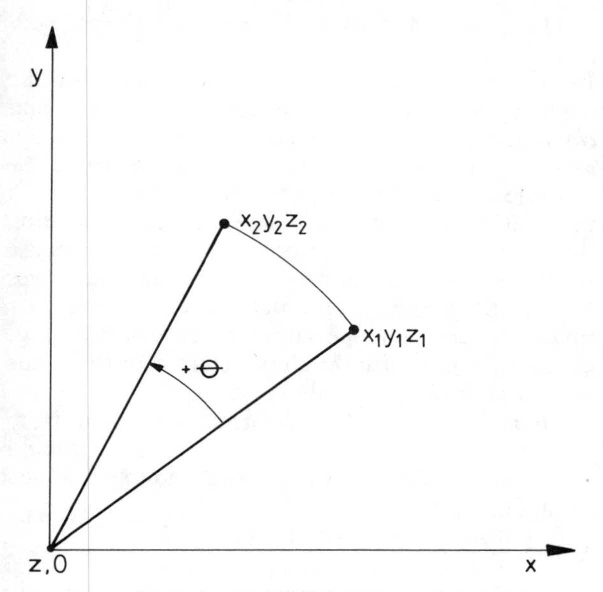

Fig.15.3 Rotation of object +⊖ in right hand co-ordinate system

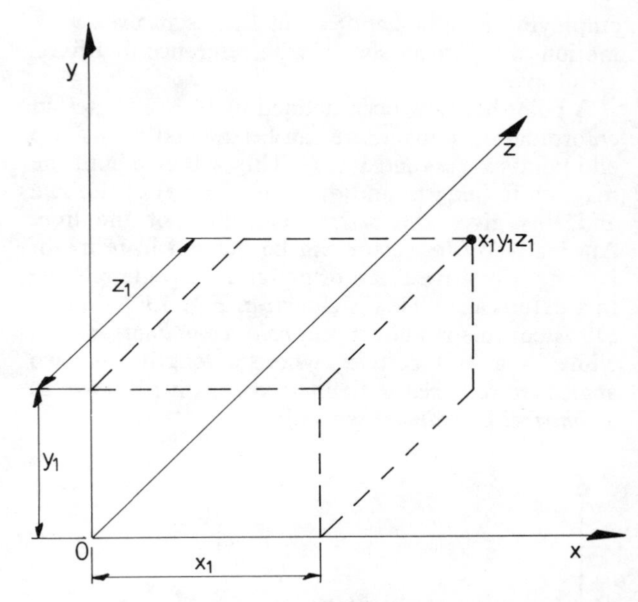

Fig.15.5 Left hand co-ordinate set of positive axes

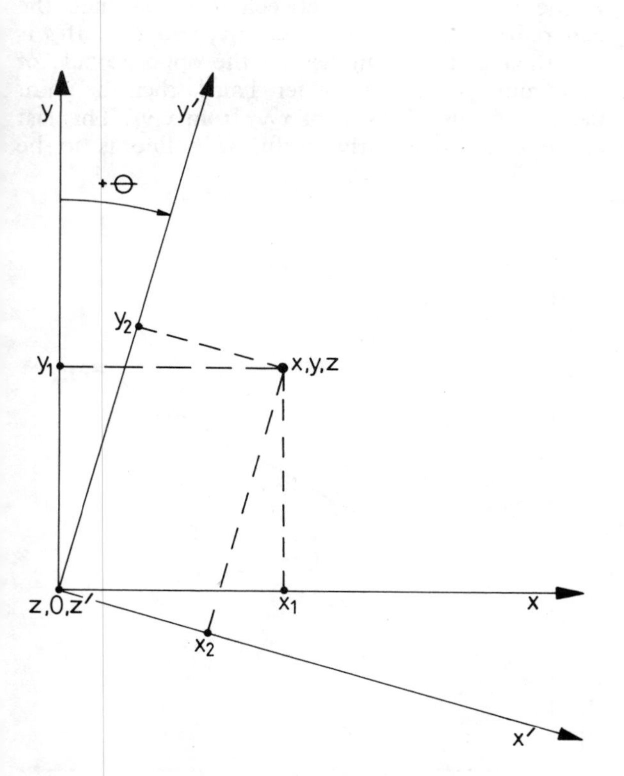

Fig.15.4 Rotation of axes by +⊖ in right hand co-ordinate system

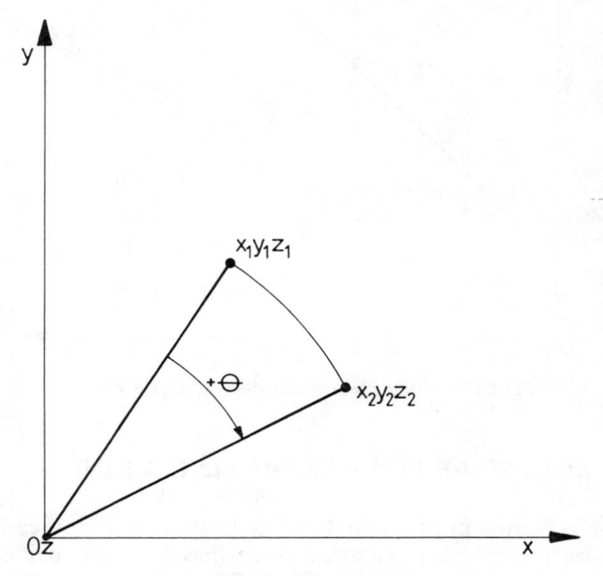

Fig.15.6 Rotation of object by +⊖ in a left hand co-ordinate system

graphics screen. In a left hand co-ordinate system, a positive rotation of the object about the origin is seen as a clockwise rotation, as shown in Fig. 15.6.

It is usual for graphics to have their origins defined at the lower left. Some screens, however, use the upper left corner as the origin.

In this text we will adopt the convention of

employing a right hand set of Cartesian axes with motion of an object shown with reference to a fixed set of axes.

A point has now been defined by its *xyz* Cartesian co-ordinates. Thus a line can be defined by its two end points $x_1y_1z_1$ and $x_2y_2z_2$. This will give both the magnitude (length) and direction (angle) of the line and this gives the *vector* definitions of the line. Alternatively the vector can be defined in terms of its length relative to an origin and its angle relative to a datum axis. This is shown in Fig. 15.7. In a 2-D system this is known as a *polar co-ordinate system*, while in a 3-D system, where a length and two angles are required to define a vector, it is known as a *spherical co-ordinate system*.

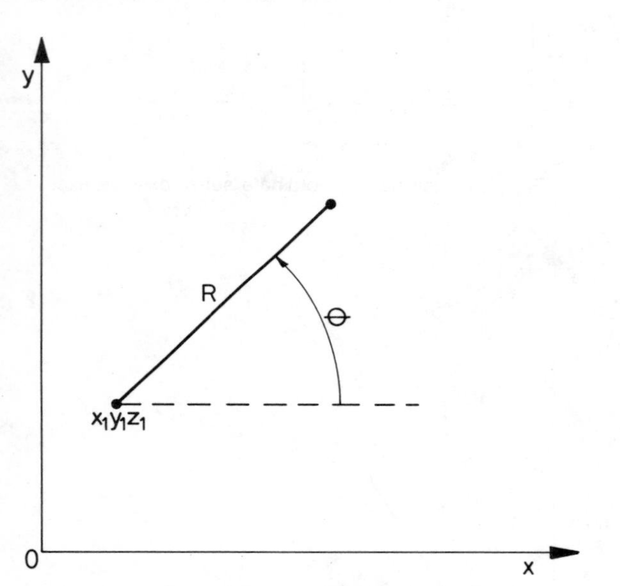

Fig.15.7 Polar co-ordinate definition of a vector

SOFTWARE FOR GENERATING A LINE

As shown in program 1, a line from x_1y_1 to x_2y_2 can be drawn on a microcomputer-based system using an instruction such as DRAW X_1Y_1, X_2Y_2. We have seen, however, in Chapter 14 that by using either raster scan or refresh display, the computer must generate a series of points between the two ends of the line corresponding to each pixel that needs to be turned on. Thus an additional series of calculations is required to find all the appropriate pixels that must be lit between the two ends of the line. There are a number of methods of doing this, all based on the definition of a line.

The general definition of a line in 2-D space is:

$$ay = bx + c$$

In the graph Fig. 15.8 b/a is the tangent of the angle made by the line with the positive x axis and c/a is the constant at which the line crosses the y axis. Making use of this equation, it would be possible to increment in the x direction by $\triangle x$, a pixel at a time and calculate the corresponding increment $\triangle y$ in the y direction. However, because the slope b/a becomes very large as the line moves towards the vertical, computational accuracy is poor unless a series of special cases is invoked, e.g. changing over to use the slope referred to the y axis when the angle moves above 45°.

An alternative and more usual treatment is to consider the line from x_1y_1 to x_2y_2 as containing a generalized point xy. A ratio p can now be defined as in Fig. 15.9 as:

$$p = \frac{\text{distance of } xy \text{ from } x_1y_1}{\text{distance from } x_1y_1 \text{ to } x_2y_2} = \frac{l}{R}$$

The generalized point then has the co-ordinates:

$$x = [(1 - p)x_1 + px_2] \text{ and}$$
$$y = [(1 - p)y + py_2]$$

If the value of p lies between 0 and 1 then the generalized point lies between x_1y_1 and x_2y_2. If p is less than 0, the point lies on the opposite side of x_1y_1 from x_2y_2. If p is greater than 1, then the point lies on the opposite side of x_2y_2 from x_1y_1. This last concept is particularly useful if a line is to be

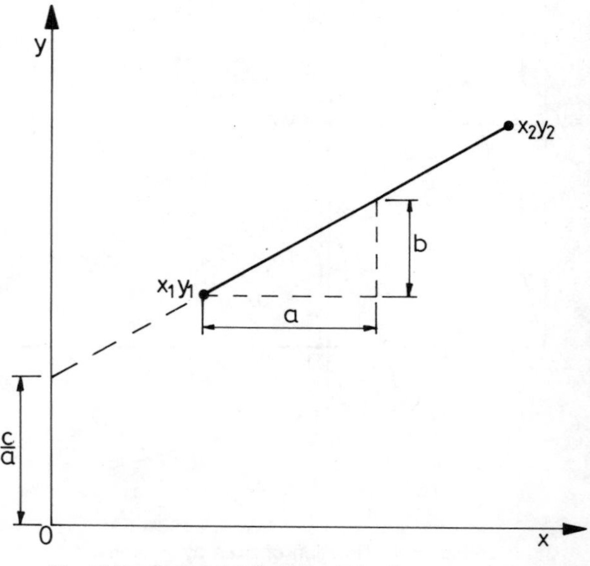

Fig.15.8 General definition of the line $ay = bx+c$

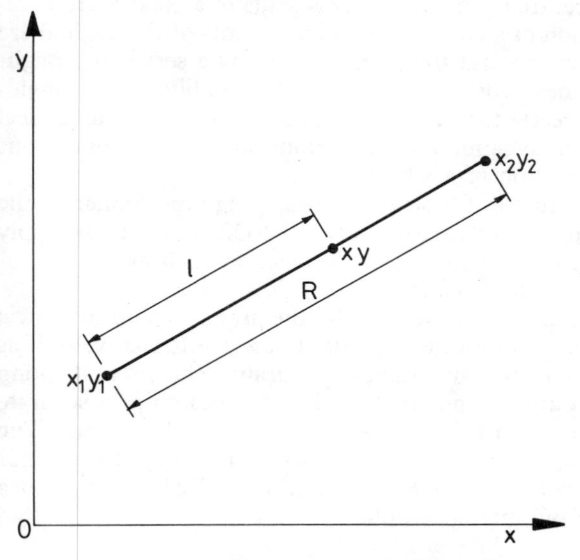

Fig.15.9 Definition of a point lying on a line

enlarged. The equations in this form of expression for a line are:

$x = x_1 + (x_2 - x_1)p$

$y = y_1 + (y_2 - y_1)p$

or, combining to eliminate p:

$(y_1 - y_2)x + (x_2 - x_1)y + x_1y_2 - x_2y_1 = 0$

Thus values of $\triangle y$ can be calculated for increments in $\triangle x$ to, once again, give those pixels which should be lit. It is this type of calculation which takes place whenever a line is drawn. However, because this is a time-consuming process, calculations at this level are usually carried out in a special-purpose microchip which is part of the graphics processor contained in most home computers with a graphics capability. Hence this calculation and the associated pixel fill are performed whenever a command such as

DRAW X1Y1,X2Y2

is given.

It can be seen that many of the tasks which are quite simple for the draughtsman, e.g. drawing a line between two points, are more complicated when carried out by a computer and often require a mathematical expression to be generated. The intuitive procedures of the draughtsman are replaced by detailed mathematical processes within the computer. Thus a study of computer graphics needs to include some mathematics concerned with the description and transformation of graphical primitives. However, these expressions are kept at a relatively simple level in this chapter.

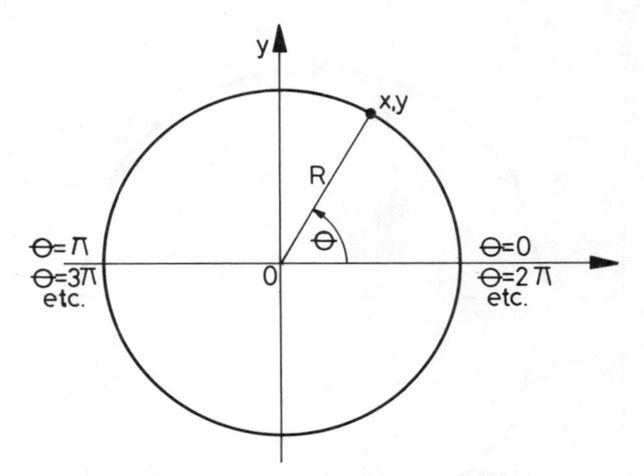

Fig.15.10 Multiple rotations resulting from the definition of a circle

SOFTWARE FOR GENERATING A CIRCLE

Circles or arcs of circles are similarly required to have their own software routines.

Complete circles

The equation for a circle with axes located at the circle centre (Fig. 15.10) is:

$y = \sqrt{(R^2 - x^2)}$

This form, in which y is expressed as a function of x, is known as an *explicit* form in which there is only one y value for each x value. However, since the circle is a closed form, the point $\theta = 0$ is also the point $\theta = 2\pi$ radians, and for multiple rotations $\theta = 4\pi$, etc. In order to deal with this closed value condition, the equation must be changed to an *implicit* form. The implicit form of the circle shown in Fig. 15.11 is:

$(x - x_1)^2 + (y - y_1)^2 - R^2 = 0$

Hence the correct point on the implicit curve can be found by calculating the roots of the algebraic equation.

A difficulty with this form of equation is that, if the increments of x are equal and the corresponding values of y are calculated, the dots shown in Fig. 15.11 are produced. Since the dots are not equi-spaced around the circle, joining them with a series of straight lines would result in a form giving a poor representation of a circle. This form of algebraic expression is known as *non-parametric*. Non-parametric curves are very dependent upon the choice of axes for their ease of use.

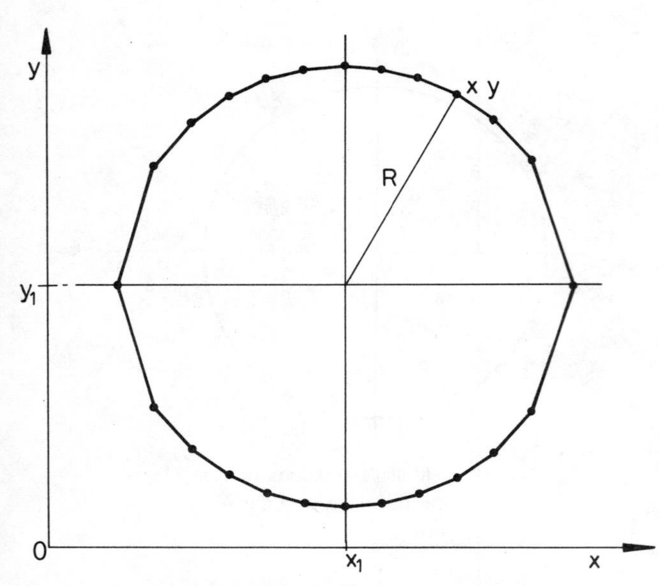

Fig.15.11 Non-parametric representation of a circle by 24 points

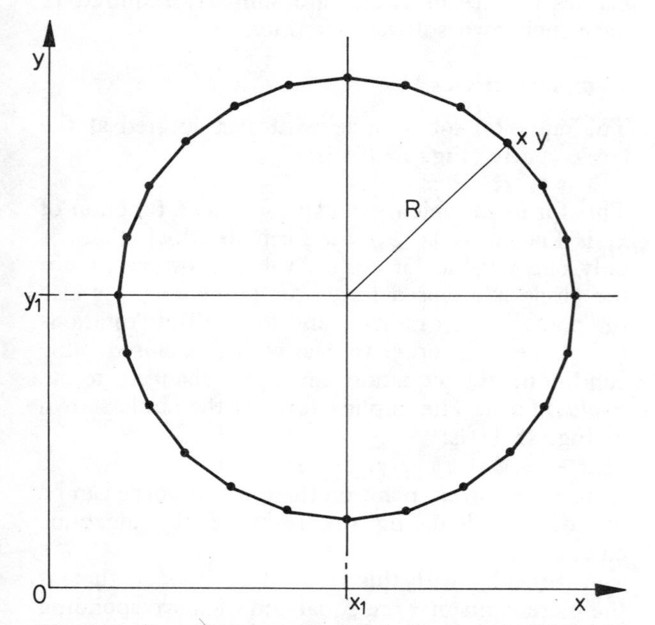

Fig.15.12 Parametric representation of a circle by 24 points

A more accurate representation of a circle, as shown in Fig. 15.12, employs a *parametric* form:

$x = x_1 + R\cos\theta$

$y = y_1 + R\sin\theta$

Here the circle is represented in polar form using the parameter θ, i.e. the angle subtended at the centre of the circle. This leads to a good representation of a circle if equal increments of the angle θ are chosen and the points joined by a series of straight lines. Also, since θ can be readily set to angles greater than 2π radians, the parametric form is ideal for dynamic representations such as the continuous rotation of a wheel.

Just as for straight lines, programs similar to the above are part of a special ROM chip. It is simply necessary to give an instruction such as

DRAW CIRCLE (X,Y,R)

to employ automatically the graphics chip to draw a circle of radius R centred at x,y. Alternatively, if as in very basic graphics programs, the circle drawing routine is not part of the graphics chip, a separate procedure for drawing circles could be set out. The following procedure could be part of a routine for drawing a circle of radius R and centre x_1y_1 on a BBC microcomputer:

```
10 DEF PROCCIRCLE (X1,Y1,R)
20 MOVE X1+R,Y1
30 FOR THETA = 10 TO 360 STEP 10
40 X = R*COS(RAD(THETA))
50 Y = R*SIN(RAD(THETA))
60 DRAW X1+X,Y1+Y
70 NEXT THETA
80 ENDPROC
```

Line 20 moves the cursor to a point on the circle to the right of the centre located at x_1y_1. Line 30 defines an angle THETA in 10 degree steps from 10° to 360°. Lines 40 and 50 give the parametric representations of the circle with angle THETA converted to radians. Line 60 draws to the point defined by $x_1 + x$, $y_1 + y$. Line 70 increments the value of THETA and returns control to line 30 to calculate the new co-ordinates of the point on the circumference of the circle. This procedure is repeated until THETA = 360°.

Circular arcs

If a circular arc were represented solely by its end points and its radius an ambiguity would arise, since the curve could be either concave or convex (Fig. 15.13). This can be avoided by attaching a convention sign to the radius, but would still lead to ambiguity if the arc angle were greater than 180°. Also the points of the arc have to be less than $2R$ apart. It is often easier and more useful if the arc centre, radius and angles corresponding to the two end points can be specified as in Fig. 15.14. This

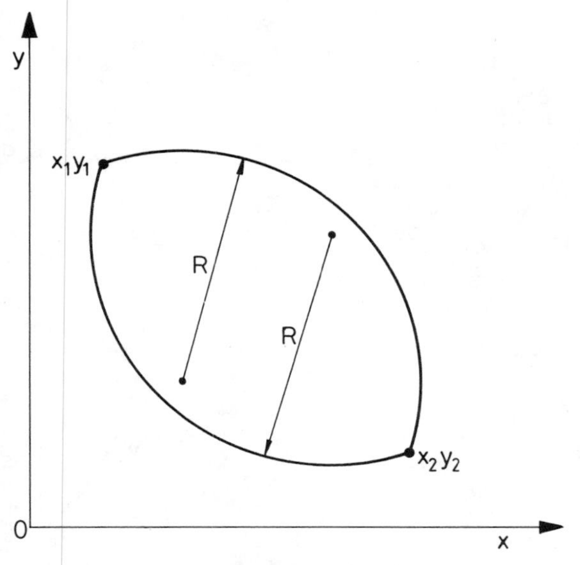

Fig.15.13 Two interpretations of an arc using end points and radius

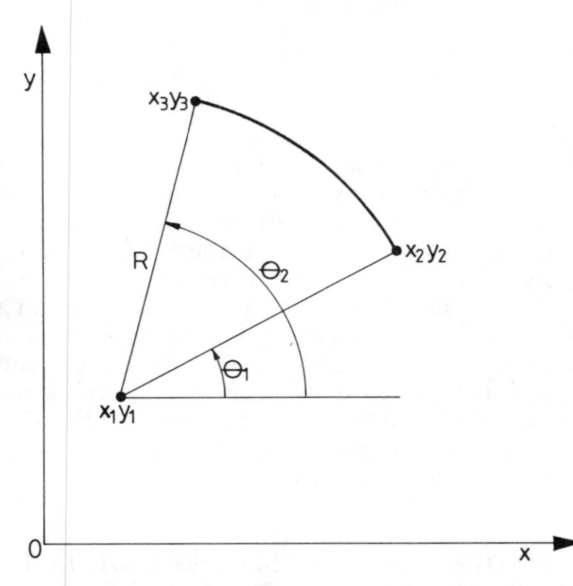

Fig.15.14 An alternative representation of an arc

representation uses the same parametric form as for a full circle. Thus the end points are given by:

$$x_2 = x_1 + R \cos \theta_1$$
$$y_2 = y_1 + R \sin \theta_1$$

and

$$x_3 = x_1 + R \cos \theta_2$$
$$y_3 = y_1 + R \sin \theta_2$$

Some devices, such as expensive plotters and refresh displays have circle generaters built into them at a hardware level. Not only do these produce fast and efficient plots, but they also plot a large number of points, giving high quality circles. For most cheaper displays, however, the circle is approximated by a number of straight lines. To ensure adequate definition of larger diameter circles, it is necessary to plot more points to ensure that the chords stay at a constant length. This is automatically adjusted in most drawing routines.

Cubic curves

Although the implicit form can be employed to represent exactly such features as circles, free-form curves and surfaces which are often required in geometrical modelling cannot be precisely represented. To obtain precise representation a parametric polynomial is required.

To draw through a pair of end points and pass near to other points (known as *control points*) a generalized curve is needed. If we also need to join two curve segments together, then the slopes at the meeting point need to be the same. The third order cubic curve is the lowest order curve that will satisfy all these criteria.

A 3-D curve will require three third order equations, one in x, one in y and one in z. This can be expressed in terms of a parameter t varying from 0 to 1. This is expressed mathematically as:

$$x(t) = a_x t^3 + b_x t^2 + c_x t + d_x$$
$$y(t) = a_y t^3 + b_y t^2 + c_y t + d_y$$
$$z(t) = a_z t^3 + b_z t^2 + c_z t + d_z$$
$$\text{where } 0 \leqslant t \leqslant 1$$

The slopes of the curves are ratios of the tangent vector components, e.g.:

$$\frac{dy}{dx} = \frac{dy/dt}{dx/dt}$$

where

$$\frac{dx}{dt} = 3a_x t^2 + 2b_x t + c_x \textit{ etc.}$$

The tangent vectors are more useful than the slopes because slopes can become infinite, leading to computational difficulties, whereas tangent vectors need never be infinite.

There are many ways of defining a cubic parametric curve. The most frequently encountered are Bezier and B-spline.

Bezier curves

These define the positions of the curve end points and use two other control points not on the curve to define the tangents at the ends. Fig. 15.15 shows

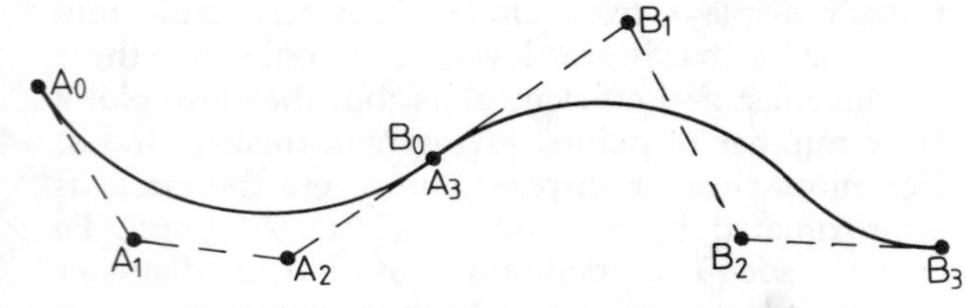

Fig.15.15 Two Bezier cubic segments

two curves $A_0A_1A_2A_3$ and $B_0B_1B_2B_3$ joined together at A_3B_0. Any of the control points A_1A_2 or B_1B_2 may be moved by the designer and the curve will smoothly modify to suit, allowing the designer to see if this is better suited to his purpose. Any changes to the vertices of a span only offset the curve within that span, leaving the rest of the curve unaffected. The tangent vectors at the ends join the points A_0A_1 and B_2B_3.

B-spline

The B-spline approximates, rather than matches, the end points but allows the first and second derivatives to be continuous at the segment end points. Bezier curves only have the first derivative continuity and so B-splines tend to have a smoother form of curve. However, neither B-spline nor Bezier curves can be employed for precisely representing conics, circles and the primitive quadric forms, e.g. cones, cylinders and spheres. Thus, in practical sophisticated CAD systems, curves must be modelled on a hybrid of cubic splines and of implicit curves.

CURVED SURFACES

Curved surfaces are made up from bicubic surfaces defined by three sets of cubic equations in two parameters *s* and *t*, instead of simply *t*, as for the cubic spline. The form of the equation is:

$$x(s,t) = a_{11}s^3t^3 + a_{12}s^3t^2 + a_{13}s^3t + a_{14}s^3 + a_{21}s^2t^3 + a_{22}s^2t^2 + a_{23}s^2t + a_{24}s^2 + a_{31}st^3 + a_{32}st^2 + a_{33}st + a_{34}s + a_{41}t^3 + a_{42}t^2 + a_{43}t + a_{44}$$

where a_{ij} is a series of constants.

Similar equations can be written for $y(s,t)$ and for $z(s,t)$. This generates a patch which defines a curved surface with four boundary lines and four corners. Each corner has its location and three slopes. Fig. 15.16 shows an arrangement of a bicubic patch which is frequently used in CAD surface generation and is known as the *Coons patch* after Steven Coons,

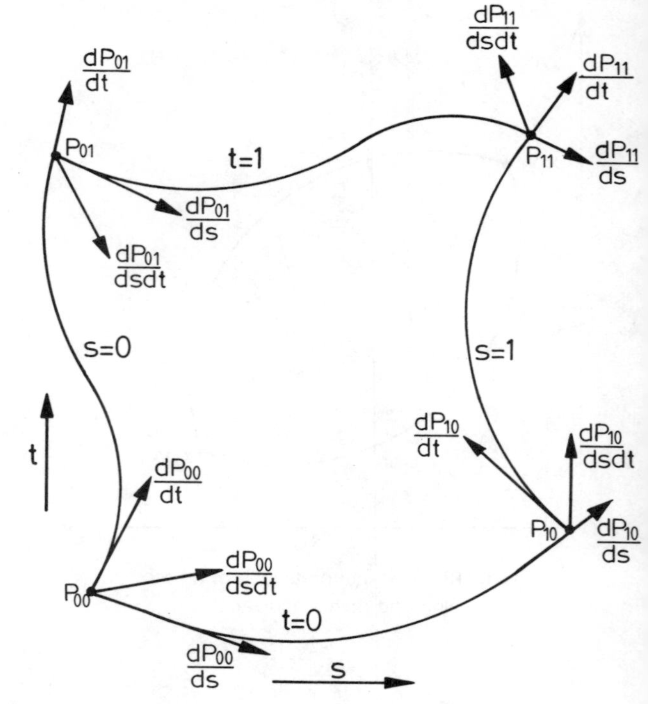

Fig.15.16 A typical 'Coons' patch

its originator. The four boundary curves each need to be defined in terms of *x*, *y* and *z*. The four corners must also be defined by their *x*, *y* and *z* co-ordinates. Each corner also requires the definition of its slopes, one along each parametric direction. Each slope again requires defining in the *x*, *y* and *z* directions. A third vector at each corner is given in terms of a partial derivative in both *s* and *t* and defines the degree of twist at the corner of the surface of a patch. A full surface can be defined by placing adjacent patches in position exactly to match the edges and their slopes.

TWO-DIMENSIONAL (2-D) DRAUGHTING SYSTEMS

In this section a number of terms and features are introduced that are commonly found in most CAD systems, ranging from the small 'educational' systems through to the largest professional systems. Rather than give a very detailed description of a specific system, at this stage the discussion is kept fairly general. A more specific detailed treatment of application packages is given in Chapter 16.

As discussed in Chapter 14, even simple CAD systems require the use of an additional input system (joystick, mouse, etc.) to position a cursor on the screen and access menu instructions quickly without the need to use the keyboard. In the graphics software of such a system there will also be what are known as *primitives*. These are elements, generally accessed through menu commands, which are the smallest building blocks used to generate images. It is not possible for the graphics user to change a primitive. Typical primitives are lines, circles, arcs, rectangles, prisms, etc.

Each primitive can be assigned what are known as *attributes*. Thus a line may be a continuous thick line, a dashed line to represent hidden detail, or a chain line for a centre line. Similarly each line may have an attribute of a specific colour, chosen from a palette of those available. In some of the cheaper systems, the attributes of line type are not fully available on the graphics screen but can be reproduced when plotted out on paper so that, e.g. a hidden detail line can be generated by a series of pen up/pen down commands to the plotter. Similarly line thickness and colour could be varied by choosing the appropriate pen for the plotter.

When an input device such as a joystick is used with a CAD system, it is not necessary to use the keyboard with instructions such as 'DRAW X,Y' in order to draw objects on the work page. Instead a cursor in the form of a simple cross can be positioned on the screen. By pressing a button this can be fixed as the object origin. A line is then drawn from the fixed cursor to a *dynamic* cursor. As the joystick is moved, so the dynamic cursor follows. The line joining the origin to the dynamic cursor is known as a *rubber band* because it can be stretched and pivoted about the fixed cursor until the line is in the desired position. Pressing a button will then fix the line and change the dynamic cursor into a new fixed cursor from which the next point can be drawn. Fig. 15.17 shows rubber banding being used in the process of completing the third side of a triangle.

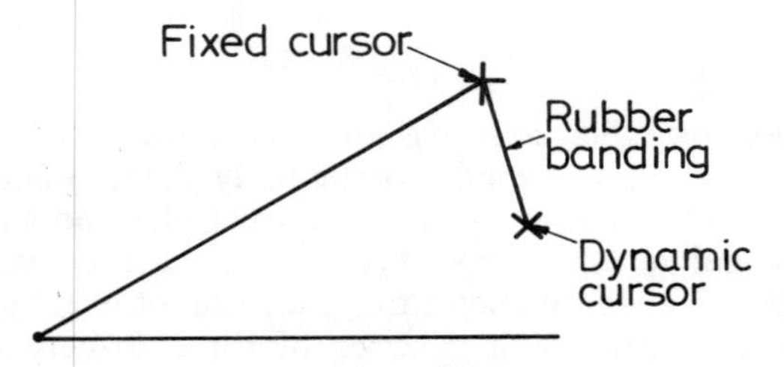

Fig.15.17 Rubber banding

While such a facility would be quite adequate for general sketches, to achieve scaled engineering drawings, it is necessary for the *x* and *y* dimensions to be dynamically displayed, relative to some previously defined origin. Alternatively, a lightly drawn grid, whose mesh size can be defined beforehand, can be laid down to aid in drawing the components.

Most CAD packages also have at least two *erase* commands. One simply erases the last item drawn, the other clears the whole of the current screen. Views of complex items can be gradually built up. As an example, Fig. 15.18 shows the development of a cone achieved by deleting the last line drawn in Fig. 15.17 and selecting the primitive *circular arc* from the menu. There are a number of possible options for choosing the size and position of an arc. These are the following:

(1) Specify the two end points of the arc with a third point lying on the arc.
(2) Specify the two end points and the arc centre.
(3) Specify the radius, centre and included angle.

Whichever is chosen depends upon the task in hand. In Fig. 15.18, the conical development is best achieved by option (2).

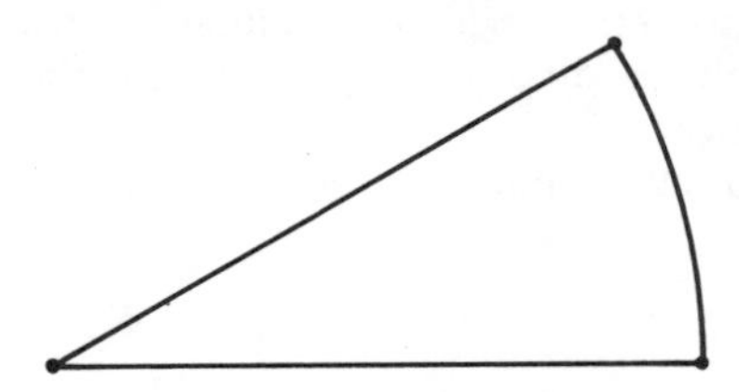

Fig.15.18 Building a cone using Fig.15.17

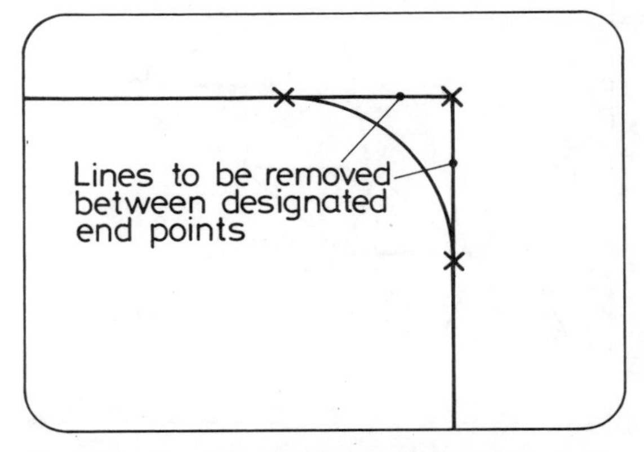

Fig.15.19 Creating a fillet radius on an enlarged view

For special features such as corner fillets it is only necessary to point at the two lines and specify, usually through the keyboard, the size of the radius for the tangential arc to be drawn. As seen in Fig. 15.19, this leaves a sharp corner to be removed. This can usually be done by enlarging the corner to fill the screen. The tangency point and the end of the line can then be accurately located, and the section of the line between them selectively erased.

Having built up a view of an object it is often advisable to file it away on to a library disk. This will not only ensure a *back-up* copy should the view be accidentally erased, but will also allow the view to be called up and modified for use on another drawing.

The view of the object can be positioned on the work page to enable other views to be projected from it in orthographic projection. The use of a grid is particularly useful at this stage in enabling the views to be projected accurately. The features in the other views can be gradually built up by enlarging the portion containing the view currently being drawn until it fills the work page in order to achieve a reasonable accuracy of drawing.

In addition to orthographic views, it is also possible to generate isometric views by laying down a dotted isometric grid to facilitate setting out distances along directions parallel to the three isometric axes.

It should be emphasized at this stage that the isometric and orthographic views held in the computer which result from the use of a 2-D graphics program do not have any information about the three-dimensional nature of the part being drawn. In the same way that a conventional draughtsman will specify a plan view from the front view using his knowledge of the 3-D nature of the part, so it is necessary for the CAD user to interpret the 3-D nature of the part shown on the screen. In this sense the computer and graphics screen are only acting as a substitute for the traditional drawing board and no 3-D properties, e.g. volume or centre of gravity, can be obtained. Indeed, except in some limited cases where a plane is specified as parallel to the plane of projection, it is not possible to determine 2-D properties, e.g. areas and centres of areas.

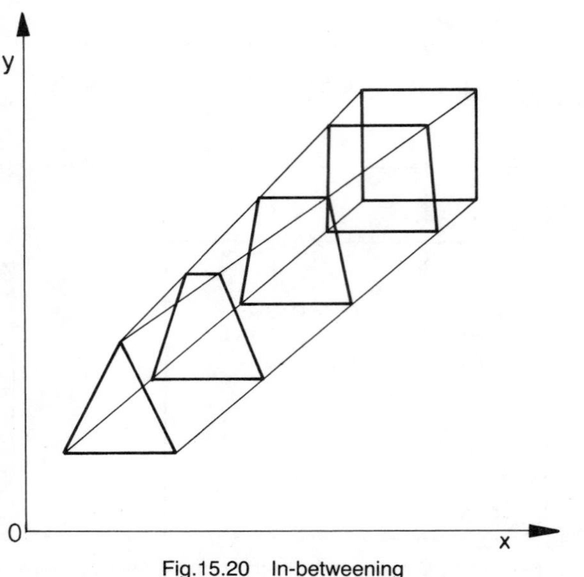

Fig.15.20 In-betweening

ADDITIONAL 2-D FACILITIES

Copy

The ability to store an image on the library disk enables a view to be called up several times over. The image can be scaled appropriately and then copied into several locations on the work page. The ability to 'copy' is a useful feature for repetitive items, e.g. nuts and bolts, which can be stored as standard files. In some systems, such items are provided as 'primitives' which are not accessible to be erased but can be scaled and positioned appropriately to fit the drawing.

Mirror

A further command frequently used in drawings is the *mirror* (or *reflect*) command which enables a part to be drawn using only one half and a centre line. If the part is then identified by a rectangular box, the mirror command will enable the missing half of the view to be drawn about the centre line, saving considerable time.

Tweening

A process called *tweening* (or *in-betweening*) can be found in some systems, particularly for animation work. The computer can take an initial and final view and generate a specified number of in-between stages. Fig. 15.20 shows the transition of a triangle into a square using a series of three in-between images.

Scale and zoom

It is not only possible to *scale* on overall drawing but, in most systems, the x direction can be scaled separately from the y. In addition to being able to define a scale for the drawing, most systems have a *zoom* facility. This enables a particular part lying at the centre of the drawing to be continuously enlarged or shrunk at the press of a button. This is particularly useful to check that two lines actually meet. The part to be enlarged can also be identified by placing it in a rectangular frame. Pressing a button will then enlarge the frame to fill the screen. However, if the part to be enlarged is off to one side at the start of the zoom, it will be quickly lost from view as the image magnifies.

Pan

Under these circumstances it is necessary to use the *pan* (or *shift*) command. This has the effect of moving the screen across the work page as if it were a moving *window*.

Windows and viewports

Let us assume that the end of a long shaft is to be drawn on a graphics screen. The shaft exists in what are called the user's (or '*world*') co-ordinates. The end of the shaft to be displayed represents a small *window* on the world and parts lying outside that window are *clipped* so that no attempt will be made to display them on any device. The device (e.g. printer, plotter, display screen) has a viewing surface on to which the image is to be mapped. The view surface can be scaled so that its maximum co-ordinates are represented by a square ranging from 0,0 to 1,0 in both the x and y directions. This is known as *normalized device co-ordinates* because it can represent any output device. The result is as shown in Fig. 15.21 with a graphics screen as an output device. The normalized device co-ordinates could be converted, in turn, into the particular device co-ordinates – e.g. the number of pixels on a display screen. Since the screen is rectangular, using normalized device co-ordinates, the right

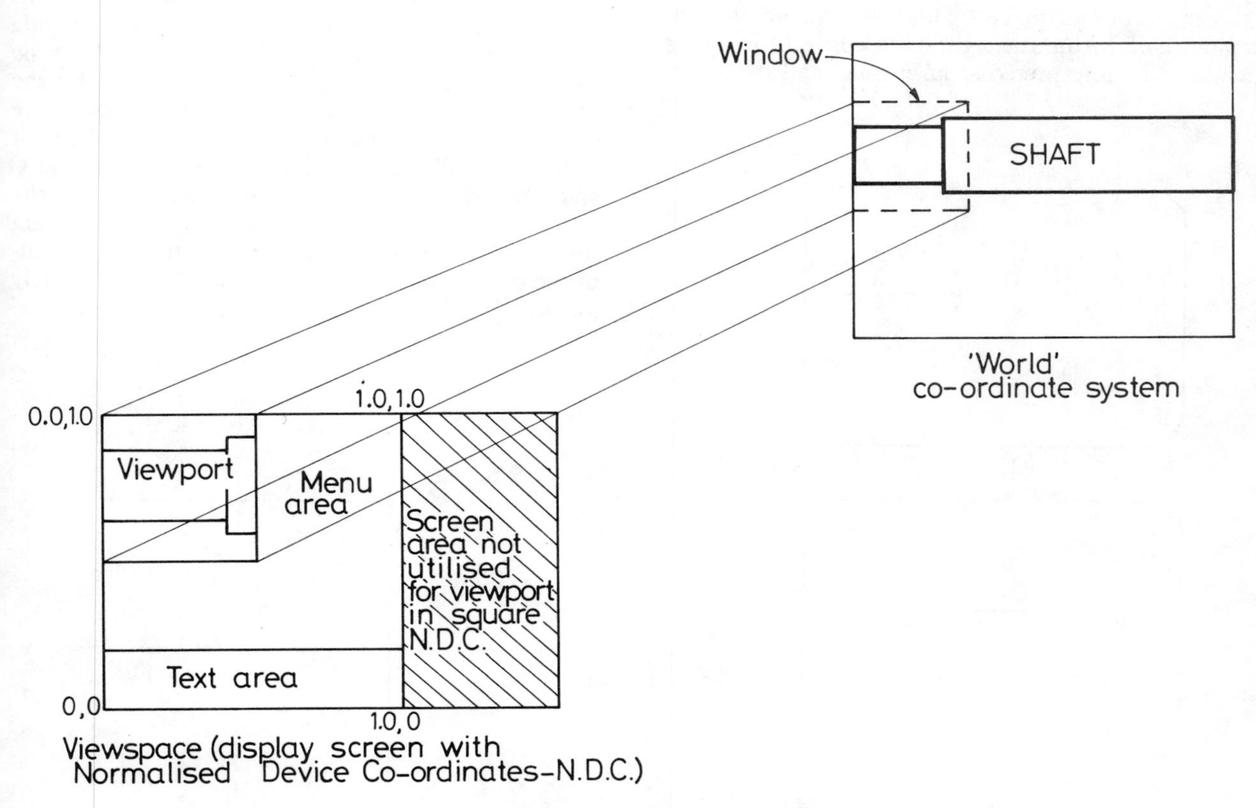

Fig.15.21 Definition of viewports and windows

hand part will not be used for graphics display and can be used for computer error messages, etc. The *viewport* containing the end portion of the shaft is shown as appearing in the top left section of the screen. This allows space on the screen for other viewports which are mapped from the world co-ordinate systems and can contain, e.g. parts which are to be assembled on to the shaft; or associated text. The viewports can be of any size and in any location on the screen. Unfortunately many modern business systems where the screen is partitioned into several sections use the term *window* incorrectly when, according to International Standard definitions, the term *viewport* should be used. This misnomer is so widespread that it is likely that the Standard will have to be revised.

Clipping

The process of *clipping* is applied to a window to ensure that the display device does not attempt to draw parts which lie outside the window. Fig. 15.22(a) shows an attempt to draw a line from point 1 to point 2, where point 2 lies outside the screen. The analogue values equivalent to the distance of 2 from the right hand edge of the screen x would be interpreted as an x value and the actual view that is drawn would be as shown in Fig. 15.22(b). This effect is known as *wraparound*.

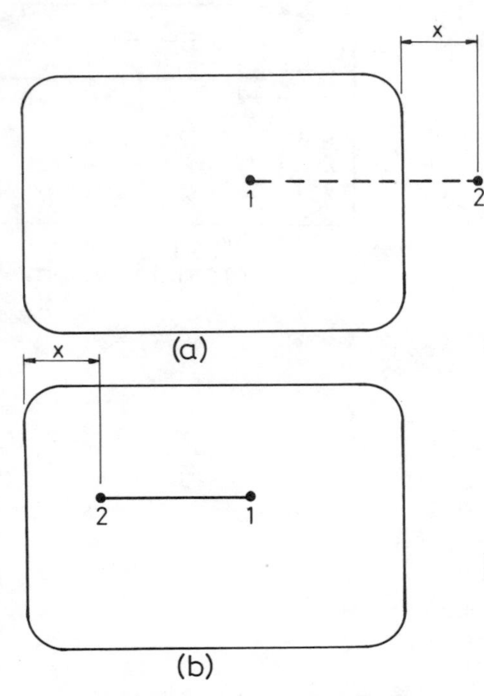

Fig.15.22 'Wraparound' effects

There are several possible routines for clipping. The most common, ascribed to Cohen and Sutherland, is shown in relation to a series of lines in Fig. 15.23. The total drawing represents a world co-ordinate system which is to be clipped to a window represented by the central square. The 'world' is divided into eight separate regions lying around the central window. Each of these regions is assigned a value as a block of 4 bits in the computer. The lowest (right hand) bit is set to one if the region lies to the left of the central window. The second bit is set if the region is to the right of the window, the third bit is set if below the window and the fourth bit if above the window. Thus, if a line is drawn across the regions and both ends are zero, then the line is entirely within the central window. If the line is totally outside the central region, it will be found that each end of the line will have the same corresponding bit set to 1. Hence a horizontal line from the top left to the top right corner will have ends 1001 and 1010 respectively, i.e. the left hand bit will be a 1 in each case. This test can be applied to reject all lines lying outside the centre. A line such as AD in Fig. 15.23 can be sub-divided at B. The section AB is tested by the above criteria and discarded as totally outside the centre. The line BD is now tested and found that it cannot be easily rejected. BD is further divided at C and the line CD found to lie entirely within the central window so that BC can be rejected. Clipping routines of this type can be set up in special-purpose graphics chips and operate extremely quickly.

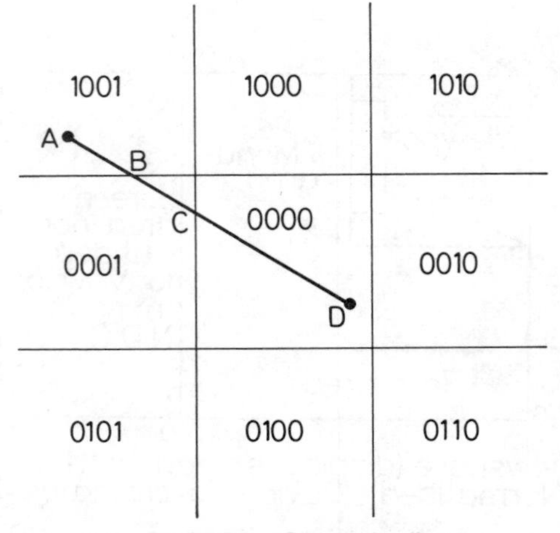

Fig.15.23 'Clipping' a line

TRANSFORMATIONS

2-D transformations

As part of the process of displaying an object on the screen, it is often necessary to change (or *transform*) a whole group of picture features, points, lines or planes. The most frequent types of transformations are: *translations*, in which the group of features is moved linearly with reference to the origin; *rotation*, in which all picture features are rotated about the origin; *scaling*, in which the whole group is enlarged or reduced with reference to the origin.

The principles underlying these transformations are illustrated graphically in this section and the mathematical process is explained. However, the majority of 2-D draughting systems, and all 3-D systems, employ a mathematical technique for representing the picture features called a *matrix* representation. All matrices can be manipulated in a standard way so that the various transformation processes, individually and in combination, can be quickly calculated using a standardized procedure. For those who have a knowledge of matrices, the matrix approach to transformation is included as Appendix A, page 211. However, it is recommended that the following section be read first, since this deals with the underlying principles of the process which are often not apparent when dealing with matrices. While the process of total transformation of a line is often intuitively obvious, the mathematical definition of the process demands a regularized procedure in which everything proceeds step by step and all transformations take place with reference to the origin.

Translation

An example is given in Fig. 15.24 of a line translated by two units in the x direction and one unit in the y direction with respect to the origin. The start of the line is translated from (1,1) to (3,2). Because the translation values for both ends of the line are the same, the new line will be parallel to the old. In general mathematical terms translation can be represented by:

$$x_1 = x + \triangle x$$
$$y_1 = y + \triangle y$$

Where x_1, y_1 are the co-ordinates of the translated point; x and y are the original co-ordinates; $\triangle x$ and $\triangle y$ are the translation displacement values. Thus translation involves a process of addition (or subtraction).

Scaling

If the line (1,1) to (2,3) is now scaled by doubling its length, the result is as shown in Fig. 15.25. As can be seen in this figure the process of scaling also changes the position of both ends of the line. Scaling therefore also involves a process of translation. The new line is also parallel to the original line. Quite often it is necessary to enlarge an object while keeping a corner fixed relative to the origin.

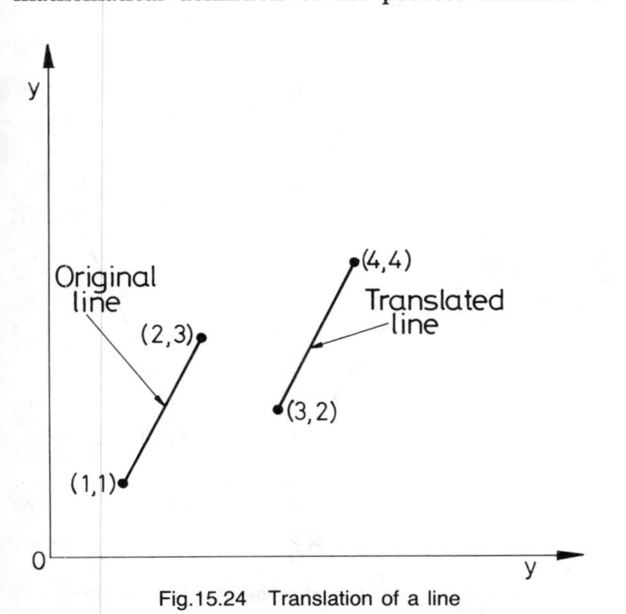

Fig.15.24 Translation of a line

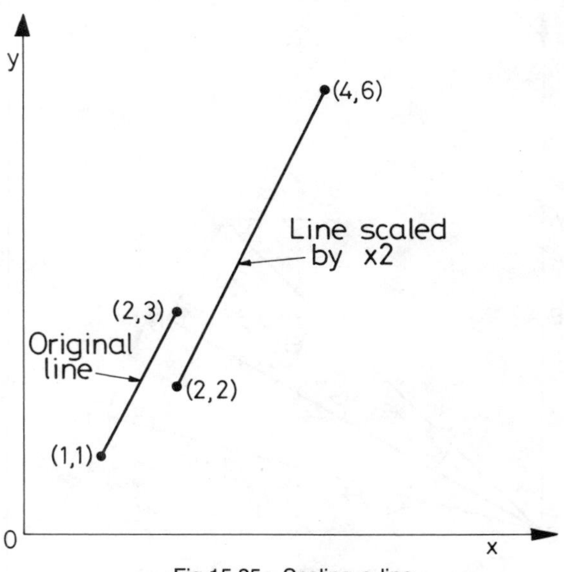

Fig.15.25 Scaling a line

This process would be similar to doubling the length of the line in Fig. 15.25 while keeping the end (1,1) in its original position. Because all processes take place with respect to the origin, a sequence of transformations is required. This sequence would involve a translation by (−1,−1) for the whole line followed by a scaling and then a re-translation by (1,1) to bring the lowest end of the line back to its earlier position. The mathematical expressions for scaling are:

$$x_1 = x \times Sx$$
$$y_1 = y \times Sy$$

where Sx and Sy are the scale factors for x and y. Scaling thus involves a process of multiplication. Theoretically there is no reason why the values Sx and Sy need to be the same. Thus the drawing can be stretched in the x direction by an amount different to that in the y direction. This is a useful facility when drawing an ellipse.

Rotation

A point P_1 at (4,3) is to be rotated about the origin by +30° (i.e. anti-clockwise). The result is readily constructed as shown in Fig. 15.26. The mathematical expression of the new co-ordinates is:

$$x' = 0x_2 = OA = BD - CD$$
$$= OD \cos\theta - DP_2 \sin\theta$$
$$= x_1 \cos\theta - y_1 \sin\theta$$

$$y' = 0y_2 = AP_2 = AC + CP_2$$
$$= OB + CP_2$$
$$= OD \sin\theta + DP_2 \cos\theta$$
$$= x_1 \sin\theta + y_1 \cos\theta$$

Where θ is the angle by which the point is rotated. If the rotation of 60° is applied to the line (1,1) to (2,3) then the result is as shown in Fig. 15.27. Because the rotation is about the origin, the process results also in the line being translated. If the line were to be purely rotated about the end (1,1) by 60°, then for the mathematical process, it would first be necessary to translate the line to the origin as shown in Fig. 15.28(a), then rotate about the origin by 60° (Fig. 15.28(b)) and finally re-translate back to the original end point (1,1) as shown in Fig. 15.28(c).

As a general rule the process of translation can be seen to involve addition, while both scaling and rotation are processes of multiplication. This has implications for the matrix manipulation described in Appendix A, page 212, and is the reason for introducing there the concept of *homogeneous co-ordinates*. A further implication for the matrix manipulation is in the fact that the order of a sequence of transformation is important. This can be clearly seen in Fig. 15.28 where the sequence is translate, rotate, translate. Had the sequence been translate, translate, rotate, then the first two translations would cancel out, leaving a pure rotation about the origin instead of one about the end of the line.

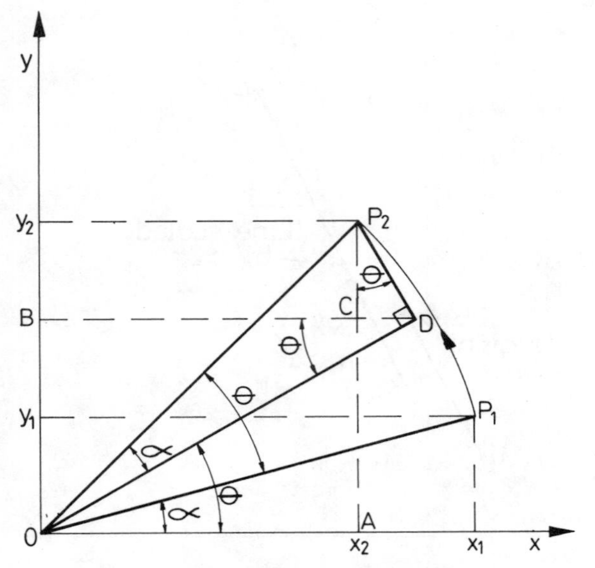

Fig.15.26 Rotation of a point

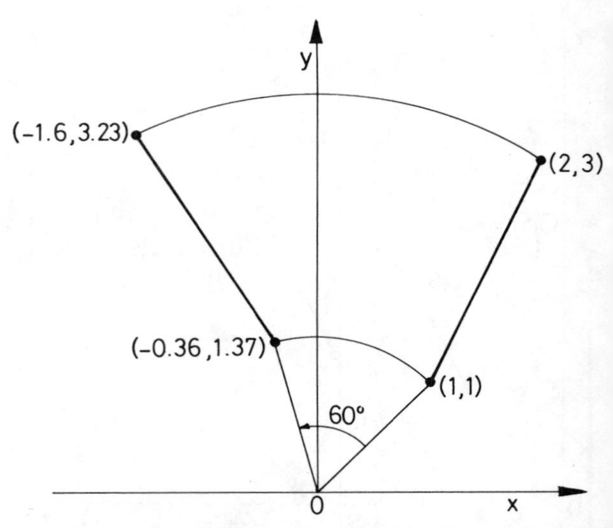

Fig.15.27 Rotation of a line about the origin

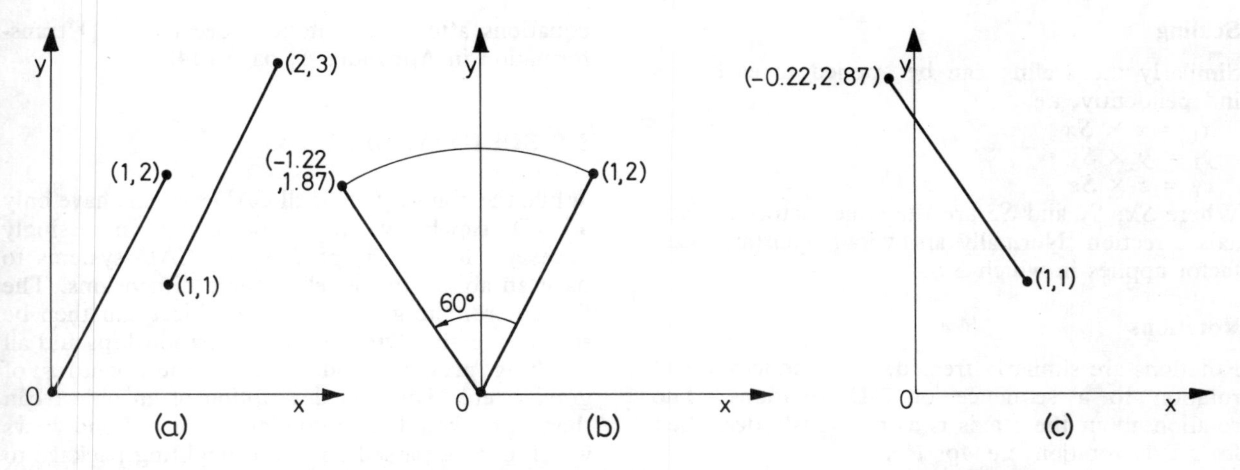

Fig.15.28 Sequence of transformations for rotation of a line about one end

3-D transformations

The addition of a third dimension to the previously defined 2-D transformations adds some complications, particularly for rotations. Fig. 15.29 shows the positive rotation directions in relation to a right hand set of positive Cartesian axes.

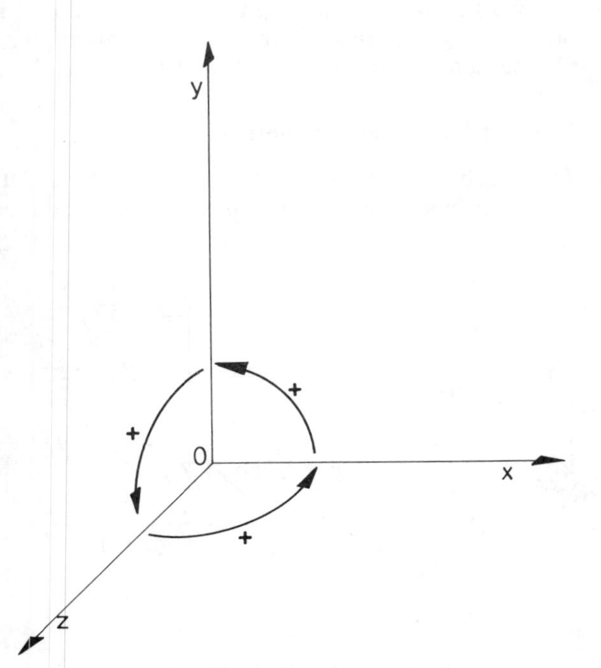

Fig.15.29 Positive rotation conventions

Translation

Pure linear transformation is little affected by the introduction of the z axis. The triangle in Fig. 15.30 shows an example of 3-D translation for which:

$$x_1 = x + \triangle x$$
$$y_1 = y + \triangle y$$
$$z_1 = z + \triangle z$$

i.e. the separate translation values $\triangle x$, $\triangle y$ and $\triangle z$ can be added independently to each axis to achieve the new translated co-ordinates x_1, y_1, z_1 for each of the corners of the triangle ABC.

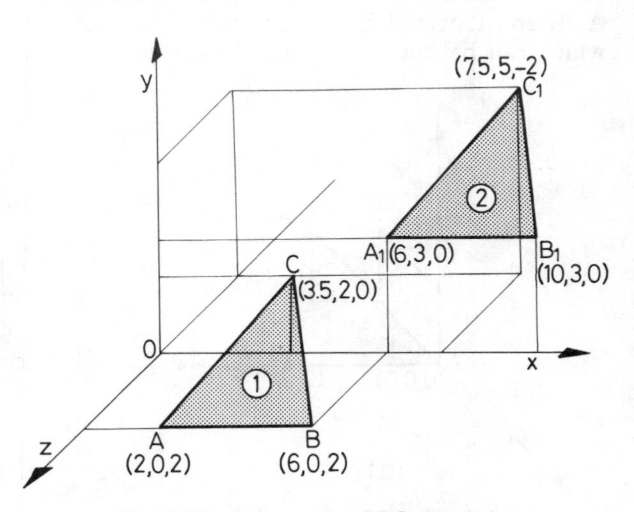

Fig.15.30 An example of 3-D translation

Scaling

Similarly the scaling can be applied to each axis independently, i.e.

$x_1 = x \times Sx$
$y_1 = y \times Sy$
$z_1 = z \times Sz$

Where Sx, Sy and Sz are the scale factors in each axis direction. Normally an overall, constant scale factor applies in which $Sx = Sy = Sz$.

Rotations

Rotations are similarly treated. This reduces a 3-D rotation to a sequence of 2-D rotations. The rotation about the z axis is as previously described for a 2-D rotation, i.e. for Rz:

$x_1 = x \cos \theta - y \sin \theta$
$y_1 = y \cos \theta + x \sin \theta$
$z_1 = z$

i.e. there is no change in the z co-ordinate due to rotation about the z axis. For Ry:

$x_1 = x \cos \theta + z \sin \theta$
$y_1 = y$
$z_1 = z \cos \theta - x \sin \theta$

and for Rx:

$x_1 = x$
$y_1 = y \cos \theta - z \sin \theta$
$z_1 = z \cos \theta + y \sin \theta$

Fig. 15.31 shows an example of successive rotations in which a triangle (Fig. 15.31(a)) with AB coincident with the x axis, is to be successively rotated about the Oz axis by +90° (Fig. 15.31(b)) and then by −60° about the Ox axis to give the final view as shown in Fig. 15.31(c). Each of the corners A, B and C would have x', y' and z' co-ordinates which can be calculated from the previously given equations after each rotation. See also 3-D transformation in Appendix A, page 214.

3-D SOLID MODELLING

While the majority of small CAD systems have only a 2-D capability, it is becoming increasingly necessary for larger, professional CAD systems to have an ability to model in three dimensions. The full co-ordinate geometry of an object can then be stored, together with its spatial relationships and all resulting properties such as volumes, centres of gravity, etc. The 3-D description of an object can then be broken down into plan, front and end views which can be passed on to a draughting package to produce dimensioned engineering drawings. It is possible to produce a complete solid model, with all the information, e.g. full surfaces and hidden detail being displayed. Alternatively an abbreviated form can be displayed, which shows cylinders as multi-faceted surfaces and no hidden lines removed. The two most common methods of fully modelling solids are *Boundary representation* and *Constructive solid geometry*. In practice, most commercial solid modellers employ a combination of these two approaches, the most appropriate being chosen for a particular task. The quality of image produced by a full solid modeller, with highlights and shadows, is often so good that it can be confused with photographs taken of the real object.

Constructive Solid Geometry (CSG)

This technique uses a series of standard 3-D 'building blocks' which are built up and combined

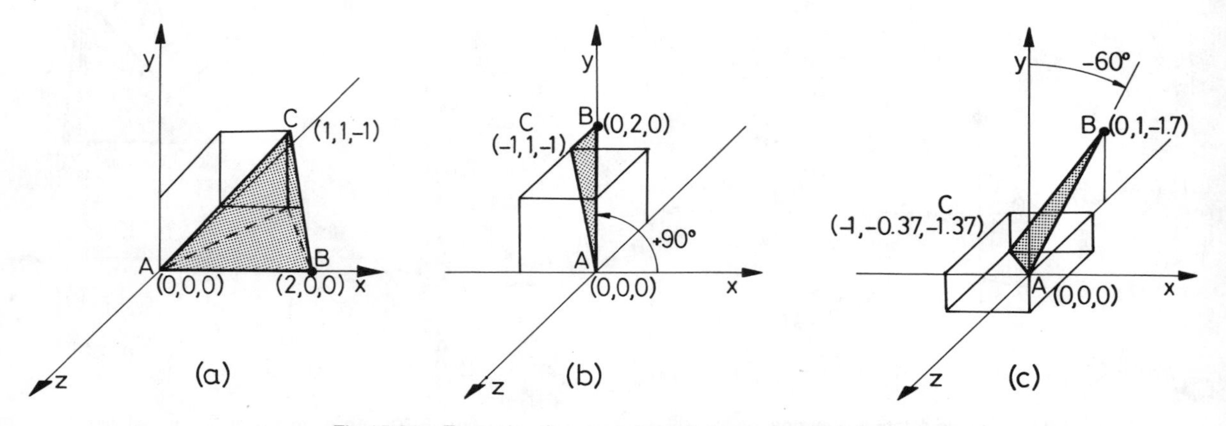

Fig.15.31 Example of successive rotations of a triangle

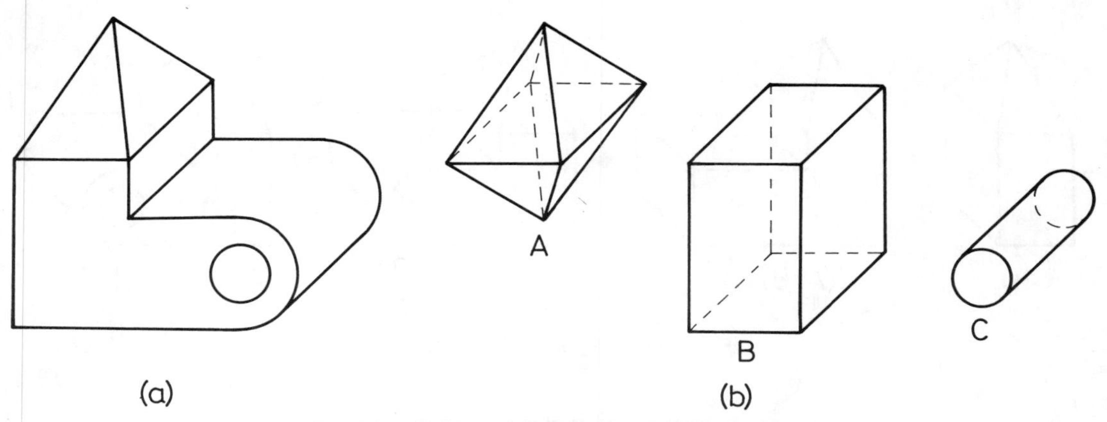

Fig.15.32 Solid model made from building blocks

mathematically by a process known as *Boolean algebra* using processes of *intersection*, *union* (or join) and *difference* (or cut). Fig. 15.32(a) shows the construction of an object using the 3-D building blocks which are illustrated separately in Fig. 15.32(b). The full Boolean operation is:

[((A + B) + B) + C] − C

The process of *intersection* is caused by the overlap of two objects and is of value for checking interference. Fig. 15.33 shows the intersection object formed from (A + B) in Fig. 15.32. The process of adding two blocks to fuse into a new block is the process of *union*, e.g. ((A + B) +B). The process of *difference* is one of subtraction as when drilling a hole, e.g. (−C).

The object can be joined together in stages as shown in Fig. 15.34.

The data base for models using CSG is a combination of data and of logical procedures for merging the various blocks. It is compact to store, but lengthy to build. If only the CSG *tree* is kept comprising of which blocks are used, how they are connected and their sizes, then the storage is very compact. The slow task of finding edge intersections is generally left to the end of the model build, prior to which the model can be easily amended by changing the tree. Once full surface information is stored, the data storage advantages are largely lost, but the model can be quickly displayed. Surfaces are stored in their algebraic form, usually as quadrics (e.g. unbounded planes, cylinders, cones and spheres) which must have a closed form of topology. CSG cannot deal with parametrically described sculptured surfaces. These must be approximated by a combination of solids having quadric surfaces.

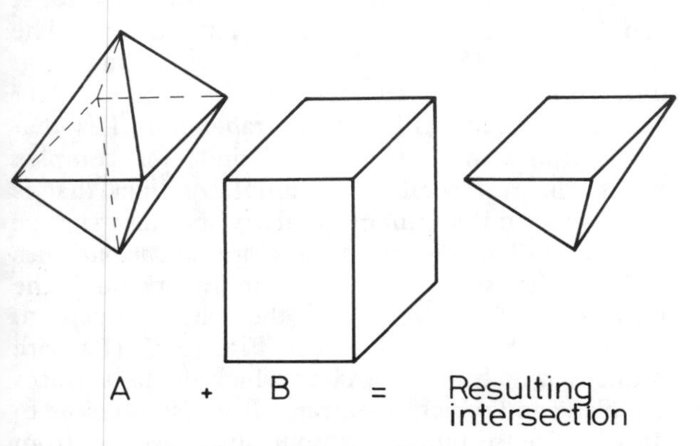

Fig.15.33 Example of intersection

Boundary Representation (B-Rep)

In a B-Rep system, a solid is defined by five views – plan, front, two ends and the reverse plan. Rubber banding lines are used to inter-relate corresponding features in the various views. B-Rep stores a description of the object in terms of its surfaces, edges and vertices as shown in Fig. 15.35. Since the boundary information is kept at all times as an explicit definition, it is quicker to build the model than using CSG, but the data base that must be stored is larger. B-Rep is very compatible with wire frame models, but modifications are more difficult to make than when using CSG. B-Rep is a useful technique for non-standard shapes, e.g. aircraft, fuselage and wing shapes and for car body styling.

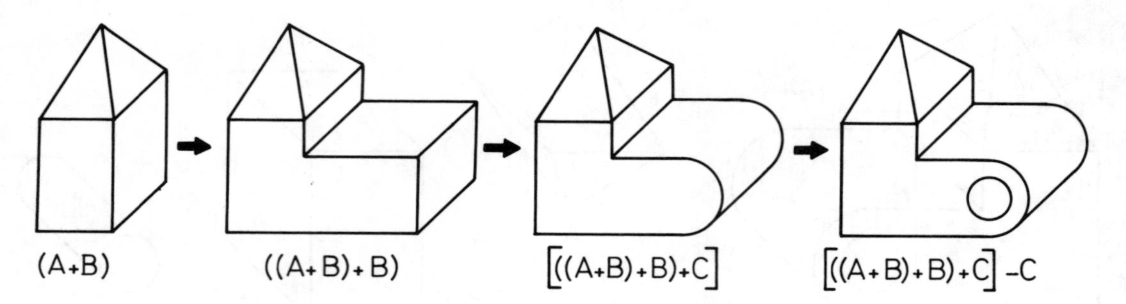

Fig.15.34 Stages in CSG construction

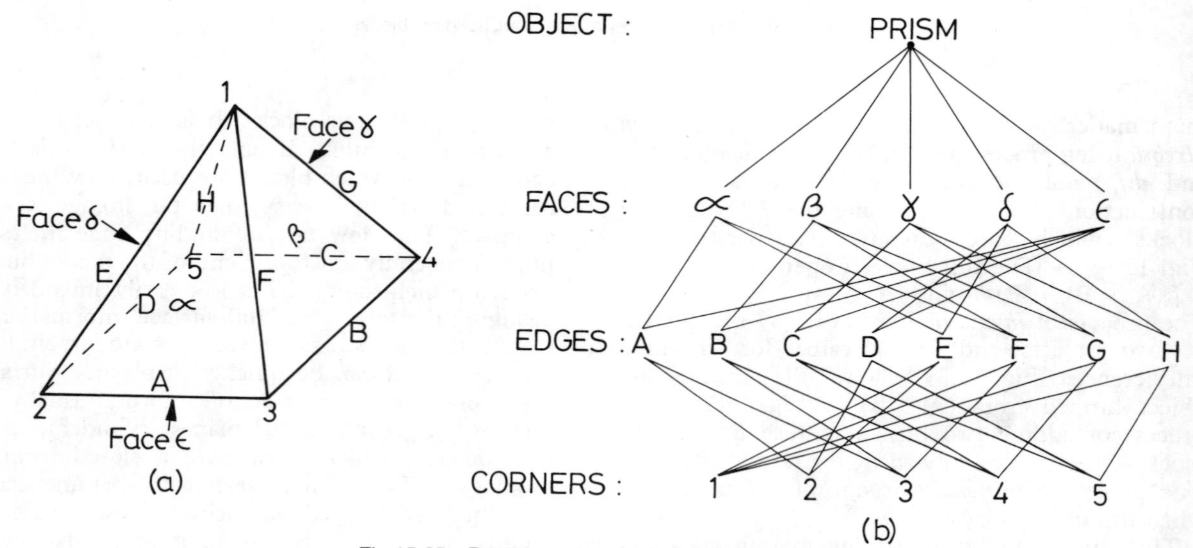

Fig.15.35 Boundary representation of a prism

Spatial enumeration

In this technique, 3-D space is divided up into a number of small 3-D 'cells'. The process is simple to program and can be implemented in a hardware chip. The intersection of two solids can be easily found by looking for the common spatial properties in each of the two sets of 3-D cells. However, an exact definition of the boundary or intersection curve is difficult to display and to change. Also surface definition is generally poor. A small increase in cell resolution leads to a vast increase in data storage.

Wire frames

A wire frame is effectively a line drawing of a 3-D object and is a method of representing the 3-D geometry of the edges and nodes of an object without a full surface representation. The object has the appearance of a frame constructed from wire. It can be quickly displayed and manipulated. The block in Fig. 15.36 is shown as a wire frame with only 16 lines and 2 circles.

The difficulty with a wire frame model is that hidden lines are not removed and, for complex items, the result can be a jumble of lines that is impossible to determine. Similarly, because surface features are not displayed there are no *contour* lines and so the surface can be ambiguous and the resulting interpretation of the object open to question. The block drawn in Fig. 15.37 is a wire frame in which it is not clear which of the surfaces are plane and which re-entrant. It is also possible to draw nonsense objects without any objection from the program.

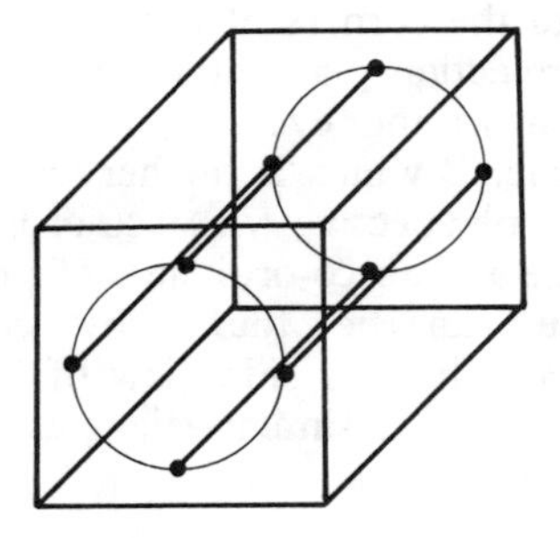

Fig.15.36 Wire frame object

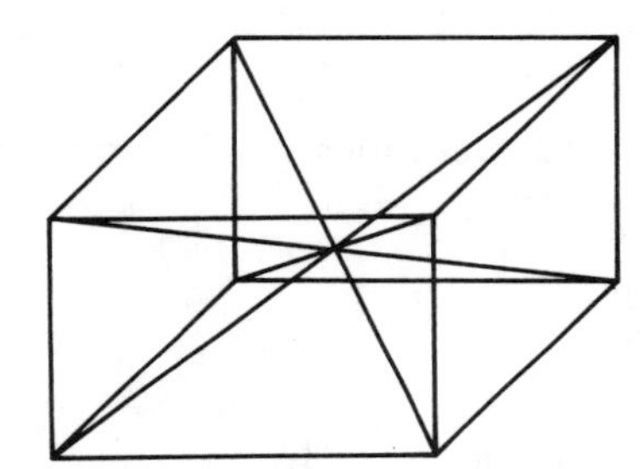

Fig.15.37 Ambiguous wire frame object

Wire frames are often used with a full solid modeller to give a quick viewing of the object without waiting for a complete surface representation, which can take a long time to generate.

2½-D objects

The term 2½-D is used for those parts which are either flat objects with a constant depth (extruded parts) or for solids of revolution. This limited class of 3-D entities can be generated by an extension of 2-D techniques and was, until recently, the only type of 3-D object that could be generated on smaller CAD systems. Flat objects can be considered as 2-D shapes which are translated, swept or extruded, into the *z* dimension. Fig. 15.38 shows a typical example. Using the 2½-D concept, the groove can be set to a shorter depth than the rest of the object to produce a recess.

Revolute objects can also be produced by sweeping a 2-D profile through 360° as shown in Fig. 15.39. The amount of storage needed for 2½-D objects can be minimized by displaying in a wire frame or a faceted form. Fig. 15.40 shows the effect of adding shading patterns and tone to a 2½-D rotational sweep. The image represents the ducting of a jet engine and is modelled on a normal BBC microcomputer with no additional memory.

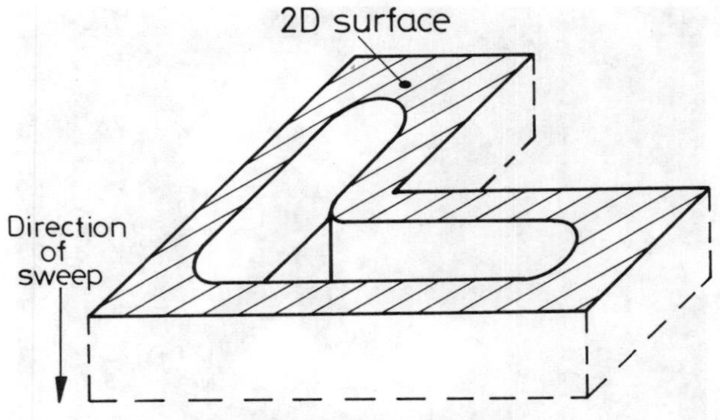

Fig.15.38 2½-D extruded shape

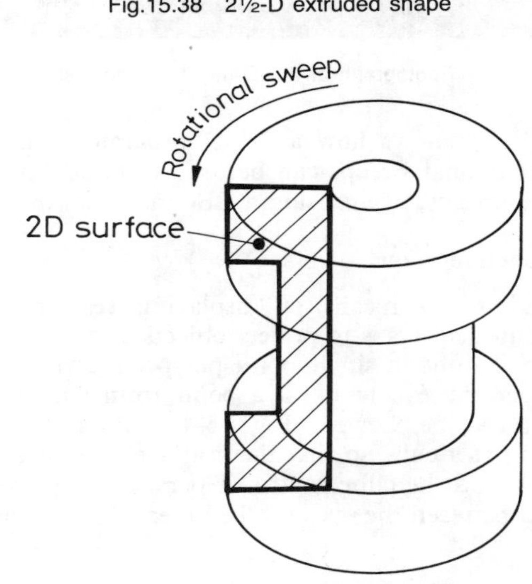

Fig.15.39 2½-D rotational shape

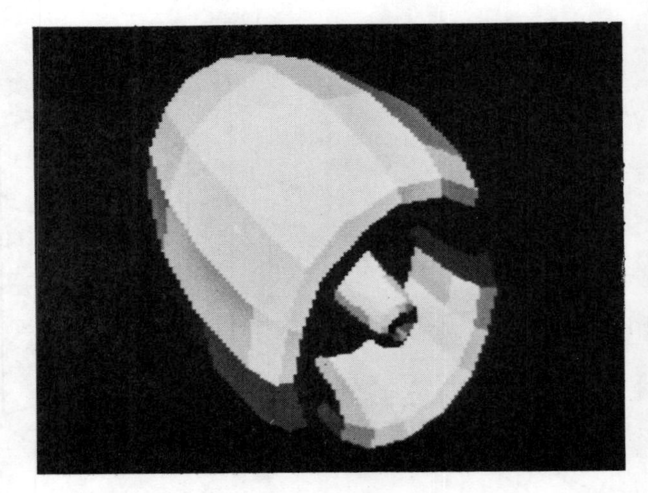

Fig.15.40 Photograph of model jet engine duct in 2½-D

Fig.15.41 Photograph of 2½-D model of robot structure

Fig. 15.41 shows how a 2½-D program of linear and rotational sweeps can be used to build up and merge images, again using a BBC microcomputer.

Perspective views

An additional means of displaying realism and depth in displays is to project objects as perspective views. To obtain single-point perspective views we consider the eye to be at a point from which the object can be viewed. Fig. 15.42 shows the eye looking at a cube so that the z axis passes through the eye and the cube centre. A perspective plane is placed between the eye and the object. Rays, drawn from the eye to the corners of the block, will pass through the projection plane and create the image. Corners nearest to the eye, e.g. A, will appear larger than corner B which is further from the eye.

To find the perspective view co-ordinates, we need to find the x, y, z co-ordinates of points such as B_1. These can be found by considering Fig. 15.43 which shows a side view of Fig. 15.42. In the side view, from similar triangles, it can be seen that the ratio

$$\frac{z_1}{y_1} = \frac{z_2}{y_2}$$

from which

$$y_1 = \frac{y_2 z_1}{z_2}$$

Similarly, horizontal ratios will be preserved as:

$$\frac{z_1}{x_1} = \frac{z_2}{x_2}$$

from which

$$x_1 = \frac{x_2 z_1}{z_2}$$

Hence the co-ordinates of B_1 are:

$$\frac{x_2 z_1}{z_2}, \frac{y_2 z_1}{z_2}, z_1$$

The resultant perspective view of a cube of side length 4, centrally viewed from a distance of 8 from the viewpoint to the cube centroid and to the projection plane $z_1 = 8$ as shown in Fig. 15.44. The effect is a vanishing point at Oz, i.e. the eye viewpoint. As the viewpoint is moved closer to the

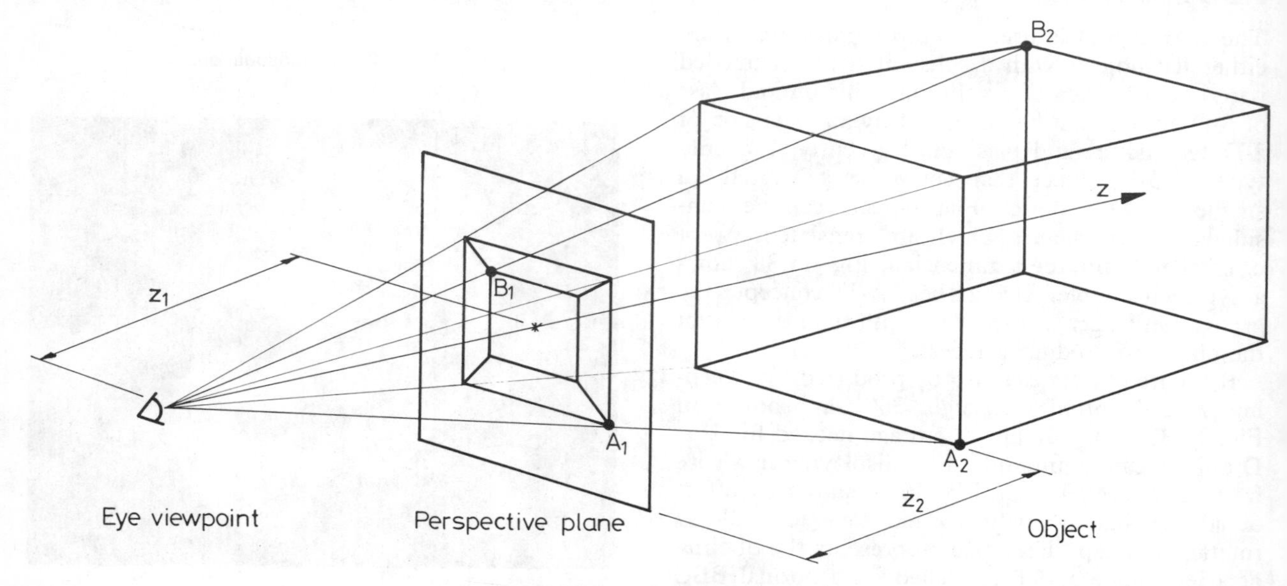

Fig.15.42 Perspective projection

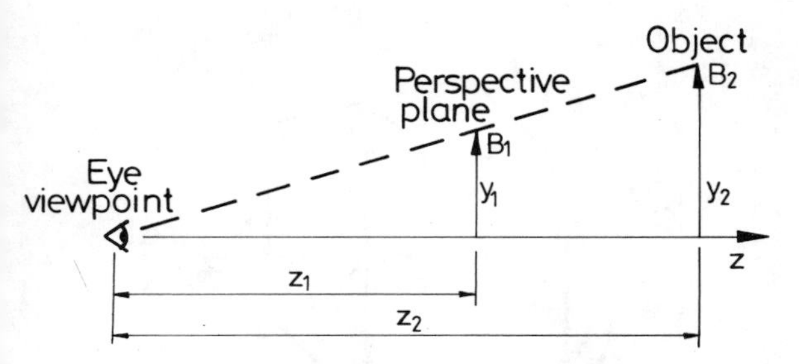

Fig.15.43 Side view of perspective projection

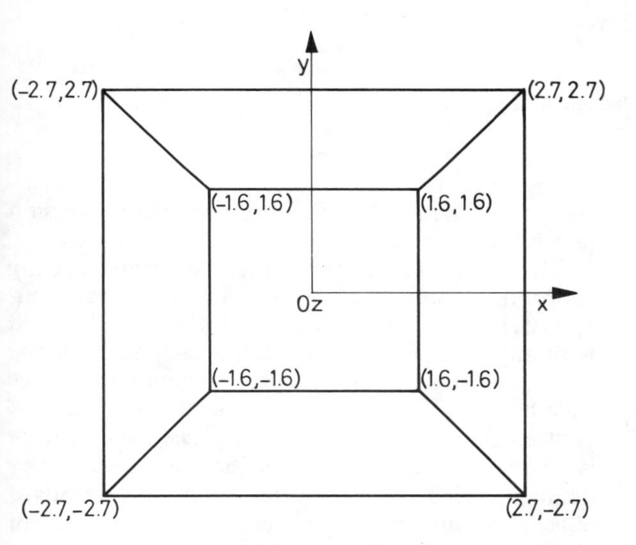

Fig.15.44 Single point perspective view of a cube

screen, the convergence effect will increase. If the object is moved further from the projection plane, it also moves further from the viewpoint and so the converging effect is diminished. The advantage of perspective views is that they enable a user to *fly around* an object to view it from many different angles – a facility that is of particular advantage to architects.

HIDDEN LINES

Because wire frame figures are confusing when all the hidden edges are left in, it is useful to be able to erase, or dot, those which are hidden behind the nearer surfaces. There are many programs for deleting hidden lines. The more general purpose are extremely complex and require both a large memory and a considerable time to execute. One of the simpler strategies can handle only convex bodies. A body is defined as convex if, when any two points on the body are joined by a line, all parts of the line lie within the body. Fig. 15.45 shows examples of convex and concave bodies. The program checks whether lines lie behind plane surface segments (or facets). In order to do so, a list of all lines, vertices and facets is required together with their relationship to each other. A surface test is used in which a line of sight is drawn to the object surface from the projection origin. A further line is drawn as a normal outward from the surface of the object. If the angle between the two lines is less than 90°, then the face and all its edges are visible. Fig. 15.46 shows a rectangle projected on to a plane. The normals to the centres of the four surfaces are N1 through to N4 and the angles made

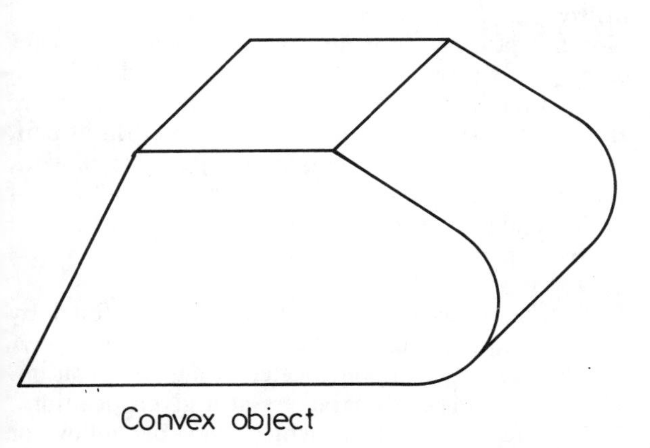

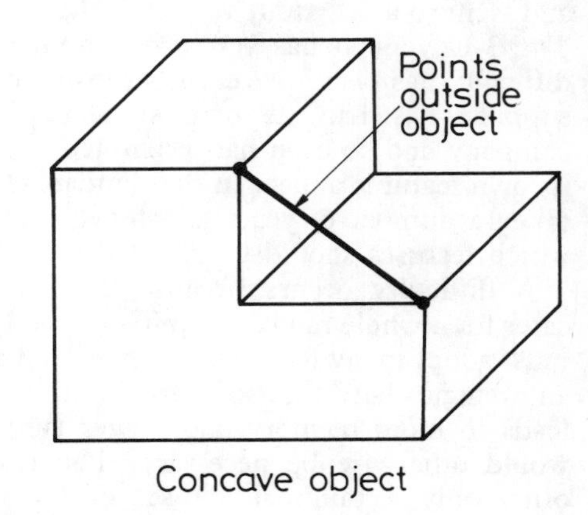

Fig.15.45 Examples of concave and convex objects

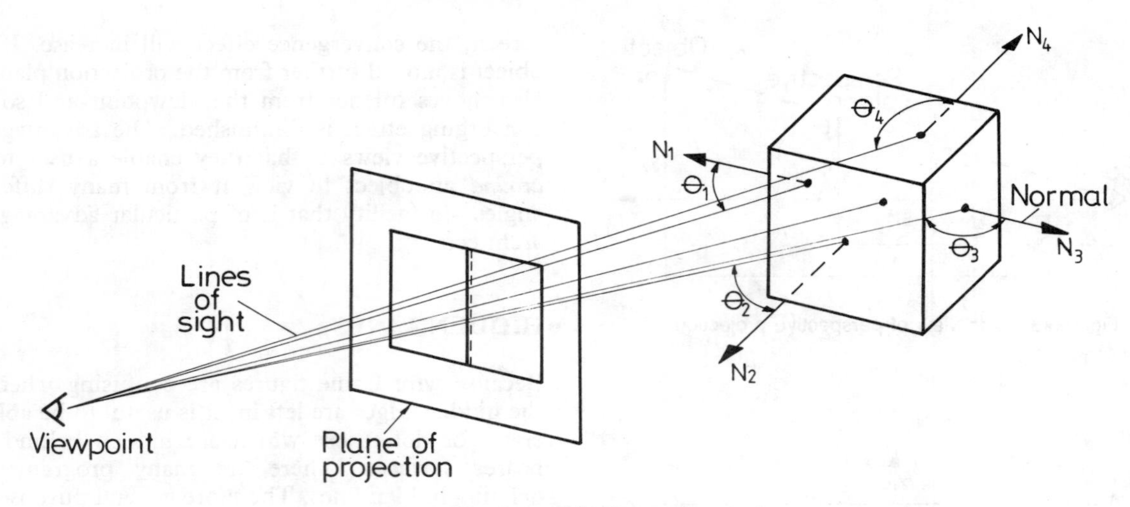

Fig.15.46 General hidden surface test

between the line of sight and these normals are θ_1 to θ_4. Since θ_1 and θ_2 are both less than 90°, faces 1 and 2 are seen in full. θ_3 and θ_4 are both greater than 90° and so represent hidden surfaces.

GRAPHICS STANDARDS

Graphics Kernel System (GKS)

The need for an international graphics standard has arisen because, without a common standard, each time a new hardware vendor attempts to use graphics software, a major re-write of the graphics programs is necessary. The process of formulating an International Standard started in the mid-1970s and went to a 2-D draft version (DIS 7942) in 1983. The 3-D version has yet to be implemented. The difficulty has been that each hardware and software supplier has had its own standards within the company and so each has attempted to ensure that its own features appear in the standards. It has thus taken a number of years to achieve a consensus on which features should be adopted.

A difficulty occurs because the standard must cater for a whole range of equipment and the coding must adopt many features which are not required in any single hardware/software combination. This leads to more memory and longer run times than would otherwise be necessary. The result is that often only a minimal sub-set of GKS is implemented, which is then further modified by the company. The result is that each company's version of GKS is slightly different.

GKS is a set of procedures for standardizing subroutine interfaces so that any hardware configuration of input and output devices can be used with any software package. GKS uses many of the concepts listed in this chapter, including features such as World and Normalized device co-ordinates. It attempts to ensure that the applications package is unaffected by any peculiarities of hardware by defining standard classes of input and standard output primitives. The device independence of GKS is introduced by defining a concept of an abstract work station. This work station is rather different from that of the *intelligent* work station defined in Chapter 14. The GKS work station utilizes a single display device which can be a plotter, printer, storage tube, refresh or raster display. If a separate display device is used, this will be identified as a separate work station. Thus there are input work stations (keyboard, tablet, light pen, etc.), output work stations and input/output work stations. The output primitives are abstractions of basic actions that a basic device can perform. The six basic primitives are:

1. *Polyline* – a set of connected lines defined by their sequence of points.
2. *Polymarker* – symbols located at a given position.
3. *Text* – strings of characters at a given position.
4. *Fill areas* – polygons which may be hollow or filled with colour, pattern or style of hatching.

5. *Pixel array* – arrays of pixels, each with its own colours.
6. *Generalized drawing primitives* – circular and elliptical arcs, splines, etc., characterized by a means of identification, a number of points and additional data, e.g. radii or angle of arc.

Each output primitive has two groups of attributes. One group is an attribute fixed when the primitive is created, e.g. text size and spacing, pattern size for filling areas, etc. The other group is a work station attribute that can identify, e.g. the type of line, line width, colour, etc. This latter facility would, for example, allow a line to be output on to one work station, consisting of a display screen, as a particular colour and when input to another work station, consisting of a plotter, convert the line to a particular type, e.g. centre line. GKS also defines *metafiles* for use in the long-term filing of graphical information. They can be used for such tasks as transporting graphical information between systems or from one place to another, e.g. by the use of magnetic tape.

Initial Graphics Exchange Specification (IGES)

IGES is a neutral file format for the exchange or interchange of design information that will link otherwise incompatible CAD installations. This will permit graphical data to be exchanged without the need for the data to be re-input each time through the keyboard. It represents one of several attempts to define an intermediary format that will allow data to be exchanged between different systems. It therefore has a different aim from GKS, which is concerned with a standardized subroutine interface. While IGES is in common use commercially, it has yet to take on the status of an International Standard. The use of a large standardized neutral file means that each supplier of CAD software and hardware will need to write an IGES pre-processor to convert its data into a form suitable for IGES to read it. A supplier will also need an IGES post-processor to read the IGES file data and convert it into a form that can be used by its system. The work of writing a single pre- and post-processor for use with the neutral IGES file, is much less than would be required to write a separate conversion file for direct connection to every vendor's hardware or software.

This chapter has dealt with the general principles underlying how computer programs generate images on a display screen. Chapter 16 considers some specific packages in order to demonstrate how these principles are applied in practice.

Exercises

(1) In a home computer, the machine code instruction STA $ 1FFF addresses the highest memory location.
 (a) How many K of memory must the computer have?
 (b) How many bits does this represent?
 (c) Represent this as a binary number.

(2) Using PROGRAM 1 as a guide (page 168) create a BASIC program which will draw an equilateral triangle of side length 50, starting at position 50,50 with one side horizontal. The computer software uses the commands MOVE X,Y to move the cursor to a position x,y and LINE X,Y to draw a line from current location of the cursor to a position x,y.

(3) Describe the use of procedures for the program in Exercise 2 to be used repeatedly to draw four equilateral triangles offset by 75 in x and y.

(4) Is the expression $y = mx + c$ implicit or explicit? What is a parametric form of this equation? Use the parametric form to generate a series of radial lines 50 long and at 30° increments from the point 100,100.

(5) Using the concepts in PROGRAM 3 (page 169) and in the procedure PROCCIRCLE (page 174) as a guide, write a BASIC program to draw an S shape consisting of two tangential semi-circles of radius 50.

(6) Discuss the relative merits of Bezier and B-spline curves.

(7) How many separate parameters are needed for the definition of four adjacent Coons' patches for a smoothly intersecting 3-D curved surface?

(8) A simple 2-D draughting system can be used for drawing isometric views but it is not thought of as a 3-D system. Why is this? What facilities would be required to make it a 3-D system?

(9) Starting with the graphics source program, discuss the sequence of files, menu and system activities required to build up and archive a simple assembly drawing.

(10) What is the function of a library file in a simple 2-D draughting system?

(11) Discuss, with the aid of diagrams, how the small end bearing of a car engine connecting rod can be mapped from world co-ordinates to be displayed as a viewport (in screen pixels) on a 256 × 312 pixel display screen.

(12) A line from 0,0 to 200,150 is to be clipped to a square viewport located from 50 to 100 in x and from 50 to 100 in y. Determine the sequence of clipping operations using the Cohen and Sutherland technique.

(13) The triangle shown in Fig. 15.31(a) is to be translated by −1 in the z direction, then rotated +60° about 0z and finally rotated +30° about 0y. Draw the positions of the triangle after each transformation and give the corner A in each case, as functions of x and y.

(14) Describe the object shown in Fig. 15.23 using the constructive solid geometry primitives of a rectangle and cylinder, together with the Boolean operations of intersection, union and difference. Also sketch the resulting intersections.

(15) Use a boundary representation to describe a cube.

(16) What are the advantages and disadvantages of using a wire frame construction for the block shown in Fig. 15.34?

(17) Describe the object in Exercise 14 by a series of 2½-D extrusions and solids of revolution, together with the Boolean operations of intersection, union and difference.

(18) Using Figs 15.42 to 15.44 as a guide, construct the perspective views of the end of a cylinder Ø40 by 60 long centrally viewed with a distance of 60 from the viewpoint to the front face of the cylinder. The projection plane is 50 from the viewpoint.

(19) A 40 side length cube is viewed along its diagonal. Describe how you would check which surfaces are hidden. Assume the picture plane is vertical and the diagonal is horizontal inclined at 45° to the picture plane.

(20) Contrast the aims of the functions of the GKS Standard with that of the IGES.

16 The application of CAD packages

This chapter aims to show a range of examples of the application of CAD in order to give an indication of the various levels of CAD activity that are provided by modern systems.

A 2-D DRAUGHTING PACKAGE

It should be emphasized that the greater majority of low-cost 2-D draughting packages, suitable for drawing engineering components, contain no features which will give an inherent knowledge of the 3-D nature of the object that is drawn. Even where pictorial views such as isometric drawings are shown, they are merely lines and distances set off along the inclined axes. It is necessary for the user to position the views, interpret which of the various lines and planes correspond in the various views, which features should be shown as hidden detail, etc.

The first example is taken from a low-cost 2-D draughting package which is very popular with both industrial and educational users. The reason for giving details of the features available and the techniques used in a particular package is that it gives a good understanding of the typical features and restrictions of this level of equipment.

This first example is the *Robocom Bitstik 2* which can be implemented on a number of microcomputers. This particular package has been chosen as an illustration because it is believed to be a good example of a method of data input that is *user friendly*, while embodying most of the features of a larger commercial draughting package. While it is inappropriate to go through all the precise details of how a drawing can be built up using this particular package, an overview of its facilities will give a feel for the typical capabilities of such a system.

Hardware required

The Robocom Bitstik 2, like most small CAD systems that are suitable for reasonably complex drawings, requires a large memory for a microcomputer. Typically around 256 K bytes are needed if a fairly complex drawing is to be stored completely in memory and not filed in separate sections. Some of this memory can be supplied in a special ROM graphics chip which reduces the main memory required. This is the case with the Bitstik.

The Bitstik will run on a number of microcomputer systems such as an IBM PC, an Apple 11 or a BBC microcomputer with additional second processor. The capability of an unexpanded BBC microcomputer is very limited in the type of engineering components that can be drawn. In addition to the microcomputer, a pair of floppy disk drives is needed. A pair is required because two disks will often need to be accessed simultaneously. A visual display screen, preferably colour, is also required. The special features of the Bitstik is that instead of using a tablet as an input device, an elaborate joystick is used as shown in Fig. 14.18 (page 160). This is used not only to move the cursor around the screen with *x*, *y* motions of the joystick, but a rotation of the stick will also give a *zoom* facility. A further three buttons provide various control instructions, e.g. confirm a selection from the screen menu, execute a command, etc.

Software

The high level programs for the graphics system are written in BASIC and are contained on a master floppy disk. The primitives, lines, circles, arcs, etc., are contained in machine code on a special graphics ROM. This is an electronic chip which is permanently plugged into the computer memory. This has the advantage that not only is the computer memory requirement reduced, but also the primitives which are most frequently required will be generated very quickly. The processes of scaling, rotating and translating are carried out internally within the software using matrix notation, as described in Appendix A, page 211. This requires a great deal of mathematical processing in order to manipulate the matrices. Instead of integers, real numbers with a reasonable precision after the decimal point are needed. Their manipulation within the matrices is the primary reason why the second processor is needed for the BBC microcomputer.

In addition to the master floppy disk containing the main software, two other disks are required. These are a library disk and a buffer working disk. Once the master program has been loaded into the computer memory, the disk can be removed from the disk drive leaving space for a further two disks. Programs are automatically loaded into the buffer disk as a temporary store, leaving the computer memory with free space to carry out complex calculations. Once these calculations are complete, the program can be loaded back into memory from the buffer disk. The second disk, which is continuously required to run a program, is a library disk. This is used to file the current working drawings (or *work page*). While many larger systems simply list the working drawings under a file name, and it is necessary for the user to remember which names refer to which drawings, the Bitstik uses a system of displaying the files as small pictures. Thus the library file can store three separate pages, each of which can have up to 16 boxes. Each box on the page will contain an exact scaled down picture of the drawing that was produced as the work page. This enables quite complex working drawings to be constructed by calling up separate boxes from a number of library disks and piecing them together on the work page. The use of a pictorial record, in place of a file name, makes the system easy to use. A number of standard components, e.g. nuts, bolts, bearings, gears, etc., can be stored on the library disk and called up to be displayed to scale wherever required on the work page.

The screen of the work page is laid out as a graphics *plot* area on which the drawings will appear (typically 288 × 216 pixels on the BBC microcomputer). Alongside this, and to the right, is a menu area (typically 32 × 216 pixels) containing a series of instructions which can be selected. Along the bottom of the plot area is a palette. Here the term palette is used not in its normal sense as a range of colours which are available to the user, but as a range of primitives and their attributes which are available for selection. Thus the Bitstik palette consists of line shapes (e.g. straight lines, arcs, circles), colours and line types (e.g. continuous lines or a range of differently spaced dots). To produce the special line types required for centre lines or hidden detail dashes, it is necessary to display these on the work page as one of the types of dotted line. When drawing on paper using a plotter, the plotter assigns the particular line type, e.g. centre line or hidden detail, whenever that particular dotted line is met. The palette also contains a *nib* command which allows closed areas to be filled, either with a solid fill or with one of a range of five spacings of hatching. This is a useful feature for hatching sectioned parts. A cursor can be moved over the whole of the screen; plot area, menu and palette by using the *x*, *y* motion of the joystick. Pressing a button on the joystick will confirm the selection of a particular menu or palette feature.

Menu functions

Two separate menu functions can be accessed; menu 1 and menu 2. Menu 1 contains the following series of instructions which can be selected:

- *Text*: allows text to be typed in, scaled and rotated.
- *Paint*: colour fills an enclosed area. If the area is not enclosed, the colour 'leaks' out of the area and appears at random over the work page.
- *Trace*: allows a stream of points to be successively plotted to form a continuous freehand line. The location of each point must be stored and so this option uses a great deal of memory.
- *File*: used to deposit a work page on to a library disk as a *library unit*.
- *Copy*: retrieves a filed drawing copy from a library disk for display on the screen. While in the copy mode, further options are available: to scale it larger or smaller; rotate through 360° in 5° steps; stretch in the *x* or *y* direction; produce a mirror image of the library unit about the vertical and horizontal axes using commands '*x* flip' and '*y* flip' respectively.
- *Erase*: deletes the last feature drawn. It can be used to step back successively through the features erasing each time.
- *Find*: steps the cursor through the series of points plotted. Not only does this function position the cursor at each point plotted, but it also gives the *x* and *y* co-ordinates of the points.
- *Move*: allows a complete library unit to be moved around the work page.
- *Duplicate*: allows any number of library units to be copied on to the work page from any library disk.

- *Exchange*: swops any library unit on the work page for another.
- *Zoom*: enables an area on the work page to be selected and expanded or contracted to any size.
- *Pan*: allows the viewpoint to move up and down or side to side to display any part of the work page. This is essential when using zoom because enlarging a feature off the centre of a screen will cause it to disappear from view and the pan command is needed to return the area on to the screen.

A second menu allows the following precision controls:

- *Angle lock*: moves the cursor along any angled line. This is particularly useful for orthogonal views since setting the angle lock to 0° will allow only horizontal or vertical lines to be drawn. The angle lock is also of value for setting out isometric views.
- *Grid lock*: sets a grid which can be spaced in *x* and *y* directions to give from 4 to 32 definable divisions. This means that the cursor will *snap* to each grid location in turn and cannot draw in between the grid lines.

DRAWING PICTURES ON THE WORK PAGE

The Bitstik uses two types of cursor for drawing on the work page; an origin cursor and a dynamic cursor, both positioned by the joystick. Positioning the origin cursor on the work page is the same as using the 'move' command in simpler microcomputer-based systems. It does not result in a line being drawn. The dynamic cursor can be moved relative to the origin cursor and a line drawn between the two. This is called the 'rubber band' line which stretches and contracts as the dynamic cursor moves relative to the origin cursor (Fig. 16.1). When the dynamic cursor is in the desired position, the 'execute' button on the joystick is pressed to fix the line and free the dynamic cursor to input the next point.

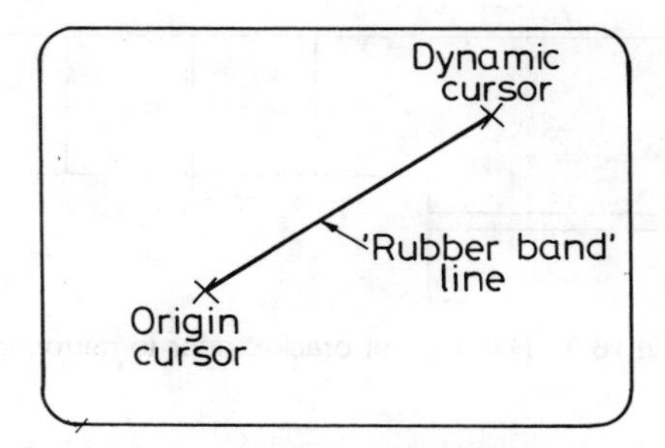

Fig.16.1 Rubber band line joins the origin to the dynamic cursor

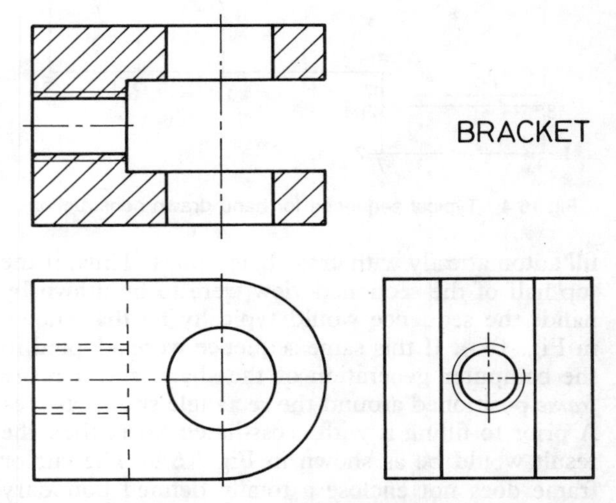

Fig.16.2 A bracket to be drawn on a 2-D draughting system

Drawing an object

The bracket shown in Fig. 16.2 is to be drawn using the Bitstik system. Using a 2-D computer draughting system requires a slightly different order of procedure to that required when drawing by hand. The exact sequence will depend on the particular 2-D package employed. As an example, the sectioned view of the bracket can be seen to have an axis of symmetry about the horizontal axis. Since most draughting systems have a *mirror* command, then it will be best to draw the view shown in Fig. 16.3 and then operate a mirror command to draw the lower half. In the case of the Bitstik, this will be the command *Y flip*. Notice that the cross-hatched section lines are not put in at this stage as the mirrored lower half will otherwise contain section lines in the opposite direction to the top half. A further difficulty which occurs with simpler draughting systems is concerned with cross-hatching. A totally universal cross-hatch routine that can correctly and automatically interpret holes, etc., is only possible using a solid modeller. The *Bitstik* package does not have an automatic cross-hatch generator. For those small 2-D packages that do, however, they require a totally enclosed area to

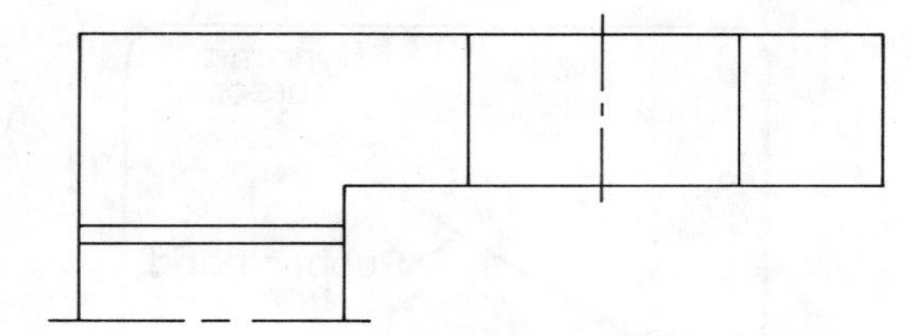

Fig.16.3 Half plan of bracket prior to mirroring

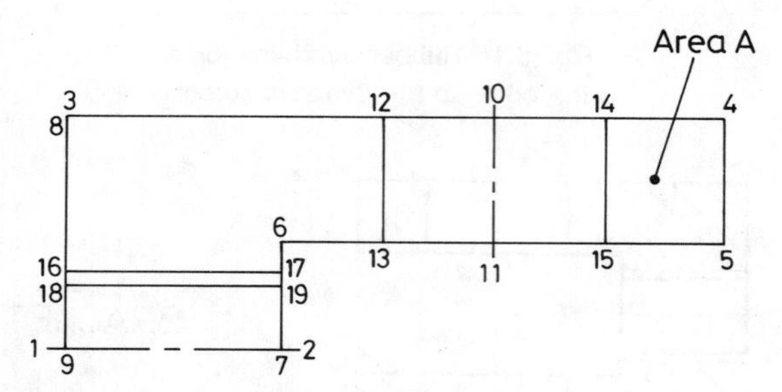

Fig.16.4 Typical sequence for hand drawn constructions

fill automatically with cross-hatch lines. Thus, if the top half of the sectioned view were to be drawn by hand, the sequence would typically be that shown in Fig. 16.4. If this same sequence were adopted in the computer generation of the shape and a *cursor frame* positioned around the rectangle shown as area A prior to filling it with cross-hatch lines, then the result would be as shown in Fig. 16.5. The cursor frame does not enclose a totally defined boundary but has lines A and B as part of the total boundary crossing the cursor frame. If an attempt were made to cross-hatch this area, in most packages the hatch lines would leak over the entire work page. Instead the part must be built up by the sequence of lines shown in Fig. 16.6 which define each piece to be sectioned as a separate area. The cursor frame can now be positioned around points 1 to 4 or 7 to 11 to achieve an enclosed area in each case, which can be correctly sectioned. Since an enclosed area is required, then the line joining points 4 to 1 must intersect with the line joining points 1 and 2.

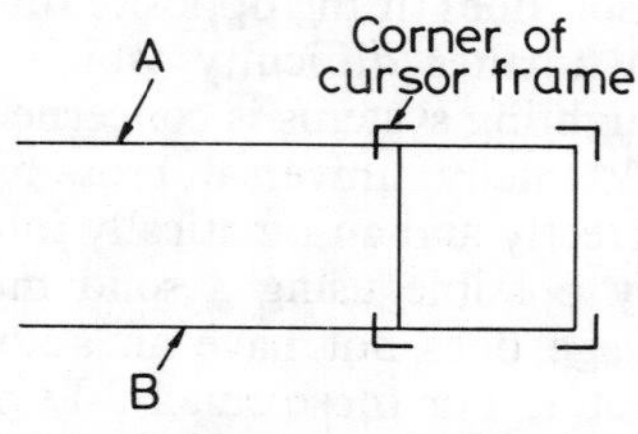

Fig.16.5 Problems in sectioning Fig.16.4

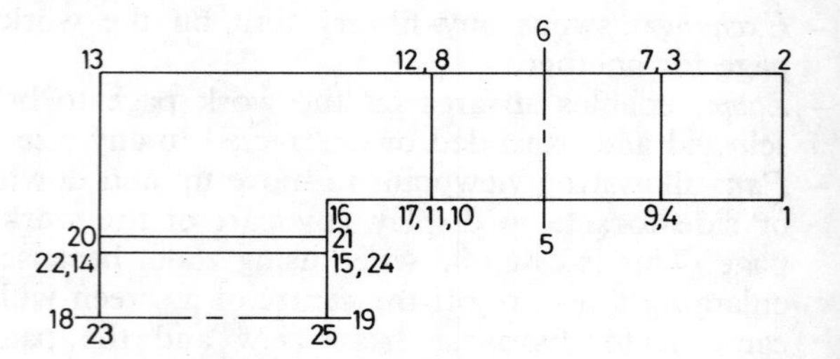

Fig.16.6 Typical sequence required for computer construction of plan

Although an automatic cross-hatch routine is not available in *Bitstik* it too requires an enclosed area for filling with colour, e.g. when using the *paint* command. To ensure this is the case it is necessary to first draw the line from 1 to 2 and use the *find* command to position the dynamic cursor at 1 before drawing the line from 4 to 1. Since all the lines in the sectional view are orthogonal, they could be drawn by setting the *Angle lock* to zero which would ensure that only horizontal and vertical lines could be drawn. Having drawn the main lines of the half plan, the view can be stored as a library unit, mirrored using *Y flip* (i.e. mirror the view about the *x* axis) and the lower half added to the upper half to form a new library unit. This new unit can now be transferred to the work page so that cross-hatch lines may be drawn. In *Bistik* this must be carried out by drawing the individual lines at an appropriate angle and spacing. In other 2-D packages with an automatic cross-hatch generator, providing enclosed areas are available, the cross-hatch lines can be generated automatically.

To set up a front view directly under a plan, it is easiest to start the whole drawing on a grid whose spacing is chosen to suit the dimensions of the whole component. This then ensures that corresponding end features of the component are in line in each view. However, it is most unlikely that all the features on the component will lie on a grid line. For those that do not it is necessary to *find* the appropriate points in plan view, note their *x* and *y* co-ordinates and use these to draw the appropriate features in the front view. (The *x* and *y* co-ordinates can be specified to six places of decimals.) The front view could then be drawn using the upper half which, in turn, could be mirrored about the horizontal centre line. However, since circles are involved it is just as easy to proceed as shown in Fig. 16.7. Here the line from 1 to 2 would be drawn using the orthogonal lock. The *Tangential*

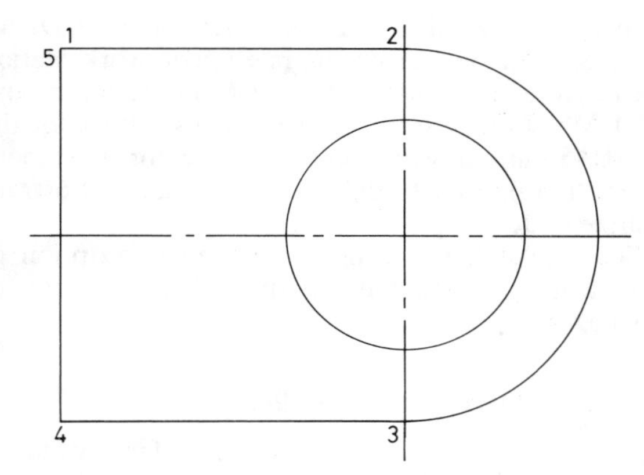

Fig.16.7 Typical sequence for computer construction of front view

Arc symbol is then selected from the palette; point 3 is then located using the appropriate x, y co-ordinates and the arc is drawn. The centre of the arc can then be located and used as the centre of the smaller circle. The command *Circle* is chosen from the palette and the circle drawn using the previously defined centre and a radius whose value is input through the keyboard. Centre lines can be specified using a consistent dotted line type which can be designated as a chain-dot centre line when the drawing is plotted. Similarly the hidden detail lines can be specified by another dotted line type which can be designated as a short dashed hidden detail line when being plotted.

Having completed the front view, this can be filed as a further library unit and the end view also completed and filed. Since the three views are available as separate files, they can be called back on to a new work page and spaced apart appropriately to allow text and dimensions to be added. Since all the views are correctly scaled as a percentage of the total work page, it is only necessary to scale the work page as a whole in the appropriate dimensions, e.g. km, m or mm, for each point on the drawing to be correctly positioned. The Bitstik 2 has automatic dimensioning facilities which allow the dimensions of a line between two points to be automatically calculated and displayed, together with appropriate dimensions and leader lines. This saves a great deal of time. On many similar packages it is necessary to type in the appropriate dimensions on the keyboard, position the text and draw the dimension lines using the cursor control.

Having produced a complete drawing, it can now be filed as a totality on a separate *archive* disk and, if desired, the library disks can be wiped clean of all separate library units, ready to start a fresh drawing.

Although the features on this level of draughting facility are much restricted compared with larger commercial packages which use both a solid modeller and draughting facility, the cost of software is about one-fiftieth, and of the hardware one-twentieth, of the price of the larger commercial packages. Draughting facilities of this level can be very effective for small companies, particularly if their designs are frequently changing and involve small changes on a basic theme. However, the full advantages (pointed out in Chapter 14) of the integrative nature of CAD with its potential for linking with other design and manufacture facilities, will not be available because the 2-D draughting package does not form a 3-D geometric data base.

AN INTEGRATED CAD/CAM PACKAGE

The following detailed example is of an integrated CAD/CAM set of software, employed by larger industrial companies to access a wide range of design, analysis and manufacture activities. At the heart of this type of facility is a solid modeller which is capable of generating the full 3-D geometry of an object. This solid modeller can be connected to other software packages so that the 3-D geometry of an object can be easily transferred from the solid modeller to, e.g. analysis, draughting or machining packages. It is important that the links between these packages should allow data to be transferred with ease to and from each package and not require the user to reformulate the data into a new structure each time a new set of software is to be used. The close links between the solid modeller and draughting package are particularly important because many designers trained in a traditional drawing board approach, prefer to use the draughting package to build up the definition of the solid model of the object. This is done by first defining the plan, front and end views and then inter-relating corresponding features in each view to build up a knowledge of the 3-D nature of the part. This is then submitted to the solid modelling package which inter-relates the features, not just of the edges but how the surfaces connect together and how the volume is generated to give a full solid model with volumetric properties. This latter phase of generating the solid model requires much CPU power and, for a complex object, can take a long time. However, while the model is being generated, the draughting package can generally be used by the designer to build up the geometry of other components.

An alternative approach often more favoured by those with less experience of traditional draughting and inter-relating orthographic views, is to generate the solid model directly. Images are generally built up as pictorial views, often using 3-D building blocks in a constructive solid geometry approach. In the early stages, views can be displayed in wire frame form to speed the process of generating images. Orthographic views can be displayed where there is ambiguity in the pictorial view. When employing this approach, there is less necessity to have a good ability to inter-relate the orthographic views into a visualization of the 3-D form. This, together with the ease with which a computer can generate a number of pictorial views taken from different viewpoints, will probably result in the solid modeller being the preferred means of generating information about the solid. In the future there is likely to be a decrease in the traditional ability to read a drawing made up from a number of orthographic views.

Having generated the solid model it is then possible to pass the geometric data to the draughting package to produce a traditional engineering drawing, fully dimensioned.

A COMMERCIAL EXAMPLE OF INTEGRATED CAD/CAM

A commonly available package called I-DEAS by Structural Dynamics Research Corporation (SDRC) is described below. These details are included, not because it is expected that the reader will use this package and become familiar with the statements it contains, but because it provides a good indication of the type of facilities that are available in a well integrated CAD/CAM system.

The full I-DEAS software package consists of a solid modeller called GEOMOD, which can also be used for kinematic display and has an associated draughting facility GEODRAW. For finite element analysis there is a program SUPERTAB which takes the solid model data and automatically generates a finite element mesh and displays the output in what is known as *finite element pre- and post-processing*. Dynamic analysis is also possible for complex assemblies to be analysed and tested using a program called SYSTAN. The whole I-DEAS package can be run on an intelligent work station with, for a single user, about 2 Mb of memory and a 71 Mb Winchester disk. The total software for the I-DEAS suite is very complex and comprises about 1 million lines of high level language (Fortran) source code.

The following is a more detailed description of the features available in the I-DEAS suite of packages.

The GEOMOD solid modeller

A solid modeller must provide a facility for a designer to be able to try out a number of design ideas speedily and compare their relative merits. In order that the solid modeller can deal with the numerous objects commonly met with in engineering and can quickly model them on a wide range of possible hardware, the following features were built into the GEOMOD program:

(1) The programs are written in a language which can be applied to a wide range of computers and have a general purpose interface program which allows a large number of display devices to be used.
(2) To allow for quick display, curved surfaces can be readily approximated by facets. The precise geometry is available for surfaces and intersections to be calculated and displayed, should these be required.
(3) Boolean set operations are provided for adding and subtracting primitives in a constructive solid geometry (CSG) approach.
(4) In addition to the CSG approach, a boundary representation file is used which stores a description of the final object by using its orientated trimmed surfaces. This allows objects to be stored very efficiently.
(5) To provide speed of display and flexibility for various levels of realism, objects can be displayed in a combination of wire frames, hidden detail and shaded images.
(6) Surfaces can be either precisely or approximately represented in a mathematical form that minimizes the calculations and data storage for surface intersections, orientations, displays and features such as the determination of tangents and normals to surfaces. This reduces the size of programs to allow them to be most easily developed, run and stored.
(7) The data can handle objects which are not

closed and which have a zero thickness structure.

(8) Objects and surfaces can be deformed by standard operations, e.g. bending, stretching, warping, filleting, etc.

(9) 2-D curves may be generated which can be extruded, revolved or skinned together to create a solid.

(10) 2-D and 3-D properties may be calculated, e.g. volume, centre of gravity, moment of inertia, principal axes, surface areas, etc.

(11) Components can be assembled into an overall system by specifying connecting points, lines, planes, curves, surfaces, etc.

(12) Interference between adjacent components or systems can be automatically detected.

(13) The kinematic relationship between objects can be stored so that performance cycles can be animated.

The generation of solid forms

The designer may require the combination of several methods of generating solids. For example a profile may be swept through 360° to form a solid of revolution and then using a Boolean operator, cut by a primitive cylinder.

The following methods of generating solid forms are available:

(1) *Primitive creation*. This is a CSG approach in which a set of widely used shapes are utilized to construct a more complex object using Boolean operators.

(2) *Boolean operators*. Three types are generally used (see Fig. 16.8):

(a) *join* or *union*. Two objects are joined to form a new object and this is successively built up, permitting the designer to work on several parts separately and join them at the end of the process.

(b) *cut* or *difference*. An object is cut by a *tool* object, e.g. a hole is created by cutting the object with a cylinder of an appropriate size.

(c) *intersect*. A new object is defined by the overlap between two objects. This is also of value for checking if parts interfere. This is usually carried out by first eliminating components by automatically placing a sphere around them to detect whether they could possibly intersect. The rest of the parts are then checked on a component by component basis. If required, the actual volume of intersection can be calculated. The identification of gaps between parts that should be touching can also be carried out using a similar procedure.

Fig.16.8 The Boolean operations, join, cut and intersect

(3) *Orientation operators*. These include rotation, translation and axis positioning. They are used to position an object in a desired location and to allow positioning for Boolean operations.

(4) *Profile boundary creation*. Because many designers are accustomed to working in 2-D and relating this to 3-D, it is necessary to have a good 2-D facility within the solid modeller. Thus a wide variety of methods for defining points, lines, circles and splines is needed. Tangents, normals and intersections are also provided. Collections of those of most value to a particular designer can be stored together. Measurements can be given, e.g. between points and various curves. A profile boundary is created by manipulating points and lines to form a 2-D composite curve, composed of

sequential segments of straight lines, circles and splines. A number of operations are required to relate the 2-D profile to an object in 3-D space. One method is to sweep the 2-D profile about an axis (rotation) or to extrude it along an axis (translation). These types of operation can be applied to a large class of objects which can be finished using Boolean and shaping operators.

(5) *Skinning*. This operation puts a 3-D *skin* over a series of cross-sections which are generated from a number of profile boundaries. This is particularly useful for irregular shapes such as are found in motor cars and in aircraft.

(6) *Shaping operations*. These are used to modify the shape in a specific manner.
   (a) *Bend*. This operator bends a component into a new shape by defining an original skeleton of an object and then repositioning it to a new desired skeleton. The geometry of the object is also modified to incorporate the changed shape of the skeleton. As an example, a tyre may be designed by defining its tread pattern in a flat plane and then bending it in two directions to form the torus of the tyre. Alternatively, a duct could be defined by a series of cross-sections along a straight centre line. The centre line could then be bent into a final shape with the profile of the duct being transformed automatically.
   (b) *Blend*. Smooths out specified regions of an object. It is of especial value for providing a fillet between two surfaces or for rounding off sharp corners and edges.
   (c) *Reflect*. Mirrors an object about an axis to allow a designer to take advantage of any symmetry which an object may possess.
   (d) *Scale*. For shrinking or enlarging an object.
   (e) *Stretch*. Elongates the object in any specified direction.
   (f) *Thick*. Adds a specified thickness to an object. This can be useful for checking if the addition of manufacture tolerances on a thickness will cause the part to overlap with another.
   (g) *Warp*. Allows the designer to push or pull the part at a point to warp or deform it in a controlled manner.
   (h) *Tweaking*. Allows the designer to access the geometry of an object. Small changes may then be implemented by modifying the geometry of a point or the merging of two lines.

(7) *Geometric property calculations*. The following properties can be automatically calculated. Volume, weight, centre of gravity, principal axes, moments of inertia about various axes, surface area. This allows the designer to compare quickly the properties of various designs, e.g. the volume of a complex geometry can be used to give the minimum weight for a fabrication.

Kinematic simulation

As a part of the GEOMOD package, there is a kinematic simulation facility. If a system, composed from a number of objects has parts which can move relative to each other, the parts are said to have *kinematic motion*. The study of kinematics involves the geometry of the parts, their range and direction of movement, together with the position and nature of their axes, rotational or linear. Because the solid modeller contains the complete geometry of the parts, it is possible to derive information, e.g. about the path which a point follows. Thus the sequence of configurations that a kinematic system passes through as it moves can be calculated, stored and displayed. The sequence of motion can be displayed forward or in reverse or at a single step at a time to give the overall envelope of operation and automatically check for potential collision of parts. The sequence of movement can be animated if required to run at real operating speeds and the result stored on film or video tape. This avoids the need for the building of expensive physical models to study the kinematics of a part.

Automatic assembly

One of the most time-consuming processes in building up a CAD assembly is in ensuring parts are correctly orientated, particularly where the components do not fit together precisely, e.g. with clearance fits. The GEOMOD solid modeller also has a special assembly program which automatically ensures a coincidence or alignment of geometric primitives, e.g. points, lines, planes, space curves and surfaces in a manner designated by the user. This avoids the necessity of the user having to zoom on to a point or line to ensure it is in exact contact, without clearance or overlap with another point or line.

Graphical display

A 3-D solid representation of a component is

modelled and stored in the CAD system data base as a geometry of all the features of a component. This geometry data base can then be used to generate any required display, e.g. wire frame, hidden lines, shaded image. The user can scale or rotate, call for perspective views and use a series of multiple viewports to display several images on the screen at the same time. Colour, reflectivity and shadows can be added to provide images of great realism. Parts of the picture can be selectively blanked out, e.g. dimensions and text to emphasize a component's relationship. Alternatively a series of layers of views can be blanked out to give a part sectional view of component assemblies under a front surface (Fig. 16.9), or the parts can be shown as exploded views as in Fig. 16.10.

Fig.16.9 A solid model of a British Rail diesel engine

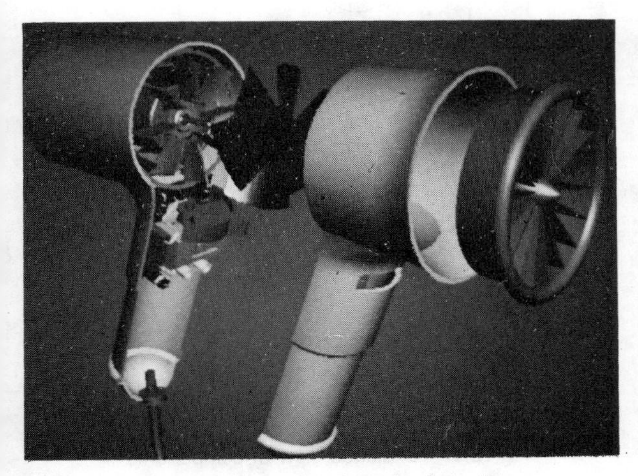

Fig.16.10 Exploded view of a hair dryer

It is often desirable to store views and display them at another time on other graphics devices. Thus, in addition to the geometry, annotation and configuration of the parts, it is necessary to also store information about the views and display parameters to enable views to be displayed automatically from the graphics display data. This is carried out with a pictorial layout package which can also be used directly to create sectioned or exploded views or to use general cutting volumes to reveal internal geometrical detail. Refresh vector graphics devices are particularly useful for animated displays and so the ability to display on raster or refresh vector devices is catered for.

These display features, together with text annotation, are of value not only for concept design and presentation, but also for advertising and marketing. With the aid of these techniques, computer generated artwork can be produced at a fraction of the time and cost of artwork produced by conventional methods.

An application example of GEOMOD

An example of an application of the GEOMOD system in operation is shown in Figs 6.11 to 6.24. This shows the design of a robotic manipulator. The overall final assembly is shown in Fig. 16.11. The first step is to lay out the overall configuration of joints and drives using a mechanism synthesis program for determining initial sizes of links and pulleys, as shown in Fig. 16.12. The geometry of new parts can be defined as shown in Figs 16.13 to 16.16, which give details of the shoulder rotation joint and the associated upper arm link. Fig. 16.13 shows the build-up of the exterior shape while Fig. 16.14 shows the desired profile. Fig. 16.15 shows the profile extruded to the desired thickness to create a solid object. Recess and holes are created by subtracting features. So far no interior surfaces

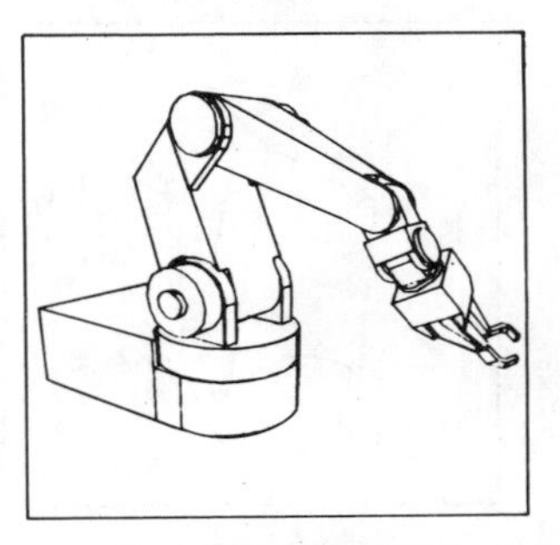

Fig.16.11 Final assembly of robotic arm

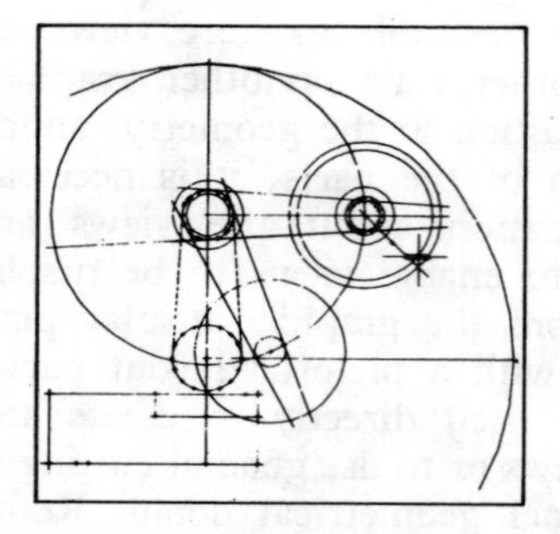

Fig.16.12 Kinematic layout of arm

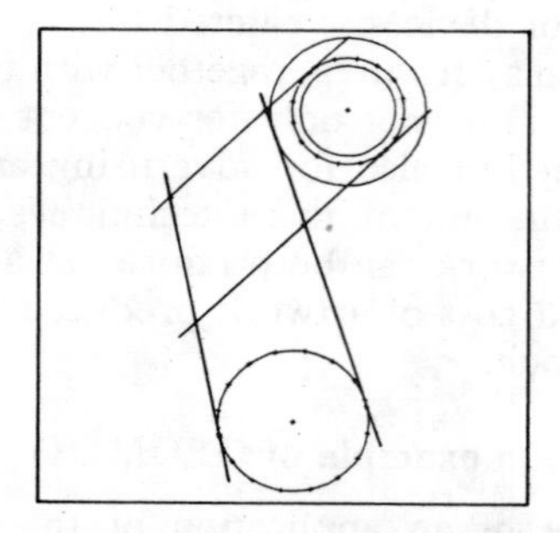

Fig.16.13 Definition of the upper arm shape

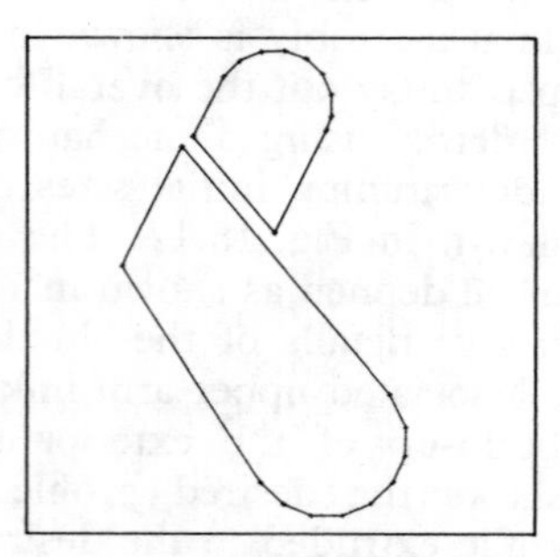

Fig.16.14 Profile of the upper arm side piece

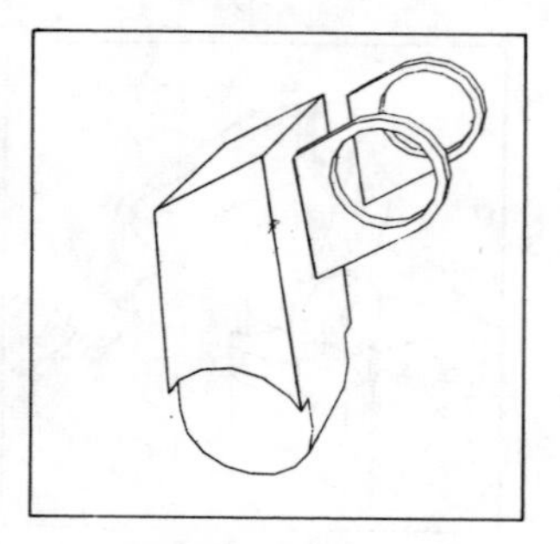

Fig.16.15 Pieces for the upper arm

have been designed and thus the object is assumed by the computer as being solid. As the robot is to be fabricated from plate material, the thickness of the main block is specified to define an interior surface (Fig. 16.16). The two plate lugs are also joined to the main block at this stage. Note the faceted construction of circles as an approximation for speed of display, although the full, precise geometry is also held in the data base for exact display tasks such as interference checks. The remainer of the parts are specified together with their connections as in Fig. 16.17. The arm is then put together (Fig. 16.18) and different configurations of the design tested to check the range of movements. Structural interference and packaging restraints can also be investigated. A potential interference zone between the waist and the forearm can be seen in Fig. 16.19 which leads to the need for an additional extension to the waist joint which can be tested in Fig. 16.20. A check on the possible trajectories is carried out (Fig. 16.21) using the kinematics analysis model. Detailed design of individual components is aided by the ability to take sectional views from such assemblies and

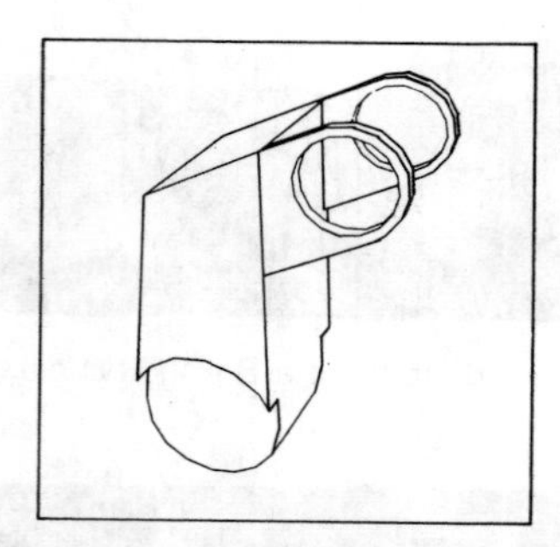

Fig.16.16 Completed upper arm

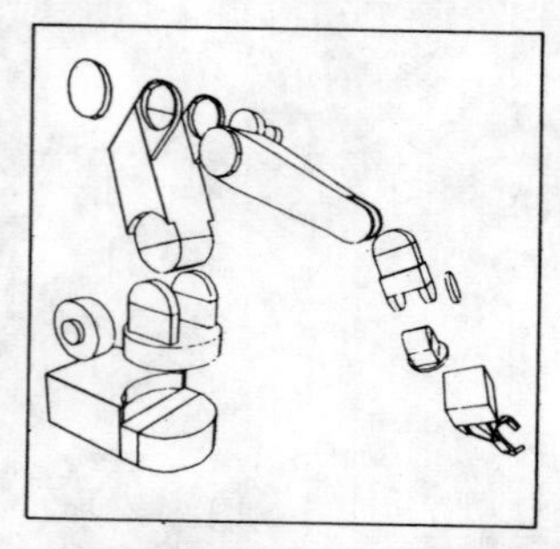

Fig.16.17 Exploded view of components which make up the robot

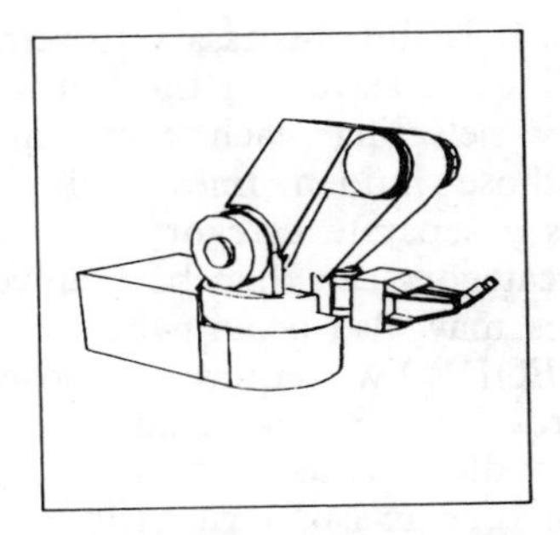

Fig.16.18 A different position of the robot

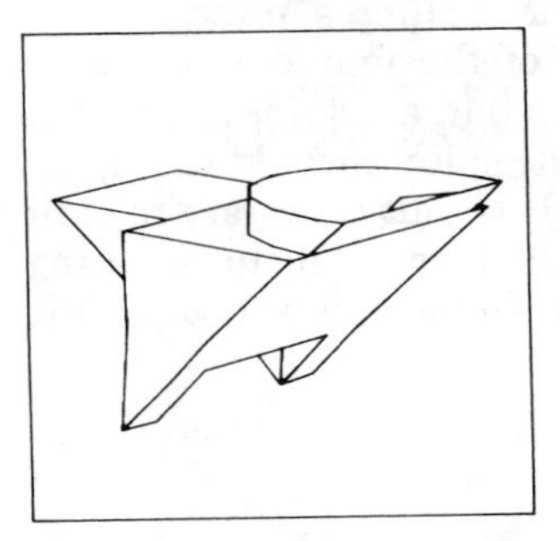

Fig.16.19 Interference zone between robot wrist and forearm

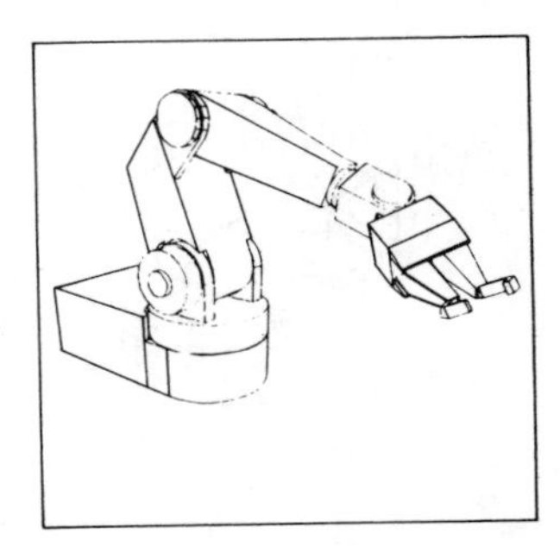

Fig.16.20 A modified design of robot wrist

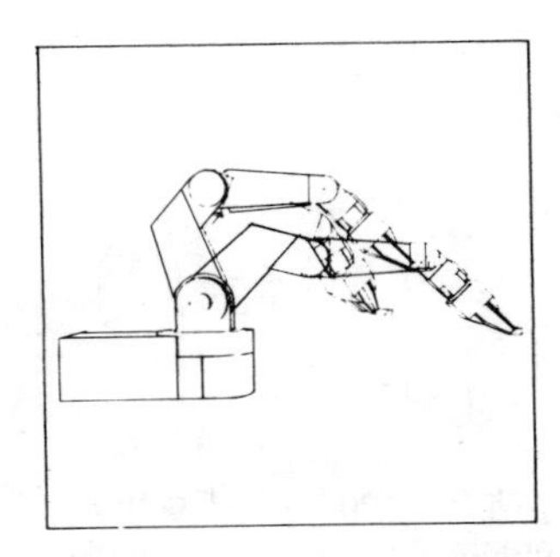

Fig.16.21 Robot trajectory using kinematic analysis

exploded views. Fig. 16.22 shows a sectional view of the base, while a complete sub-assembly of a drive joint is sectioned in Fig. 16.23. The drive joint is shown as an exploded view in Fig. 16.24.

The overall geometry of the robot is also available to other software packages for further analysis. For example the I-DEAS suite of software also has a dynamic analysis module and a solid element mesh generation package for finite element stress analysis.

THE 2-D DRAUGHTING MODULE: GEODRAW

There are two possible ways of using the GEODRAW draughting module. Either the geometry of an object can be created in GEOMOD and the geometry files transferred to GEODRAW for automatic dimensioning, sectioning, plotting, etc., or a new object can be created afresh using GEODRAW. The latter method generates a 3-D geometry file in GEODRAW which can, in turn, be passed back to the solid modeller for further manipulation. This close integration of the various modules in the I-DEAS suite is a further example of the considerable advantages gained when designing components.

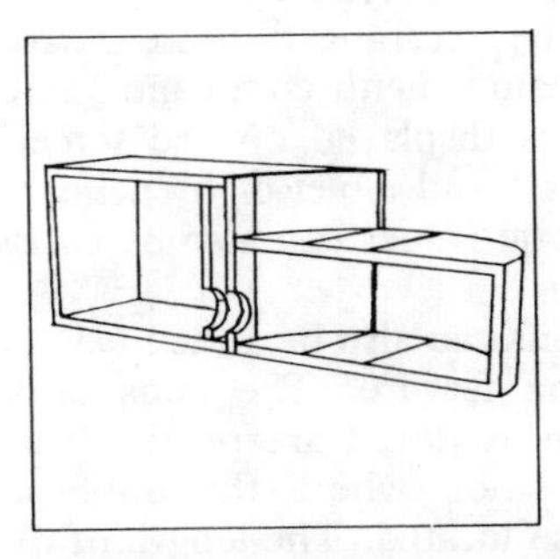

Fig.16.22 Sectioned view of the base platform

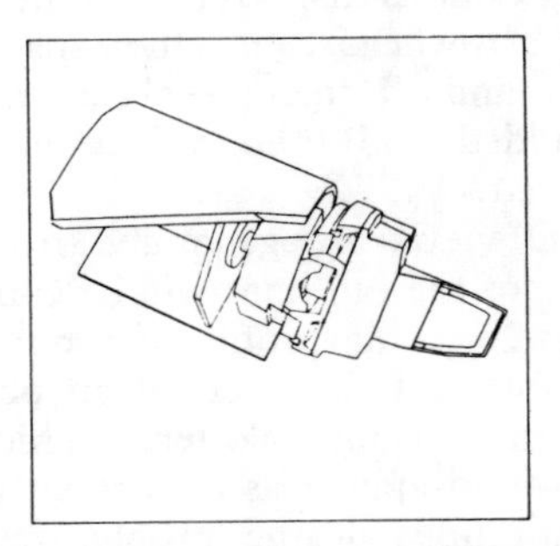

Fig.16.23 Sectioned view of the joint drive

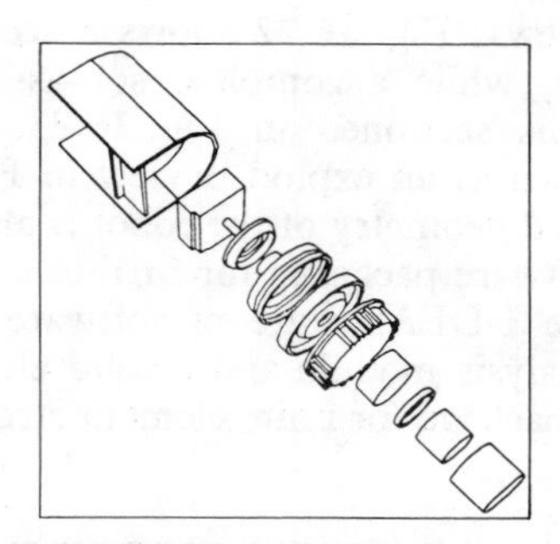

Fig.16.24 Exploded view of the joint drive

Using a file generated by the solid modeller

The full geometry of an object can first be defined in the solid modeller, e.g. as a 3-D wire frame. The views can be rotated in turn to give the plan, front, end and isometric views which can be displayed together using separate viewports on the display screen. Section planes can also be defined to give additional views which show internal features of the object. Still within GEOMOD, the hidden detail can be selectively removed or shown as hidden detail lines. Each of the views can then be stored as a file on disk, transferred to the GEODRAW program and displayed again on the screen. The views can be rearranged if necessary and scaled separately using menu commands in GEODRAW. The menu is displayed on the screen and picked using a mouse and tablet or by using the keyboard. Exact numeric values can also be entered using the keyboard.

Dimensions can also be added using an automatic dimensioning feature. The ends of a line whose dimension is required are picked using the cursor and the position where the dimension is to be placed is also located. The length of the line is then automatically retrieved from the geometric data base and its value is displayed, together with leader lines and arrowheads, in the space that was indicated. Standard tolerances can also be automatically added and their value changed if and when required.

Since 2-D views are generated from 3-D geometry, some of the full lines will be coincident with hidden ones, e.g. the profile of a cube represents both the front and the back of an object. If this view were drawn using a plotter, the hidden back of the object would appear as coincident dashed lines over the full lines of the profile, resulting in a thicker plotted line. To achieve good quality plots of drawings, it is thus necessary to remove hidden coincident lines to leave just the full lines. This is achieved by selecting each view in turn and specifying those hidden lines which are to be displayed as a separate category. All hidden lines not in that category can then be removed.

Difficulties may also occur when cross-hatching surfaces. GEODRAW requires a closed chain of lines and arcs for cross hatching. Splines (curves) cannot be handled. Thus if the item in Fig. 16.25 were generated as an isometric view in GEOMOD, the holes which were circles in orthographic views would appear as ellipses in the isometric view. Thus the corners of the four cut surfaces would not be seen as arcs but as splines. For the purposes of sectioning the splines would disappear, as shown in Fig. 16.26. It is thus necessary to close each area by picking each corner in turn, using the cursor, before cross-hatching as shown in Fig. 16.27.

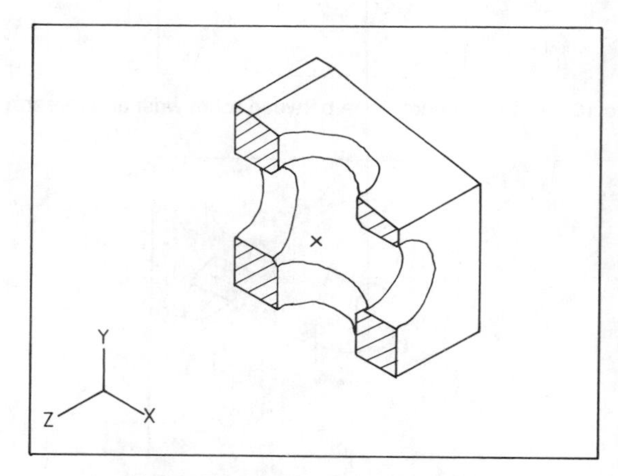

Fig.16.25 Isometric view of a block

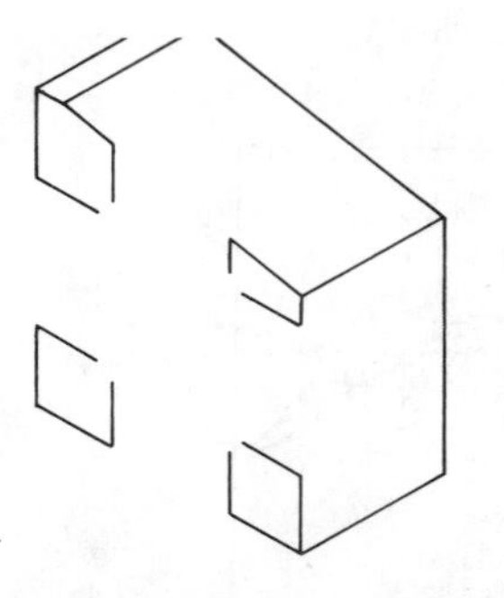

Fig.16.26 Block showing open areas when splines are removed

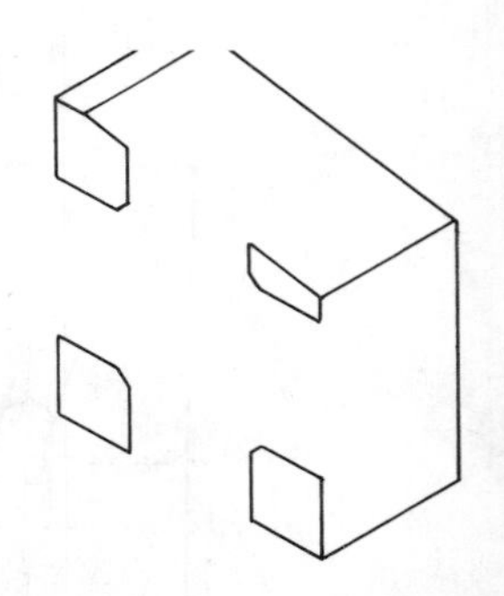

Fig.16.27 Corner areas of block are closed prior to cross-hatching

Using GEODRAW to build the basic geometry of an object

A single view of an object can be defined using GEODRAW by selecting the size of a viewport and defining the origin. All the facilities that were previously described in the Bitstik package are also available in GEODRAW. However, GEODRAW has a far greater range of options available for defining individual features, e.g. there are a larger number of possible ways for generating lines, arcs and circles. Having fully defined a view of an object it can be labelled, e.g. as front view, and then filed and transferred to the GEOMOD package so that the geometry can be available for modelling. Other separately defined orthogonal views can be sent to GEOMOD so that a full solid model can be generated. Automatic dimensioning and text may be added to the views in GEODRAW in the normal way.

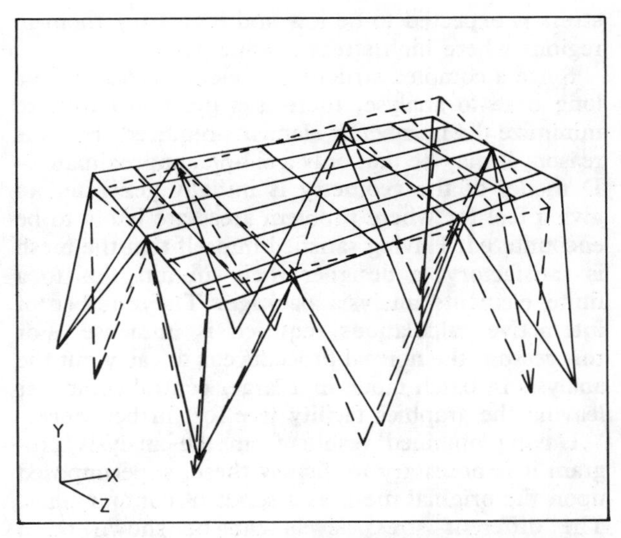

Fig.16.28 A dynamic analysis package can be used to show the displacement of a structure

SYSTEM ANALYSIS

The SDRC package SYSTAN can be used to analyse the dynamic forced response of a system. The same data base as was generated in GEOMOD is employed, so that a full geometry is available for analysis. The mass, stiffness and damping characteristics of each connection of an assembly can be defined. A variety of forces, excitation frequencies and displacements can be input to the model to test the resulting response of the assembly. The resulting displacement of the structure can be shown (Fig. 16.28) or a series of graphs generated which show aspects such as vibration frequency and amplitude resulting from a variety of input disturbances. Because SYSTAN is part of an integrated suite of software, it is easy to pass data direct to and from other packages in the I-DEAS suite, e.g. in *finite elements* analysis and in *Frame* analysis (used for static, dynamic and buckling analysis of structures represented by interconnected beams and shells) and *Fatigue* analysis which can estimate the institution of a fatigue crack forming in a mechanical component.

FINITE ELEMENT ANALYSIS

In finite element analysis, a component is broken down into a series of polygons to form a mesh. The forces applied to the component are then recalculated to form resultant stresses at the nodes of the particular meshes where the forces act. These stresses are then applied to the appropriate nodes of the next mesh element and the resultant stresses at the adjacent nodes are calculated. This process is continued until the stresses have been calculated at every node point right across the object. The production of finite element programs tend to be a specialist business, with different programs available for different geometries and types of problem. Thus finite element analysis programs are provided by specialist software houses.

If the number of elements required to define the surface of the object is quite small, the process of dividing the object up into a mesh could be performed by hand and the resultant stresses could be plotted (also by hand) as stress levels or contour lines shown on the surface of the object. However, the majority of objects require many meshes, typically several hundred, and thus a special mesh generation program (or *pre-processor*) is required. To plot out by hand the resultant stresses as contour lines would take far too long and so the results of a finite element analysis have to be converted back into a visual form using a *post-processor*.

The 3-D geometry available from a solid modeller is then passed to a mesh generator in the pre-processor. The resultant mesh can then be displayed on a graphics terminal. An experienced user will then examine the mesh and modify it appropriately, reducing the number of elements where stress is expected to be low and increasing them in regions where high stress is anticipated.

Since a complex structure of elements will take a long time to analyse, there is a great incentive to minimize the number of elements required. For this reason, it may be that only a simple, approximate 3-D model of the geometry is initially generated to give a feel for where problem areas are likely to be encountered. Having satisfied himself that the mesh is satisfactory, a designer then submits this to a finite elements analysis package. The number of interactive calculations required is immense. For this reason, the normal procedure is to carry out the analysis in batch mode in a larger central computer leaving the graphics facility free for further work.

Having obtained results from the analysis program it is necessary to display these, superimposed upon the original mesh as a series of contour lines. The different stress levels can be shown on a monochrome display as a series of anotations on each line. However, for complex structures this is difficult to interpret and it is of greater value to use colour displays where each colour represents a particular stress level. It then becomes easy to identify areas of stress concentration. Because the designer will generally wish to try out the effect of different loads or a variety of geometries, this procedure of pre-processing, analysing and post-processing may have to be repeated many times.

In the I-DEAS system the finite elements package is called SUPERTAB and consists of a pre-processor mesh generater which can automatically generate solid elements as well as surface meshes (Fig. 16.29). Loads, restraints, couples and material properties can all be easily specified. The finite elements analysis program can be supplied by a specialist software house or a SUPERTAB version can be employed, which can treat both static and dynamic stresses. The results can then be displayed

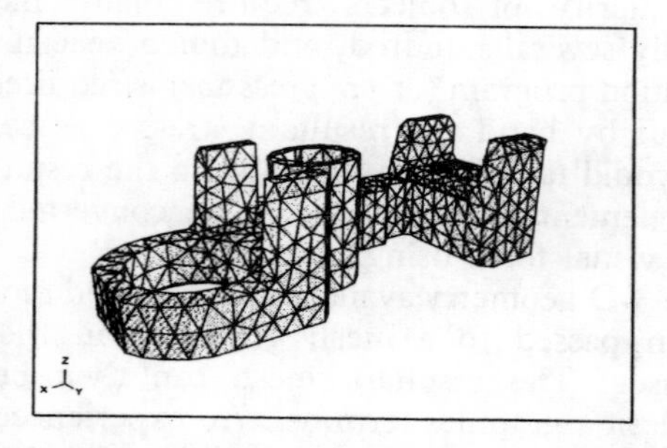

Fig.16.29 Automatic mesh generation of a component using a finite element pre-processor

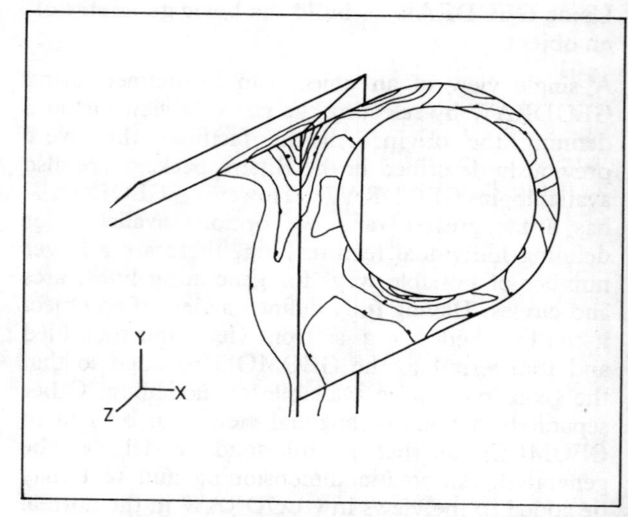

Fig.16.30 Strain distribution in a component shown using a finite element post-processor

as stress levels using a post-processor (Fig. 16.30). Colour animation may be used where dynamic stresses are present.

In addition to modelling stresses, the finite element method can also be used to model any field effects such as fluid dynamics in determining pressure fields or thermo dynamics to determine temperature distributions or in nuclear physics, to determine radiation fields in nuclear reactors.

COMPUTER INTEGRATED MANUFACTURE

As discussed in Chapter 15, in addition to generating the geometry of a part for design purposes, the same geometric data base can be used for manufacturing the object. The most usual *computer aided manufacture* (CAM) activity is in the use of *numerical control* (NC) machine tools. In a large integrated CAD package, the geometric data from the solid model can be passed to the NC program code generator directly. However, rotational parts can be machined on an NC lathe using a profile of the part which is used to generate the 2½-D solid model by a rotation about the axis of the object. Similarly profiles of parts which are extruded in a 2½-D solid model may be machined using a numerically controlled milling machine. Hence the area of NC machining can often be implemented with a relatively simple 2½-D modelling system.

There are a number of specialized NC machining systems commercially available which both design the part in profile, allow the cutter tool path and sequence of cuts to be decided upon and then displayed on the graphics screen. From this information, with a minimum of help from the user, the computer can generate the series of coded instructions which the NC machine requires to give the correct machining instructions. Fig. 16.31 shows an example of such an NC system called PATHTRACE. The example shows a part displayed on a display screen. The part is to be turned on an NC lathe. The lower horizontal edge represents the centre of rotation. The outer rectangle represents the bar of material from which the part is to be machined. The inner lighter coloured shape is the part which is to be machined. The straight lines are a representation of the tool path while it is cutting, while the dotted lines show the rapid traverse of the tool. An information window at the top of the screen displays information about the machine tool program, such as feed rates, spindle speeds, coolant state, the correct position and a machining time estimation. The lathe turning tool can be selected from a library of up to 1800 tools. A representation of the tool currently being used is displayed in the top left hand corner of the screen. The geometry of the component profile can be first defined using a separate program which has additional commands to make the display easier, such as mirror, add chamfers, add blend radii, etc. The geometry of the profile can then be loaded into the appropriate NC program for lathe or mill. Fixtures and clamps can also be shown. The tool path for milled components can be automatically offset from the geometry of the component once the tool diameter is specified (Fig. 16.32).

SIMULATION

In addition to the above simulation on the graphics screen of the NC machine showing the cutting tool moving around the part, it is possible to simulate other activities graphically as an aid to production.

Machine tool layouts

One of the more usual applications of graphical simulation as an aid to production is in the motion of machine tools. A typical example is shown in Fig. 16.33. Here the physical motions of a robot are simulated together with those of adjacent machine tools, conveyors, etc. The individual motions are built up using a specially designed program called GRASP, which facilitates the display of the outlines of various machines and their relative motions. Using this approach it is possible to select the robot structure which is the most appropriate for a task and then try out various movements in relation to the machine tool to ensure it can carry out the required tasks.

If the robot and machine tool dimensions are sufficiently accurate it is possible to decide on the sequence and range of motions which the robot must have to carry out the task. The robot

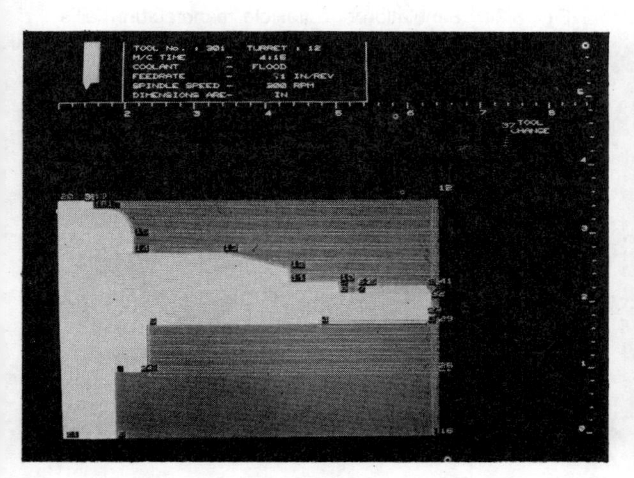

Fig.16.31 Tool path simulation of a part to be machined on a numerically controlled lathe

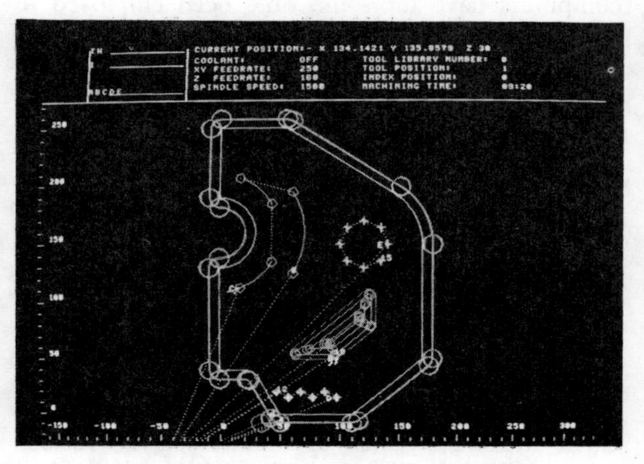

Fig.16.32 Tool path simulation of a part to be machined on a numerically controlled milling machine

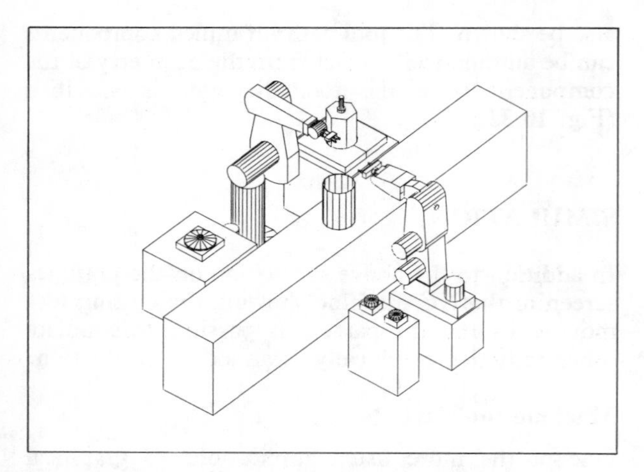

Fig.16.33 Simulation of a robot and machine tool cell

simulation can then be employed to produce a program of robot motions which can be sent direct to the robot controller. Thus the robot can be programmed for a new task *off-line* so that it can switch directly from one task to another. This avoids the robot and associated machines being out of use, often for long periods of time while the robot is taught a new sequence of motions by leading it through by hand. The use of graphic simulation for off-line programming of robots, machine tools and automatic guided vehicles can load to considerable improvements in production efficiency.

A further use for graphical simulation is as an adjunct to the manufacture planning process. As an aid to planning the layout of a manufacture activity, computers have for some time been employed to simulate a series of manufacture processes. Thus the time to order a part to be made, the time for the material to be drawn from stores and the time to manufacture on a variety of machines can all be simulated as a process in the computer. The planning department can then decide on whether to bring in additional lathes, milling machines, etc., to improve the production rate in order to meet required delivery dates. The effect of the additional machines can then be judged by running the computer model of the manufacture process in a speeded up time. The build-up of a queue of parts at various stages of manufacture can be used to assess the necessity of speeding up machining cycles or of introducing new machine tools at various stages. Traditionally the throughput individual cycle times and other data were given as a large sequence of numbers which required considerable skill to interpret. The advent of cheap graphical display systems enables the processes to be displayed on a screen in a form which can be easily understood.

The workshop foreman can now use a package with graphical display to determine the best machine utilization given the current availability of machine tools at any given time. Fig. 16.34 shows the simulation of a flexible manufacture cell displayed using a graphical simulation program called DRAFT. The cell consists of two lathes, a grinding machine and gauging station. The input of orders, selection of raw materials from stores and the final packaging of the parts is also simulated. With a known distribution of frequency of orders, together with machine performance, the likely production can be dynamically displayed with a full day's production being simulated in a few minutes, with

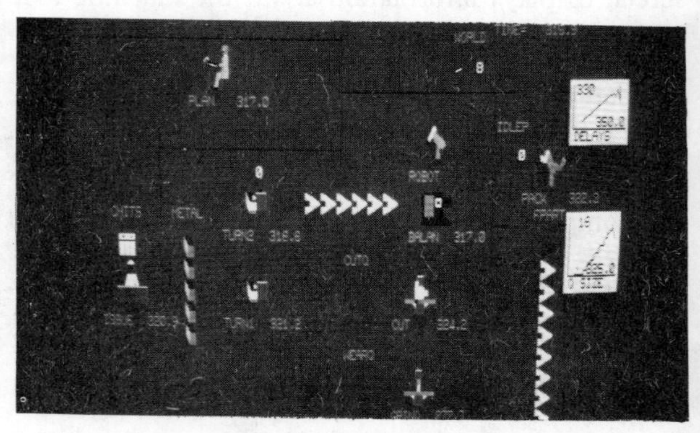

Fig.16.34 Simulation of a flexible manufacture cell's production capabilities showing bottleneck at packing station

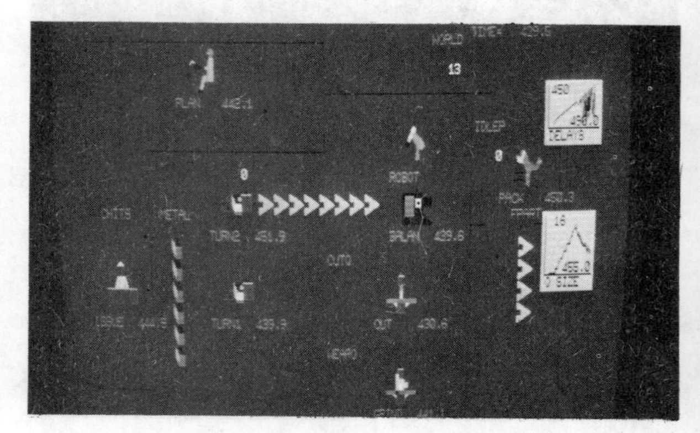

Fig.16.35 Simulation of a flexible manufacture cell showing effect of an additional packer

various bottleneck stages identified. Fig. 16.35 shows the same cell simulated with an additional packer to reduce the bottleneck which was occurring at the final packing station.

Exercises

(1) Why do many smaller microcomputer based draughting systems have a special graphics ROM?
(2) What is the usual procedure for drawing centre lines and hidden detail lines on a smaller draughting system, e.g. Robocom Bitstik 2?
(3) In the Robocom system, how could you sign your name? Why is this expensive in memory?
(4) How does drawing a line using a draughting system, e.g. Bitstik 2, contrast with that using a simpler draughting system, e.g. BBC microcomputer?
(5) What are the typical menu instructions available in a simpler type of draughting system, e.g. Bitstik 2?
(6) The *universal joint yoke* (Fig. 4.9) is to be drawn on a simple draughting system such as Bitstik 2.
   (a) List the sequence of commands required to draw the front view.
   (b) How would the plan and end views be constructed in line with the corresponding features in the front view?
   (c) How would you construct the end views? Particular emphasis should be placed on the construction to ensure that the cross-hatch lines will not *leak*. Contrast this procedure with that normally used to draw the view by hand.
   (d) How would you proceed to draw an isometric view of the object using Bistik 2?
(7) Describe the potential benefits of using a small draughting system such as Bitstik 2 for a small company making a range of similar pneumatic valves, many of which are specially commissioned by the customers.
(8) An integrated CAD system is to be used to build up the geometry of an object. What are the relative merits of using a solid modeller, compared with an integrated draughting system for this purpose?
(9) A solid model of the *brake crankshaft lever* (Fig. 12.7) is to be constructed in an integrated modeller, e.g. GEOMOD. Discuss the relative merits of the various ways in which the solid geometry can be built up.
(10) The *brake crankshaft lever assembly* (Fig. 12.7) is to be assembled using separate models of ① the *crankshaft*, ③ the *fork*, and ⑤ the *bush liner*. What aspects of the GEOMOD solid modeller could be used to assist with this assembly process? How could the Boolean operations help to check the correct function of the assembly?
(11) How could the kinematic part of the GEOMOD program assist in constructing the assembly of items used in Exercise 10?
(12) Why is it that display programs often use faceted cylinder or wire frame forms, even though the full geometry is available in the data base?
(13) Describe the sequence of activities necessary to model the *brake crankshaft lever assembly* (Fig. 12.7) in a solid modeller such as GEOMOD.
(14) Describe how ① the *gear bracket*, modelled in Exercise 13, could be passed to a draughting system such as GEODRAW for dimensioning.
(15) Contrast the facilities available in a 2-D draughting system which is part of an integrated CAD system such as GEODRAW, with that of a simpler draughting system.
(16) How might the dynamic analysis package SYSTAN and the finite element package SUPERTAB be used to aid the design analysis of the gear lever assembly in Exercise 13?
(17) Why is it that a comparatively simple numerical control machine tool can be used to machine components designed on a 2½-D CAD system?
(18) Why is the use of graphical simulation so useful in the off-line programming of robots? How can it aid in the design of a manufacturing cell?

Appendix A

MATRIX NOTATION FOR GRAPHICAL TRANSFORMATIONS

This appendix is not intended as an introduction to matrix notation but serves to supplement the principles given in Chapter 15 concerning transformations by using the shorthand of matrix notations.

2-D TRANSFORMATIONS

A generalized point in 2-D can be represented by its x and y co-ordinates as

$$P = [x_1, y_1]$$

where $[x_1, y_1]$ is a 1×2 matrix. Similarly a line in 2-D can be represented by its end points as a 2×2 matrix:

$$L = \begin{bmatrix} x_1 & y_1 \\ x_2 & y_2 \end{bmatrix}$$

The general 2-D point (x, y) can be transferred into the point $(x_1 y_1)$ as

$$\begin{aligned} x_1 &= ax + by \\ y_1 &= cx + dy \end{aligned} \qquad \text{(A.1)}$$

where the transform T can be expressed in matrix form as:

$$T = \begin{bmatrix} a & c \\ b & d \end{bmatrix}$$

Equation (A.1) can now be expressed in matrix form as

$$(x_1, y_1) = (x, y) \begin{bmatrix} a & c \\ b & d \end{bmatrix} \qquad \text{(A.2)}$$

i.e. x_1 can be found by multiplying the row vector (x, y) by the first column

$$\begin{bmatrix} a & . \\ b & . \end{bmatrix}$$

and y_1 by multiplying (x, y) by the second column

$$\begin{bmatrix} . & c \\ . & d \end{bmatrix}.$$

Similarly a pair of matrix transformations can be multiplied together to give one combined (or *concatenated*) form. Thus if

$$T_1 = \begin{bmatrix} a & c \\ b & d \end{bmatrix}$$

and

$$T_2 = \begin{bmatrix} e & g \\ f & h \end{bmatrix}$$

then the concatenated transform

$$T = T_1.T_2 = \begin{bmatrix} a & c \\ b & d \end{bmatrix} \begin{bmatrix} e & g \\ f & h \end{bmatrix}$$

or

$$T = \begin{bmatrix} (ae + cf) & (ag + ch) \\ (be + df) & (bg + dh) \end{bmatrix}$$

$$T = \begin{bmatrix} j & l \\ k & m \end{bmatrix}$$

where $j = ae + cf$, i.e. j is formed by taking the sum of the products of the first row of T_1 with the first column of T_2.
$k = be + df$, i.e. k is formed by taking the sum of the products of the second row of T_1 with the first column of T_2.
$l = ag + ch$, i.e. l is formed by taking the sum of the products of the first row of T_1 with the second row of T_2.
$m = bg + dh$, i.e. m is formed by taking the sum of the products of the second row of T_1 with the second column of T_2.

TRANSLATION

The expressions given in Chapter 15 for translation of a point are

$$x_1 = x + \Delta x, y_1 = y + \Delta y$$

where x_1 and y_1 are co-ordinates of the translated point, i.e.

$$(x_1, y_1) = (x, y) + T$$

where

$$T = [\Delta x, \Delta y]$$

Similarly a line L can be translated as

$$\begin{bmatrix} x'_1 & y'_1 \\ x'_2 & y'_2 \end{bmatrix} = \begin{bmatrix} x_1 & y_1 \\ x_2 & y_2 \end{bmatrix} + T$$

$$\textit{where } T = \begin{bmatrix} \Delta x_1 & \Delta y_1 \\ \Delta x_2 & \Delta y_2 \end{bmatrix}$$

$$\textit{i.e. } \begin{bmatrix} x'_1 & y'_1 \\ x'_2 & y'_2 \end{bmatrix} = \begin{bmatrix} x_1 & y_1 \\ x_2 & y_2 \end{bmatrix} + \begin{bmatrix} \Delta x_1 & \Delta y_1 \\ \Delta x_2 & \Delta y_2 \end{bmatrix}$$

$$= \begin{bmatrix} (x_1 + \Delta x_1) & (y_1 + \Delta y_1) \\ (x_2 + \Delta x_2) & (y_2 + \Delta y_2) \end{bmatrix} \quad \text{(A.3)}$$

Thus in Fig. 15.24, the line

$$L = \begin{bmatrix} 1 & 1 \\ 2 & 3 \end{bmatrix}$$

which is translated by two units in x and one unit in y as

$$T = \begin{bmatrix} 2 & 1 \\ 2 & 1 \end{bmatrix}$$

Hence from eqn (A.3), the transform is

$$L + T = \begin{bmatrix} 1 & 1 \\ 2 & 3 \end{bmatrix} + \begin{bmatrix} 2 & 1 \\ 2 & 1 \end{bmatrix} = \begin{bmatrix} 3 & 2 \\ 4 & 4 \end{bmatrix}$$

i.e. $x_1, y_1 = 3,2$
$x_2, y_2 = 4,4$ as in Fig. 15.24.

SCALING

Scaling involves enlarging or reducing size, e.g. the point

$$(x', y') = (x, y)S$$

where

$$S = \begin{bmatrix} \Delta x & 0 \\ 0 & \Delta y \end{bmatrix}$$

the scaling matrix. This scales by Δx in the x direction and by Δy in the y direction. An enlargement (Δx, $\Delta y > 1$) also translates further from the origin, while a reduction (Δx, $\Delta y < 1$) translates nearer the origin.

In the example Fig. 15.25, the line

$$L = \begin{bmatrix} 1 & 1 \\ 2 & 3 \end{bmatrix}$$

is doubled in size, i.e.

$$S = \begin{bmatrix} 2 & 0 \\ 0 & 2 \end{bmatrix}$$

and:

$$L.S. = \begin{bmatrix} (1 \times 2 + 1 \times 0) & (1 \times 0 + 1 \times 2) \\ (2 \times 2 + 3 \times 0) & (2 \times 0 + 3 \times 2) \end{bmatrix} = \begin{bmatrix} 2 & 2 \\ 4 & 6 \end{bmatrix}$$

i.e. $x_1, y_1 = 2,2$
$x_2, y_2 = 4,6$ as in Fig. 15.25.

ROTATION

In a 2-D transformation, points are rotated about Oz in an anti-clockwise direction for positive values of θ, using a right hand co-ordinate system, e.g. for a point (x_1, y_1)

$$x_1 = x \cos\theta + y \sin\theta$$
$$y_1 = y \cos\theta - x \sin\theta$$

where x_1 and y_1 are the transformed co-ordinates of the point (x, y), or

$$(x_1, y_1) = (x, y)R$$

where

$$R = \begin{bmatrix} \cos\theta & \sin\theta \\ -\sin\theta & \cos\theta \end{bmatrix}$$

the rotation matrix.

In the example given in Fig. 15.27, the line

$$L = \begin{bmatrix} 1 & 1 \\ 2 & 3 \end{bmatrix}$$

is rotated by $\theta = 60°$ about the origin, i.e.

$$R = \begin{bmatrix} \cos 60° & \sin 60° \\ -\sin 60° & \cos 60° \end{bmatrix}$$

and

$$L.R. = \begin{bmatrix} -0.366 & 1.366 \\ -1.598 & 3.232 \end{bmatrix}$$

HOMOGENEOUS CO-ORDINATES

To achieve a pure rotation about the end (1,1) of a line, it would be necessary to translate the end (1,1) to the origin, perform the rotation and then re-translate the end of the line back to the position (1,1). The advantage and strength of matrix multiplication is that the successive processes of translation, rotation and translation can be combined into a single transformation matrix. However, the desire to combine the above 2×2 matrices into a single multiplication matrix gives rise to difficulties because the translation transform is an additive process, while rotation and scaling are multiplicative. To achieve a similar multiplicative form with translation, the concept of homogeneous co-ordinate transforms is introduced.

To treat all 2-D processes as multiplicative, the translation process must be turned into a *dot product* form. The transformations can then all be treated similarly (or *homogeneously*). This is carried out by considering the xy plane containing the line L to be scaled in the z direction. The xy plane is then only one of an infinite number of planes in the z direction. The z axis then represents a scaling factor F which ranges from 0 to ∞ as shown in Fig. A.1. A point $p(x_1, y_1)$ is now represented as $p(F.x_1, F.y_1, F)$ where scale factor $F \neq 0$ giving the homogeneous co-ordinate representation for a point as $P(XYF)$. The 2-D Cartesian co-ordinates are given by $x = X/F$, $y = Y/F$. In practice F is normally chosen as 1 and thus division by F is not required.

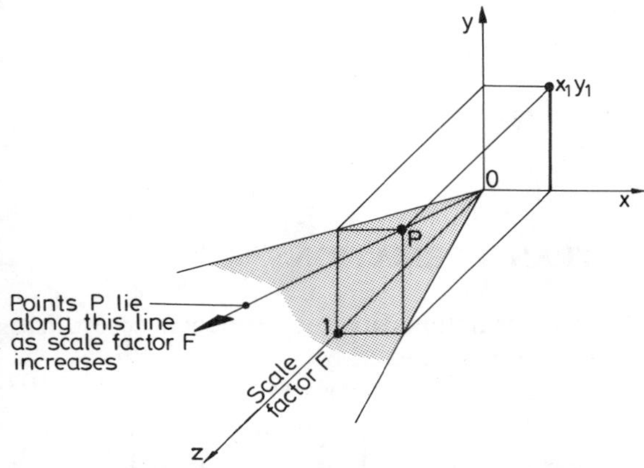

Fig.A.1 Homogeneous co-ordinate representation of a point by use of a scale factor F

For 2-D representation in homogeneous form, a point now becomes a three element row vector $[x, y, 1]$ and a translation becomes the dot product

$$[x'y'1] = [xy1].T(\Delta x\ \Delta y)$$

where $[x'y'1]$ is the transformed point at $F = 1$ and $[xy1]$ is the original point at $F = 1$ and

$$T(\Delta x\ \Delta y) = \begin{bmatrix} 1 & 0 & 0 \\ 0 & 1 & 0 \\ \Delta x & \Delta y & 1 \end{bmatrix}$$

A series of translations one after the other, can be accomplished by first finding the dot products of all the translation matrices to give a concatenated form as a single translation matrix whose elements will be the sum of the individual elements.

A scaling is now

$$[x'y'1] = xy1. \begin{bmatrix} \Delta x & 0 & 0 \\ 0 & \Delta y & 0 \\ 0 & 0 & 1 \end{bmatrix}$$

The concatenated form of successive scalings one after the other will be the product of the individual elements.

A rotation is now

$$[x'y'1] = [xy1]. \begin{bmatrix} \cos\theta & \sin\theta & 0 \\ -\sin\theta & \cos\theta & 0 \\ 0 & 0 & 1 \end{bmatrix}$$

Concatenation of successive rotations will be the sum of individual elements.

Example

Rotate a square about a corner P through an angle θ. Because transformations are with respect to the origin, this process has three parts:

(1) translate P to the origin;
(2) rotate through an angle θ;
(3) re-translate back to the original position of P as shown in Fig. A.2.

The net transformation matrix is:

$$\begin{bmatrix} 1 & 0 & 0 \\ 0 & 1 & 0 \\ -x_1 & -y_1 & 1 \end{bmatrix} . \begin{bmatrix} \cos\theta & \sin\theta & 0 \\ -\sin\theta & \cos\theta & \\ 0 & 0 & 1 \end{bmatrix} . \begin{bmatrix} 1 & 0 & 0 \\ 0 & 1 & 0 \\ x_1 & y_1 & 1 \end{bmatrix}$$

$$= \begin{bmatrix} \cos\theta & \sin\theta & 0 \\ -\sin\theta & \cos\theta & 0 \\ x_1(1-\cos\theta)+y_1\sin\theta & y_1(1-\cos\theta)-x_1\sin\theta & 1 \end{bmatrix}$$

This single transformation matrix can then be applied to all four corners of the square to give their final co-ordinates. The order of the above steps is clearly vital. If a rotation about P were followed by two translations, the result would be quite different and thus matrices are not, in general, commutative. The only transforms in which order is unimportant are:

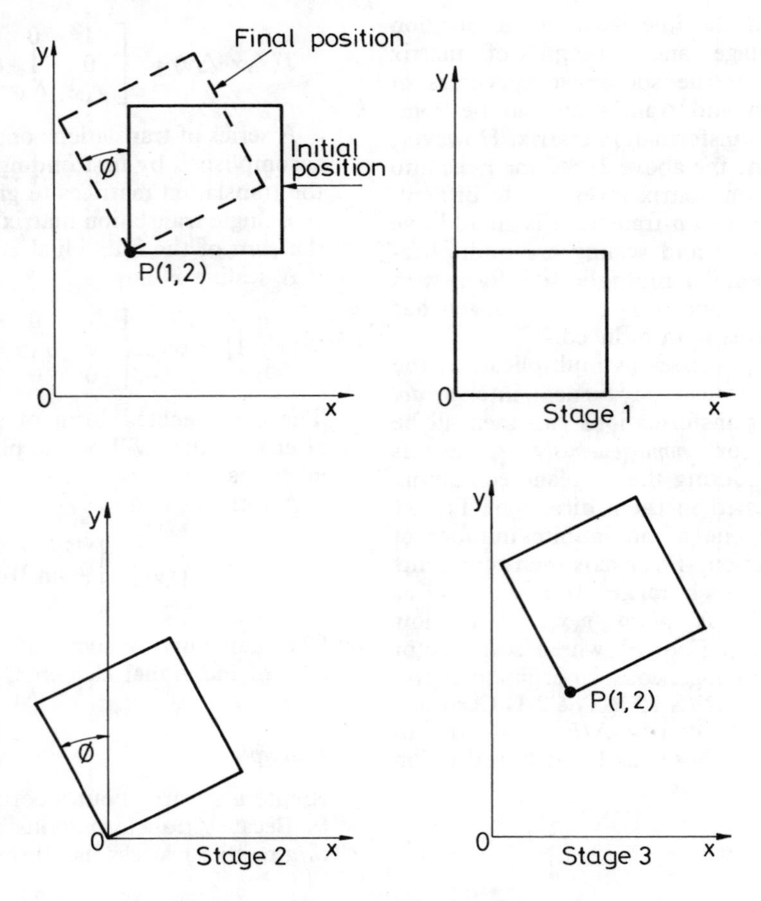

Fig.A.2 Stages in the rotation of a square

(1) a series of translations;
(2) successive scalings;
(3) successive rotations;
(4) when a scaling (with the same x and y scale factor) is followed by a rotation.

Computational efficiency

Although the individual matrices need to be kept as a 3 × 3 matrix, the final transformation matrix can have the last column ignored. Thus the transformation of a 2-D point uses four multiplications and four aditions, instead of nine multiplications and six additions. The resulting saving of computation time can be worth while for the transformation of complex items or where speed is important, as in dynamic displays.

3-D TRANSFORMATIONS

3-D transformations in homogeneous co-ordinates involve a 4 × 4 matrix.

A 3-D translation becomes:

$$T(\triangle x, \triangle y, \triangle z) = \begin{bmatrix} 1 & 0 & 0 & 0 \\ 0 & 1 & 1 & 0 \\ 0 & 0 & 1 & 0 \\ \triangle x & \triangle y & \triangle z & 1 \end{bmatrix}$$

A 3-D scaling becomes:

$$S(\triangle x, \triangle y, \triangle z) = \begin{bmatrix} \triangle x & 0 & 0 & 0 \\ 0 & \triangle y & 0 & 0 \\ 0 & 0 & \triangle z & 0 \\ 0 & 0 & 0 & 1 \end{bmatrix}$$

A 3-D rotation becomes:

Rotation about the x axis

$$R_x = \begin{bmatrix} 1 & 0 & 0 & 0 \\ 0 & \cos\theta & \sin\theta & 0 \\ 0 & -\sin\theta & \cos\theta & 0 \\ 0 & 0 & 0 & 1 \end{bmatrix}$$

Rotation about the y axis

$$R_y = \begin{bmatrix} \cos\theta & 0 & -\sin\theta & 0 \\ 0 & 1 & 0 & 0 \\ \sin\theta & 0 & \cos\theta & 0 \\ 0 & 0 & 0 & 1 \end{bmatrix}$$

Rotation about the z axis

$$R_z = \begin{bmatrix} \cos\theta & \sin\theta & 0 & 0 \\ -\sin\theta & \cos\theta & 0 & 0 \\ 0 & 0 & 1 & 0 \\ 0 & 0 & 0 & 1 \end{bmatrix}$$

The example given in Fig. 15.31, which involves a rotation of a triangle ABC, first about 0_z by +90° and then by −60° about the 0_x axis, is now considered.

Since corner A is placed at the origin, and always remains there, it can be ignored.

The matrix rotation for the two stages of rotation of B is:

$$x'_B\, y'_B\, z'_B = [x_B\, y_B\, z_B\, 1] \,.\, R_{0z}$$

$$= [x_B\, y_B\, z_B\, 1] \,.\, \begin{bmatrix} \cos 90^\circ & \sin 90^\circ & 0 \\ -\sin 90^\circ & \cos 90^\circ & 0 \\ 0 & 0 & 0 \\ 0 & 0 & 1 \end{bmatrix}$$

and since

$$x_B = 2,\ y_B = 0,\ z_B = 0$$

$$x'_B\, y'_B\, z'_B = [0,\ 2,\ 0]$$

and

$$x''_B\, y''_B\, z''_B = [x'_B y'_B z'_B\, 1] \,.\, R_{0x}$$

$$= [x'_B\, y'_B\, z'_B\, 1] \,.\, \begin{bmatrix} 1 & 0 & 0 & 0 \\ 0 & \cos\theta & \sin\theta & 0 \\ 0 & -\sin\theta & \cos\theta & 0 \\ 0 & 0 & 0 & 1 \end{bmatrix}$$

$$= [\ 0,\ 2,\ 0,\ 1\ ] \,.\, \begin{bmatrix} 1 & 0 & 0 & 0 \\ 0 & 0.5 & -0.866 & 0 \\ 0 & 0.866 & 0.5 & 0 \\ 0 & 0 & 0 & 1 \end{bmatrix}$$

$$= [0,\ 1.0,\ -1.732,\ 1]$$

More usually, the above two rotation matrices could be concatenated to produce a single transform as:

$$T = \begin{bmatrix} \cos\theta & \sin\theta & 0 & 0 \\ -\sin\theta & \cos\theta & 0 & 0 \\ 0 & 0 & 1 & 0 \\ 0 & 0 & 0 & 1 \end{bmatrix} \cdot \begin{bmatrix} 1 & 0 & 0 & 0 \\ 0 & \cos\phi & \sin\phi & 0 \\ 0 & -\sin\phi & \cos\phi & 0 \\ 0 & 0 & 0 & 1 \end{bmatrix}$$

where $\theta = 90^\circ$ and $\phi = -60^\circ$

$$\text{or } T = \begin{bmatrix} \cos\theta & \sin\theta\cos\phi & \sin\theta\sin\phi & 0 \\ -\sin\theta & \cos\theta\cos\phi & \cos\theta\sin\phi & 0 \\ 0 & \sin\phi & \cos\phi & 0 \\ 0 & 0 & 0 & 1 \end{bmatrix}$$

$$= \begin{bmatrix} 0 & 0.5 & -0.866 & 0 \\ -1 & 0 & 0 & 0 \\ 0 & 0.866 & 0.5 & 0 \\ 0 & 0 & 0 & 1 \end{bmatrix}$$

Hence

$$[x \quad y \quad z \quad 1].T$$

$$= [2 \quad 0 \quad 0 \quad 1] \,.\, \begin{bmatrix} 0 & 0.5 & -0.866 & 0 \\ -1 & 0 & 0 & 0 \\ 0 & 0.866 & 0.5 & 0 \\ 0 & 0 & 0 & 1 \end{bmatrix}$$

$$= [0,\ 1{,}0,\ -1.732,\ 1] \text{ as before.}$$

Appendix B

A selection of symbols taken from BS3939: *Graphical symbols for electrical power, telecommunications and electronics diagrams* is given below. These are the symbols most commonly found in electrical and electronics circuits.

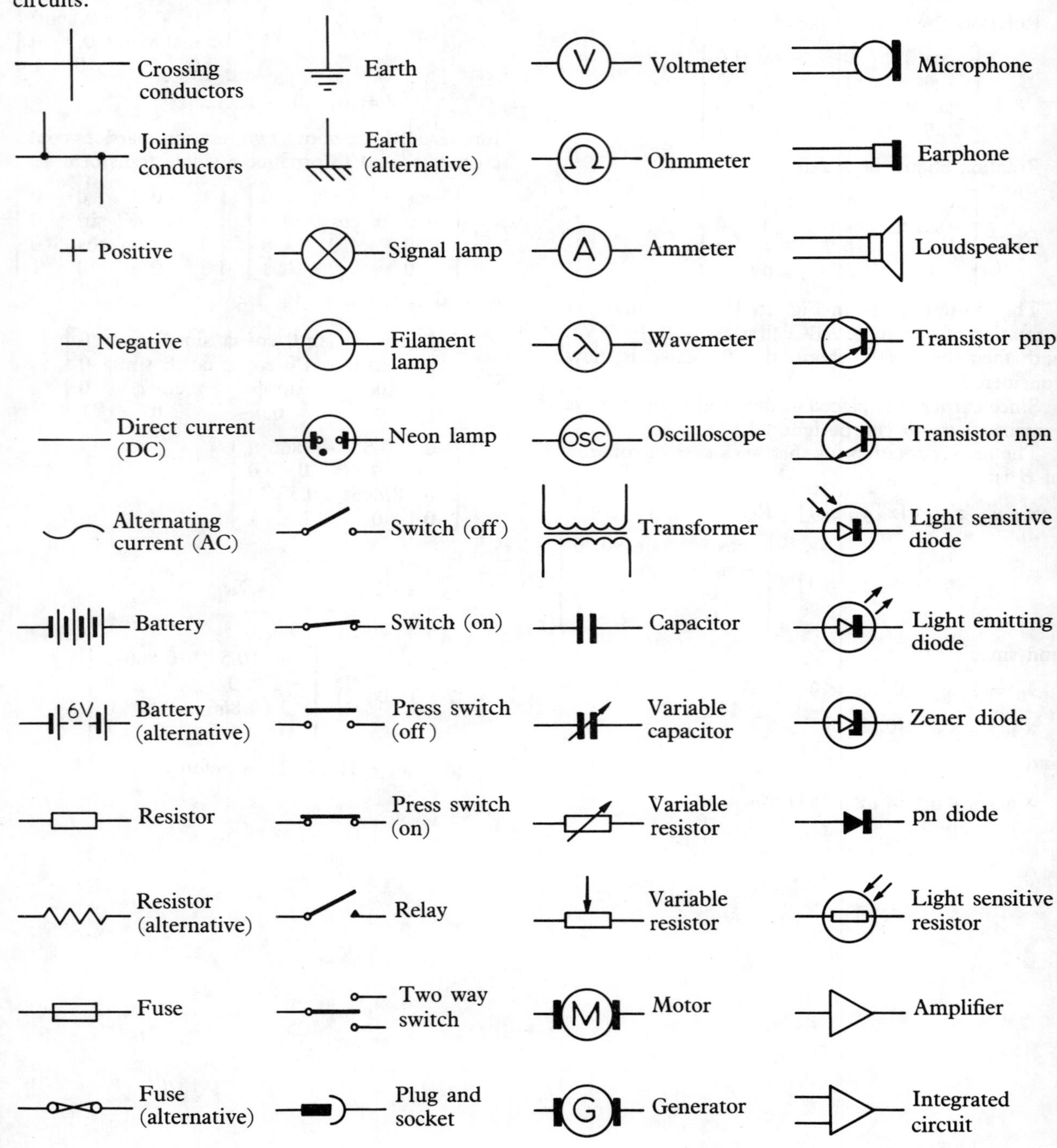

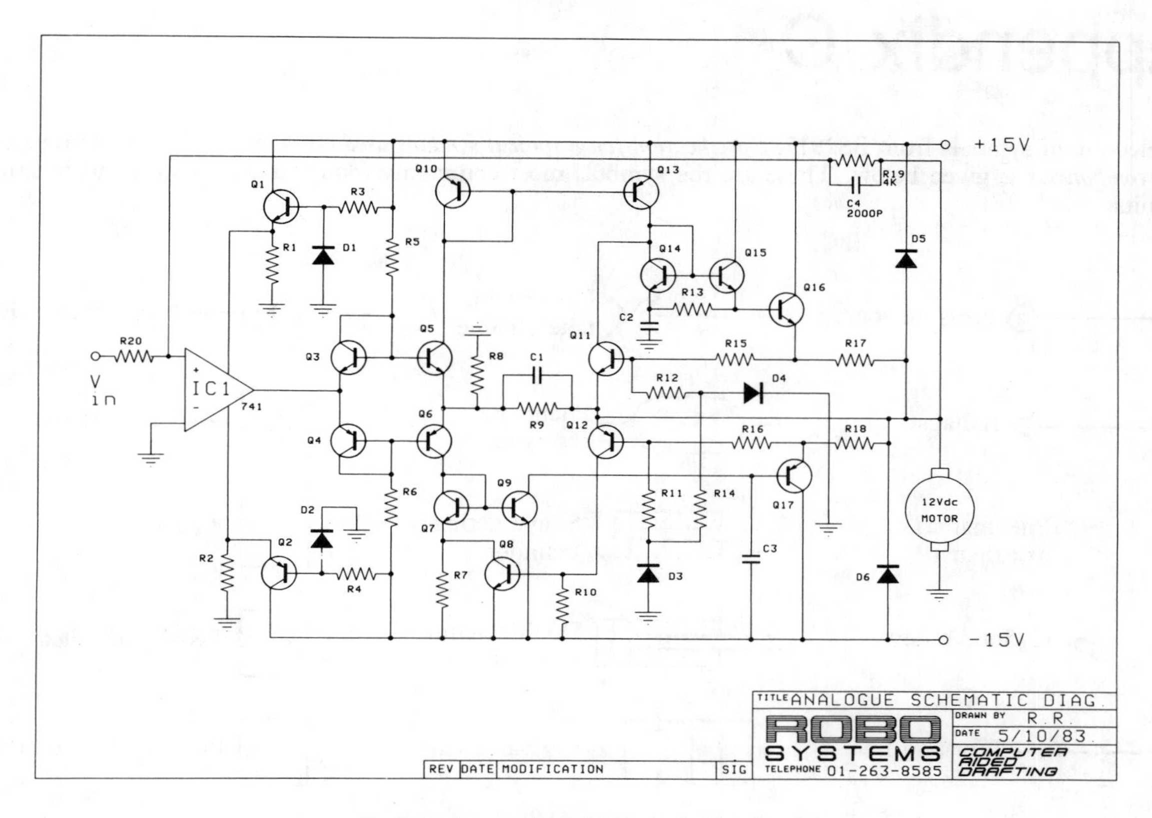

Fig.B.1 A computer printed electronics circuit

Appendix C

A selection of symbols from BS2917: *Specification for graphical symbols used on diagrams for fluid power systems and components* is given below. These are the symbols most commonly found in pneumatics and hydraulics circuits.

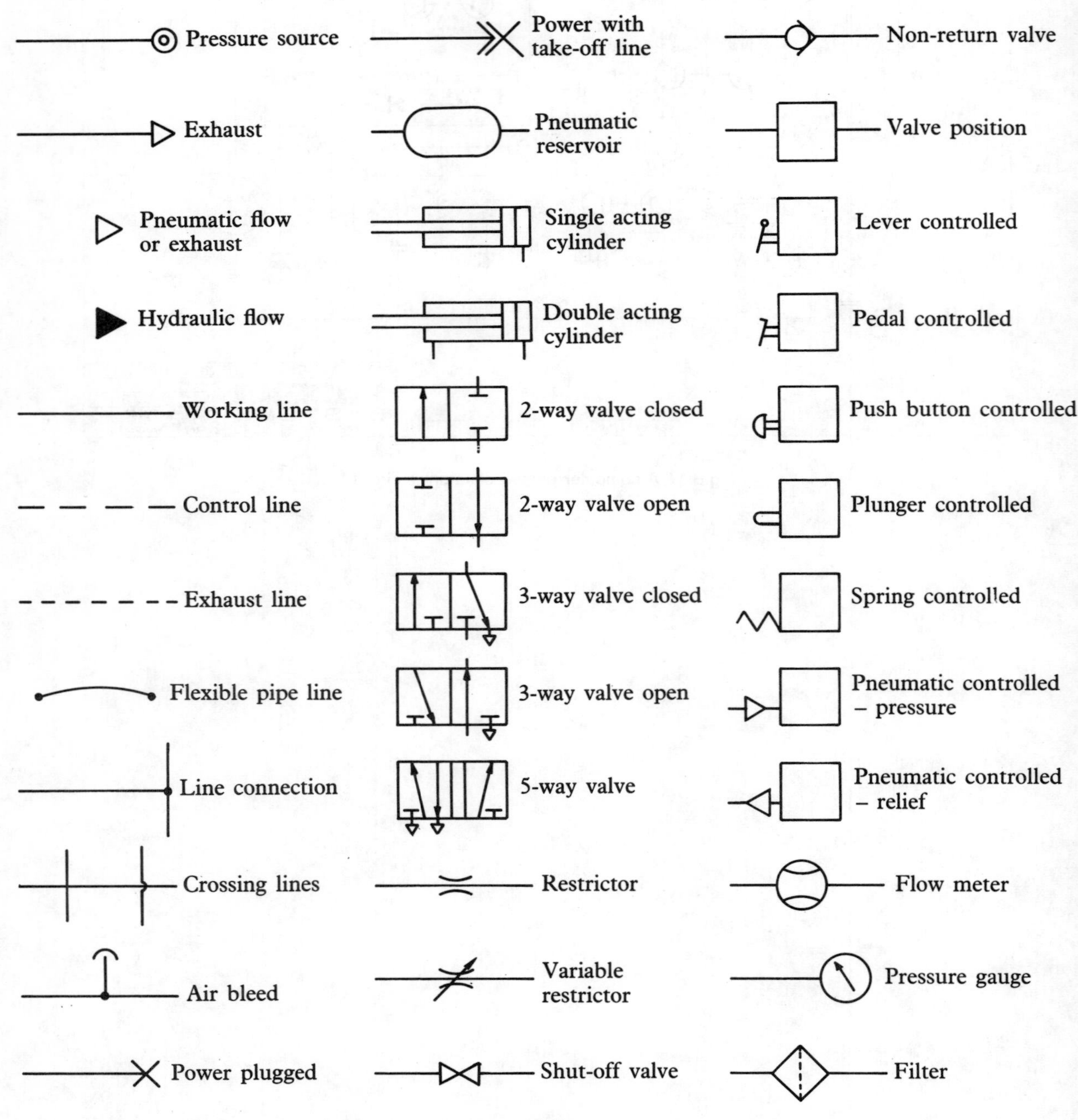

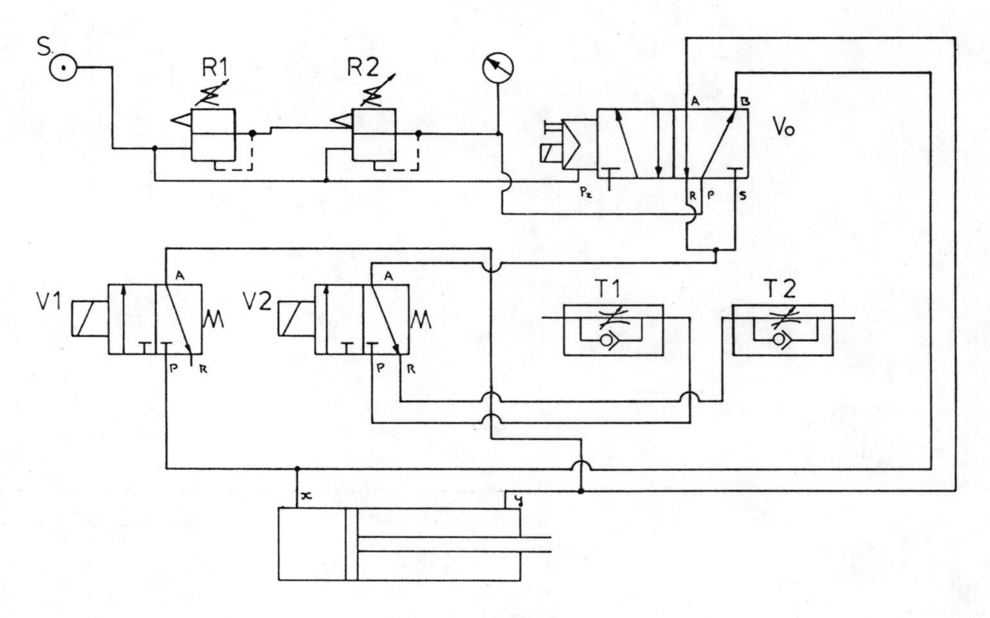

Fig.C.1 A hydraulics circuit

Index